ELECTRON PARAMAGNETIC RESONANCE

ELECTRON PARAMAGNETIC RESONANCE

by
S. A. Al'tshuler and B. M. Kozyrev
Kazan State University, Kazan, U.S.S.R.

Translated by SCRIPTA TECHNICA, Inc.

Translation Editor
Charles P. Poole, Jr.
Gulf Research and Development Corp.
Pittsburgh, Pennsylvania

1964

ACADEMIC PRESS • New York and London

ACADEMIC PRESS INC.
111 FIFTH AVENUE
NEW YORK, NEW YORK 10003

United Kingdom Edition
Published by
ACADEMIC PRESS INC. (LONDON) LTD.
BERKELEY SQUARE HOUSE, LONDON W. 1

Library of Congress Catalog Card Number: 63-21398

Originally printed in Russian under the title:
ELEKTRONNIY PARAMAGNITNIY REZONANS

Published by

State Press for Physico-Mathematical Sciences
Moscow, U. S. S. R. 1961

PRINTED IN THE UNITED STATES OF AMERICA

Editor's Preface to the English Edition

This book is a comprehensive treatise on the field of electron paramagnetic resonance, covering both the theoretical background and the results of experiment. The text includes discussions of much Russian work that has never before been available in English and extensive references to the original literature. Another particularly useful feature is the extensive tabulation of all the experimental data and literature references on transition metal ions, complete to the end of 1958.

Charles P. Poole, Jr.

Preface

Discovered in 1944 by Ye. K. Zavoyskiy, electron paramagnetic resonance (EPR) has become one of the most powerful tools of physical research. Its realm of application is extremely broad. In ionic crystals it makes it possible to determine the structure of the energy levels in magnetic centers, elucidate the fine structure of the crystalline lattice, and define the parameters that characterize the kinetics of magnetization. The study of crystal lattice defects by means of EPR is of extreme interest. In liquid salt solutions, electron paramagnetic resonance affords the possibility of investigating solvate shell structure. Interesting data concerning the properties of conduction electrons in metals and semiconductors have been obtained through it. In nuclear physics, paramagnetic resonance has proved valuable as a method for determining nuclear moments, and it is one of the most effective means of polarizing nuclei.

The method of paramagnetic resonance has been particularly fruitful in chemistry. It has enabled the first detection of free radicals in 10^{-10}- to 10^{-13}-mole quantities. The study of paramagnetic resonance in biological materials has been successfully initiated.

Most recently, paramagnetic resonance has found important applications in radio engineering in the construction of a new kind of low-noise amplifier.

These examples explain the intense current interest in this method that is shown not only by physicists but also by chemists, biologists, and radio engineers.

The present book is the first attempt to give, as far as possible, a complete review of research in the field of electron paramagnetic resonance. Due to space limitations, the authors were in most cases forced to omit detailed calculations and descriptions of experimental methods; these, however, are well presented in readily available texts in Russian. In this work the most detailed expositions cover theoretical materials and experimental data on ionic crystals, since these are the materials that have been most extensively studied by the methods of paramagentic resonance.

This book encompasses all the basic literature on EPR up to 1959. In addition, the authors have attempted to give a résumé of all the more important results of theoretical calculations and all the experimental data that merit the greatest confidence.

Chapter I was written by both authors; Chapters II, IV and VII and Sections 5.5 and 5.7 of Chapter V are the work of B. M. Kozyrev; Chapters III, VI and VIII and Sections 5.1–5.4, 5.6 and 5.8–5.10 of Chapter V were written by S. A. Al'tshuler.

The authors wish to express their deep gratitude to Ye. K. Zavoyskiy for helpful discussion of many of the topics considered in this book. We are also extremely grateful to R. Sh. Nigmatullin, who reviewed the manuscript of Chapter II, to V. B. Shteynshleiger, who reviewed the section of the book devoted to paramagnetic amplifiers, and to N. G. Koloskova, for the great assistance she rendered in compiling the tables.

S. A. Al'tshuler and B. M. Kozyrev

Kazan, July 15, 1959

Contents

Basic Notation

A—magnetic hyperfine interaction constant;
a—spin Hamiltonian constant;
a_0—Bohr radius;
B—magnetic hyperfine interaction constant;
c—velocity of light;
D, E—spin Hamiltonian constants;
e—electron charge;
e_{eff}—effective charge;
F—spin Hamiltonian constant;
g—spectroscopic splitting factor;
g_0—Landé g factor;
g_x, g_y, g_z—principal values of the g tensor;
g_N—nuclear g factor;
$g(\nu)$—shape function of the paramagnetic resonance absorption line;
H_0—static magnetic field intensity;
H_r—amplitude of the oscillatory magnetic field;
$\mathcal{H}_{\text{cr}}$—electron energy in the electric field of the crystal;
$h \equiv 2\pi\hbar$—Planck's constant;
I—nuclear spin quantum number;
J—total quantum number of the electron shell;
J, J_{ik}—exchange integral;
k—Boltzmann constant;
L—electron orbital angular momentum quantum number;
M—quantum number of the projection of J;
M_k—k-th moment of the resonance line;
M—number of ions per unit cell;
M_m—number of magnetically nonequivalent ions per unit cell;
m_e—electron mass;
N_0—number of unpaired spins per cm^3;
N_k—number of unpaired spins on level k per cm^3;
n—population difference of two neighboring spin sublevels;
n_0—population difference of two neighboring spin sublevels in the equilibrium state;
P—hyperfine quadrupole interaction constant;
P—power of the radio-frequency field adsorbed in 1 cm^3 of a paramagnetic sample;
$p_{MM'}$—probability of transition of the system from level M to level M' under the influence of an oscillatory magnetic field;

Q—quality factor;
q—nuclear quadrupole moment;
q_{lk}—saturation factor;
R—equilibrium distance from the center to the edge of the octahedral complex;
S—spin quantum number of the electron;
S'—effective spin;
T—absolute temperature;
T_1—longitudinal paramagnetic relaxation time;
T_2—transverse paramagnetic relaxation time;
T_{21}—cross-relaxation time;
v—mean velocity of sound;
Z—nuclear charge;
β_0—Bohr magneton;
β_N—nuclear magneton;
γ—gyromagnetic ratio;
$\Delta\nu$—line width of paramagnetic resonance in cps;
ΔH—line width in gauss;
θ—Debye temperature;
χ_0—static paramagnetic susceptibility;
χ—complex paramagnetic susceptibility;
χ'—real part of χ;
χ''—imaginary part of χ;
μ—magnetic moment of a particle;
ν—frequency of the oscillatory magnetic field;
ν_0—Larmor precession frequency;
ρ—density pf a substance;
σ—absorption coefficient of ultrasound;
τ—spin-lattice relaxation time;
τ'—spin-spin relaxation time.

CHAPTER I

Introduction

1.1. Elementary Magnetic Resonance

Many contemporary methods of investigating the properties of particles possessing nonzero magnetic moments are based on the phenomenon which may be called elementary magnetic resonance. The use of magnetic resonance made possible Rabi's well-known molecular beam method for the determination of nuclear magnetic moments [1], the measurement of the magnetic moment of a neutron by Alvarez and Bloch [2], the determination of the value of the fine structure of the positronium ground state by Deutsch [3], the discovery of a new optical effect by Kastler [4], etc. This phenomenon of elementary magnetic resonance is also the basis of paramagnetic resonance and of several other related effects exhibited by substances containing particles with nonzero magnetic moments.

The fundamentals of elementary magnetic resonance may be understood in terms of simple classical concepts. Suppose a particle having a magnetic moment μ is placed in a magnetic field of intensity H_0. Then, the moment μ will precess around H_0 with the Larmor frequency $\nu_0 = g_0 (eH_0/4\pi m_0 c)$, where g_0 is the Lande g factor, which equals 2 for particles with pure electronic spin, and equals 1 for particles with pure electronic orbital magnetism.

Suppose that a weak magnetic field H_1 is applied at right angles to H_0 and rotates around it at a frequency ν (Figure 1.1). If $\nu = \nu_0$, then the additional rotary moment which arises due to the action of the field H_1 is always directed so that the magnetic moment μ tends to be located in the equatorial plane. As a result there occurs a rapid fluctuation in the orientation of the moment μ.

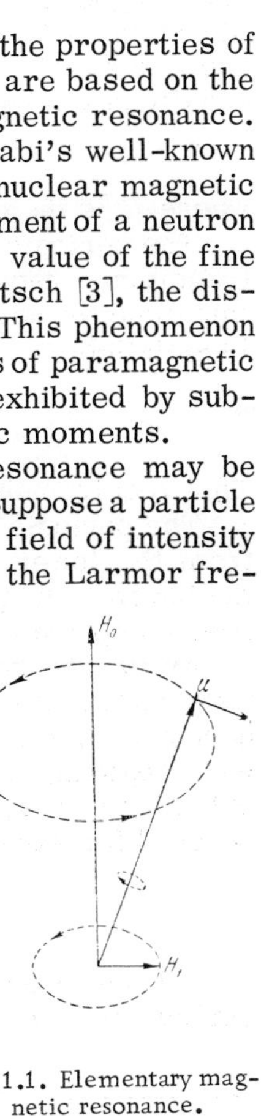

Fig. 1.1. Elementary magnetic resonance.

If the frequencies ν and ν_0 differ appreciably, the effect of the field H_1 will be negligible because the resulting motion of the moment μ rapidly changes phase with respect to the precessional motion. For the same reason, the effect of the field will also be small if the direction of rotation of H_1 is opposite to the direction of precession. In practice this fact enables one to replace the rotating field by an oscillating field, which can be represented as the composition of two fields of identical magnitudes, rotating in opposite directions at the same frequency.

The question may arise as to what extent the magnitude of the resonant effect depends on how close ν is to ν_0. The smaller the ratio H_1/H_0 the greater will be the sharpness of the magnetic resonance.

Let us proceed to consider the quantum picture of elementary magnetic resonance. Suppose that a particle possesses mechanical and magnetic moments, whose maximum components along the direction of H_0 are represented by $J\hbar$ and μ, respectively. As we know, $\mu = g_0\beta J$, and hence the magnetic field H_0 gives rise to $2J+1$ equally spaced energy levels,[1] namely:

$$E_M = g_0\beta H_0 M, \tag{1.1}$$

where M is the magnetic quantum number, $J \geq M \geq -J$.

The periodic magnetic field $H_r \cos 2\pi\nu t$ induces magnetic dipole transitions between adjacent energy levels ($\Delta M = \pm 1$), provided this field is perpendicular to H_0,[2] and if the resonance condition is satisfied:

$$E_M - E_{M-1} = g_0\beta H_0 = h\nu. \tag{1.2}$$

This requirement is identical with the classical condition: $\nu = \nu_0$.

The periodic field induces with equal probability the transitions from the lower to the upper energy levels and from the upper to the lower. The probabilities of these nonadiabatic transitions have been computed by Guttinger [5], Majorana [6] and Rabi [1].

As can be readily calculated from Eq. (1.2), for all magnetic field intensities encountered in present-day experiments the frequency of Larmor precession lies in the radio-frequency or microwave regions. This fact is of great practical significance. Because of it, highly sensitive and convenient radio engineering apparatus may be used for experiments based on elementary magnetic resonance.

1.2. Paramagnetic Resonance

Let us proceed from the treatment of an isolated magnetic particle to a macroscopic body containing a large number of such

---

[1]If the magnetic moment of a particle is comprised of both a spin and an orbital part, we shall assume that the field H_0 is not capable of disrupting the spin-orbit coupling.

[2]If the magnetic particle is not isolated, but is, for instance, located in a crystalline lattice, resonance transitions are possible in several cases for a parallel arrangement of the periodic and of the steady magnetic fields (see Chapter III).

particles. We shall call these bodies paramagnetic regardless of the magnitude of the diamagnetic component of the total magnetic moment of the substance. The behavior of a paramagnetic substance in a magnetic field will depend essentially on the interaction of the paramagnetic particles with one another and with the neighboring diamagnetic particles. These interactions will favor the establishment of a thermodynamic equilibrium, if that equilibrium is disturbed for any reason. Hence, if the equilibrium state has been attained in a static magnetic field H_0 and the distribution laws of classical statistics are applicable, the populations of the individual energy levels are determined by the Boltzmann factor $e^{-g_0\beta H_0 M/kT}$. The populations of the lower energy levels are greater than those of the upper levels; therefore, when a periodic magnetic field with the resonance frequency is switched on, the number of absorption events produced by the field will exceed the number of induced radiation events, and as a result the substance will absorb energy from the radio-frequency field. Thus, two opposing processes take place in paramagnetic resonance: the radio-frequency field tends to equalize the populations of the various magnetic levels, and the internal interactions tend to restore the Boltzmann distribution by conversion of the energy absorbed from the radio-frequency field into heat.

A steady state is finally established: the populations of the magnetic levels cease to change, and the radio-frequency energy is uniformly absorbed by the paramagnetic substance. In addition, if the intensity of the periodic field is very high, the populations of the various magnetic levels in the steady state will level off, after which no additional energy is absorbed when the radio-frequency field power is increased (saturation sets in).

The paramagnetic resonance absorption effect is thus found to be intimately related to processes determining the kinetics of the magnetization of paramagnetic substances, or in other words, to paramagnetic relaxation. The hypothesis of Casimir and Du Pre [7, 8], suggesting that the magnetization of a paramagnetic substance be considered a two-stage process, was found to be exceedingly fruitful in the theory of paramagnetic relaxation: 1) equilibrium is established inside the "spin system," that is, the system of the magnetic moments of all the paramagnetic particles, and 2) an exchange of energy occurs between the spin system and the "lattice" which comprises all the remaining degrees of freedom of the paramagnetic substance. It is clear that such a treatment is possible provided the interactions within the spin system (spin-spin interactions) are much stronger than the interactions of the spin system with the lattice (spin-lattice interactions).

If we exclude very low temperatures, the lattice temperature may be regarded as constant because its heat capacity is much greater than that of the spin system. Hence the lattice acts like a thermostat in which the spin system is immersed. A certain temperature which is, in general, different from the lattice temperature may also be attributed to the spin system. The process of establishing an equilibrium between the spin system and the lattice may be considered as an exchange of energy between the systems, leading to temperature equalization. The rate of this process may be characterized by the spin-lattice relaxation time, which will be denoted by τ. There may be dramatic differences in the mechanisms of spin-lattice relaxations from one substance to another. Therefore, in addition to being strongly dependent on the temperature of a paramagnetic substance, the magnitude of τ varies over wide limits from one substance to another.

The rate at which equilibrium is established within the spin system may be characterized by the spin-spin relaxation time τ'. Obviously, the very possibility of dividing a paramagnetic substance into a spin system and a lattice system presupposes that $\tau' \ll \tau$. In contrast with time τ, the magnitude of τ' depends very little on lattice temperature. We note one more difference between spin-spin and spin-lattice relaxation. The process of establishing an equilibrium within a spin system consists in an exchange of energy between its various parts, although the total energy of the spin system is conserved. Spin-lattice relaxation, however, is associated with a change in the energy of the spin system.

In his phenomenological theory of paramagnetic resonance, Bloch [9] introduced two relaxation times: the longitudinal T_1 and the transverse T_2. Let the paramagnetic substance be situated in a static field H_0. The time T_1 then characterizes the rate at which the equilibrium state is established if there is an instantaneous change in the magnitude of the field H_0, assuming its direction is preserved. The time T_2 determines the relaxation if there is an instantaneous change in the direction of the field H_0 while its absolute magnitude is preserved. The time T_1 characterizes the process of establishment of the equilibrium, related to the change in spin system energy, and may therefore be identified with the spin-lattice relaxation time τ. The time T_2 describes the rate of the relaxation process whereby the energy of the spin system remains unchanged; it may be identified with the time τ'. However, the equivalences of the times τ to T_1, and τ' to T_2 will not always hold. This is because the concepts of longitudinal and transverse relaxation times T_1 and T_2 may always be introduced, while the times τ and τ' have meaning only if $\tau \gg \tau'$. We are here totally omitting the question of whether the two parameters T_1 and T_2 are sufficient for a description of the complex process of paramagnetic relaxation. It will be seen later that certain cases require the introduction of a greater number of parameters (see Chapter V).

The internal interactions in a paramagnetic substance not only cause energy absorption from the radio-frequency field but also produce broadening in the paramagnetic resonance line. If for an isolated particle the sharpness of the magnetic resonance depends on the ratio H_1/H_0, in the absence of saturation the sharpness of the resonance and the related absorption line width for a paramagnetic substance are determined by the spin-spin and spin-lattice interactions. Let us assume that spin-spin interactions are much stronger than spin-lattice interactions and let us consider two neighboring magnetic particles. Assuming these particles to be isolated, as a first approximation, we may assign the system of energy levels (1.1) to each of them. Let the first particle be located in level with a magnetic quantum number M_1 and let the second particle be in level M_2. Due to spin-spin interactions, there arises a certain probability A' that within 1 second these particles will exchange energy. Thus, if the first particle makes a transition to a level with the magnetic quantum number $M_1 + 1$, the second jumps to the level $M_2 - 1$. The spin-spin relaxation time τ' will be of the order $1/A'$; it, as we can see, determines the lifetime of a particle in a given magnetic energy level. Consequently, the width of the absorption line due to spin-spin interactions may be estimated as $1/\tau'$.

If the spin-lattice interactions predominate, the concept of the time τ' loses meaning. However, the spin-lattice relaxation time τ may be introduced if we consider the probability of a transition of an individual paramagnetic particle from one magnetic energy level to another under the influence of thermal motion. If this probability per second equals A, $\tau \sim 1/A$ and the absorption line width will be of the order of $1/\tau$. In the general case, however, the absorption line width may be estimated as $1/\tau + 1/\tau'$. No general form of the rigorous correlation between relaxation time and line width can be given, however, because that correlation depends greatly on the shape of the absorption line.

From our knowledge of the temperature dependence of the relaxation time it follows that if the line width of a paramagnetic resonance absorption is determined by spin-lattice interactions, it will decrease rapidly as the temperature decreases. If, on the other hand, spin-spin interactions play a dominant role, the temperature dependence of the line width will be very slight.

The position and number of lines of paramagnetic resonance absorption also depend on the internal interactions of a paramagnetic substance. If the form of the energy spectrum produced by the field H_0, were not influenced by the internal interactions, the system of energy levels would be given by Eq. (1.1), as before; furthermore, if the selection rules for transition between the levels under the influence of the periodic magnetic field were also preserved, only one absorption line would exist. The position of this line for the given field intensity H_0 would be determined by the magnitude of the Landé factor g_0. In actuality, however, even though systems of equidistant magnetic energy levels are preserved in many paramagnetic substances, the g factor deviates from its value for a free particle because of these internal interactions. Figure 1.2 shows the curve of paramagnetic resonance absorption in chromium chloride; the absorption maximum corresponds to a g factor ≈ 2, as may be easily computed by means of (1.2), whereas for the ground state $^4F_{3/2}$ of a free Cr^{3+} ion, the Landé g factor is 2/5. The absorption curve in the figure shows the magnitude of the energy absorbed by the paramagnetic substance from the radio-frequency field per second, as a function of the strength H_0 of the static magnetic field. The reason for these coordinates is that in the vast majority of cases the experiments are performed with a fixed frequency ν and a variable field H_0.

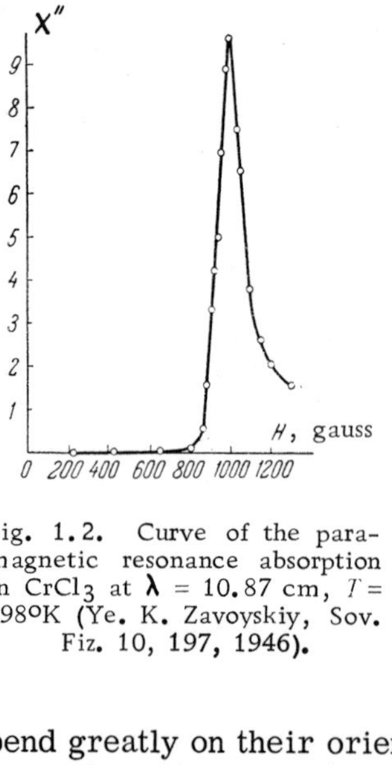

Fig. 1.2. Curve of the paramagnetic resonance absorption in $CrCl_3$ at λ = 10.87 cm, T = 298°K (Ye. K. Zavoyskiy, Sov. Fiz. 10, 197, 1946).

In condensed media, as Kittel [10] has noted, the g factor, which determines the magnitude of the splitting of the energy levels in a magnetic field, does not coincide with the factor giving the gyromagnetic ratio which is obtained from measurements of magnetomechanical effects. We shall therefore follow Kittel and call the g factor resulting from paramagnetic resonance experiments the spectroscopic splitting factor.

The system of Zeeman energy levels in many paramagnetic substances, especially those whose magnetism is not purely spin, ceases to be equally spaced. For this reason, several absorption lines arise instead of one, and we say that fine structure is observed in the paramagnetic resonance spectrum. The form of the spectrum in single crystals may depend greatly on their orientation with respect to the field $\mathbf{H}_0$. As an example, Figure 1.3 is a diagram of the splitting of the ground level of a Cr^{3+} ion situated in the lattice of an Al_2O_3 crystal, as a function of the intensity of a magnetic field $\mathbf{H}_0$, applied parallel to the trigonal axis of the crystal. In this figure $\epsilon = E_M/D$, $x = g\beta H_0/D$ and $2D$ is the zero-field splitting. Figure 1.4 shows photographs of the fine structure of the paramagnetic resonance spectrum for two different crystal orientations; the trigonal axis is parallel or perpendicular to the field H_0.

It is apparent from Figure 1.3 that even in the absence of the field H_0 there is in the radio-frequency region a splitting of the ground level of the paramagnetic particle. Thus, in many cases resonance absorption of the radio-frequency energy may occur by means of magnetic dipole transitions between sublevels existing even in the absence of the steady magnetic fields.

Finally, we note that the selection rules are altered because of the internal interactions. For instance, transitions between other than adjacent Zeeman energy levels become possible; thus, a paramagnetic substance in which these levels are equidistant will show satellites at $2\nu_0$, $3\nu_0$, etc., in addition to the main absorption line corresponding to the Larmor frequency ν_0.

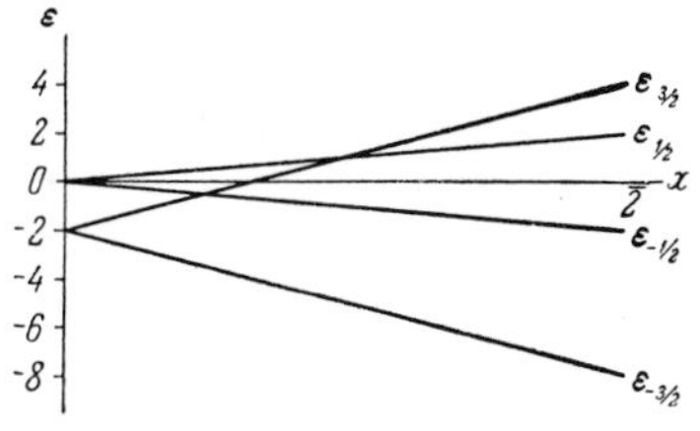

Fig. 1.3. Diagram of the splitting of the ground level of a Cr^{3+} ion located in a trigonal crystalline field and in a magnetic field H_0 applied parallel to the trigonal axis.

The form of the paramagnetic resonance spectrum depends on the existence of magnetic moments in the nuclei of the paramagnetic

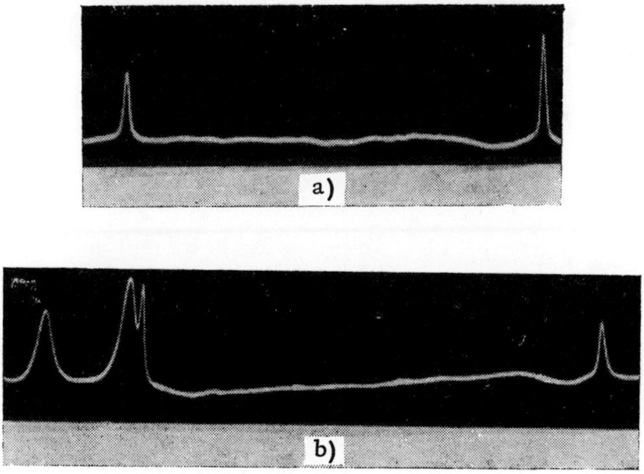

Fig. 1.4. Photographs of fine structure spectrum of Cr^{3+} in Al_2O_3. a—H_0 parallel to the trigonal axis of the crystal; b—H_0 perpendicular to the trigonal axis of the crystal.

atoms (molecules). The interactions of the magnetic moment of the nucleus and the magnetic moment of the electron shell both with each other and with the static magnetic field H_0 create a new system of energy levels in the paramagnetic substance. It is of essence whether 1) the field H_0 is so strong that the coupling between the electronic and nuclear moments breaks down, or whether 2) the field H_0 is so weak that this coupling is preserved. In the first case, the position of the paramagnetic resonance absorption line arising from the magnetic moments of the electron shells of the atoms (molecules) is unchanged, but hyperfine structure appears: each line breaks up into several components, their number depending on the nuclear spin. In the second case the spectral pattern changes completely because the g factors which determine the location of the absorption line assume entirely different values.

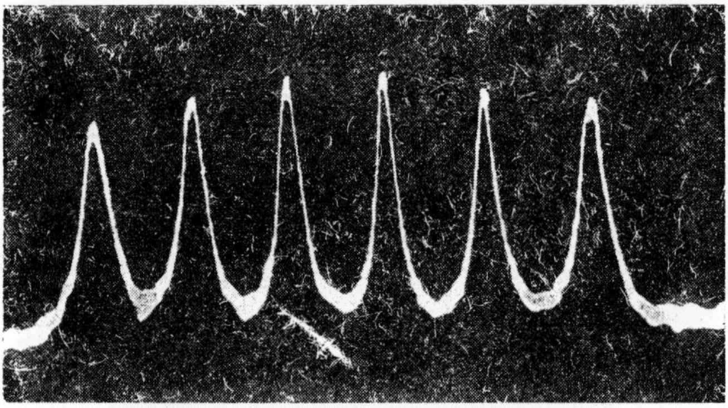

Fig. 1.5a. Hyperfine structure of the spectrum of Mn^{2+} in an aqueous solution of $MnCl_2$ at $\nu = 9345$ Mc.

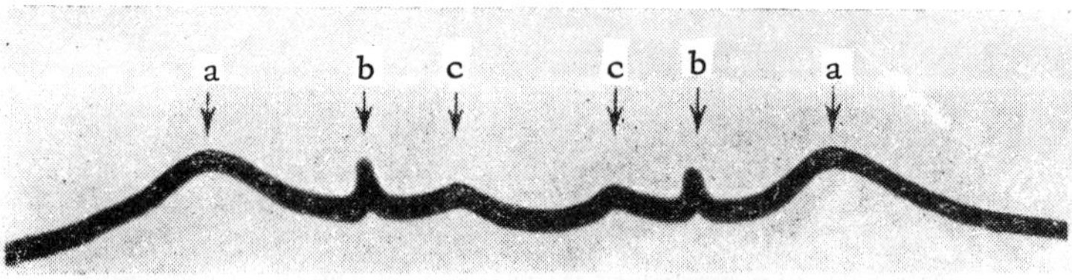

Fig. 1.5b. Influence of the nuclear spin on the spectrum of Mn^{2+} in an aqueous solution of $MnCl_2$ at $\nu = 147$ Mc. a—$^{55}Mn^{2+}$ ($g = 1$); b—free radical ($g = 2$); c—Fe^{3+} impurity in the glass ampoule.

Figure 1.5a shows the absorption spectrum observed in an aqueous solution of $MnCl_2$ at $\nu = 9345$ Mc in a strong field H_0, which varies over the range of 2900 to 3400 gauss. The center of the spectrum corresponds to $g = 2.000$, and this g factor would determine the position of the absorption line if that line were not split by the magnetic moment in the manganese nucleus. Figure 1.5b shows the absorption spectrum, which consists of one line, when observed in the same solution of $MnCl_2$ at a frequency of 147 Mc and in a weak field H_0 varying over the range of -175 to +175 gauss. This absorption maximum corresponds to a value of g almost exactly equal to one. Thus, the interaction with the nucleus in weak fields decreases the g factor by a factor of two in our case. Figure 1.6 shows the typical fine structure and hyperfine structure of the Mn^{2+} spectrum observed in a single crystal of apatite.

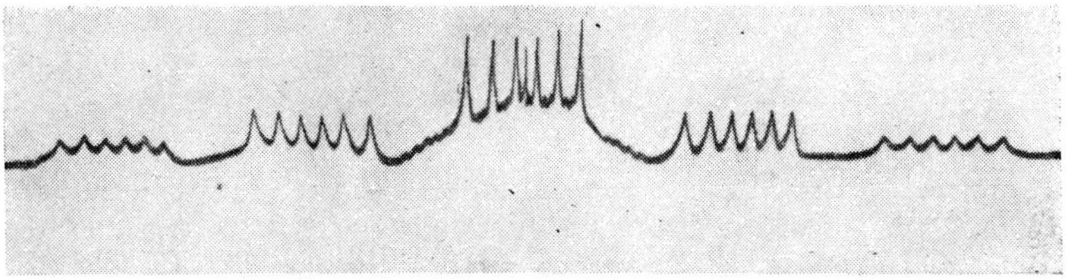

Fig. 1.6. Fine structure and hyperfine structure of the spectrum of Mn^{2+} in manganese apatite at $\nu \approx 10^{10}$ cps; each of the five lines of the fine structure is split into six hyperfine components. (The narrow line at the center of the third group is due to a free radical.)

Several other phenomena are closely related to paramagnetic resonance absorption. It can easily be deduced that under conditions of resonance the action of a periodic magnetic field on the paramagnetic substance should change its magnetization. As a result, the paramagnetic susceptibility shows a strong dependence on the frequency ν, and if ν is close to ν_0 the dispersion of the susceptibility becomes anomalous. The rotation of the plane of polarization of the radio waves and other magneto-optical phenomena also have an anomalous character, provided the experimental conditions are such that the magnetic vector of the wave is perpendicular to the applied static magnetic field and the frequencies ν and ν_0 are almost equal.

We have examined the different aspects of the paramagnetic resonance effect and we may now give a general definition for it.

Paramagnetic resonance is the body of phenomena related to quantum transitions taking place between the energy levels of a macroscopic system under the influence of a periodic magnetic field of resonance frequency.

In this definition we speak of a body of phenomena because in addition to paramagnetic resonance absorption we observe paramagnetic resonance dispersion, paramagnetic resonance rotation, etc. Moreover, we emphasize here that the phenomena are observed in macroscopic systems where spin-spin, spin-lattice and similar interactions occur; this distinguishes paramagnetic resonance from Rabi's resonance experiments with molecular beams, from those of Alvarez and Bloch with neutron beams, etc.

Finally, if we accept that Debye dispersion and absorption of electromagnetic waves in dielectrics take place as a result of electric dipole transitions induced by the electric component of the wave, then the phenomena studied by us are due to magnetic dipole transitions which are excited by the magnetic field.

In the vast majority of cases, paramagnetic resonance is studied by application of two magnetic fields to a paramagnetic substance. Thus, a strong static and a weak periodic field are used. However, we have seen in the example of the Cr^{3+} ion that under the influence of a radio-frequency field there is a possibility of magnetic dipole transitions even in the absence of a static magnetic field. It is natural also to classify under paramagnetic resonance the phenomena connected with transitions of this type.

The great difference in magnitudes of the magnetic moments of electrons and nuclei produces a natural subdivision into electronic and nuclear paramagnetic resonance, although the experimental investigative methods and the theory of both effects have much in common. Nuclear paramagnetic resonance should also include nuclear quadrupole resonance—a phenomenon due to magnetic dipole transitions which, in the absence of an external static magnetic field, occur between the energy levels produced by the interaction of the nuclear quadrupole moments with electric fields inside condensed media.

1.3. Magnitude of the Effect

We shall now establish several quantitative relations. Suppose that under the influence of an external magnetic field and internal forces the ground energy level of a magnetic particle is split into η sublevels, which are labeled by the quantum numbers M and M'. According to the quantum theory of radiation, the probability per second that the oscillating magnetic field $H_r \cos 2\pi\nu t$ will cause a transition from level M to level M' is equal to

$$p_{MM'} = \frac{8\pi^3}{h^2} |\langle M | \mu_x | M' \rangle|^2 \rho_\nu, \tag{1.3}$$

where $\langle M | \mu_x | M' \rangle$ is the matrix element of the component of the magnetic moment of the particle in the direction of the periodic magnetic field, and $\rho\nu$ is the mean spectral density of the electromagnetic energy, which in our case may be given by the expression

$$\rho_\nu = \frac{H_r^2}{8\pi} g(\nu). \tag{1.4}$$

We have introduced here a shape factor $g(\nu)$, which takes into account the fact that the absorption line is not infinitely narrow, but has a noticeable width. The function $g(\nu)$ reproduces the absorption line shape and is normalized so that

$$\int_0^\infty g(\nu)\,d\nu = 1. \tag{1.5}$$

If the temperature of the paramagnetic substance is sufficiently high, so that $E_M - E_{M'} = h\nu \ll kT$, then for a volume of 1 cm^3 containing N_0 magnetic particles the difference in populations of the pair of levels M and M' will equal:

$$N_M - N_{M'} = \frac{N_0}{\eta}\,\frac{h\nu}{kT}. \tag{1.6}$$

From Eqs. (1.3), (1.4) and (1.6) we obtain the following expression for the power absorbed per unit volume of the paramagnetic substance in the transitions from the level M to the level M':

$$\begin{aligned} P_{MM'} &= (N_M - N_{M'})\,p_{MM'}\,h\nu = \\ &= \pi^2 \frac{N_0}{\eta kT} \left| \langle M | \mu_x | M' \rangle \right|^2 H_r^2 \nu^2 g(\nu). \end{aligned} \tag{1.7}$$

To obtain the total power P absorbed as the result of transitions between all the sublevels, it is necessary to sum over all possible values of M and M'. Since the static paramagnetic susceptibility equals [11]:

$$\chi_0 = \frac{2N_0}{\eta kT} \sum_{M>M'} \left| \langle M | \mu_x | M' \rangle \right|^2, \tag{1.8}$$

then

$$P = \frac{\pi^2}{2}\,\chi_0 H_r^2 \nu^2 g(\nu). \tag{1.9}$$

The total power is of interest when the matrix elements $\langle M | \mu_x | M' \rangle \neq 0$ for those pairs of levels which have identical separations, since in this case the transitions between the various pairs of levels give the same absorption line.

The Q factor of a loaded paramagnetic circuit may be determined from the equation

$$\frac{1}{Q} = \frac{\left(\frac{P}{\nu}\right)}{2\pi\,(H_r^2/8\pi)} = 2\pi^2 \chi_0 \nu g(\nu). \tag{1.10}$$

The maximum absorption, which occurs at the frequency $\nu = \nu_0$, may be related to the width $\Delta\nu$, for if we write

$$g(\nu_0) = \frac{q}{\Delta\nu}, \tag{1.11}$$

then it is apparent from (1.5) that $q \approx 1$. The precise value of q depends on the shape of the absorption line; if the line has a Gaussian shape, $q = 0.939$; while with a Lorentzian shape, $q = 0.636$ (see Sec. 1.4).

Equation (1.7) is valid if the field H_r is considered to be so small that it does not disturb the equilibrium energy level distribution of the particles. Disturbances may set in as the intensity of the radio-frequency radiation is increased; these disturbances lead to a saturation effect. Let us establish a quantitative criterion for the existence of this effect. Let us consider the simplest case of paramagnetic particles possessing only two energy sublevels. Let us designate by n the excess population of the lower sublevel over the population of the upper sublevel; in the equilibrium state let $n = n_0$. It may be deduced that from the definition of the spin-lattice relaxation time that in the absence of a radio-frequency field, the transition to the equilibrium state will be determined by the equation

$$\frac{dn}{dt} = -\frac{n - n_0}{\tau}. \tag{1.12}$$

With a radio-frequency field present, the equation for n takes the form:

$$\frac{dn}{dt} = -\frac{n - n_0}{\tau} - 2np_{MM'}. \tag{1.13}$$

Under steady-state conditions, we have

$$\frac{n}{n_0} = [1 + 2\tau p_{MM'}]^{-1}. \tag{1.14}$$

An energy level split in a magnetic field into two sublevels may always be assigned an effective spin $S' = 1/2$ and a spectroscopic splitting factor g, whose method of calculation will be indicated in Chapter III. We may therefore write

$$< M | \mu_x | M' > = < -\tfrac{1}{2} | g\beta S'_x | +\tfrac{1}{2} > = g\beta. \tag{1.15}$$

Substituting (1.3) into (1.14) and using (1.4), (1.11) and (1.15) we obtain

$$\frac{n}{n_0} = \left[1 + \frac{2\pi^2 q g^2 \beta^2 \tau H_r^2}{h^2 (\Delta\nu)}\right]^{-1}. \tag{1.16}$$

The ratio $n/n_0 = 1$ at equilibrium and tends to zero as saturation is approached. The quantity $q_n = n/n_0$ is called the saturation factor. If the frequency of Larmor precession in a field of strength H_r is denoted by $\nu_r = g\beta H_r/h$, the following condition is the criterion of saturation:

$$\nu_r^2 \gg \Delta\nu \frac{1}{\tau}. \tag{1.17}$$

1.4. Paramagnetic Resonance as a Part of the General Study of Magnetism

The present-day study of paramagnetism is characterized by the transition from the investigation of magnetic properties of materials under static conditions to the study of phenomena observed in periodic magnetic fields. The body of contemporary knowledge of dynamic paramagnetism is developing along three directions: 1) adiabatic demagnetization, 2) paramagnetic relaxation, and 3) paramagnetic resonance.

The relationship between these fields is so close that some authors [12] regard paramagnetic resonance, for instance, as part of the study of paramagnetic relaxation, while others [13], on the contrary, look upon paramagnetic relaxation as a paramagnetic resonance caused by a transition of zero frequency. This close link allows an over-all theoretical treatment of a number of problems relevant to all three fields, as well as gathering of mutually complementary data on various physical constants, such as magnetic heat capacity, relaxation times, etc.

The study of the behavior of substances in steady magnetic fields is fundamentally characterized by the static susceptibility χ_0. However, in the study of dynamic phenomena it is convenient to look upon the susceptibility as a complex quantity: $\chi = \chi' - i\chi''$. That part of the magnetization which changes in phase with the field is determined by the dynamic susceptibility χ', while the absorption of the energy from the periodic field by the paramagnetic substance is determined by the quantity χ''. The problem confronting the theory of paramagnetic absorption and dispersion is the establishment of the dependence of the quantities χ' and χ'' on the frequency of the periodic field and the intensity of the applied static field. The general relation between the coefficients χ' and χ'' is given by the Kramers-Kronig equations [14]

$$\chi'(\nu) = \frac{2}{\pi}\int_0^\infty \frac{\nu_1\chi''(\nu_1)}{\nu_1^2 - \nu^2}\, d\nu_1 + \text{const}, \quad \chi''(\nu) = -\frac{2}{\pi}\int_0^\infty \frac{\nu\chi'(\nu_1)}{\nu_1^2 - \nu^2}\, d\nu_1. \tag{1.18}$$

The dispersion formulas were obtained in closed form only for gases [15]. Obviously, a simple solution of this problem is hardly possible for condensed systems, with their very complicated internal interactions. It is therefore necessary to use approximate equations. A comparison of (1.18) at $\nu = 0$ with (1.5) gives a relation between the magnitude of χ'' and the line shape function $g(\nu)$:

$$\chi''(\nu) = \frac{\pi}{2}\nu\chi_0 g(\nu). \tag{1.119}$$

When comparing with experiment the usual form of $g(\nu)$ is either a Gaussian-type function such as

$$g(\nu) = \frac{1}{\sqrt{2\pi}\,\sigma}\left\{e^{-\frac{(\nu-\nu_0)^2}{2\sigma^2}} + e^{-\frac{(\nu+\nu_0)^2}{2\sigma^2}}\right\} = g_1(\nu) + g_2(\nu), \tag{1.20}$$

or a Lorentzian-type function

$$g(\nu) = \frac{\Delta\nu}{2\pi}\left\{\frac{1}{(\nu-\nu_0)^2 + \frac{1}{4}\Delta\nu^2} + \frac{1}{(\nu+\nu_0)^2 + \frac{1}{4}\Delta\nu^2}\right\} = g_1(\nu) + g_2(\nu). \tag{1.21}$$

Here $\nu_0 = g\beta H_0/h$, $\sigma = \Delta\nu/(2\sqrt{2\ln 2})$, and $\Delta\nu$ is the width of the absorption line at high frequencies. The second terms on the right-hand sides of Eqs. (1.20) and (1.21) vanish for $\nu \gg \Delta\nu$; however, it is necessary to introduce them in order to determine the parity of the absorption effect with respect to the field H_0 [16].

In electron paramagnetic resonance experiments one studies the dependence of χ' and χ'' on the magnitude of the field H_0 for ν = const. The form of the Kramers-Kronig relation must therefore be modified [16]:

$$\left.\begin{aligned} \chi_0 - \chi'(H_0) &= \frac{1}{\pi}\int_0^\infty \frac{F(H_0+H) - F(H_0-H)}{H}\,dH, \\ F(H_0) &= \frac{1}{\pi}\int_0^\infty \frac{\chi'(H_0+H) - \chi'(H_0-H)}{H}\,dH, \end{aligned}\right\} \tag{1.22}$$

where $F(H_0) = \chi''(H_0) - \pi\nu\chi_0 g_2(\nu)$. Since $g_2(\nu)$ is a monotonically decreasing function, it is not important what expression is used for it. In the majority of cases paramagnetic resonance is studied by measuring $\chi''(H_0)$. Paramagnetic dispersion under resonance conditions was first observed by Zavoyskiy [17] in the salt $MnSO_4$; subsequent measurements of $\chi'(H_0)$ are described in [18]. Figure 1.7 shows typical curves of paramagnetic resonance absorption and dispersion.

Paramagnetic resonance may be detected not only by measuring χ' and χ'', but also by observing the rotation of the plane of polarization of microwaves in paramagnetic substances under the influence of a static magnetic field. This effect has been theoretically studied by a number of authors [19], and the corresponding measurements have been made [20].

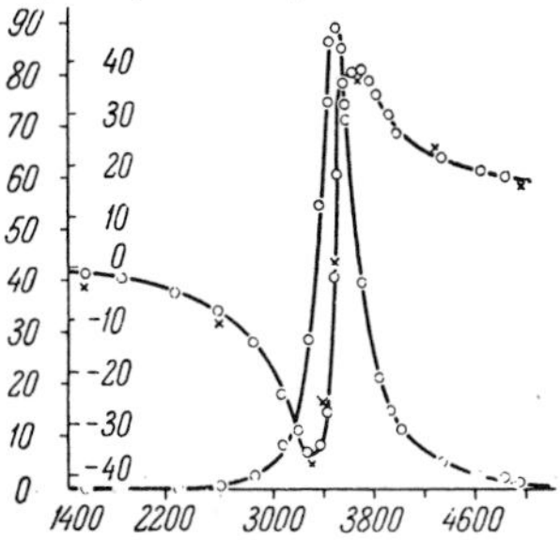

Fig. 1.7. Curves of paramagnetic resonance absorption and dispersion of the susceptibility in $MnSO_4$ at ν = 9620 Mc (B. M. Kozyrev, S. G. Salikhov, Yu. Ya. Shamonin, Zh. Exp. i Teor. Fiz. 22, 56, 1952).

Between the angle of deflection of the plane of polarization and the paramagnetic absorption there exists a simple integral relation [21]:

$$\varphi = \frac{4\pi\nu\sqrt{\varepsilon}}{c} \int_0^\infty \frac{\chi''(H_0 + H) - \chi''(H_0 - H)}{H} dH. \tag{1.23}$$

Here ϵ is the dielectric constant of the paramagnetic substance. A typical curve of $\varphi(H_0)$ is given in Figure 1.8.

Integral relations (1.22) and (1.23) allow checking for the accuracy of the form of the experimental curves of paramagnetic resonance. Other analogues of magneto-optical phenomena in microwaves under conditions of magnetic resonance such as the Cotton-Mouton effect [22] are being investigated.

The body of results obtained by means of paramagnetic resonance gives important characteristics of various substances. It will be sufficient to name but a few: the determination of the magnetic and mechanical moments of atoms, molecules and atomic nuclei; paramagnetic relaxation times; etc.

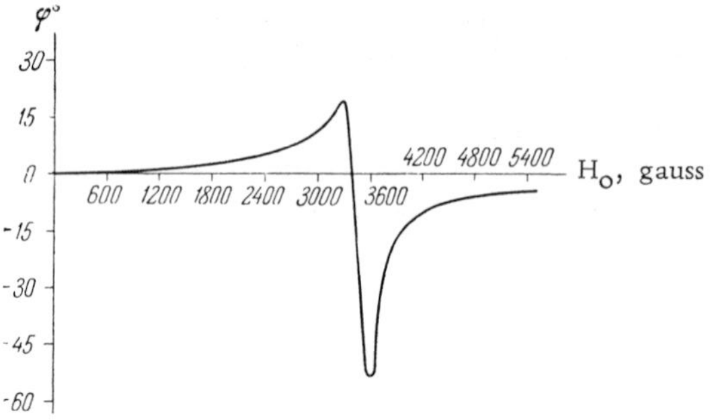

Fig. 1.8. Curves of the paramagnetic resonance rotation in $CuSO_4 \cdot 5H_2O$ (N. N. Neprimerov, Izv. AN SSSR, Ser. fiz., 18, 368, 1954).

1.5. Paramagnetic Resonance and Spectroscopy

Paramagnetic resonance is an integral part of spectroscopy, as it provides a means for determining the position of the energy levels of magnetic particles. It is interesting to consider the peculiar features of paramagnetic resonance in comparison with optical spectroscopy.

1. Let us first note that the frequencies used in magnetic resonance experiments range from 10^6 to 10^{11} cps. These frequencies, situated below the limits of the infrared part of the spectrum, allow highly accurate investigation of energy level splittings so small that they are inaccessible or almost inaccessible by optical methods.

2. The probability of spontaneous transition in the radiofrequency region is very small, since this probability is proportional to ν^3. Therefore, in paramagnetic resonance studies one is forced to deal only with induced absorption and emission.

3. While in the great majority of cases optical spectra arise from electric dipole transitions between energy levels, the lines of paramagnetic resonance absorption arise exclusively from magnetic dipole transitions. Consequently, the Einstein coefficients for induced absorption and emission will, in the case of paramagnetic resonance, be smaller by roughly four orders of magnitude.

4. As a result, the paramagnetic resonance effect is exceedingly small; that it can be observed at all is due to the high sensitivity of electronic methods of detection and the enormous number of photons coming into play. Thus, 1 mw corresponds to $n \approx 10^{20}$ photons per sec at a frequency of 10^{10} cps.

5. From the uncertain relation between the number of photons and the phase of the electromagnetic wave it follows that because of the extremely large magnitude of n, the phase can be determined with very great precision in paramagnetic resonance. Thus, the electromagnetic field may be considered as a classical quantity in radio-frequency spectroscopy.

6. In the optical frequency region the line width is always very small in comparison with the fundamental frequency. In paramagnetic resonance the relation between these quantities becomes quite different, since the interactions causing a broadening of the lines can be of the same order of magnetude as the energy splitting which determines the resonance frequency. Because of this the width of paramagnetic resonance lines is often comparable to the fundamental frequency and can be measured with great accuracy. This opens up wide possibilities for investigation of different types of interactions in paramagnetic substances by means of analysis of the shape and width of a paramagnetic resonance line and of the character of its dependence upon various factors.

7. The most important factors determining the line width are magnetic dipole interactions, exchange forces, local electrical fields created by neighboring magnetic particles, and finally, thermal motion; the natural line widths of radio-frequency spectra are completely negligible.

8. In contrast with optical experiments, in radio-frequency spectroscopy it is customary to use radiation which is so monochromatic that the generated band of frequencies is incomparably narrower than the absorption line width.

9. Paramagnetic resonance spectra are not studied by varying the frequency of the incident radiation, but by varying the characteristic frequencies of the absorbing systems. This is achieved by varying the static magnetic field.

1.6. History of the Discovery of Paramagnetic Resonance

Paramagnetic resonance was discovered in Kazan by Ye. K. Zavoyskiy (1944). His first experiments dealt with resonance absorption in salts of the iron group ions. Zavoyskiy's discovery was preceded by some theoretical assumptions on the nature of the expected effect. Following the well-known Stern-Gerlach experiments on spatial quantization, Einstein and Ehrenfest [24] advanced a number of arguments concerning quantum transitions between magnetic sublevels of atoms under the influence of equilibrium radiation. On the basis of these considerations, Dorfman suggested in 1923 the possibility of resonance absorption of electromagnetic waves by paramagnetic substances, naming this phenomenon the photomagnetic effect [25].

In 1932, there appeared the fundamental work of I. Waller [26], performed at the suggestion of Pauli and containing a quantum theory of paramagnetic relaxation in solids. This work served as a basis for the further development of the theory of dynamic phenomena in paramagnetic substances and, in particular, of paramagnetic resonance.

In the mid-thirties Gorter and his co-workers [8] began a systematic study of the absorption and dispersion of radio-frequency electromagnetic waves by paramagnetic substances. The studies were conducted at frequencies of 10^6–$3 \cdot 10^7$ cps in the presence of static magnetic fields. But Gorter's attempt to detect paramagnetic resonance was fruitless [27] because of imperfections in technique and the use of insufficiently high frequencies.

Zavoyskiy [23] developed new and highly sensitive methods for the study of paramagnetic resonance: instead of calculating the amount of heat liberated by the paramagnetic substance, as did Gorter, he began to measure the weakening of the energy of the high-frequency field as a result of absorption. In order to obtain fully resolved lines of paramagnetic resonance absorption, he widened the range of utilized frequencies to $3 \cdot 10^9$ cps. Not only did he succeed in discovering the phenomenon of paramagnetic resonance, but he also investigated a number of its properties and considerably enlarged the scope of paramagnetic relaxation studies.

The first theoretical interpretation of Zavoyskiy's experiments was advanced by Ya. I. Frenkel' [28].

The discovery of an analogous effect in atomic nuclei, made by Purcell [29] and Bloch et al. [30] within two years after publication of Zavoyskiy's work, was a natural sequel to the study of paramagnetic resonance determined by the magnetic moments of electrons. Finally, in 1950 Dehmelt and Kruger [31] discovered a paramagnetic resonance determined by transitions between nuclear quadrupole energy levels in crystals in the absence of an external magnetic field.

In the postwar years, there appeared an enormous number of papers based on this method. The great progress in microwave engineering on the one hand and, on the other, the discovery of very valuable applications of the paramagnetic resonance method to the solution of certain problems in solid-state physics, nuclear physics, chemistry and engineering gave a great impetus to the study of this field.

Literature for Chapter I

1. Rabi, I. I. Phys. Rev. 51, 652, 1937.
2. Alvarez, Z. W., Bloch F. Phys. Rev. 57, 111, 1940.
3. Deutsch, M. Phys. Rev. 84, 601, 1951; 85, 1047, 1951.

4. Kastler, A. J. J. Phys. Radium 11, 255, 1950; Physica 17, 191, 1957.
5. Guttinger, P. Z. Phys. 73, 169, 1931.
6. Majorana, E. Nuovo Cimento 9, 43, 1932.
7. Casimir, H. B. G., du Pré, F. K. Physica 5, 507, 1938.
8. Gorter, C. Paramagnetic Relaxation, Elsevier, Amsterdam, 1947.
9. Bloch, F. Phys. Rev. 70, 460, 1946.
10. Kittel, C. Phys. Rev. 76, 743, 1949.
11. Van Vleck, J. H. The Theory of Electric and Magnetic Susceptibilities, Oxford, 1932.
12. Shaposhnikov, I. G. Doctor's Dissertation, Moscow, FIAN, 1949.
13. Gorter, C. Uspekhi Fiz. Nauk. 53, 545, 1954.
14. Kramers, H. A. Atti Congr. Fis., Como, 545, 1927; Kronig, R. J. Opt. Soc. Amer. 12, 547, 1926.
15. Van Vleck, J. H., Weisskopf, V. F. Rev. Mod. Phys. 17, 227, 1945; Frolich, H. Nature 157, 478, 1948.
16. Al'tshuler, S. A. Zh. Eksp. Teor. Fiz. 20, 1047, 1950.
17. Zavoyskiy, Ye. K. Zh. Eksp. Teor. Fiz. 17, 155, 1947.
18. Kozyrev, B. M., Salikhov, S. G., Shamonin, Yu. Ya. Zh. Eksp. Teor. Fiz. 22, 56, 1952; Romanov, I. M. Uch. Zap. KGU 113, 187, 1953; Neprimerov, N. N. Izv. AN SSSR, Ser. Fiz., 18, 360, 1954.
19. Kastler, A. J. Compt. Rend. 228, 1640, 1949; Tsirul'nikova, L. M., Shaposhnikov, I. G. Izv. AN SSSR, Ser. Fiz., 20, 125, 1956. Shekun, L. Ya. Izv. AN SSSR, Ser. Fiz., 20, 1262, 1956.
20. Wilson, M. C., Hull, G. F. Phys. Rev. 74, 711, 1948; Neprimerov, N. N. Izv. AN SSSR, Ser. Fiz., 18, 368, 1954.
21. Shekun, L. Ya. Izv. AN SSSR, Ser. Fiz., 20, 1262, 1956.
22. Battaglia, A., Gozzini, A., Polacco, E. Nuovo Cimento 10, 1205, 1953; Hedvig, P. Acta Phys. Hung. 6, 489, 1957.
23. Zavoyskiy, Ye. K. Doctor's Dissertation, Moscow, FIAN, 1944; J. Phys. USSR. 9, 245, 1945.
24. Einstein, A., Ehrenfest, P. A. Phys. 11, 31, 1922.
25. Dorfman, Ya. Ga. Z. Phys. 17, 98, 1923.
26. Waller, I. Z. Phys. 79, 370, 1932.
27. Gorter, C. J. Physica 3, 995, 1936; 9, 591, 1942; Deikstra, Z. F. Thesis, Amsterdam, 1943.
28. Frenkel', Ya. I. Zh. Eksp. Teor. Fiz. 15, 409, 1945.
29. Purcell, E. M., Pound, R. V., Torrey, N. S. Phys. Rev. 69, 37, 1946.
30. Bloch, F., Hansen, W. W., Packard, N. Phys. Rev. 69, 127, 1946.
31. Dehmelt, H. G., Kruger, H. Naturwiss. 37, 111, 1950; Z. Phys. 129, 401, 1951.

CHAPTER II

Methods of Measurement

2.1. Microwave Spectroscopy

The currently used technique for measuring paramagnetic resonance is based on the determination of a change of some parameter in the oscillating system containing the paramagnetic substance. Such a change occurs as a result of absorption, dispersion of the paramagnetic susceptibility, or rotation of the plane of polarization in the substance under investigation.

Techniques of this type were first developed by Zavoyskiy both for the frequency region 10^7-10^8 cps [1] and for higher frequencies of the order 10^9 cps [2], which approach the microwave region.

Before the discovery of paramagnetic resonance, the experiments performed by Gorter and his school [3], concerned with studies of paramagnetic losses of a nonresonant character at frequencies up to 10^7 cps, were conducted by means of calorimetric measurement of the heat evolved in a paramagnetic substance. This heat evolution was determined from the rate of heating of the sample due to the losses occurring in it. Because of its low sensitivity and the difficulty of separating paramagnetic absorption from other forms of loss (dielectric loss, losses by electrical conduction), such a method could not be used for the study of paramagnetic resonance. Although Gorter's technique of measuring the dynamic susceptibility χ' belongs to the category of indirect electrical methods, it is suitable only for very low frequencies. Thus, the foundation of contemporary methods of radio-frequency spectroscopy were actually established by Zavoyskiy.

Of course the measuring technique is different for the microwave-frequency region ($\nu \approx 10^{10}$ cps) on one hand, and for the radio-frequency region ($\nu \approx 10^6$-10^9 cps) on the other. This fact gives some authors a basis for distinguishing between radio-frequency and microwave magnetic spectroscopy. However, such a distinction has little foundation, since the nature of the phenomena under investigation is the same in both cases.

We shall first consider the methods employed in the microwave region. Every microwave magnetic spectrometer consists of the following basic parts: 1) a microwave oscillator with a stabilized frequency and power supply and frequency and power controls; 2) an absorption cell in the form of a cylindrical or rectangular cavity resonator; 3) a detector; 4) an amplifier and recording device; and 5) a source of a steady magnetic field. In the majority of cases we must add to these parts 6) a system for modulation of the steady magnetic field (see, for instance, Fig. 2.2).

The cavity resonator containing the sample of the substance under investigation is placed between the poles of an electromagnet in such a way that the static and microwave magnetic fields acting on this substance are mutually perpendicular. The sample is placed at a site in the cavity such that the microwave magnetic field is maximal and the electric field is minimal (to reduce the nonmagnetic losses). During the measurement process, the frequency of the microwave oscillator exciting the electromagnetic oscillations in the cavity is kept constant. However, the intensity of the static magnetic field is variable. The selection of these experimental conditions is dictated by the fact that a study of the dependence of the paramagnetic absorption coefficient on the microwave frequency for $H_0 = \text{const}$ would introduce additional experimental difficulties connected with changes in oscillator power during changes in the frequency of the radiation produced by it.

Two basic types of microwave magnetic spectrometers are used. In the first type the paramagnetic resonance absorption is detected by the change in power transmitted through the cavity resonator containing the substance (the transmitted wave method), and in the second, absorption is detected by the change in power reflected from the cavity containing the substance (the reflected wave method).

The transmitted wave method was first applied experimentally by Cummerow, Holliday and Moore [4], who showed that the coefficient of paramagnetic absorption may be determined by measuring the output power of the cavity resonator.

The second method enables us to evaluate the coefficient of paramagnetic absorption from the coefficient of reflection of the cavity resonator containing the material under investigation. Whitmer, Weidner, Hsiang and Weiss [5] have constructed a microwave magnetic spectrometer which operates on the principle of a T bridge with the use of a double T joint. From the measured power P, which arises as the result of an unbalance of the bridge due to paramagnetic losses, one may determine the reflection coefficient γ, which is related to the dynamical susceptibility of the paramagnetic substance:

$$P \sim \gamma^2 = \text{const}\,(\chi'^2 + \chi''^2). \tag{2.1}$$

In modern spectrometers both the transmitted wave method and the reflected wave method are used.

Before proceeding to a treatment of actual individual experimental arrangements, which differ mainly in the method of detection of the transmitted or reflected power, we shall discuss several factors that determine the sensitivity of a magnetic spectrometer. By virtue of (1.9) and (1.19) a paramagnetic sample placed in an oscillating magnetic field $H_r \cos 2\pi\nu t$ absorbs power $P = \pi\nu \chi'' H_r^2$. The power absorbed by the cavity resonator itself may be expressed as $P_0 = (1/Q_0)\nu(H_r^2/4)V$, where Q_0 is the Q factor of an unloaded cavity, and V is its effective volume. Therefore, the ratio of the power absorbed by the sample under investigation to the power dissipated by the cavity itself equals

$$\frac{P}{P_0} = \frac{4\pi\chi'' Q_0}{V}. \tag{2.2}$$

It is apparent from (2.2) that the maximum sensitivity of the apparatus for the measurement of the coefficient of paramagnetic absorption χ'' will be achieved with the smallest volume and the largest Q factor of the unloaded cavity resonator.

For a sample containing paramagnetic particles with spin $S = 1/2$, the absorption coefficient will be $\chi'' \approx \chi_0(\nu/\Delta\nu)$ where χ_0 is the static magnetic susceptibility of the sample, ν is the frequency of the oscillating magnetic fields, and $\Delta\nu$ is the width of the resonance absorption line, expressed in units of frequency. When $S = 1/2$ and $g = 2$ the static magnetic susceptibility of one mole of a material equals $\chi_0 = 0.38/T$. If the wavelength of the microwave oscillator is $\lambda \approx 3$ cm, and the width of the paramagnetic resonance line is of the order of 1 gauss,[1] i.e., $\sim 10^{-4}$ cm^{-1}, at room temperature $\chi''_{\text{mole}} \approx 4$. Therefore, in order to decrease the Q factor of the cavity to 1/2 of its value $Q_0 \approx 5000$ in the absence of a load, we must place in the cavity $\sim 10^{-5}$ mole of our paramagnetic substance, if we assume for the effective volume $V \approx 2$-3 cm^3.

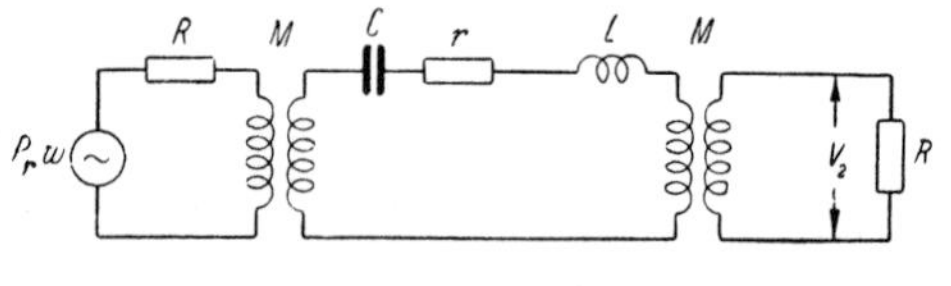

Fig. 2.1. Equivalent circuit (for the determination of the sensitivity of a microwave spectrometer).

According to Bleaney and Stevens [6], to evaluate the limiting sensitivity of the spectrometer, we may consider an equivalent circuit, where the resonant cavity is represented by a tuned circuit of series resistance r (Figure 2.1). Microwave radiation is coupled into this circuit through a mutual inductance M from an oscillator

---

[1] Such line widths can usually be observed with free radicals.

of available power P_1 and of internal impedance R. The radiation is detected by a receiver also of impedance R. If the oscillator has angular frequency ω and is exactly tuned to the resonant circuit, the voltage across the detector is

$$V_2 = \frac{r'(RP_1)^{\frac{1}{2}}}{r+r'},$$

where $r' = 2\omega^2 M^2 / R$.

If, owing to paramagnetic absorption, the series resistance r changes by δr, the change in the detector voltage is

$$\delta V_2 = \frac{r'(RP_1)^{\frac{1}{2}} \delta r}{(r+r')^2}.$$

Since r' depends on the tightness of coupling into the resonant circuit, we can adjust it by changing the coupling (i.e., the value of M). The sensitivity will be greatest when the voltage δV_2 at the detector reaches a maximum, which occurs when $r = r'$. We express δV_2 in terms of the power P_2, reaching the receiver. We have then $\delta V_2 = \delta r\, RP_2\,)^{1/2} / (r + r')$. This expression shows that the fractional change $\delta V_2 / (RP_2\,)^{1/2}$ in the voltage at the receiver equals $\delta r/(r+r')$. Thus, as we increase the coupling, P_2 goes up, but compensating for this the value of the loaded Q falls due to the heavier coupling. At the optimum, the detector voltage change due to the paramagnetic absorption becomes

$$\delta V_2 = (RP_1)^{\frac{1}{2}} \frac{\delta r}{4r}.$$

If the receiver has a noise factor N and bandwidth df, then the signal output will equal the noise output when the condition $\delta V_2 = (NkTdfR)^{1/2}$ is observed.

Also, $\delta r / r$ represents the ratio of the power absorbed by the sample to that dissipated by the cavity resonator, which as we have seen equals $4\pi \chi'' Q_0 / V$. Thus, for the minimum value of χ'' which can be recorded by the equipment, we find the condition

$$\chi''_{\min} = \frac{V}{\pi Q_0} \left(\frac{NkTdf}{P_1} \right)^{\frac{1}{2}}. \tag{2.3}$$

With the resonant cavity assumed previously, at $Q_0 = 5000$ and $\lambda = 3$ cm, at $N = 10$, $df = 1$ cps, and oscillator power of 40 mw and

$V = 2\text{-}3\ cm^3$, the theoretical minimum value of χ''_{min} is approximately 10^{-13} at room temperature. With an absorption line width $\sim 10^{-4}\ cm^{-1}$ this should correspond to the possibility of obtaining a signal at this noise level from $\sim 2.5 \cdot 10^{-13}$ mole of paramagnetic particles with $S = 1/2$ (at 300°K). Actually the sensitivity which can be achieved in the apparatus, as a rule, is much lower than this value and depends greatly on many factors, in particular on the applied frequency and on the method of measuring the signal.

The existing spectrometers may be divided into several groups according to the method of detection of paramagnetic resonance microwave spectra: 1) DC detection; 2) detector and audio amplifier; 3) double modulation method; and 4) superheterodyne method. Recently there have appeared papers [7] in which investigation of very narrow lines of electron paramagnetic resonance are carried out by the spin echo method, previously used only for nuclear paramagnetic resonance.

The first method is the simplest to realize, but because of its low sensitivity it was employed only in the early stages of the development of magnetic radio-frequency spectroscopy, when the investigations dealt with relatively coarse effects occurring in undiluted paramagnetic substances with broad and intense absorption lines. In this method the microwave signal from a transmission or reflection cavity is rectified and is fed through a compensating circuit to a sensitive galvanometer. The paramagnetic absorption curve is plotted by the "point-by-point" method: the galvanometer deflections, which are proportional to the power passing through the detector, are recorded for different values of the steady magnetic field intensity H_0. For each value of H_0 the cavity is previously tuned to the oscillator frequency.

On converting to an investigation of the narrower and weaker absorption lines observable in diluted paramagnetic substances, methods giving greater sensitivity and enabling one to obtain either an oscilloscope image or a tracing of the spectral pattern are required.

A method satisfying these requirements consists in the use of modulation of the steady field H_0 by an audiofrequency magnetic field; such modulation was first employed by Zavoyskiy [1] in 1944 during research in the radio-frequency region. If the amplitude of the field H which modulates the given external steady magnetic field sweeps across a paramagnetic resonance absorption line, there will be a corresponding modulation of the power reflected or transmitted by the resonant cavity. This modulated power can be amplified and displayed on an oscilloscope whose horizontal sweep is synchronized with the field modulation. During a single modulation period the resonant values of the field H_0 will be passed through twice; therefore the part of the spectrum that is encompassed by the amplitude modulation (or at sufficiently large amplitude, the entire spectrum) will be displayed on the screen of an oscilloscope in a form which is doubled and symmetrical with respect to the center of the picture, and which represents the function $\chi''(H_0)$. Such a method of studying paramagnetic resonance is quite satisfactory for an initial examination of paramagnetic spectra, but a study of the details of these spectra, however, is more conveniently conducted by using an amplitude modulation that is very small compared to the width of the line under investigation. In this case when the field H_0 gradually passes through the resonance region, we obtain a curve for the dependence of the derivative $d\chi''/dH_0$ on H_0 which is usually recorded.

A block diagram of a microwave spectrometer with low-frequency modulation of the magnetic field and with a transmission type resonant cavity is illustrated in Figure 2.2.

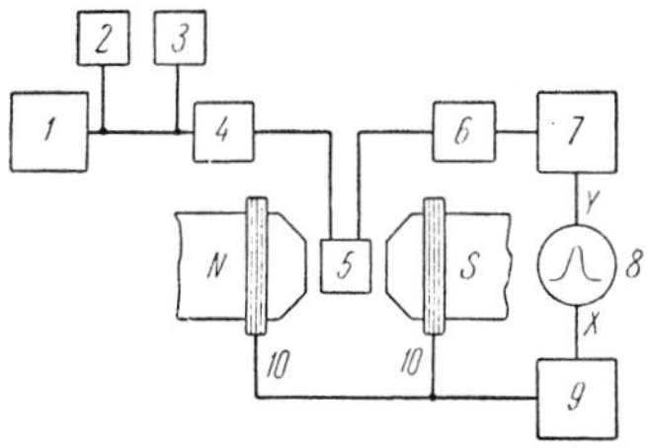

Fig. 2.2. Microwave spectrometer with flow-frequency modulation of the magnetic field (transmitted wave method).
1—Microwave generator; 2—frequency control; 3—power control; 4—attenuator; 5—resonant cavity with the sample; 6—crystal detector; 7—audio-frequency amplifier; 8—oscilloscope; 9—phase shifter; 10—modulation coil.

An apparatus with the same field modulation, but operating according to the reflected wave method, is described by Manenkov and Prokhorov [8]. It is illustrated in Figure 2.3.

The sensitivity of this type of spectrometer is limited mainly by the low-frequency noise of the crystal detector. By constructing a spectrometer using a bolometer as their detector, Beringer and Castle [9] have eliminated this noise and thereby obtained greater sensitivity. With a bolometer it is possible to detect power of the order of a milliwatt without any appreciable low-frequency noise. In the Beringer and Castle apparatus the transmitted wave method is used. The microwave generator is frequency stabilized and the narrowband phase-sensitive amplifier operates at a frequency of 30 cps, which also serves as the field modulation frequency. The experimentally estimated sensitivity of this spectrometer does not differ greatly from the theoretically attainable value. A block diagram of the Beringer and Castle spectrometer is shown in Figure 2.4. This spectrometer was designed for the study of very weak paramagnetic resonance lines observable in rarefied gases.

Another method of increasing the sensitivity of a microwave spectrometer was first used by Smaller and Yasaitis [10] for paramagnetic resonance measurements. It consists in the use of double modulation of the magnetic field. The spectrometer constructed on this principle by Buckmaster and Scovil [11] has a sensitivity no less than that of a spectrometer with a bolometer. The double modulation principle consists in the following: the spectral noise density of a crystal detector is inversely proportional to the frequency (at least over the range 1 to $24 \cdot 10^9$ cps). Consequently, if in addition to a large amplitude modulation at the audiofrequency ν_2 we apply a second modulation of the magnetic

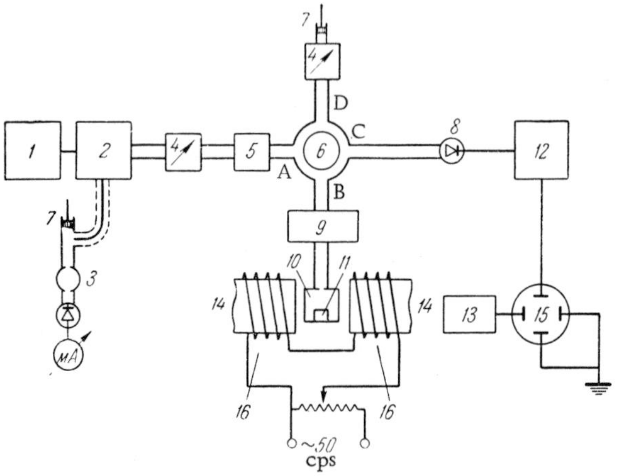

Fig. 2.3. Microwave spectrometer with low-frequency modulation of the magnetic field (reflected wave method) [8]. 1—Stabilized voltage source; 2—klystron oscillator; 3—wavemeter; 4—attenuator; 5—phase shifter; 6—hybrid ring (magic T); 7—plunger; 8—crystal detector; 9—stub; 10—cavity resonator; 11—sample; 12—low-frequency amplifier; 13—sweep; 14—electromagnet; 15—oscilloscope; 16—modulation coil.

field at frequency ν_2, which is sufficiently high that the fractional excess low-frequency noise over the thermal noise in the crystal detector becomes negligibly small, and if the amplification is carried out at the frequency ν_2, then the sensitivity (in comparison with audiofrequency amplification) should increase sharply. We note that the amplitude of the high-frequency modulation must not exceed the half-width of the spectral lines under investigation [12].

In the Buckmaster and Scovil spectrometer a cylindrical cavity is excited in the TE_{111} mode, and the power source is a microwave generator at $\lambda = 1.2$ cm. The frequency of the first modulation is $\nu_1 = 60$ cps and the frequency of the second modulation is $\nu_2 = 462.5$ kc. A block diagram of this spectrometer is given in Figure 2.5. The microwave power from a reflex klystron is fed through a transmission resonant cavity to a diode crystal detector. Instrumentation is placed in front of the cavity to regulate and control the incoming microwave power and to measure the wavelength. The video signal obtained at the output of the crystal detector passes through an amplifier tuned at 462 kc having an amplification factor of 10^6 and a passband width of 8 kc; amplification occurs up to a level at which the signal can be detected linearly. The output of either an ordinary linear detector or a phase-sensitive detector is fed to an oscilloscope. In the first case, the oscillogram gives the modulus of the derivative of the line shape, and in the second case it gives the derivative itself. The voltage of the time sweep on the oscillograph is fed through the phase shifter from the power source of the low-frequency modulation of the magnetic field (Helmholtz coil). By using the method of narrowband amplification instead of applying a magnetic field of frequency ν_1, a slow and linear passage of the field H_0 is obtained.

The greatest difficulty is the realization of high-frequency modulation, because this necessitates the introduction of a radio-frequency magnetic field inside the resonant cavity. For this purpose the resonant cavity is partially slotted in a plane passing through its axis. If the slot width is small in comparison with the wavelength λ, the Q of the cavity changes little. Only the modulation current flowing along the inner surface of the cavity is effective in producing a radio-frequency field. This was made sufficiently large to ensure at the site of the investigated substance a radio-frequency magnetic field with an amplitude up to 50 gauss.

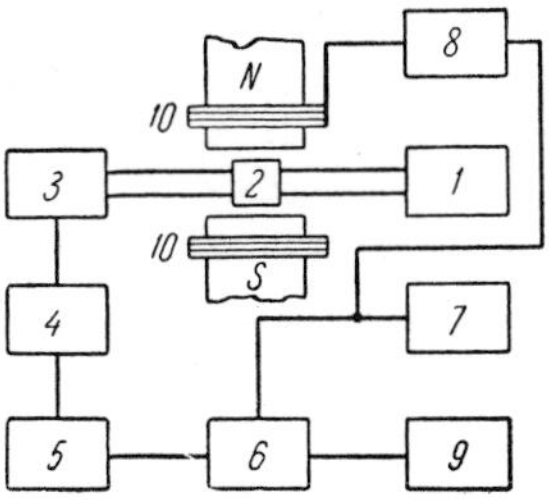

Fig. 2.4. Microwave spectrometer using a bolometer [9]. 1—Stabilized microwave oscillator; 2—cavity resonator; 3—bolometer; 4—DC bridge; 5—high gain 30 cps amplifier; 6—lock-in amplifier; 7—30 cps power amplifier; 9—long-time constant galvanometer; 10—modulation coil.

An experimental estimate of the sensitivity of the Buckmaster and Scovil spectrometer with amplification at a frequency of 462 kc and with an amplifier bandwidth of 8 kc shows that, at 290°K, 10^{-11} mole of a free radical with a line width of 3.5 gauss gives a signal-to-noise ratio of 2:1 for a standard derivative of the line shape. Calculations show that with the use of very narrowband amplification (1 cps) the ultimate sensitivity should be of the order of 10^{-13} mole of a free radical at 290°K.

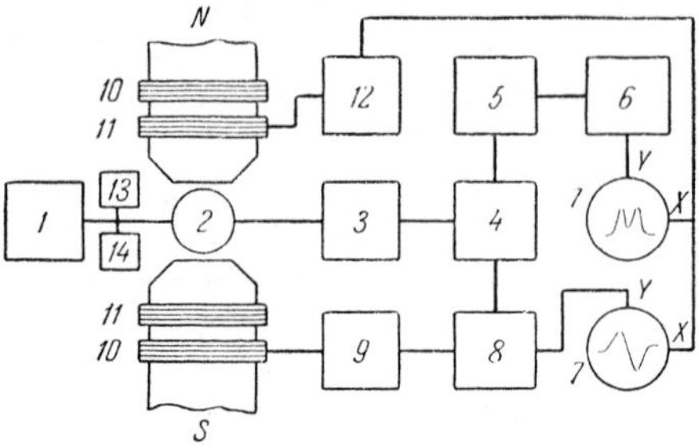

Fig. 2.5. Microwave spectrometer with double modulation of the magnetic field [11]. 1—Stabilized oscillator; 2—resonant cavity with the sample; 3—detector; 4—amplifier at the frequency $\nu_2 + \Delta\nu$; 5—linear detector; 6—amplifier at ν_1; 7—oscilloscope; 8—phase-sensitive detector; 9—phase shifter at ν_2; 10—modulation coil at ν_2; 11—modulation coil at ν_1; 12—phase shifter ν_1; 13—frequency meter; 14—power monitor.

The microwave magnetic spectrometer of Semenov and Bubnov [13] is also based on the principle of double modulation. It utilizes high-frequency modulation at 975 kc and low-frequency modulation at 50 cps. The amplitude of the low-frequency modulation is on the order of 300 gauss. The spectrometer provides a system for automatically tuning the oscillation frequency of the klystron generator to the cavity resonator. A voltage of approximately 15 mv is supplied to the reflex klystron from the automatic frequency control generator (630 kc). This voltage frequency-modulates the microwave oscillations produced by the klystron. If the oscillation frequency of the klystron is detuned with respect to the cavity resonator, there arises an amplitude modulation of the microwave oscillation. The phase of this "automatic frequency control" signal is determined by the sign of the detuning, and the amplitude is proportional to the magnitude of the detuning. After detection of the microwave oscillations the frequency control signal is amplified by a resonant amplifier (630 kc, 10^5 gain) and is fed to a phase-sensitive detector, whence it proceeds to the reflector electrode of the klystron. As a result there exists a frequency tuning of the klystron to the resonance frequency of the cavity containing the substance under investigation.

This device gives the Semenov and Bubnov microwave spectrometer a very high operational stability. Consequently, it is particularly suited to an investigation of the rate of chemical reactions. When oscillographic signal recording is used, its sensitivity is approximately $4 \cdot 10^{-10}$ mole of diphenylpicrylhydrazyl and approximately $8 \cdot 10^{-12}$ mole of the same substance when using a slow recorder trace. A block diagram of the spectrometer is given in Figure 2.6.

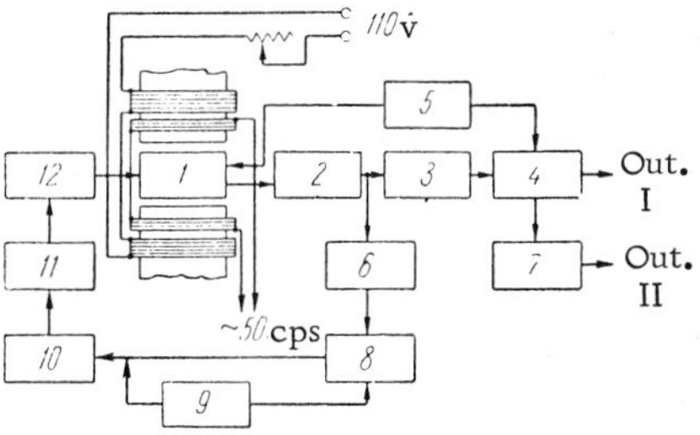

Fig. 2.6. Microwave spectrometer with double modulation and automatic frequency control [13].
1—Cavity resonator with sample; 2—microwave crystal detector; 3—amplifier (ν = 975 kc); 5—HF oscillator (ν = 975 kc); 6—signal amplifier with automatic frequency control AFC (ν = 630 kc); 7—DC amplifier; 8—AFC phase sensitive detector; 9—AFC oscillator (ν = 630 kc); 10—klystron oscillator (λ = 3.2 cm); 11—ferrite isolator; 12—variable attenuator.

The superheterodyne method of detection was first used for the study of paramagnetic resonance by England and Schneider [14]. It is based on the use of a balanced T bridge (or hybrid ring), which receives power from the measuring klystron with frequency f_1 and from the auxiliary klystron with frequency f_2. The frequency difference $f_1 - f_2$ is chosen equal to several tens of megacycles. At this intermediate frequency we amplify the signal arising as a result of the unbalancing of the bridge due to paramagnetic absorption. The low-frequency noise of the crystal detector is thereby made negligibly, small. As the difference $f_1 - f_2$ increases, however, intermediate frequency amplifier noise increases. When both of these factors are taken into account the theoretical optimum for the frequency $f_1 - f_2$ lies at about 30 Mc [15].

A specimen block diagram of a spectrometer with superheterodyne detection [16] is given in Figure 2.7.

In the absence of paramagnetic absorption, no signal should exist in the fourth arm of the bridge, when it is exactly tuned and balanced. The absorption causes an unbalance due to the variation in the reflection coefficient and as a result the power from klystron 1 begins to enter the fourth arm and is mixed in the crystal mixer with power from the auxiliary klystron, giving an intermediate frequency signal which enters the amplifier.

It should be kept in mind that the power δP reflected in the fourth arm does not equal the absorbed power ΔP, but is only part of it; according to Gordy [17]

$$\frac{\delta P}{\Delta P} = \frac{\Delta P}{P},$$

where P is the total power in the resonant cavity.

The differences in the form of the microwave magnetic spectrometer that we considered briefly make it possible to study with great accuracy the position and, with somewhat lesser accuracy, the shape of the paramagnetic resonance line. The accuracy with which the position of the line is determined depends mainly on the accuracy of measurement of the intensity of the steady magnetic field H_0 at resonance, since the resonance frequency ν can usually be measured without a large error.

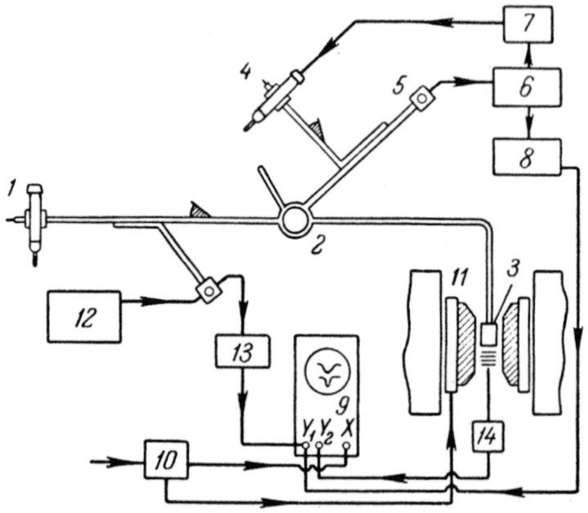

Fig. 2.7. Microwave spectrometer operating in accordance with the superheterodyne method [16]. 1—Klystron; 2—hybrid ring (or T bridge); 3—resonant cavity; 4—local heterodyne[a]; 5—mixer; 6—intermediate frequency (i.f.) amplifier; 7—automatic frequency control; 8—video amplifier; 9—oscilloscope; 10—phase shifter; 11—modulation coil; 12—frequency multiplier[b]; 13—receiver; 14—proton magnetometer.

[a] [Local oscillator klystron.]
[b] [Frequency standard and multiplier.]

As a rule the determination of the magnetic field intensity reduces also to the measurement of a certain frequency, which is generally the frequency of the proton paramagnetic resonance observed in the given magnetic field. At the present time magnetometers constructed on the principle of proton resonance are used in all cases that require a precise measurement of magnetic field. One of the methods of using proton resonance to determine the position of a paramagnetic resonance line is given in Figure 2.7. The frequency of a proton magnetometer is changed smoothly until the position of the maxima of electron and proton resonances observable on the screen of a double-beam oscilloscope are coincident at the same abscissa. One of the possible circuits of a proton magnetometer [18] is given in Figure 2.8.

Clearly the narrower the line and the higher the frequency at which we measure the paramagnetic resonance, the more accurately the position of the line can be determined. For a line with $\Delta H \approx 1$ gauss and at frequencies corresponding to the millimeter region, the accuracy of determination of the effective g factor is in the range of hundredths of a percent. In undiluted paramagnetic salts with broad lines, however, the effective g factor can be determined only to an accuracy no greater than tenths of a percent, and usually even less accuracy is obtained.

The study of the shape of a paramagnetic resonance line is a more difficult problem. Thanks to the fact that paramagnetic absorption χ'' is always accompanied by dispersion of the paramagnetic susceptibility χ'', generally speaking the observed line $\chi''(H_0)$ must be deformed to some extent as a result of an admixture of χ'. It is not difficult, however, to show [8] that the influence of dispersion on the line shape can be neglected if two conditions are observed: 1) the natural frequency of the resonant cavity under magnetic resonance conditions exactly equals the frequency of the microwave oscillator, and 2) the amount of the paramagnetic material used for the measurement is sufficiently small, so that the paramagnetic losses in the sample are small in comparison with the total losses in the cavity resonator.

A number of special methods have been developed which make it possible to separate out the pure effect $\chi''(H_0)$ or $\chi' H_0)$ [19-21]. They are essential when, for some reason or another, condition (2) cannot be fulfilled.

The technique of measuring paramagnetic rotation of the plane of polarization is reported in [22].

For lack of space we are unable to describe the separate units and details of the apparatus used in the construction of microwave spectrometers. Such descriptions can be found in the books by Gordy, Smith and Trambarulo [23], Strandberg [24] and Ingram [16], and in special radio engineering literature.

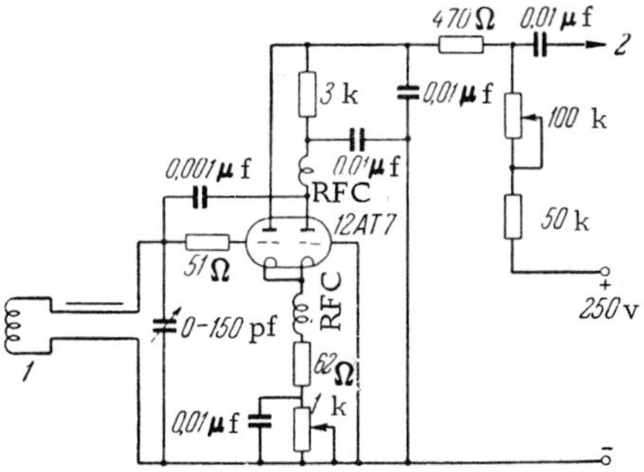

Fig. 2.8. Proton magnetometer [18]. 1—Coil with a sample of the magnetic field; 2—to the amplifier and oscilloscope; RFC are radio-frequency coils.

We shall limit ourselves here merely to a consideration of apparatus connected with low-temperature and high-temperature measurements of paramagnetic resonance.

The first extensive investigations of paramagnetic spectra at hydrogen and helium temperatures were conducted by Bleaney and his co-workers at Oxford [16]. For work at $\lambda = 1.25$ cm at liquid nitrogen and liquid hydrogen temperatures, they used a special form of a cylindrical resonant cavity with an inner diameter of 12 mm and a height from 6 to 11 mm with input and output irises located in the top of the cavity resonator for convenience in placing the resonator in a Dewar. The crystal under investigation was fastened to a small platform which covers the third orifice located at the center of the top cover of the cavity resonator. This platform was fastened to a long thin-walled silver tube, which makes it possible to turn the crystal in a chosen plane through any angle with respect to the external magnetic field. The waveguides, which conduct the microwave power to and from the cavity resonator, are made of thin-walled silver,[1] have inner dimensions 2.5 × 6 mm, and are filled with distrene almost to the upper uncooled end, where they gradually taper off. A cross-sectional view of such a cavity resonator is presented in Figure 2.9. Similar apparatus is also used for other wavelengths.

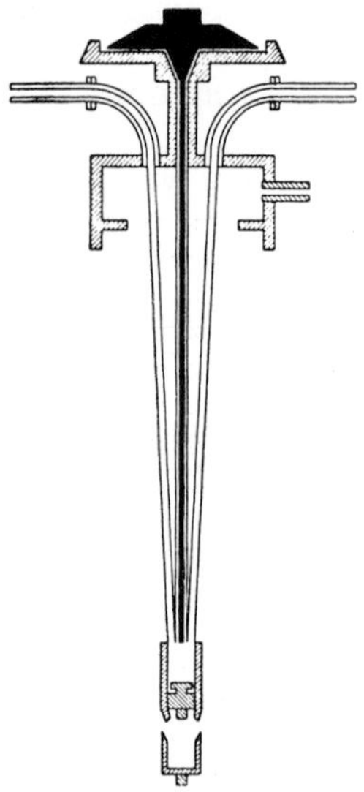

Fig. 2.9. Cavity resonator for measurement at low temperatures at a wavelength of 1.25 cm [16].

Besides this method of measurement at low temperatures, others are also used. In particular, it is highly advantageous to use a rectangular cavity resonator, in which the TE_{012} made is excited, or a cylindrical cavity resonator, in which the TE_{011} mode is excited. The distribution of the magnetic lines of force of the microwave field in such cavity resonators is indicated in Figure 2.10. In the narrow wall (or in the front of the cylinder) of the cavity resonator an orifice is cut, in which a phenoplast vessel with the sample under investigation is inserted [13]. When the necessary conditions regarding the position and dimensions of the orifice are satisfied, its presence does not very strongly effect the quality factor of the cavity resonator and consequently does not appreciably affect the sensitivity of the apparatus. Of course, a necessary condition for any measurements with a Dewar or with a phenoplast vessel placed inside the cavity resonator is a highly stable operation of the spectrometer, so that boiling of the liquid coolant does not cause distortion of the observed spectrum.

A similar technique makes it possible to make measurements both at reduced and at elevated temperatures [25]. The investigations at elevated temperatures can also be

[1] Currently for this purpose a low thermal conductivity alloy (copper-nickel, stainless steel, etc.) is most frequently used.

carried out by means of a special heating device, described in [26].

It must be remembered that in several cases (for instance in the investigation of relaxation time by the method of saturation of a paramagnetic resonance line) it is necessary to use large amplitudes of the microwave magnetic field. Pulse techniques are customarily used for such work [27, 28].

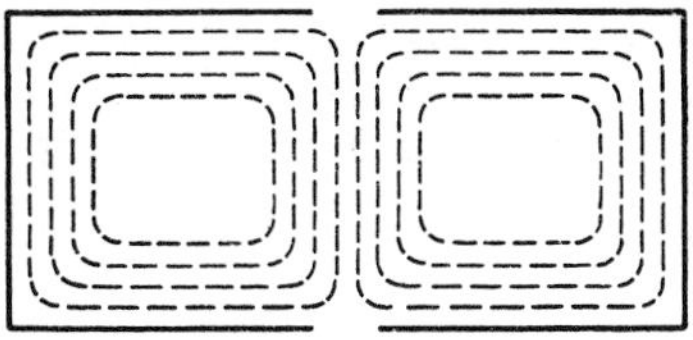

Fig. 2.10. Cavity resonator with an orifice for measurements at low temperatures.

2.2. Methods of Measurement in the Radio-Frequency Region

In the radio-frequency region at present, two types of methods of measuring $\chi''(H)$ are chiefly used: one of them may be called the method of reaction on the generator; the other is based on a determination of the change in the Q factor of the oscillatory circuit (or resonance cavity) due to paramagnetic loss.

It was already mentioned that the first investigations of Gorter on nonresonant paramagnetic absorption, observable at low frequencies, were carried out by a direct calorimetric method. The inconvenience of this method and its inapplicability to very high frequencies compelled Zavoyskiy to seek an indirect electrical method that would take paramagnetic losses into account. He developed the method of reaction on the generator [1, 2], which is widely used at present for the study of both electron and nuclear paramagnetic resonance [29, 30].

For work in the radio-frequency region, the investigated substance is not normally placed in the resonant cavity, but instead is placed in an induction coil, which is either a component part of the circuit of an electronic oscillator or is inductively coupled to it. The technique of Zavoyskiy's radio-frequency measurements is based on the fact that under certain conditions a change in the watt load ΔW on the generator, which creates the electromagnetic oscillations, causes a change in the grid ΔI_g or anode ΔI_a current of the generator, which is proportional to this change ΔW. The proportionality between ΔW and ΔI_g or ΔI_a must hold if the power dissipated by the substance due to paramagnetic absorption is small in comparison with the total losses in the circuit.

Work with radio-frequency magnetic spectrometers becomes very much simpler, and their sensitivity is greatly increased, by modulating the steady magnetic field with a low-frequency field. This modulation, which was already discussed in the preceding section, was in fact first used by Zavoyskiy for the radio-frequency region.

The simplest schematic diagram of an apparatus operating according to the method of Zavoyskiy is given in Figure 2.11.

A very simple method was used in [31] to measure the absolute values of paramagnetic absorption in the radio-frequency region. It consists in a determination of the Q factor of the induction coil of an oscillating circuit by means of a somewhat modified Q meter. This change in the quality factor is proportional to the magnitude of χ'':

$$\Delta Q = -4\pi\eta\chi'' Q^2,$$

where η is the filling factor of the coil. Similar equipment was proposed previously for the measurement of nuclear magnetic resonance [30].

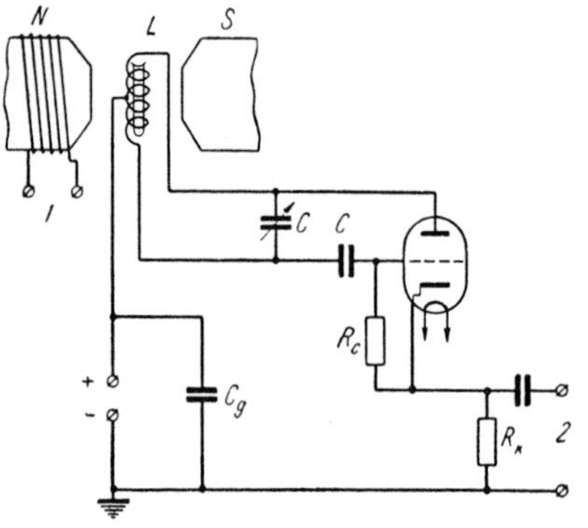

Fig. 2.11. Block diagram of a radio-frequency spectrometer operating on the method of reaction on the generator [1]. 1—Modulation winding of the electromagnet; 2—input to a low-frequency amplifier.

Radio-frequency spectrometers in which the absorption cell is the induction coil of an oscillating circuit have the advantage of conveniently placing the sample under study in a high-frequency field and easily afford the opportunity of carrying out measurements at low or high temperatures. However, the low quality factor of the coil gives such equipment a sensitivity which is not always adequate. Therefore, in certain cases, when a particularly high sensitivity is required, the induction coil of a radio-frequency spectrometer is replaced by a cavity resonator with a high Q factor. This type of radio-frequency spectrometer was constructed by Feher and Kip [32] for measurements of paramagnetic resonance in metals. A block diagram of this spectrometer is presented in Figure 2.12. In this apparatus an improved signal-to-noise ratio was achieved due to the use of a lock-in detector.

In conclusion we shall discuss briefly the sources of the steady magnetic field used in the study of paramagnetic resonance. In experiments conducted in the microwave region, where the resonance values of H_0 usually have a magnitude of 3000 gauss and higher, electromagnets are the only suitable sources for producing these fields. Since in the majority of cases the width of a paramagnetic resonance line is tens and sometimes hundreds of gauss, particularly rigid requirements regarding the uniformity of the magnetic field are not established. However, in individual cases we may observe very narrow lines, of the order of tenths of a gauss. For such measurements we use appropriate stabilization with a type of electromagnet that is employed in nuclear magnetic resonance [29].

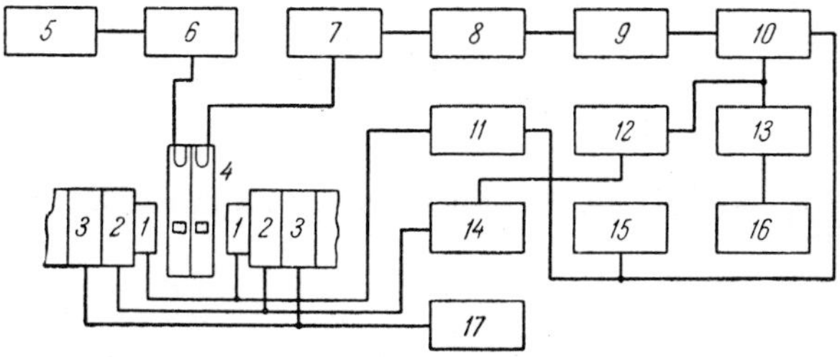

Fig. 2.12. Block diagram of a radio-frequency spectrometer, using the method of measuring the Q factor with a phase sensitive detector [32].
1—Modulation coil for obtaining the sinusoidal magnetic field; 2—modulation coil for obtaining a slowly varying magnetic field; 3—coil for obtaining a steady magnetic field; 4—high-Q cavity resonator (Q = 1000-1500); 5—high-frequency oscillator; 6, 7—impedance-matching transformers; 8—vacuum tube detector; 9—narrowband amplifier; 10—lock-in detector; 11—amplifier for the recording instruments; 14—sawtooth current generator; 15—reference sinusoidal voltage generator; 16—recording instruments; 17—power supply source of the coil [3].

Along with electromagnets, Helmholtz coils may be used to create the steady magnetic field in measurements of electron paramagnetic resonance at radio frequencies, since in this case the required field intensity is small. Determination of the position of the paramagnetic resonance line in the radio-frequency region is made either with the aid of a measurement of the resonance field intensity H_0 by a proton magnetometer or with the aid of a standard substance, for example, diphenylpicrylhydrazyl, for which the value of the g factor is known with sufficient accuracy.

Literature for Chapter II

1. Zavoyskiy, Ye. K. Doctoral Dissertation, Moscow, Phys. Inst. Acad. Sci., 1949; Zh. Eksp. Teoret. Fiz. 16, 603, 1946.
2. Zavoyskiy, Ye. K. J. Phys. USSR 9, 245, 1945.

3. Gorter, C. Paramagnetic Relaxation, Elsevier, Amsterdam, 1947.
4. Cummerow, R. L., D. Holliday, G. E. Moore. Phys. Rev. 72, 1233, 1947.
5. Whitmer, C. A., R. T. Weidner, J. S. Hsiang, P. R. Weiss. Phys. Rev. 74, 1478, 1948.
6. Bleaney, B., K. W. H. Stevens. Rep. Progr. Phys. 16, 108, 1953.
7. Blume, R. J. Phys. Rev. 109, 1867, 1958; Gordon, J. P., K. D. Bowers. Phys. Rev. Letters 1, 368, 1959.
8. Manenkov, A. A., A. M. Prokhorov. Radiotekh. i Elektron. 1, 469, 1956.
9. Beringer, R., J. G. Castle, Jr. Phys. Rev. 78, 581, 1950.
10. Smaller, B., E. L. Yasaitis. Rev. Sci. Instr. 24, 337, 1953.
11. Buckmaster, H. A., H. E. D. Scovil. Canad. J. Phys. 34, 711, 1956.
12. Smaller, B. Phys. Rev. 83, 812, 1951.
13. Semenov, A. G., N. N. Bubnov. Pribory Tekh. Eksp. No. 1, 92, 1959.
14. England, T. S., E. E. Schneider. Nature 166, 437, 1950.
15. Strum, P. D. Proc. Inst. Radio Eng. 41, 875, 1953.
16. Ingram, D. J. E. Spectroscopy at Radio and Microwave Frequencies, London, 1955.
17. Gordy, W. Rev. Mod. Phys. 20, 668, 1948.
18. Pound, R. V., W. D. Knight. Rev. Sci. Instr. 21, 219, 1950.
19. Weidner, R. T., C. A. Whitmer. Rev. Sci. Instr. 23, 75, 1952.
20. Hirshon, J. M., C. K. Fraenkel. Rev. Sci. Instr. 26, 34, 1955.
21. Ruter, C., R. Lacroix, C. R. Extermann. Onde Electr. 35, 338, 1955.
22. Neprimerov, N. N. Izvest. Akad. Nauk SSSR, Ser. Fiz., 18, 360, 1954.
23. Gordy, W., W. Smith, P. Trambarulo. Microwave Spectroscopy, John Wiley & Sons, N. Y., 1953.
24. Strandberg, V. Microwave Spectroscopy, IL, 1956.
25. Avvakumov, V. I., N. S. Garif'yanov, B. M. Kozyrev, P. G. Tishkov. Zh. Eksp. Teoret. Fiz. 37, 1564, 1959.
26. Bickford, L. R., Jr. Phys. Rev. 78, 449, 1950.
27. Bloembergen, N., S. Wang. Phys. Rev. 93, 72, 1954.
28. Nigmatullin, R. Sh., R. M. Valishev. Reports on Paramagnetic Resonance Conference, Kazan, 1959.
29. Andrew, E. Nuclear Magnetic Resonance, Cambridge Univ. Press, 1953.
30. Grivet, P. (editor). La Résonance paramagnétique nucléaire,
31. Paris, 1955.
32. Tishkov, P. G. Zh. Eksp. Teoret. Fiz. 36, 1337, 1959.
Feher, G., A. F. Kip. Phys. Rev. 98, 337, 1955.

CHAPTER III

Theory of Spectra of Ionic Crystals

3.1. Introduction

Of all the various classes of paramagnetic substances, ionic crystals are the most extensively studied. Paramagnetism is an inherent property of ionic crystals containing elements of the transition groups, since only atoms of these elements are able to preserve their unfilled electron shells during the process of crystal formation.

In order to construct a theory of the energy spectra of ionic paramagnetic crystals, it is necessary first of all to consider the interaction of the electrons with one another and with the nuclei within each ion; then the electrostatic, magnetic and exchange interactions among the different ions; and finally the effect of the external magnetic field. The magnetic and exchange forces produce narrow quasi-continuous energy bands because these forces are weak in substances which are not very magnetically concentrated, while the number of possible orientations of the angular momenta of the crystal's magnetic particles relative to one another is enormous. As a result the magnetic and exchange interactions usually do not influence the form of the paramagnetic resonance spectrum,[1] but cause only a broadening of the individual lines. Therefore, we shall discuss these interactions in Chapter V, which deals with the shape of the absorption lines.

The electrostatic reaction between free ions will be accounted for approximately by assuming that each ion is located in a certain mean electric field arising from all the surrounding particles. For brevity, we shall call this field the crystalline field. The effect of the crystalline field is always weaker than the Coulomb interaction among the electrons inside the atom. Therefore, we can use the self-consistent field method and speak of the configuration of the electrons forming the unfilled shell of the paramagnetic ion. The ions of the various transition groups have the following electron configurations: iron group (from Ti to Cu) — $3d^n$, palladium group (from Zr to Ag) — $4d^n$, rare earths (from Ce to Yb) — $4f^n$, platinum group (from Hf to Au) — $5d^n$, actinides (from U on) — $6d5f^n$.

---

[1] Certain exceptions will be discussed below (see Sec. 3.11).

The self-consistent field method does not fully account for the electrostatic interaction between the electrons. Hence for the usually employed perturbation calculations, one must know what relationship exists between the neglected part of this repulsion between the electrons and 1) the magnetic coupling between their spin and orbital momenta, and 2) the crystalline field forces. We distinguish three cases. The crystalline field is called weak if it is unable to disrupt the coupling between the orbital and spin moments of the entire unfilled electron shell. The field is called intermediate if it is stronger than the spin-orbit coupling of electrons but considerably weaker than the interaction between the individual electrons. Finally, it is called strong if its effect is greater than the coupling between the electrons of the unfilled shell. The first two cases are realized in hydrated salts of rare earth elements and of iron-group elements, respectively. The strong field case is not encountered in pure form, because should the crystalline field come to be more effective than the interaction between the individual electrons, the ionic bond is replaced and a covalent bond between the paramagnetic atom and its immediate environment comes forcibly into play.

The character of the splitting of energy levels of paramagnetic ions by the crystalline field depends to a great extent on the symmetry of this field. This circumstance enabled Bethe [1] to obtain a qualitative solution of this problem with the aid of group theory. Tables 3.1 and 3.2 indicate how the energy levels are split for the cases of integral and half-integral angular-momentum quantum numbers J. In the third and subsequent columns it is shown how the energy sublevel arises in a field of corresponding symmetry, where the numbers in parentheses denote the degree of degeneracy of these sublevels.

Table 3.1

J	Degree of degeneracy of a free atom	Splitting in a field				
		Icosahedral symmetry*	Cubic symmetry	Trigonal symmetry	Tetragonal symmetry	Rhombic symmetry
0	1	1(1)	1(1)	1(1)	1(1)	Total splitting
1	3	1(3)	1(3)	2 = 1(1)+1(2)	2 = 1(1)+1(2)	
2	5	1(5)	2 = 1(2)+1(3)	3 = 1(1)+2(2)	4 = 3(1)+1(2)	
3	7	2 = 1(3) + 1(4)	3 = 1(1)+2(3)	5 = 3(1)+2(2)	5 = 3(1)+2(2)	
4	9	2 = 1(4) + 1(5)	4 = 1(1)+1(2)+2(3)	6 = 3(1)+3(2)	7 = 5(1)+2(2)	
5	11	3 = 2(3) + 1(5)	4 = 1(2)+3(3)	7 = 3(1)+4(2)	8 = 5(1)+3(2)	
6	13	4 = 1(1) + 1(3) + 1(4) + 1(5)	6 = 2(1)+1(2)+3(3)	9 = 5(1)+4(2)	10 = 7(1)+3(2)	
7	15	4 = 2(3) + 1(4) + 1(5)	6 = 1(1)+1(2)+4(3)	10 = 5(1)+5(2)	11 = 7(1)+4(2)	
8	17	4 = 1(3) + 1(4) + 2(5)	7 = 1(1)+2(2)+4(3)	11 = 5(1)+6(2)	13 = 9(1)+4(2)	

*See page 70 regarding icosahedral symmetry in ionic crystals.

Table 3.2

J	Degree of degeneracy of a free atom	Splitting in a field		
		Icosahedral symmetry	Cubic symmetry	Lower symmetry
1/2	2	1 = 1(2)	1(2)	1(2)
3/2	4	1 = 1(4)	1(4)	2(2)
5/2	6	1 = 1(6)	2 = 1(2) + 1(4)	3(2)
7/2	8	2 = 1(2) + 1(6)	3 = 2(2) + 1(4)	4(2)
9/2	10	2 = 1(4) + 1(6)	3 = 1(2) + 2(4)	5(2)
11/2	12	3 = 1(2) + 1(4) + 1(6)	4 = 2(2) + 2(4)	6(2)
13/2	14	4 = 2(2) + 1(4) + 1(6)	5 = 3(2) + 2(4)	7(2)
15/2	16	3 = 1(4) + 2(6)	5 = 2(2) + 3(4)	8(2)

It is apparent from Table 3.2 that in the case of a half-integral spin, the energy sublevels always remain at least doubly degenerate. This fact is a consequence of a general theorem due to Kramers [2], which is of fundamental importance in the theory of paramagnetism. The theorem states that no electrical force can completely remove the degeneracy of an energy level system containing an odd number of electrons. It follows from this that paramagnetic resonance can always be observed in paramagnetic ions containing an odd number of electrons, because by removing the degeneracy of the ground state, the magnetic field is able to bring about splittings lying in the radio-frequency region. When the number of electrons is even, all the levels may be nondegenerate, even in the absence of a magnetic field, and lie so far from one another that no magnetic field attainable in practice can draw them close enough together that RF resonance absorption can take place.

The effect of a crystalline field on the static susceptibility of paramagnetic salts was first examined by Van Vleck [3]. Penney and Schlapp made detailed calculations for a number of salts of rare earths [4] and of elements of the iron group [5]. Similar calculations were then carried out by other authors [6], but only after an accumulation of experimental data on paramagnetic resonance in ionic crystals did it become possible to construct a systematic theory of the energy spectra of paramagnetic ions.

3.2. Matrix Elements of a Crystalline Field

In perturbation-theory calculation of the effect of a crystalline field on the energy levels of paramagnetic ions, it is first necessary to calculate the matrix elements of the energy $\mathscr{H}_{cr}$ of electrons of the unfilled shell in the electric field of the crystal. The energy $\mathscr{H}_{cr}$ can be represented in the form

$$\mathscr{H}_{\text{cr}} = \sum_i -eV(x_i, y_i, z_i), \tag{3.1}$$

where V is the potential of the crystalline field, and x_i, y_i, z_i are the coordinates of the i-th electron of the unfilled shell. By assuming that the energy shells of the paramagnetic ion and the surrounding particles do not overlap, and consequently that the potential V satisfies Laplace's equation, we may expand V in a series of spherical harmonics:

$$V = \sum_{n,\, m} A_n^m r^n Y_n^m(\vartheta, \varphi). \tag{3.2}$$

This expression may be considerably simplified by retaining only some of the series terms. In ionic crystals only the d and f shells of paramagnetic atoms may be unfilled. When the perturbation matrix $\mathscr{H}_{\text{cr}}$ is calculated with the aid of wave functions of the d electrons, the spherical harmonics for which $n > 4$ will give matrix elements equal to zero [7]. Analogously, in the case of f electrons the terms in the series with $n > 6$ can be discarded. We must also omit terms of the series with odd n: the matrix elements of odd-order spherical harmonics equal zero, since the electron wave functions are invariant under an inversion transformation; we keep in mind that all the crystals studied up to the present time have a center of symmetry. The term with $n = 0$ gives a negligible additive constant, which may be set equal to zero. Finally, since V is real, it follows that $A_n^m = (A_n^{-m})^*$. Further simplications of (3.2) can be obtained if one takes into account the symmetry of the crystalline field. We note that the surface spherical harmonic $Y_n^m(\vartheta, \varphi)$ has axial symmetry when $m = 0$, tetragonal symmetry when $m = \pm 4$, trigonal symmetry when $m = \pm 3$, hexagonal symmetry when $m = \pm 6$, and finally rhombic symmetry when $m = \pm 2$. Thus, it follows that if we denote $A_n^0 r^n Y_n^0(\vartheta, \varphi)$ by U_n^0 and $[A_n^m Y_n^m(\vartheta, \varphi) + A_n^{-m} Y_n^{-m}(\vartheta, \varphi)]$ by $U_n^{|m|}$, the potentials of the fields of different symmetry will become

$$V_{\text{tetr}} = U_2^0 + U_4^0 + U_4^4 + U_6^0 + U_6^4 \text{ (tetragonal)}, \tag{3.3a}$$

$$V_{\text{trig}} = U_2^0 + U_4^0 + U_4^3 + U_6^0 + U_6^3 + U_6^6 \text{ (trigonal)}, \tag{3.3b}$$

$$V_{\text{hex}} = U_2^0 + U_4^0 + U_6^0 + U_6^6 \text{ (hexagonal)}, \tag{3.3c}$$

$$V_{\text{rhom}} = U_2^0 + U_2^2 + U_4^0 + U_4^2 + U_4^4 + U_6^0 + U_6^2 + U_6^4 + U_6^6 \text{ (rhombic)}, \tag{3.3d}$$

$$V_{\text{tricl}} = \sum_{m=0}^{2} U_2^m + \sum_{m=0}^{4} U_4^m + \sum_{m=0}^{6} U_6^m \text{ (triclinic)}. \tag{3.3e}$$

For a field of cubic symmetry, where the polar axis (Z axis) coincides with a fourfold axis of symmetry, the potential takes the form

$$V_{\text{cub}} = A_4^0 r^4 \left\{ Y_4^0(\vartheta, \varphi) + \sqrt{\frac{5}{14}} \left[Y_4^4(\vartheta, \varphi) + Y_4^{-4}(\vartheta, \varphi) \right] \right\} + \\ + A_6^0 r^6 \left\{ Y_6^0(\vartheta, \varphi) - \sqrt{\frac{7}{2}} \left[Y_6^4(\vartheta, \varphi) + Y_6^{-4}(\vartheta, \varphi) \right] \right\}. \tag{3.4a}$$

However, if the polar axis is parallel to a body diagonal of the cube and is therefore a threefold axis of symmetry,

$$V_{\text{cub}} = D_4 r^4 \left\{ Y_4^0(\vartheta, \varphi) + \sqrt{\frac{10}{7}} \left[Y_4^3(\vartheta, \varphi) + Y_4^{-3}(\vartheta, \varphi) \right] \right\} + \\ + D_6 r^6 \left\{ Y_6^0(\vartheta, \varphi) + \frac{1}{8} \sqrt{\frac{70}{3}} \left[Y_6^3(\vartheta, \varphi) + Y_6^{-3}(\vartheta, \varphi) \right] + \\ + \frac{1}{8} \sqrt{\frac{77}{3}} \left[Y_6^6(\vartheta, \varphi) + Y_6^{-6}(\vartheta, \varphi) \right] \right\}. \tag{3.4b}$$

The tetragonal field may be represented by the sum of an axial field and a cubic field given by an expression of the type (3.4a); in the same way, the trigonal field can be broken down into the sum of an axial field and a cubic field given by expression (3.4b).

For further calculations it is advantageous to pass over to Cartesian coordinates. If V_n^m denotes the following homogeneous polynomials of degree n of coordinates x, y, z:

$$\left. \begin{aligned} & V_2^0 = 3z^2 - r^2, \quad V_2^1 = xz, \quad V_2^2 = x^2 - y^2, \\ & V_4^0 = 35z^4 - 30r^2z^2 + 3r^4, \quad V_4^1 = (7z^2 - 3r^2)\,xz, \\ & V_4^2 = (7z^2 - r^2)(x^2 - y^2), \quad V_4^3 = (x^2 - 3y^2)\,xz, \\ & V_4^4 = x^4 - 6x^2y^2 + y^4, \quad V_6^0 = 231z^6 - 315r^2z^4 + 105r^4z^2 - 5r^6, \\ & V_6^1 = 33xz^5 - 30xz^3r^2 + 5r^4xz, \\ & V_6^2 = 16z^4(x^2 - y^2) - 16(x^4 - y^4)z^2 + x^6 + x^4y^2 - y^4x^2 - y^6, \\ & V_6^3 = (11z^2 - 3r^2)(x^2 - 3y^2)xz, \quad V_6^4 = (11z^2 - r^2)(x^4 - 6x^2y^2 + y^4), \\ & V_6^5 = x^5z - 10x^3y^2z + 5xy^4z, \quad V_6^6 = x^6 - 15x^4y^2 + 15x^2y^4 - y^6, \end{aligned} \right\} \tag{3.5}$$

we have $U_n^m = B_n^m V_n^m$, where

$$\left. \begin{aligned} & B_2^0 = \frac{1}{4}\sqrt{\frac{5}{\pi}}\, A_2^0, \quad B_2^1 = \sqrt{\frac{15}{2\pi}}\, |A_2^1|, \quad B_2^2 = \frac{1}{2}\sqrt{\frac{15}{2\pi}}\, |A_2^2|, \\ & B_4^0 = \frac{3}{16\sqrt{\pi}}\, A_4^0, \quad B_4^1 = \frac{3}{4}\sqrt{\frac{5}{\pi}}\, |A_4^1|, \quad B_4^2 = \frac{3}{4}\sqrt{\frac{5}{2\pi}}\, |A_4^2|, \\ & B_4^3 = \frac{3}{4}\sqrt{\frac{35}{\pi}}\, |A_4^3|, \quad B_4^4 = \frac{3}{8}\sqrt{\frac{35}{2\pi}}\, |A_4^4|, \quad B_6^0 = \frac{1}{32}\sqrt{\frac{13}{\pi}}\, A_6^0, \\ & B_6^1 = \frac{1}{8}\sqrt{\frac{13 \cdot 21}{2\pi}}\, |A_6^1|, \quad B_6^2 = \frac{1}{32}\sqrt{\frac{13 \cdot 105}{\pi}}\, |A_6^2|, \\ & B_6^3 = \frac{1}{16}\sqrt{\frac{13 \cdot 105}{\pi}}\, |A_6^3|, \quad B_6^4 = \frac{3}{32}\sqrt{\frac{13 \cdot 14}{\pi}}\, |A_6^4|, \\ & B_6^5 = \frac{3}{16}\sqrt{\frac{13 \cdot 77}{\pi}}\, |A_6^5|, \quad B_6^6 = \frac{1}{32}\sqrt{\frac{13 \cdot 21 \cdot 11}{\pi}}\, |A_6^6|. \end{aligned} \right\} \tag{3.6}$$

The potential of the cubic field (3.4a) in Cartesian coordinates is*

$$V_{\text{cub}} = C_4\left(x^4 + y^4 + z^4 - \frac{3}{5}r^4\right) + \\ + C_6[2(x^6 + y^6 + z^6) - 15(x^4y^2 + y^4x^2 + \\ + z^4x^2 + x^4z^2 + z^4y^2 + y^4z^2) + 180x^2y^2z^2], \quad (3.7)$$

where $C_4 = (15/4\sqrt{\pi})\,A_4^0 = 20B_4^0$, $C_6 = (1/4)\,(\sqrt{13/\pi})\,A_6^0 = 8\,B_6^0$.

Now that analytic expressions have been obtained for the crystalline field potential, we shall discuss certain general facts concerning the calculation of the perturbation matrix elements. Let ψ_M $(M = J,\ J-1,\ J-2,\ \ldots,\ -J)$ be the ground state wave functions of the free atom under the assumption that we account for only those electron interactions which are much greater than $\mathcal{H}_{\text{cr}}$. J and M denote the quantum numbers of the constants of motion, namely, the angular momentum and its projection on the Z axis, respectively. It is easy to show that the matrix elements

$$\langle JM|\Sigma V_n^m|JM'\rangle \equiv \int \psi_M^* \Sigma V_n^m \psi_{M'}\,d\tau$$

vanish if $M \neq m + M'$. The symbol Σ in accordance with (3.1) designates a summation over all electrons of the unfilled shell.

To find the nonzero matrix elements associated with states having the same J, the method of equivalent operators [8, 9] is usually employed. The set of functions Y_n^m $(m = 0, \pm 1, \pm 2, \ldots, \pm n)$ forms the basis of an irreducible representation of the rotation group of dimensionality $2n + 1$. Each of the functions of the electron coordinates ΣV_n^m may be associated with an equivalent operator, i.e., an analogous function of operators of the projections of angular momenta $\hat{J}_x$, $\hat{J}_y$, $\hat{J}_z$, which have the same transformation properties. Thus, for instance, the functions $\Sigma\,(x^2 - y^2)$ and $\Sigma\,(3z^2 - r^2)$ correspond to the operators $\hat{J}_x^2 - \hat{J}_y^2$ and $3\,\hat{J}_z^2 - J(J+1)$. It is more difficult to find the equivalent operators, because in contrast with x, y, z the operators J_x, J_y, J_z do not commute. Hence, when finding the operator equivalent to the expression $x^k y^l z^m$, one must choose the arithmetic means of $(k+l+m)!/k!\,l!\,m!$ possible permutations of the operators $\hat{J}_x \ldots \hat{J}_x \hat{J}_y \ldots \hat{J}_y \hat{J}_z \ldots \hat{J}_z$. For instance, the function $\Sigma\,xy$ corresponds to the operator $1/2\ (J_xJ_y + J_yJ_x)$.

The matrix elements of the functions ΣV_n^m and the corresponding equivalent operators coincide exactly except for a certain common factor, which is identical for all functions with a given n.

Thus the tedious direct calculations of the matrix elements of the crystalline field potential may be replaced by simple calculations of the matrix elements of polynomials of the second, fourth and sixth degree in $\hat{J}_x$, $\hat{J}_y$, $\hat{J}_z$. Direct calculations of all the matrix elements are necessary in order to determine the common factors α, β, γ, but for this purpose it is sufficient to make a calculation

* [see Table 4 of Low [90] - Ed.]

of only one matrix element of ΣV_n^m for each electron configuration and of only one potential function with a given n.

Table 3.3 gives the linearly independent equivalent operators of the polynomials V_n^m of the second, fourth and sixth degree. The

Table 3.3

$$\hat{V}_2^0 = \alpha\overline{r^2}\,[3\hat{J}_z^2 - J(J+1)];$$

$$\hat{V}_2^1 = \frac{\alpha\overline{r^2}}{2}\,[\hat{J}_x\hat{J}_z + \hat{J}_z\hat{J}_x] = \frac{\alpha\overline{r^2}}{4}\,\{\hat{J}_z(\hat{J}_+ + \hat{J}_-) + (\hat{J}_+ + \hat{J}_-)\hat{J}_z\};$$

$$\hat{V}_2^2 = \frac{\alpha\overline{r^2}}{2}\,[\hat{J}_+^2 + \hat{J}_-^2];$$

$$\hat{V}_4^0 = \beta\overline{r^4}\,[35\hat{J}_z^4 - 30J(J+1)\hat{J}_z^2 + 25\hat{J}_z^2 - 6J(J+1) + 3J^2(J+1)^2];$$

$$\hat{V}_4^1 = \frac{\beta}{4}\overline{r^4}\,\{[7\hat{J}_z^3 - 3J(J+1)\hat{J}_z - \hat{J}_z](\hat{J}_+ + \hat{J}_-) + $$
$$+ (\hat{J}_+ + \hat{J}_-)[7\hat{J}_z^3 - 3J(J+1)\hat{J}_z - \hat{J}_z]\};$$

$$\hat{V}_4^2 = \frac{\beta}{4}\overline{r^4}\,\{[7\hat{J}_z^2 - J(J+1) - 5](\hat{J}_+^2 + \hat{J}_-^2) + (\hat{J}_+^2 + \hat{J}_-^2)[7\hat{J}_z^2 - J(J+1) - 5]\};$$

$$\hat{V}_4^3 = \frac{\beta}{4}\overline{r^4}\,\{\hat{J}_z(\hat{J}_+^3 + \hat{J}_-^3) + (\hat{J}_+^3 + \hat{J}_-^3)\hat{J}_z\};$$

$$\hat{V}_4^4 = \frac{\beta}{2}\overline{r^4}\,(\hat{J}_+^4 + \hat{J}^4);$$

$$\hat{V}_6^0 = \gamma\overline{r^6}\,\{231\hat{J}_z^6 - 315J(J+1)\hat{J}_z^4 + 735\hat{J}_z^4 + 105J^2(J+1)^2\hat{J}_z^2 - 525J(J+1)\hat{J}_z^2 + $$
$$+ 294\hat{J}_z^2 - 5J^3(J+1)^3 + 40J^2(J+1)^2 - 60J(J+1)\};$$

$$\hat{V}_6^1 = \frac{\gamma}{4}\overline{r^6}\,\{[33\hat{J}_z^5 - 30J(J+1)\hat{J}_z^3 + 15\hat{J}_z^3 + 5J^2(J+1)^2\hat{J}_z - 10J(J+1)\hat{J}_z + $$
$$+ 12\hat{J}_z](\hat{J}_+ + \hat{J}_-) + (\hat{J}_+ + \hat{J}_-)[33\hat{J}_z^5 - 30J(J+1)\hat{J}_z^3 + 15\hat{J}_z^3 + $$
$$+ 5J^2(J+1)^2\hat{J}_z - 10J(J+1)\hat{J}_z + 12\hat{J}_z]\};$$

$$\hat{V}_6^2 = \frac{\gamma}{4}\overline{r^6}\,\{[33\hat{J}_z^4 - 18J(J+1)\hat{J}_z^2 - 123\hat{J}_z^2 + J^2(J+1)^2 + 10J(J+1) + 102] \times$$
$$\times (\hat{J}_+^2 + \hat{J}_-^2) + (\hat{J}_+^2 + \hat{J}_-^2)[33\hat{J}_z^4 - 18J(J+1)\hat{J}_z^2 - 123\hat{J}_z^2 + J^2(J+1)^2 + $$
$$+ 10J(J+1) + 102]\};$$

$$\hat{V}_6^3 = \frac{\gamma}{4}\overline{r^6}\,\{[11\hat{J}_z^3 - 3J(J+1)\hat{J}_z - 59\hat{J}_z](\hat{J}_+^3 + \hat{J}_-^3) + (\hat{J}_+^3 + \hat{J}_-^3) \times$$
$$\times [11\hat{J}_z^3 - 3J(J+1)\hat{J}_z - 59\hat{J}_z]\};$$

$$\hat{V}_6^4 = \frac{\gamma}{4}\overline{r^6}\,\{[11\hat{J}_z^2 - J(J+1) - 38](\hat{J}_+^4 + \hat{J}_-^4) + (\hat{J}_+^4 + \hat{J}_-^4)[11\hat{J}_z^2 - J(J+1) - 38]\};$$

$$\hat{V}_6^5 = \frac{\gamma}{4}\overline{r^6}\,\{\hat{J}_z(\hat{J}_+^5 + \hat{J}_-^5) + (\hat{J}_+^5 + \hat{J}_-^5)\hat{J}_z\};$$

$$\hat{V}_6^6 = \frac{\gamma}{2}\overline{r^6}\,\{\hat{J}_+^6 + \hat{J}_-^6\},$$

where $\hat{J}_+ = \hat{J}_x + i\hat{J}_y$, $\hat{J}_- = \hat{J}_x - i\hat{J}_y$.

summation sign in the expressions ΣV_n^m is omitted everywhere, and r denotes the distance between an electron and a nucleus.

The problem of calculating matrix elements that correspond to states of differing J requires special treatment, since in such cases the method of equivalent operators becomes considerably more complicated. The results of several calculations are given in Sec. 3.6.

When calculating the matrix elements of the function V_n^m it is useful to remember that

$$\langle J+k, J_z-m|V_n^m|J, J_z\rangle=(-1)^{m+k}\langle J+k, m-J_z|V_n^m|J, -J_z\rangle. \quad (3.8)$$

3.3. Compounds of the Iron-Group Elements

It is well known [10] from studies of the static magnetic susceptibility that the effect of a crystalline field in these substances is usually stronger than spin-orbit coupling but weaker than forces which determine the ground state term of the ion. It is appropriate therefore to write the Hamiltonian for a paramagnetic ion of the iron group in the following form:

$$\hat{\mathscr{H}}=\hat{\mathscr{H}}^0+\hat{\mathscr{H}}_{\mathrm{cr}}+\hat{\mathscr{H}}_{LS}+\hat{\mathscr{H}}_{SS}+\hat{\mathscr{H}}_Z. \quad (3.9)$$

Here $\hat{\mathscr{H}}^0$ is the main part of the Hamiltonian, including all interactions in the free atom which do not depend on the spin variables. The remaining terms of the Hamiltonian can be considered as a perturbation, where

$$\hat{\mathscr{H}}_{LS}=\lambda\hat{\boldsymbol{L}}\hat{\boldsymbol{S}}$$

is the spin-orbit interaction operator,

$$\hat{\mathscr{H}}_{SS}=-\rho\left[(\hat{\boldsymbol{L}}\hat{\boldsymbol{S}})^2+\frac{1}{2}(\hat{\boldsymbol{L}}\hat{\boldsymbol{S}})-\frac{1}{3}L(L+1)S(S+1)\right]$$

is the spin-spin interaction operator [11], and

$$\hat{\mathscr{H}}_Z=\beta(\hat{\boldsymbol{L}}+2\hat{\boldsymbol{S}})\boldsymbol{H}_0$$

is the energy of the electrons in the external magnetic field (Zeeman energy). The splittings caused by the perturbing forces are of the order:

$$\mathscr{H}_{\mathrm{cr}}\approx 10^4\ \mathrm{cm}^{-1},\quad \mathscr{H}_{LS}\approx 10^2\ \mathrm{cm}^{-1},\quad \mathscr{H}_{SS}\approx 1\ \mathrm{cm}^{-1},\quad \mathscr{H}_Z\approx 1\ \mathrm{cm}^{-1}.$$

If we take only the main Hamiltonian into account, the total orbital angular momentum L and spin angular momentum S obviously will be constants of motion. We shall assume that the problem of the possible eigenstates of $\hat{\mathscr{H}}^0$ has been solved by the self-consistent field method. In perturbation calculations, we shall begin with the ground state of $\hat{\mathscr{H}}^0$, which is characterized by a definite electron configuration and definite values of L and S. Higher approximations that take into account the influence of the excited terms of $\hat{\mathscr{H}}^0$ are in most cases unnecessary. Table 3.4 gives the configurations and the ground-state terms of various iron-group ions.

Table 3.4

Ion	Con-figu-rations	Ground state terms	λ, cm^{-1}	α	β
Ti^{3+}	d^1	^2D	154	$-\frac{2}{21}$	$\frac{2}{63}$
V^{3+}	d^2	^3F	104	$-\frac{2}{105}$	$-\frac{2}{315}$
V^{2+}	d^3	^4F	55	$\frac{2}{105}$	$\frac{2}{315}$
Cr^{3+}	d^3	^4F	87	$\frac{2}{105}$	$\frac{2}{315}$
Cr^{2+}	d^4	^5D	57	$\frac{2}{21}$	$-\frac{2}{63}$
Mn^{3+}	d^4	^5D	85	$\frac{2}{21}$	$-\frac{2}{63}$
Mn^{2+}	d^5	^6S	—	—	—
Fe^{3+}	d^5	^6S	—	—	—
Fe^{2+}	d^6	^5D	—100	$-\frac{2}{21}$	$\frac{2}{63}$
Co^{2+}	d^7	^4F	—180	$-\frac{2}{105}$	$-\frac{2}{315}$
Ni^{2+}	d^8	^3F	—335	$\frac{2}{105}$	$\frac{2}{315}$
Cu^{2+}	d^9	^2D	—852	$\frac{2}{21}$	$-\frac{2}{63}$

The perturbation calculations can be divided into several steps. A comparison of the magnitudes of the perturbing forces indicates that initially a calculation of the splitting of the $(2L+1)$-fold orbital level under the influence of the crystalline field $\mathscr{H}_{cr}$ may be made, while disregarding the remaining interactions.

Since we shall deal with d electrons, Eqs. (3.3) and (3.4) for the crystalline field potentials may be simplified by omitting the term U_n^m for $n = 6$. The matrix elements of the potential functions V_n^m may be calculated with the aid of the equivalent operators of Table 3.3. The coefficients α and β remain to be determined. For this purpose it is sufficient to calculate one matrix element of any potential function V_n^m with $n = 2$ and one with $n = 4$. We choose the functions V_2^0 and V_4^0, because they have only diagonal matrix elements. To proceed further one must express some of the wave functions of the ground-state term of the paramagnetic atom in terms of single-electron d functions. This is done most simply if we take the state with the maximum values of the projection of the spin and orbital angular momenta $\{\overset{+}{2}\ \overset{+}{1}\ \overset{+}{0}\ \ldots\}$, since these will obviously be characterized by a symmetric spin function and an antisymmetric linear combination of single-electron d functions: $f_m = R(r)\,Y_2^m\ (\vartheta, \varphi)$ with $m = 2, 1, \ldots$ Thus, from the $2L + 1$ different coordinate functions ψ_M corresponding to the ground state of $\hat{\mathscr{H}}^0$, we chose the function with the greatest value of magnetic quantum number M. If there are less than five d electrons it is easy to prove that

$$\int \psi_M^* \sum V_n^0 \psi_M \, d\tau = \int f_2^* V_n^0 f_2 \, d\tau + \int f_1^* V_n^0 f_1 \, d\tau + \ldots \tag{3.10}$$

The number of integrals on the right-hand side of this equation is equal to the number of d electrons. However, if the number of d electrons is greater than five, the calculation is carried out with the number of additional electrons to fill the d shell, and the result is taken with the opposite sign.[a] Values of α and β calculated in this manner are given in Table 3.4.

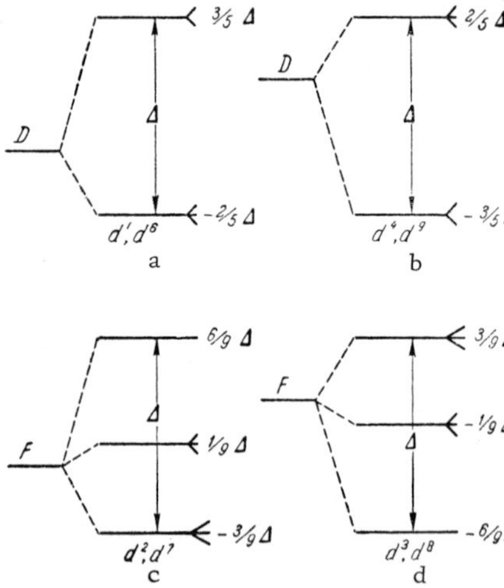

Fig. 3.1. Diagram of the splitting of the ground orbital states of iron-group ions in a cubic field.

In the majority of the salts studied the crystalline field may be decomposed into two components: a strong field of cubic symmetry and a weak field of lower symmetry, such as a trigonal

[a][For example, configurations $3d^3$ and $3d^7$ have α and β of the same magnitude but opposite sign (see Table 3.4).]

or tetragonal field. The energy $\hat{\mathscr{H}}_{\mathrm{cr}}$ is thus given by the sum $\hat{\mathscr{H}}_{\mathrm{cr}} = \hat{K} + \hat{T}$. The cubic field $\hat{K}$ is usually created by six molecules of water situated at the vertices of an octahedron whose center is occupied by the paramagnetic ion. This field changes little when changing from one element of the iron group to another, or even from one salt to another. This is evidently explained by the fact that the dimensions of the octahedron are determined by the diameter of the paramagnetic atom.

The field T has a double nature: first it is established by all the ions of the crystal and has its symmetry; second, it arises from the deformation of the octahedron which occurs as a result of the Jahn-Teller effect. According to the well-known theorem of Jahn and Teller [12], the stable state of a nonlinear system of atoms is one which possesses the least possible degeneracy.

First of all the effect of the cubic field must be determined. We see from Table 3.4 that free ions of the iron group elements contain only S-, D and F terms. Ions in S states will be considered separately. A qualitative picture of the splittings of D and F terms may be obtained at once from group-theoretical considerations (Table 3.1). In a field of cubic symmetry the F term splits into one singlet and two triplets (Figures 3.1 c and d), while the D term splits into a doublet and a triplet (Figures 3.1 a and b). A quantitative calculation by perturbation theory gives the following values for the energy and the corresponding ψ functions [9], computed for two cases:

1) Axis of quantization coincides with the trigonal axis of the cube:

2) Axis of quantization coincides with the tetragonal axis of the cube:

$$L=2 \qquad \frac{3}{5}\Delta\begin{cases}\sqrt{\frac{1}{3}}\psi_{-2}-\sqrt{\frac{2}{3}}\psi_1\\ \sqrt{\frac{1}{3}}\psi_2+\sqrt{\frac{2}{3}}\psi_{-1}\end{cases} \qquad \begin{cases}\psi_0\\ \frac{1}{\sqrt{2}}(\psi_2+\psi_{-2})\end{cases}$$

$$-\frac{2}{5}\Delta\begin{cases}\psi_0\\ \sqrt{\frac{2}{3}}\psi_{-2}+\sqrt{\frac{1}{3}}\psi_1\\ \sqrt{\frac{2}{3}}\psi_2-\sqrt{\frac{1}{3}}\psi_{-1}\end{cases} \qquad \begin{cases}\psi_1\\ \psi_{-1}\\ \frac{1}{\sqrt{2}}(\psi_2-\psi_{-2})\end{cases}$$

$$\Delta = 6\beta\overline{r^4}C_4 \tag{3.11}$$

$$L=3 \qquad \frac{1}{3}\Delta\begin{cases}\frac{2}{3}\psi_0+\frac{1}{3}\sqrt{\frac{5}{2}}(\psi_3-\psi_{-3})\\ \sqrt{\frac{5}{6}}\psi_2+\sqrt{\frac{1}{6}}\psi_{-1}\\ \sqrt{\frac{5}{6}}\psi_{-2}-\sqrt{\frac{1}{6}}\psi_1\end{cases} \qquad \begin{cases}\sqrt{\frac{3}{8}}\psi_{-1}+\sqrt{\frac{5}{8}}\psi_3\\ \sqrt{\frac{3}{8}}\psi_1+\sqrt{\frac{5}{8}}\psi_{-3}\\ \psi_0\end{cases}$$

1) Axis of quantization coincides with the trigonal axis of the cube:

2) Axis of quantization coincides with the tetragonal axis of the cube:

$$-\frac{1}{9}\Delta\begin{cases}\frac{1}{\sqrt{2}}(\psi_3+\psi_{-3})\\ \sqrt{\frac{1}{6}}\psi_2-\sqrt{\frac{5}{6}}\psi_{-1}\\ \sqrt{\frac{1}{6}}\psi_{-2}+\sqrt{\frac{5}{6}}\psi_1\end{cases} \qquad \begin{cases}\sqrt{\frac{5}{8}}\psi_{-1}-\sqrt{\frac{3}{8}}\psi_3\\ \sqrt{\frac{5}{8}}\psi_1-\sqrt{\frac{3}{8}}\psi_{-3}\\ \frac{1}{\sqrt{2}}(\psi_2+\psi_{-2})\end{cases}$$

$$-\frac{2}{3}\Delta\left\{\frac{\sqrt{2}}{3}(\psi_3-\psi_{-3})-\frac{\sqrt{5}}{3}\psi_0\right. \qquad \frac{1}{\sqrt{2}}(\psi_2-\psi_{-2}) \tag{3.11 Cont'd}$$

$$\Delta=54\beta\overline{r^4}C_4$$

The absolute value of Δ denotes the total splitting in a cubic field.

Gorter [15] has considered the subject of the sequential arrangement of the energy levels which arise under the influence of the field of an octahedron of water molecules, or in other words, the subject of the sign of the quantity C_4. It was found that $C_4>0$. From this it follows that if the ion contains only one d electron, its lower orbital level will be a triplet and its upper a doublet. The electron configuration d^6 differs from d^1 by the addition of five electrons. Since the configuration d^5 corresponds to the term ^6S, in which the effect of the cubic field is manifested only in higher approximations, the picture of the splittings of the orbital level for both cases d^1 and d^6 will be identical (Figure 3.1 a). The d^9 configuration may be considered as a filled shell with one hole or, in other words, one positive electron. A similar correspondence exists between the d^6 and d^4. configurations. Hence in the d^9 and d^4 cases the sequence of the energy levels will be reversed (Figure 3.1 b).

For configurations which produce F terms, it is easy to see that in the d^3 and d^8 cases the lower orbital level will be a singlet (Figure 3.1 d); configurations d^7 and d^2 correspond to a reverse sequence of levels, and therefore the lower level is a triplet.

Gorter has also demonstrated that in tetrahedral complexes the cubic field parameter $C_4<0$. Consequently, the order of the sublevels will be the reverse of that indicated for ions in the octahedral environment.

We now proceed to an examination of the remaining perturbations, which according to (3.9) can be written in the form

$$\mathcal{H}'=T+\lambda(\hat{L}\hat{S})-\rho\left[(\hat{L}\hat{S})^2+\frac{1}{2}(\hat{L}\hat{S})-\frac{1}{3}L(L+1)S(S+1)\right]+ +\beta(\hat{L}+2\hat{S})H_0. \tag{3.12}$$

Experiments are usually conducted at such temperatures that only those energy levels can be considered occupied which are at a distance less than several hundred cm^{-1} above the ground state. Therefore, only the lowest orbital level arising in a cubic field is of interest to us. It is essential to know if a given level is nondegenerate or degenerate.

We shall assume that the lower level is nondegenerate. If we take the electron spin into consideration, a $(2S+1)$-fold degeneracy appears. The field T does not act on the electron spin and so can produce only an insignificant level shift. In a singlet orbital state the mean angular momentum L is equal to zero, and therefore to a first approximation the spin-orbit interaction $\mathcal{H}_{LS}$ will also be equal to zero. We must therefore consider the second approximation, which gives an orbital level splitting equal roughly to $\lambda^2/\Delta \approx 1\ cm^{-1}$, i.e., of the same order of magnitude as the Zeeman energy and the spin-spin interaction.

In [16, 17], a method was developed for calculating the ground-state splitting of a magnetic ion. It found extensive application in experimental studies of paramagnetic resonance and was named the spin Hamiltonian method. This method consists of the following. The usual perturbation theory procedure will be carried out in two stages. The matrix elements of $\hat{\mathcal{H}}'$ are first computed with the aid of the coordinate wave functions, which is possible since the unperturbed Hamiltonian is independent of the spin variables. As a result the perturbation energy turns out to be a function of the spin operator $\hat{S}$ and this function is called the spin Hamiltonian.

It is not difficult to show that the spin Hamiltonian has the form

$$\hat{\mathcal{H}}_{sp} = D_{ij}\hat{S}_i\hat{S}_j + \beta g_{ij} H_{0i}\hat{S}_i, \tag{3.13}$$

where the tensors D_{ij} and g_{ij} are determined from the formulas

$$\left.\begin{aligned} &D_{ij} = -\lambda^2\Lambda_{ij} - \rho l_{ij};\quad g_{ij} = 2(\delta_{ij} - \Lambda_{ij});\\ &\Lambda_{ij} = \sum_{n\neq 0}\frac{\langle 0\,|\,L_i\,|\,n\rangle\langle n\,|\,L_j\,|\,0\rangle}{E_n - E_0};\\ &l_{ij} = \frac{1}{2}\langle 0\,|\,L_iL_j + L_jL_i\,|\,0\rangle - \frac{1}{3}L(L+1)\delta_{ij}. \end{aligned}\right\} \tag{3.14}$$

Here $i, j = x, y, z$, and E_0 and E_n denote the energy of the ground and excited orbital states, respectively.

If $\mathcal{H}_{cr}$ has tetragonal or trigonal symmetry, the tensors D_{ij} and g_{ij} are characterized by two principal values, corresponding to the two directions: parallel and perpendicular to the symmetry axis. Taking the Z axis as the symmetry axis, we obtain:

$$\begin{aligned} \hat{\mathcal{H}}_{sp} = D\left[\hat{S}_z^2 - \frac{1}{3}S(S+1)\right] + \beta g_{\parallel} H_{0z}\hat{S}_z + \\ + \beta g_{\perp}(H_{0x}\hat{S}_x + H_{0y}\hat{S}_y). \end{aligned} \tag{3.15}$$

The deviation from tetragonal symmetry can be taken into account by adding the term $E(\hat{S}_x^2 - \hat{S}_y^2)$ and replacing $g_{\perp}$ by the coefficients

g_x, g_y. The part of the spin Hamiltonian which is proportional to D (and E) determines the splitting of the orbital level in the absence of an external magnetic field. Terms which are proportional to H_{0x}, H_{0y}, H_{0z}, indicate an anisotropy of the atom's magnetic moment in the crystal; deviation of the g factor from the value $g = 2$ means that the spin moment of the electron is augmented by a small fraction of the moment associated with orbital motion.

The spin Hamiltonian method makes it possible to characterize the paramagnetic resonance spectrum by a small number of constants: D, E, $g_{\|}$, $g_{\perp}$, ... The determination of these constants from the form of the spectrum is the main object of paramagnetic resonance experiments. The aim of this theory is to obtain these constants on the basis of a given crystal model.

The theory expounded here is applicable in the first place to ions whose lowest orbital level in a cubic field is a singlet. To this category belong Cr^{3+}, V^{2+} and Ni^{2+} ions; Cr^{2+}, Mn^{3+}, and Cu^{2+} also belong to this group when the field T has tetragonal symmetry. In these ions $L = 2$ and the effect of the cubic field is to make the lowest level an orbital doublet, which according to (3.11) is uninfluenced by the spin-orbit coupling $\mathscr{H}_{LS}$; the tetragonal field, however, splits the doublet level. Thus, the lowest orbital level will again be nondegenerate and its spin degeneracy as before will be $2S + 1$.

We shall consider a more general case, in which the degeneracy of the lowest orbital level in a cubic field makes the matrix elements of the spin-orbit coupling $\mathscr{H}_{LS}$ different from zero in the first approximation. Now the perturbations caused by the spin-orbit coupling $\mathscr{H}_{LS}$ and the field T are of the same order of magnitude and must be taken into account simultaneously. Due to the Jahn-Teller effect, the paramagnetic ion under the action of these forces must possess minimal degeneracy. If we apply the Kramers theorem, we reach the following important conclusion: under the influence of $\mathscr{H}_{LS}$ and the low symmetry field T, the splitting of the energy levels of paramagnetic ions having an even number of electrons will be complete. In such a case, not only the orbital but also the spin levels will be nondegenerate. As a rule, the intervals between these levels are greater than 1 cm^{-1}, and therefore observation of paramagnetic resonance is possible only by means of millimeter radio-frequency fields.

If the paramagnetic ion has an odd number of electrons, the twofold Kramers degeneracy will be preserved. In that case the splitting of the energy level in an external magnetic field can be calculated by introducing an effective spin equal to 1/2. The spin Hamiltonian will have the following simple form:

$$\mathscr{H}_{\text{sp}} = \beta \{ g_x H_{0x} \hat{S}'_x + g_y H_{0y} \hat{S}'_y + g_z H_{0z} \hat{S}'_z \}, \tag{3.16}$$

where the $\hat{S}_i'$ are Pauli matrices. The relation of the coefficients g_x, g_y, g_z with λ and the crystalline field constants will not be dealt with.

A number of papers have been devoted to a detailed theoretical treatment of the paramagnetic resonance spectra of salts of the following: cobalt [18, 19], nickel [20-22], and copper [23-25]. Many theoretical investigations are especially devoted to chrome alums [26-34], which find extensive application in adiabatic demagnetization.

To determine the form of the paramagnetic resonance spectra it is necessary to know not only the system of lowest energy levels of paramagnetic ions, but also the probability of magnetic dipole transitions between them. The probability of a transition between any two levels M and M' is proportional to the square of the off-diagonal matrix element of the projection of the magnetic moment of the electron on the direction of the periodic magnetic field. A calculation of these matrix elements is particularly simple if the spin Hamiltonian has been established. If the position of the vector intensity of the periodic magnetic field is defined by the directional cosines α_1, α_2, α_3, the operator of the components of magnetic angular momentum may be presented in the form

$$\hat{\mu}_{H_1} = \alpha_1 g_x \beta \hat{S}_x + \alpha_2 g_y \beta \hat{S}_y + \alpha_3 g_z \beta \hat{S}_z. \qquad (3.17)$$

It remains to calculate the matrix elements of $\hat{S}_x$, $\hat{S}_y$, $\hat{S}_z$ by means of the proper spin wave functions of the levels M and M'.

3.4. Paramagnetic Resonance Spectrum of an Ion of Nickel in an Axial Crystalline Field

To illustrate the general method of calculating the paramagnetic resonance spectrum, we shall consider a Ni^{2+} ion located in a tetragonal or a trigonal crystal field. These calculations apply in particular to extensively investigated nickel fluosilicate, whose crystalline field symmetry is tetragonal. The lowest level in Ni^{2+} is a singlet (Figure 3.1 d), and therefore the spectrum may be calculated with the aid of the spin Hamiltonian (3.15) if the tetragonal axis is directed along the Z axis.

The nonzero matrix elements of the vector $\boldsymbol{S}$ may be calculated from the familiar formulas (7):

$$\left.\begin{array}{c} \langle M | S_x - iS_y | M+1 \rangle = \sqrt{S(S+1) - M(M+1)}, \\ \langle M | S_z | M \rangle = M. \end{array}\right\} \qquad (3.18)$$

In our case $S = 1$, and the nonzero matrix elements of $\boldsymbol{S}$ take the following values:

$$\left.\begin{aligned}\langle -1|S_x|0\rangle=\langle 0|S_x|1\rangle=\frac{1}{\sqrt{2}};\\ \langle -1|S_y|0\rangle=\langle 0|S_y|1\rangle=\frac{i}{\sqrt{2}};\\ \langle -1|S_z|-1\rangle=-1;\ \langle 1|S_z|1\rangle=1.\end{aligned}\right\} \tag{3.19}$$

First we assume that the static magnetic field H_0 is parallel to the tetragonal axis of the crystal. Then the possible energy values of the spin levels E_i and the corresponding spin wave functions η_i are determined from the equation

$$\mathscr{H}_{\text{sp}}\,\eta_i\equiv(D\hat{S}_z^2+g_{\|}\beta H_0\hat{S}_z)\,\eta_i=E_i\eta_i. \tag{3.20}$$

It is convenient to choose the quantity D as the unit of energy. We therefore introduce the following notation:

$$\varepsilon_i=\frac{E_i}{D},\qquad x_{\|}=\frac{g_{\|}\beta H_0}{D},\qquad x_{\perp}=\frac{g_{\perp}\beta H_0}{D}. \tag{3.21}$$

The eigenfunction of $\hat{S}_z$ corresponding to the eigenvalue M is denoted as η_M. Since a representation in which S_z is diagonal will be used, then obviously matrix (3.20) must also be diagonal, and consequently the eigenvalues of $\hat{\mathscr{H}}_{\text{sp}}$ and the corresponding eigenfunctions will equal

$$\varepsilon_a=0,\ \eta_a=\eta_0,\ \varepsilon_b=1-x_{\|},\ \eta_b=\eta_{-1},\ \varepsilon_c=x_{\|}+1,\ \eta_c=\eta_1. \tag{3.22}$$

From (3.22), (3.19) and (3.17) it is an easy conclusion that magnetic dipole transitions between the spin levels can only be brought about under the action of the component of the periodic magnetic field perpendicular to the Z axis. According to (3.19) two absorption lines of equal intensity ($\sim g_{\perp}^2\beta^2/4$) should appear, corresponding to the $-1\to 0$ and $0\to 1$ transitions.

Let us assume now that the magnetic field H_0 is perpendicular to the crystal axis. If this field H_0 is directed along the X axis, the spin Hamiltonian becomes

$$\mathscr{H}_{\text{sp}}=D\hat{S}_z^2+g_{\perp}\beta H_0\hat{S}_x. \tag{3.23}$$

From (3.18) we obtain the following secular equation for the determination of the spin energy levels:

$$\begin{vmatrix}1-\varepsilon & \frac{x_{\perp}}{\sqrt{2}} & 0\\ \frac{x_{\perp}}{\sqrt{2}} & -\varepsilon & \frac{x_{\perp}}{\sqrt{2}}\\ 0 & \frac{x_{\perp}}{\sqrt{2}} & 1-\varepsilon\end{vmatrix}=0. \tag{3.24}$$

The solution of this equation gives the following eigenvalues and eigenfunctions:

$$\left.\begin{aligned}
&\varepsilon_a=\frac{1}{2}(1-\xi),\quad \eta_a=\frac{x_\perp}{\sqrt{\xi^2+\xi}}\left(\eta_{-1}-\frac{\xi+1}{\sqrt{2}\,x_\perp}\eta_0+\eta_{+1}\right),\\
&\varepsilon_b=1,\quad \eta_b=\frac{1}{\sqrt{2}}(\eta_{-1}-\eta_1),\\
&\varepsilon_c=\frac{1}{2}(1+\xi),\quad \eta_c=\frac{x_\perp}{\sqrt{\xi^2-\xi}}\left(\eta_{-1}-\frac{\xi-1}{\sqrt{2}\,x_\perp}\eta_0+\eta_1\right),\\
&\qquad\qquad \xi=\sqrt{1+4x_\perp^2}\,.
\end{aligned}\right\} \tag{3.25}$$

The matrix elements of the components of the vector $\boldsymbol{S}$ calculated with the aid of the spin functions (3.25) equal

$$\left.\begin{aligned}
&\langle a|S_x|b\rangle=\langle b|S_x|c\rangle=0,\quad \langle a|S_x|c\rangle=-\frac{1}{\xi},\\
&\langle a|S_y|b\rangle=-i\sqrt{\frac{\xi+1}{2\xi}},\quad \langle b|S_y|c\rangle=i\sqrt{\frac{\xi-1}{2\xi}},\\
&\qquad\qquad \langle a|S_y|c\rangle=0,\\
&\langle a|S_z|b\rangle=-\frac{\sqrt{2}\,x_\perp}{\sqrt{\xi^2+\xi}},\quad \langle b|S_z|c\rangle=-\frac{\sqrt{2}\,x_\perp}{\sqrt{\xi^2-1}},\\
&\qquad\qquad \langle a|S_z|c\rangle=0.
\end{aligned}\right\} \tag{3.26}$$

It is apparent from these formulas that in strong magnetic fields, when $x_\perp \gg 1$, paramagnetic resonance occurs only if the periodic magnetic field is perpendicular to field H_0. In weak and intermediate

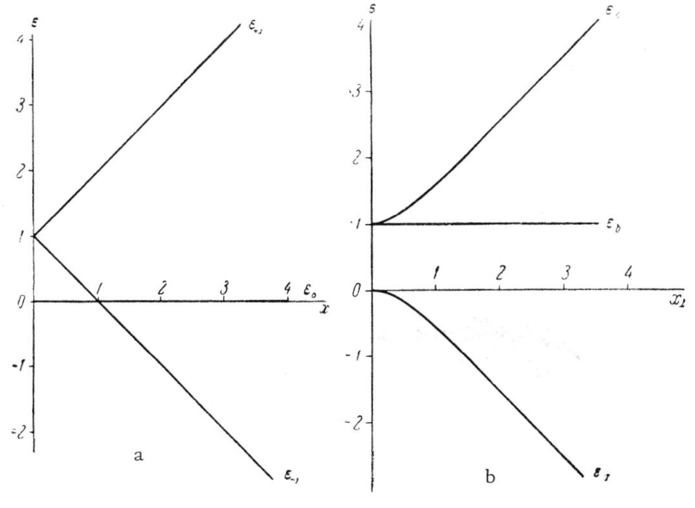

Fig. 3.2. Graph of the spin energy levels of the Ni^{2+} ion in a fluosilicate as a function of the magnetic field intensity H_0. a- H_0 is parallel to the tetragonal axis of the crystal; b- H_0 is perpendicular to the tetragonal axis.

magnetic fields, the matrix element $\langle a | S_x | c \rangle \neq 0$, and hence paramagnetic resonance absorption is possible between levels a and c if the static and periodic magnetic fields are parallel to one another. An energy level scheme and the possible transitions are given in Figure 3.2.

3.5. Hyperfine Structure of Paramagnetic Resonance Spectra

The theory of the hyperfine structure of atomic spectra was worked out a long time ago. What is new here in the application of this theory to the paramagnetic resonance spectra of crystals is the necessity of taking into account the influence of the crystalline field and certain other effects which are of no importance to optical investigations. The first calculations of the hyperfine structure of paramagnetic resonance spectra dealing with copper salts, namely, Tutton salts [35] and copper fluosilicates [36], show a clear disagreement with experimental data. The discrepancy between theory and experiment became especially pronounced when, counter to the predictions of theory, the hyperfine structure of the paramagnetic absorption lines of Mn^{2+} salts was experimentally established.

All these contradications have been eliminated by the hypothesis of "*s*-configuration interaction" [37]. It is well known [38] that the magnetic interaction of s electrons with a nucleus is very much stronger than that of electrons with $l \neq 0$. It has been assumed that in the ground state of a paramagnetic ion, besides the generally accepted $3d^n$ configuration, there also exists a small admixture of a configuration containing an unpaired s electron. It is most probable that the hyperfine structure is explained by the admixture of a $3sp^6d^n4s$ configuration, because, first of all, the transition of a $3s$ electron to a $4s$ orbital requires a comparatively small expenditure of energy and second, in this configuration, the quantum numbers of the total orbital and spin angular momenta may take on the very values of L and S that Hund's rule for the ground state of an ion would indicate. The *s*-configuration interaction occurs in free atoms and depends little on the crystalline field.

A verification of the *s*-configuration interaction hypothesis may therefore be found in the isotropy of the hyperfine structure of the paramagnetic resonance spectra and the approximately equal magnitude of the hyperfine splitting constants for all the Mn^{2+} salts that were studied. It should be noted that the *s*-configurational effect is especially important for iron group salts, since in these crystals the orbital magnetism is quenched (orbital singlet levels), which greatly decreases the hyperfine splitting.

The general theory of the hyperfine structure of the paramagnetic resonance spectra of the iron group was developed in [17]. If the nuclear spin of the paramagnetic ion differs from zero, the following expression is added to the Hamiltonian (3.9):

$$\hat{\mathcal{H}}_{\text{sp}}^{N}=p\{(\hat{L}\hat{I})+[\xi L(L+1)-k](\hat{S}\hat{I})-\frac{3}{2}\xi(\hat{L}\hat{S})(\hat{L}\hat{I})-\\ -\frac{3}{2}\xi(\hat{L}\hat{I})(\hat{L}\hat{S})\}+q'\left\{(\hat{L}\hat{I})^{2}+\frac{1}{2}(\hat{L}\hat{I})\right\}-g_{N}\beta_{N}(H\hat{I}), \tag{3.27}$$

where

$$p=\frac{2g_{N}\beta\beta_{N}}{r^{3}},\quad q'=\frac{\eta e^{2}q}{2I(2I-1)r^{3}},\quad \xi=\frac{(2l+1)-4S}{S(2l-1)(2l+3)(2L-1)}.$$
$$\eta=\pm 2S\xi.$$

Here I is the spin of the nucleus, $g_N\beta_N$ is the magnetic moment, q is the quadrupole moment of the nucleus; the plus or minus sign for η is taken depending on whether the first or second half of the atom's d shell is filled. In Eq. (3.27) the first term takes into account the interaction between the electrons and the nuclear magnetic moments; the second term, that between the electrons and the quadrupole nuclear moment; and the third includes the energy of the nucleus in an external magnetic field. The coefficient k is introduced to take into account the effect of the s configuration interaction. Theoretical calculation of the magnitude of k is extremely complex. However, comparison with experiment data reveals an interesting fact: the coefficient k is almost identical for all ions of the iron group.

The change from (3.27) to the spin Hamiltonian can be accomplished by the method described in Sec. 3.3. We know that two cases should be distinguished depending on whether the state of the atom after the action of the cubic crystalline field is non-degenerate or degenerate. In the first case the spin Hamiltonian which takes into account the interaction of the nuclear moments with the electron shell and with the external magnetic field is:

$$\hat{\mathcal{H}}_{\text{sp}}^{N}=A_{ij}\hat{S}_{i}\hat{I}_{j}+P_{ij}\hat{I}_{i}\hat{I}_{j}-g_{N}\beta_{N}\boldsymbol{H}_{0}\hat{\boldsymbol{I}}. \tag{3.28}$$

If the resultant crystalline field has tetragonal or trigonal symmetry,

$$\hat{\mathcal{H}}_{\text{sp}}^{N}=A\hat{S}_{z}\hat{I}_{z}+B(\hat{S}_{x}\hat{I}_{x}+\hat{S}_{y}\hat{I}_{y})+P\left(\hat{I}_{z}^{2}-\frac{1}{3}I(I+1)\right)-g_{N}\beta_{N}\boldsymbol{H}_{0}\hat{\boldsymbol{I}}. \tag{3.29}$$

In the second case the spin Hamiltonian has the same form, although $\hat{S}$ is to be understood as the effective spin $\hat{S}'$. We shall not pause here to discuss the relationship of the coefficients A and B with the crystalline field constants and with the nuclear moments, but it is obvious that the magnetic hyperfine structure constants A and B are proportional to $g_N\ \overline{(1/r^{3})}$, and the quadrupole interaction constant P is proportional to $q\ (\overline{1/r^3})$. The intensities of the individual hyperfine components of the paramagnetic resonance spectrum will, as before, be determined only by the magnitude of the matrix element of the electron magnetic moment (3.17), since the nuclear magnetic moment is extremely small. Therefore, in the simplest cases, when the component of the nuclear angular momentum I_z is a constant of motion, the magnetic quantum number obeys the selection rule $\Delta m = 0$.

Most theoretical calculations and experimental studies have concerned strong magnetic fields, whose effect on unpaired electrons of paramagnetic atoms is much greater than the interaction of the latter with the nuclear moments. Calculations of the hyperfine splitting in weak magnetic fields are much more complicated and have been carried out only for a few special cases [39].

To substantiate the hypothesis of s-configuration interaction, an analysis was conducted in [37] of experimental data from the optical spectra of neutral atoms and the paramagnetic resonance spectra of ions of $3d$ transition-group elements; it confirmed the statement made by Fermi long ago [38] that when no s electrons exist in the ground state of an atom, the major portion of the hyperfine splitting is often determined by unpaired s electrons of the excited level. A quantitative estimate of the coefficient k has also been made [40] by means of Hartree-Fock functions, which gave a magnitude approximately less by a factor of ten than the observed value. The discrepancy between theory and experiment may perhaps be explained by the inapplicability of the Hartree-Fock method to calculations of wave functions close to the nucleus.

3.6. Crystalline Field Parameters. Jahn-Teller Effect

Previously, all calculations of the energy spectra of paramagnetic ions and crystals were conducted by the crystalline field method. The crystalline field parameters A_n^m were generally determined by a comparison of theoretical results with experimental data on paramagnetic resonance, the temperature dependence of the static paramagnetic susceptibility, optical absorption spectra, etc. It would be of interest to make a theoretical estimate of the magnitude of the crystalline field, in particular, and the magnitude of its principal cubic component. Van Vleck [13] and Polder [6] made a numerical calculation, assuming that the cubic field is created by six point charges e_{eff} or six dipoles of moment μ_e, situated at the vertices of an octahedron at a distance R from the center. It follows from this model that the parameter C_4 introduced in (3.7) equals

$$C_4 = -\frac{35}{4}\frac{ee_{\text{eff}}}{4R^5}, \quad \text{or} \quad C_4 = \frac{175}{4}\frac{e\mu_e}{R^6}. \tag{3.30}$$

X-ray analysis of alums [41] showed that R = 2.0 A. To calculate splitting Δ it is necessary to know the magnitude of r^4 for the 3d electron. If 3d hydrogenlike functions are used, we obtain

$$\overline{r^2} = 126a_0^2Z^{-2} = 4.40a_0^2, \quad \overline{r^4} = 25.515a_0^4Z^{-4} = 31.2a_0^4. \tag{3.31}$$

We have here taken Z = 5.35, which follows from the experimental value of 43 ev for the ionization potential of Ti^{3+}. If we assume that $e_{\text{eff}} \approx -e$ or $\mu_e = 2 \cdot 10^{-18}$ cgs electrostatic units, the calculated spacings between the energy levels in a cubic field are in good agreement with experimental values. This agreement must nevertheless be acknowledged as accidental, since the adopted model is very crude. Kleiner [42] made a more accurate calculation for chrome alums by taking the distribution of the electron cloud in the oxygen ion into consideration. The water molecules are rotated toward the center of the octahedron by the oxygen atoms, which can be taken as O^-. The results of the calculations were found to be in complete contradiction to the experimental data, since even the sign of the parameter C_4 was incorrect. Tanabe and Sugano [43] considered the covalent bonds between the central ions and the neighboring atoms (see Sec. 3.8). As a result of exchange effects, a reversal of the energy levels takes place, and the order becomes correct. The resulting absolute magnitude of C_4 is found to be approximately 3/2 times as great as the experimental value.

We have already pointed out that in iron group salts the crystalline field surrounding the paramagnetic particle possesses cubic symmetry only to a first approximation. In reality, however, there are significant deviations. On the strong cubic field there is superimposed a weak field of much lower symmetry, whose origin is connected with the three following diverse causes [26].

1. Direct action on the paramagnetic particle by the electric field of remote particles located outside the octahedral complex. In alums, for example, this field has trigonal symmetry and can be represented in the following form:

$$V_{\text{trig}} = (G + 30Hr^2)(xy + yz + zx) - 35H(x^3y + xy^3 + \\ + y^3z + yz^3 + zx^3 + z^3x) + C. \tag{3.32}$$

Here x, y, and z are Cartesian coordinates of the electron referred to the principal cubic axes; G and H are constants which are independent of r; C is a polynomial having cubic symmetry and therefore unimportant for our purposes. If we introduce the spherical coordinates R_i, α_i, β_i, which determine the position of the charge e_i with respect to the paramagnetic center, we obtain the following expressions for the constants G and H:

$$\left.\begin{aligned} G &= -\sum e_i e R_i^{-3}\left(\frac{3}{2}\cos^2\alpha_i - \frac{1}{2}\right), \\ H &= -\frac{1}{63}\sum e_i e R_i^{-5}\Big[35\cos^4\alpha_i - 30\cos^2\alpha_i + 3 + \\ &\qquad + 7\sqrt{2}\cos\alpha_i\sin^3\alpha_i\cos 3\beta_i\Big]. \end{aligned}\right\} \tag{3.33}$$

Calculations show that for titanium alums, for instance, the splitting of the lower energy level by the field (3.32) equals approximately 350 cm^{-1}.

2. Indirect effect of remote particles. The remote particles deform the octahedral complex and distort the cubic field created by them. If we have three point charges a, b and c, the direct effect of charge a on c is greater than the indirect effect arising due to the motion of charge b under the influence of charge a. In our case, however, the indirect effect may be considerably more direct, since the electron clouds of the particles forming the paramagnetic octahedral complex overlap. One proof of the importance of the indirect effect is the well-known fact that the zero-field splitting of the spin levels of iron alums increases with magnetic dilution through the replacement of iron ions by aluminum ions. The direct effect may not change noticeably, because iron and aluminum ions have the same charge, and the radii of these ions are very small in comparison to the distances between the trivalent atoms. Deformation of the octahedron, however, may depend significantly on whether an iron or aluminum ion is located at its center.

3. Jahn-Teller effect. This cause of lattice deformation which lowers the symmetry of the crystalline field is often very important. The original Jahn-Teller theorem was demonstrated for molecules [13]. Later it was extended to crystals [13, 14]. According to this theorem, if the electronic state of a molecule is degenerate, the geometrical configuration of its nuclei cannot be stable, except in the following two situations: a) the molecule is linear, i.e., the nuclei are located on a single straight line; b) the molecule contains an odd number of electrons and the electron state has a twofold Kramers degeneracy, i.e., a degeneracy that cannot be removed by any alteration of the electrostatic forces.

If we exclude these two cases, a lowering of the symmetry of the nuclear configuration removes the degeneracy of the electron states. It can be proved that after the splitting of the energy level the mean value of the different electron states is unchanged. Thus, after the deformation of the molecule at least one electron level will lie below the initial level.

Van Vleck [13] realized the transition from molecules to crystals by considering the behavior of an octahedral paramagnetic complex in an external trigonal field. The Hamiltonian $\mathscr{H}$ of the electron state will contain as parameters the distances between the centers of the particles (atoms or molecules) that form the complex. Arbitrary displacements of these particles may be described by means of 21 normal vibration coordinates [a] Q_i. Expanding the Hamiltonian function in a power series in Q_i, we obtain

$$\hat{\mathscr{H}} = \hat{\mathscr{H}}_0 + \hat{V}_{\text{trig}} + \sum_i \hat{V}_i Q_i. \tag{3.34}$$

Here $\hat{\mathscr{H}}_0$ contains all the interactions inside the regular octahedral complex which do not depend on the electron spin of the paramagnetic ion; $\hat{V}_{\text{trig}}$ takes the effect of the remote atoms of the crystalline lattice into account. Suppose W_0 is one of the eigenvalues of $\hat{\mathscr{H}}_0$. One of the set of wave functions given in (3.11) is related to the energy W_0. Considering the second and third terms of (3.34) as perturbations, we may set up and solve a secular equation which gives a first-order correction to the energy W_0. Thus, the energy of the entire system is some function of the displacements Q_i. Solving the system of equations

$$\frac{\partial W}{\partial Q_i} = 0 \qquad (i = 1, 2, 3, \ldots), \tag{3.35}$$

we may find those displacements Q_i^0 which correspond to the minimum energy of W and consequently to the most stable configuration of the paramagnetic complex. Van Vleck made detailed calculations for titanium, vanadium and chrome (excited state) alums. It was found that Q_i^0 are of the order 10^{-9} cm. The potential of the low-symmetry crystalline field arising due to distortion of the octahedral configuration of water molecules will be a quadratic function of Q_i^0. The splitting of the orbital energy levels caused by this field, as the calculations show, are of the order 10^2 cm^{-1}. The potential energy of the f electron of rare earth atoms in a crystalline field is approximately 1/100 of the energy of the d electrons of iron group atoms. In rare earth crystals, therefore, $Q_i^0 \approx 10^{-11}$ cm, and consequently the splitting of the energy levels due to the Jahn–Teller effect should be equal approximately to $10^2 \cdot (10^{-2})^2 = 10^{-2}$ cm^{-1}. As we shall see below, experiments confirm this conclusion.

The Van Vleck theory was developed in the papers of Pryce and his co-workers [14]. From general considerations they reached the conclusion that the Jahn–Teller effect is relevant not only to degenerate but also to nearly degenerate systems. Interesting examples of such nearly degenrate systems include linear triatomic molecules of type BAB.

In addition, these researchers extensively studied octahedral complexes, which as we know are not only found in paramagnetic salts but are also encountered in crystals containing F centers, luminescent centers, exciton states, etc. The degeneracy of the electron state of an octahedral paramagnetic complex may be

[a] [More precisely, the complex MX_6 has 21 degrees of freedom but only 15 normal vibrational coordinates, since there are three rotational and three translational degrees of freedom.]

threefold or twofold. If the degeneracy of the energy level is threefold, the deformation of the complex during a change to a stable configuration of nuclei sometimes occurs along the (100) axis, in other cases along (111). As a result, the complex will have either tetragonal or trigonal symmetry. If the degeneracy is twofold the situation becomes more complex. In this case the energy splitting caused by deformation of the complex is proportional to $Q_2^2 + Q_3^2$, where Q_2 and Q_3 denote certain even type normal modes of the octahedron. It is convenient to introduce the new variables ρ and α:

$$Q_2 = \rho \sin \alpha, \quad Q_3 = \rho \cos \alpha. \tag{3.36}$$

It is clear that the splitting is independent of α. Thus, there exists an infinite set of configurations of equal energy. When anharmonic effects are considered, it turns out that the most stable configuration results if the octahedron is extended along one of the tetragonal axes.

As Abragam and Pryce [36] pointed out, these results serve to explain why in copper salts whose crystals have trigonal symmetry, the g factor is isotropic, and the hyperfine structure constant is isotropic and small. In a field of cubic symmetry the lowest orbital level of a copper ion is twofold degenerate, and according to (3.11) is associated with the wave functions $\varphi_1 = \psi_0$ and $\varphi_2 = (\psi_2 + \psi_{-2})/\sqrt{2}$.

Neither spin-orbit interaction nor a field of trigonal symmetry can remove the degeneracy. The only cause of the splitting of this orbital level is the Jahn-Teller effect. The following wave functions belong to the energy sublevels

$$\psi_{\mathrm{I}} = \varphi_1 \cos \alpha + \varphi_2 \sin \alpha, \quad \psi_{\mathrm{II}} = \varphi_1 \sin \alpha - \varphi_2 \cos \alpha. \tag{3.37}$$

The principal values of the g tensor, calculated by means of these functions, equal:

$$\left.\begin{aligned} g_x &= 2 - 2\frac{\lambda}{\Delta}(\cos \alpha - \sqrt{3} \sin \alpha)^2, \\ g_y &= 2 + 2\frac{\lambda}{\Delta}(\cos \alpha + \sqrt{3} \sin \alpha)^2, \\ g_z &= 2 - 8\frac{\lambda}{\Delta}\cos^2 \alpha. \end{aligned}\right\} \tag{3.38}$$

If we average over α, we obtain $\bar{g}_x = \bar{g}_y = \bar{g}_z = 2 - 4\lambda/\Delta$. The isotropy of the hyperfine structure of the paramagnetic resonance spectra can be explained in a similar way.

3.7. Salts of Rare Earth Elements

It is well known that the static magnetic susceptibility of rare earth salts at room temperature can be computed if it is assumed that the carriers of paramagnetism are free rare earth ions occurring in states determined by Hund's rule [10]. This premise is also supported by optical data [44]. From this one may conclude, first, that deviations from the normal type of coupling (Russell-Saunders), at least in the ground state, are small, and second, that the effect of the crystal field on the paramagnetic ion is weak and is not able to disrupt the spin-orbit coupling. This last fact is explained by the following two features of rare earth ions:

1. The magnetic properties of rare earth ions are caused by the low-lying $4f$ electrons, whose mean distance from the nucleus is much less than for $3d$ electrons. In addition, the outer electron shell exerts a screening effect. Therefore, the crystalline field causes a splitting of the energy levels of rare earth elements, which is of the order of 100 cm^{-1}, i.e., approximately 1/100 of that of ions of the iron group.

2. Multiplet splitting in rare earth ions is much greater than in ions of the iron group; its order of magnitude is 10^3 - 10^4 cm^{-1}.

Thus the spin-orbit coupling is much stronger than the influence of the crystalline field, and therefore the Hamiltonian for a paramagnetic ion should be written in the form

$$\mathscr{H} = \hat{\mathscr{H}}^0 + \hat{\mathscr{H}}_{cr} + \hat{\mathscr{H}}_Z. \quad (3.39)$$

Here $\hat{\mathscr{H}}^0$ is the Hamiltonian of a free ion. In perturbation theory calculations, one starts from the ground state of $\hat{\mathscr{H}}^0$, in which the total angular momentum J and the orbital and spin angular momenta L and S may be considered as constants of motion. Sometimes it is essential to go to higher approximations, which take into account the effect of the excited levels of $\hat{\mathscr{H}}^0$; usually it is sufficient to consider the first excited multiplet level. For many elements, the spacings between the ground and first excited levels are known from optical and magnetic measurements. For the remaining elements, the multiplet structure constant may be estimated, according to [45], from the following formula:

$$\lambda = 200\,(Z - 55)\ \text{cm}^{-1}. \quad (3.40)$$

Table 3.5 gives the ground states of rare earth ions, and also data taken from experiment and obtained from (3.40) pertinent to the first excited energy level.

We proceed to a consideration of the splitting of the $(2J + 1)$-fold energy level of a free ion in the crystalline field $\hat{\mathscr{H}}_{cr}$. In contrast with hydrated iron-group salts, in which the paramagnetic ion is usually surrounded by an octahedron of water molecules, which produces a strong electric field of cubic symmetry, in most salts of rare earth elements the neighborhood of a paramagnetic ion produces a field of trigonal symmetry [47]. Therefore, the energy levels of ions containing an odd number of electrons are split into $J + 1/2$ doublets (Table 3.2); while when the number of electrons is even, we obtain singlets and doublets (Table 3.1).

Table 3.5

Energy Levels of Free Rare-Earth Ions

Element (X^{3+})	z	Ground state	Excited state	$E_1 - E_0$ (theor.), cm^{-1}	$E_1 - E_0$ (expt.), cm^{-1}	Source
Ce	58	$f^1\,{}^2F_{5/2}$	${}^2F_{7/2}$	2 100	2 240	[46]
Pr	59	$f^2\,{}^3H_4$	${}^3H_5$	2 000	—	
Nd	60	$f^3\,{}^4I_{9/2}$	${}^4I_{11/2}$	1 800	—	
Pm	61	$f^4\,{}^5I_4$	${}^5I_5$	1 500	—	
Sm	62	$f^5\,{}^6H_{5/2}$	${}^6H_{7/2}$	980	1 100	[3]
Eu	63	$f^6\,{}^7F_0$	${}^7F_1$	270	300, 340	[3, 47]
Gd	64	$f^7\,{}^8S_{7/2}$				
Tb	65	$f^8\,{}^7F_6$	${}^7F_5$	2 000	—	[46]
Dy	66	$f^9\,{}^6H_{15/2}$	${}^6H_{13/2}$	3 300	—	
Ho	67	$f^{10}\,{}^5I_8$	${}^5I_7$	4 800	5 050	[48]
Er	68	$f^{11}\,{}^4I_{15/2}$	${}^4I_{13/2}$	6 500	8 000	[48]
Tm	69	$f^{12}\,{}^3H_6$	${}^3H_5$	8 400	8 250	[49]
Yb	70	$f^{13}\,{}^2F_{7/2}$	${}^2F_{5/2}$	10 500	10 300	[48]

For a quantitative calculation, one must first of all find an expression for the crystal field potential.[1] In the case of C_{3v} symmetry (formates), the potential can be expressed by formula (3.3 b), in which all six coefficients A_n^m differ from zero. For the somewhat higher symmetry C_{3h} (ethylsulfates, bromates) $A_4^3 = A_6^3 = 0$. The matrix elements of $\mathscr{H}_{cr}$, necessary for first-order perturbation theory calculations, may be obtained with the aid of equivalent operators (Table 3.3); the common factors α, β, γ for all rare earth ions may be determined by means of the ψ functions corresponding to the states with maximum J_z, by means of a transformation from the J, J_z representation to the L_z, S_z representation and then to the l_z, s_z representation [8].

Calculation of the splitting caused by $\hat{\mathscr{H}}_{cr}$ in the second-order approximation requires knowledge of the matrix elements of $\hat{\mathscr{H}}_{cr}$ connecting the ground and first excited states:

$$\langle J+1,\ J_z+m \,|\, V_n^m \,|\, J,\ J_z \rangle .$$

[1] In this section, we shall not touch upon salts with ions occurring in S states.

For this purpose, in [45, 51] the following formulas were obtained:

$$\langle J+1, J_z | V_2^0 | J, J_z \rangle = \alpha' \overline{r^2} J_z \sqrt{(J+1)^2 - J_z^2},$$
$$\langle J+1, J_z | V_4^0 | J, J_z \rangle = \beta' \overline{r^4} J_z (7J_z^2 - 3J^2 - 6J + 2) \sqrt{(J+1)^2 - J_z^2},$$
$$\langle J+1, J_z | V_6^0 | J, J_z \rangle = \gamma' \overline{r^6} J_z [33J_z^4 - 5J_z^2 (6J^2 + 12J + 15) + 5J^4 + $$
$$+ 20J^3 - 5J^2 - 50J + 12] \sqrt{(J+1)^2 - J_z^2},$$
$$\langle J+1, J_z+3 | V_4^3 | J, J_z \rangle = -\frac{1}{40} \beta' \overline{r^4} (4J_z - J + 5) \sqrt{\frac{(J+J_z+4)!(J-J_z)!}{(J+J_z)!(J-J_z-2)!}},$$
$$\langle J+1, J_z+3 | V_6^3 | J, J_z \rangle = -\frac{1}{28} \gamma' \overline{r^6} [22J_z^3 - 11J_z^2 (J-8) - J_z (4J^2 +$$
$$+ 41J - 142) + (J-2)(J-7)(J+6)] \sqrt{\frac{(J+J_z+4)!(J-J_z)!}{(J+J_z)!(J-J_z-2)!}},$$
$$\langle J+1, J_z+6 | V_6^6 | J, J_z \rangle = -\frac{1}{14} \gamma' \overline{r^6} \sqrt{\frac{(J+J_z+7)!(J-J_z)!}{(J+J_z)!(J-J_z-5)!}}.$$

Values of the coefficients α, β, γ and α', β', γ' are cited in Table 3.6. The magnitudes of α, β, γ may be calculated also with the aid of Racah coefficients [52].

After the secular equation has been solved, and hence the energy levels of an ion in a crystalline field and the corresponding wave functions have been found, one must proceed to a calculation of the splitting of these levels by the external magnetic field. We know that under the influence of $\hat{\mathscr{H}}_{\mathrm{cr}}$ either doublets (ions with an odd number of electrons) or doublets and singlets (ions with an even number of electrons) arise. Since the spacings between the energy levels in a crystalline field are much greater than the Zeeman splittings in the usual magnetic fields, we shall not consider the effect of the magnetic field on each level individually. Since the spin-lattice interaction in salts of rare earth elements is very great at room temperature (see Sec. 5.3), the experiment must be set up at temperatures so low that in practice only the lowest level is populated.[1] It is clear that observations of paramagnetic resonance will be possible if this level is not a singlet. With the aid of wave functions of the lower doublet, the matrix elements of the interaction $\hat{\mathscr{H}}_Z = \beta \boldsymbol{H}_0(\hat{\boldsymbol{L}} + 2\hat{\boldsymbol{S}})$ are calculated from the following formulas:

$$\langle J, \ldots | \hat{\boldsymbol{L}} + 2\hat{\boldsymbol{S}} | J, \ldots \rangle = g_0 \langle J \ldots | \hat{\boldsymbol{J}} | J \ldots \rangle, \tag{3.41}$$

where g_0 is the Landé factor for a free ion, and

$$\left.\begin{aligned} &\langle J+1, J_z | \hat{L}_z + 2\hat{S}_z | J, J_z \rangle = g' \sqrt{(J+1)^2 - J_z^2}, \\ &\langle J+1, J_z \pm 1 | \hat{L}_x + 2\hat{S}_x | J, J_z \rangle = \langle J+1, J_z \pm \\ &\pm 1 | \pm i(\hat{L}_y + 2\hat{S}_y) | J, J_z \rangle = \mp g' \sqrt{(J \pm J_z + 1)(J \pm J_z + 2)}, \end{aligned}\right\} \tag{3.42}$$

---

[1] Exceptions are encountered: for example, in cerium ethylsulfate, even at liquid helium temperature the two lowest levels of the ion are markedly populated.

where

$$g' = \left\{ \frac{(J+L+S+2)(-J+L+S)(J-L+S+1)(J+L-S+1)}{4(J+1)^2(2J+1)(2J+3)} \right\}^{\frac{1}{2}}. \quad (3.43)$$

The values of g_0 and g' for individual ions are cited in Table 3.6.

The second-rank perturbation matrix has a trace equal to zero, and can be represented in the form $\beta H_0 g S'$, where S' is a Pauli matrix vector, and g is a tensor with the principal values $g_{\parallel}$, $g_{\perp}$, $g_{\perp}$. If the wave functions of our doublet, which we designate symbolically by $|+\rangle$ and $|-\rangle$, are chosen so that the matrix $L_z + 2S_z$ is diagonal,

$$\left. \begin{aligned} g_{\parallel} &= 2|\langle + | \hat{L}_z + 2\hat{S}_z | + \rangle|, \\ g_{\perp} &= 2|\langle + | \hat{L}_x + 2\hat{S}_x | - \rangle|. \end{aligned} \right\} \quad (3.44)$$

Table 3.6

Ion	α	β	γ	α'
Ce^{3+}	$\frac{-2}{5 \cdot 7}$	$\frac{2}{3^2 \cdot 5 \cdot 7}$	0	$\frac{2^2}{3 \cdot 5 \cdot 7}$
Pr^{3+}	$\frac{-2^2 \cdot 13}{3^2 \cdot 5^2 \cdot 11}$	$\frac{-2^2}{3^2 \cdot 5 \cdot 11^2}$	$\frac{2^4 \cdot 17}{3^4 \cdot 5 \cdot 7 \cdot 11^2 \cdot 13}$	$\frac{13\sqrt{66}}{3^3 \cdot 5^2 \cdot 11}$
Nd^{3+}	$\frac{-7}{3^2 \cdot 11^2}$	$\frac{-2^3 \cdot 17}{3^3 \cdot 11^3 \cdot 13}$	$\frac{-5 \cdot 17 \cdot 19}{3^3 \cdot 7 \cdot 11^3 \cdot 13^2}$	$\frac{2\sqrt{14}}{11^2 \cdot 13}$
Pm^{3+}	$\frac{2 \cdot 7}{3 \cdot 5 \cdot 11^2}$	$\frac{2^3 \cdot 7 \cdot 17}{3^3 \cdot 5 \cdot 11^3 \cdot 13}$	$\frac{2^3 \cdot 17 \cdot 19}{3^3 \cdot 7 \cdot 11^2 \cdot 13^2}$	$\frac{-1}{3 \cdot 5 \cdot 11}\sqrt{\frac{14}{11}}$
Sm^{3+}	$\frac{13}{3^2 \cdot 5 \cdot 7}$	$\frac{2 \cdot 13}{3^3 \cdot 5 \cdot 7 \cdot 11}$	0	$\frac{-2^2 \cdot 13}{3^3 \cdot 7 \cdot \sqrt{30}}$
Tb^{3+}	$\frac{-1}{3^2 \cdot 11}$	$\frac{2}{3^3 \cdot 5 \cdot 11^2}$	$\frac{-1}{3^4 \cdot 7 \cdot 11^2 \cdot 13}$	$\frac{1}{3 \cdot 5 \cdot \sqrt{11}}$
Dy^{3+}	$\frac{-2}{3^2 \cdot 5 \cdot 7}$	$\frac{-2^3}{3^3 \cdot 5 \cdot 7 \cdot 11 \cdot 13}$	$\frac{2^2}{3^3 \cdot 7 \cdot 11^2 \cdot 13^2}$	$\frac{2^2\sqrt{7}}{3 \cdot 5 \cdot 7 \cdot 13}$
Ho^{3+}	$\frac{-1}{2 \cdot 3^2 \cdot 5^2}$	$\frac{-1}{2 \cdot 3 \cdot 5 \cdot 7 \cdot 11 \cdot 13}$	$\frac{-5}{3^3 \cdot 7 \cdot 11^2 \cdot 13^2}$	$\frac{1}{2 \cdot 3 \cdot 5 \cdot 7\sqrt{5}}$
Er^{3+}	$\frac{2^2}{3^2 \cdot 5^2 \cdot 7}$	$\frac{2}{3^2 \cdot 5 \cdot 7 \cdot 11 \cdot 13}$	$\frac{2^3}{3^3 \cdot 7 \cdot 11^2 \cdot 13^2}$	$\frac{-2^2\sqrt{14}}{3 \cdot 5^2 \cdot 7 \cdot 13}$
Tm^{3+}	$\frac{1}{3^2 \cdot 11}$	$\frac{2^3}{3^4 \cdot 5 \cdot 11^2}$	$\frac{-5}{3^4 \cdot 7 \cdot 11^2 \cdot 13}$	$\frac{-1}{3 \cdot 5 \cdot \sqrt{55}}$
Yb^{3+}	$\frac{2}{3^2 \cdot 7}$	$\frac{-2}{3 \cdot 5 \cdot 7 \cdot 11}$	$\frac{2^2}{3^3 \cdot 7 \cdot 11 \cdot 13}$	$\frac{-2^2}{3 \cdot 5 \cdot 7}$

Thus, the paramagnetic resonance spectra can be interpreted with the aid of the spin Hamiltonian with an effective spin $S' = 1/2$:

$$\mathscr{H}_{sp} = \beta g_{\parallel} H_{0z} \hat{S}'_z + \beta g_{\perp} (H_{0x} \hat{S}'_x + H_{0y} \hat{S}'_y). \tag{3.45}$$

Ions with an even number of electrons require special consideration. In this case it is easy to show that the off-diagonal matrix element $\langle + | \hat{L}_x + 2\hat{S}_x | - \rangle = 0$. From this it follows that the paramagnetic resonance effect should not exist. Actually if the field H_0 is parallel to the trigonal axis of the crystal, magnetic dipole transition between the magnetic sublevels will be forbidden, while if H_0 is perpendicular to the trigonal axis, $g_{\perp} = 0$.

Table 3.6

β'	γ'	g_0	g'	N	N'
$\frac{-2^3}{3^2 \cdot 7 \cdot 11}$	$\frac{2^3}{3^2 \cdot 11 \cdot 13}$	$\frac{6}{7}$	$\frac{1}{7}$	$\frac{2^4 \cdot 3}{5 \cdot 7}$	$-\frac{1}{14}$
$\frac{2^2 \sqrt{66}}{3^3 \cdot 7 \cdot 11^2}$	$\frac{-17 \sqrt{66}}{3^4 \cdot 5 \cdot 11^2 \cdot 13}$	$\frac{4}{5}$	$\frac{\sqrt{66}}{5 \cdot 11}$	$\frac{2^3 \cdot 37}{3^2 \cdot 5^2}$	$\frac{-7 \sqrt{66}}{2 \cdot 3^2 \cdot 5^2}$
$\frac{2^5 \cdot 17 \cdot \sqrt{14}}{3^3 \cdot 7 \cdot 11^3 \cdot 13}$	$\frac{2 \cdot 5 \cdot 19 \sqrt{14}}{3 \cdot 7 \cdot 11^3 \cdot 13^2}$	$\frac{8}{11}$	$\frac{\sqrt{14}}{2 \cdot 11}$	$\frac{2^2 \cdot 7 \cdot 17}{3 \cdot 11^2}$	$\frac{-193 \sqrt{14}}{2^2 \cdot 3^2 \cdot 11^2}$
$\frac{-2^5 \cdot 17}{3^3 \cdot 11^2 \cdot 13 \cdot \sqrt{154}}$	$\frac{-2 \cdot 17 \cdot 19}{3^2 \cdot 11^2 \cdot 13^2 \cdot \sqrt{154}}$	$\frac{3}{5}$	$\frac{1}{5}\sqrt{\frac{14}{11}}$	$\frac{2^5 \cdot 7}{3 \cdot 5 \cdot 11}$	$\frac{-133}{5 \cdot 2^2 \cdot 3 \cdot 11}\sqrt{\frac{14}{11}}$
$\frac{-2^4 \cdot 5 \cdot 17}{3^3 \cdot 7 \cdot 11^2 \cdot \sqrt{30}}$	$\frac{2^4 \cdot 5 \cdot 17}{3^4 \cdot 11^2 \cdot 13 \sqrt{30}}$	$\frac{2}{7}$	$\frac{\sqrt{30}}{2 \cdot 7}$	$\frac{2^3 \cdot 61}{3^2 \cdot 5 \cdot 7}$	$\frac{-19 \cdot 23 \cdot \sqrt{30}}{4 \cdot 3^2 \cdot 5^2 \cdot 7}$
$\frac{-1}{3^3 \cdot 11 \cdot \sqrt{11}}$	$\frac{1}{3^4 \cdot 11 \cdot 13 \cdot \sqrt{11}}$	$\frac{3}{2}$	$\frac{1}{2 \sqrt{11}}$	$\frac{7^2}{2 \cdot 3^2 \cdot 5}$	$\frac{-\sqrt{11}}{2 \cdot 3^2}$
$\frac{2^5 \sqrt{7}}{3^3 \cdot 7 \cdot 11^2 \cdot 13}$	$\frac{-2^3 \sqrt{7}}{3^4 \cdot 11^2 \cdot 13^2}$	$\frac{4}{3}$	$\frac{1}{3 \sqrt{7}}$	$\frac{2^5}{3^2 \cdot 5}$	$\frac{-\sqrt{7}}{2 \cdot 3^2}$
$\frac{\sqrt{5}}{2 \cdot 3^2 \cdot 7 \cdot 11 \cdot 13}$	$\frac{5 \sqrt{5}}{3^2 \cdot 11^2 \cdot 13^2}$	$\frac{5}{4}$	$\frac{1}{4 \sqrt{5}}$	$\frac{23}{2 \cdot 3 \cdot 5}$	$\frac{-4}{3 \cdot 5 \cdot \sqrt{5}}$
$\frac{-2^2 \sqrt{14}}{3^2 \cdot 7 \cdot 11^2 \cdot 13}$	$\frac{-2 \sqrt{14}}{3^2 \cdot 11^2 \cdot 13^2}$	$\frac{6}{5}$	$\frac{2}{5 \sqrt{14}}$	$\frac{2^4 \cdot 11}{3^2 \cdot 5^2}$	$\frac{-83}{3^2 \cdot 5^2 \cdot \sqrt{14}}$
$\frac{2^2}{3^4 \cdot 11 \cdot \sqrt{55}}$	$\frac{\sqrt{55}}{3^4 \cdot 11^2 \cdot 13}$	$\frac{7}{6}$	$\frac{5}{6 \sqrt{55}}$	$\frac{7}{3^2}$	$\frac{-11}{2 \cdot 3^2 \cdot \sqrt{55}}$
$\frac{2^3}{3^2 \cdot 7 \cdot 11}$	$\frac{-2^3}{3^2 \cdot 11 \cdot 13}$	$\frac{8}{7}$	$\frac{1}{7}$	$\frac{2^4}{3 \cdot 7}$	$\frac{-1}{14}$

[The values for β-Yb^{3+}, N-P_n^{3+}, α'-Nd^{3+}, N'-Ce^{3+} and N'-Dy^{3+} have been corrected to conform to (45) - Ed.]

In an experiment with praseodymium salts, for instance, the resonance effect is observed. The Jahn–Teller theorem [12] provides an explanation of this: in crystals containing ions with an even number of electrons, the symmetry of the electric field is lowered so that the degeneracy is completely removed, and the doublets are split. As shown by Van Vleck [13], these splittings in rare earth ions are very small and do not interfere with observations of paramagnetic resonance at the usual magnetic field strength. The paramagnetic resonance spectrum of ions with an even number of electrons can be computed with the aid of the spin Hamiltonian

$$\hat{\mathscr{H}}_{\text{sp}} = \beta g_{\|} H_{0z} \hat{S}_z' + \Delta_x \hat{S}_x' + \Delta_y \hat{S}_y', \qquad (3.46)$$

where $\Delta = \sqrt{\Delta_x^2 + \Delta_y^2}$ is the doublet splitting due to the Jahn–Teller effect in the absence of magnetic field H_0.

A number of papers have been devoted to detailed theoretical treatment of the paramagnetic resonance spectra of individual rare earth elements: cerium ethylsulfate [53, 50], Nd, Sm, Dy, Er, Yb ethylsulfates [54, 55], Ce, Pr, Nd, Sm double nitrates [56]. The attempt to interpret the observed paramagnetic resonance spectrum in dysprosium double nitrate led to an interesting result. It was found that the crystalline field can be divided into two parts [57]: a strong field of very high symmetry, namely, icosahedral, and a weak trigonal field. For the icosahedral symmetry

$$A_6^3 = \left(\pm \frac{14}{\sqrt{5}}\right) A_6^0, \quad A_6^6 = 14 A_6^0, \qquad (3.47)$$

and all the remaining $A_n^m = 0$. The method proposed in [58] is suitable for calculation of the splitting of levels in fields of high symmetry.

The large number (up to 6) of field constants A_n^m makes it difficult to interpret unequivocally the observed paramagnetic resonance spectra. Consequently it is customary to resort to optical data, results of investigations of temperature dependence of static magnetic susceptibility, and information concerning the Faraday effect. It is true that some difficulties arise because of the fact that paramagnetic resonance is observed in very dilute solid solutions of paramagnetic salts, whereas other experiments are conducted with concentrated paramagnetic crystals. In the case of dilution, moreover, the electric field of the crystal changes noticeably; in cerium ethylsulfate these changes even cause an inversion of the two lowest energy levels that are close to one another.

In [45] the general theory of hyperfine structure of paramagnetic resonance spectra of rare earth ions is also examined. A calculation of the hyperfine splitting of the electron energy levels may be conducted with the aid of spin Hamiltonian (3.29) with effective spin $S' = 1/2$. Thus, if the magnetic electron-nuclear interaction operator is denoted by $(\bar{a}/\bar{I})\hat{N}\hat{I}$, the hyperfine structure constants become

$$A = 2\bar{a}\langle + | \hat{N}_z | + \rangle, \qquad B = 2\bar{a}\langle + | \hat{N}_x | - \rangle. \tag{3.48}$$

The nonzero matrix elements of operator $\hat{N}$ may be calculated with the aid of the following formulas:

$$\left.\begin{aligned} \langle J, \ldots | \hat{N} | J, \ldots \rangle &\equiv N \langle J, \ldots | \hat{J} | J, \ldots \rangle, \\ \langle J+1, J_z | \hat{N}_z | J, J_z \rangle &= N' \sqrt{(J+1)^2 - J_z^2}. \end{aligned}\right\} \tag{3.49}$$

The coefficients N and N' are given in Table 3.6.

The rare earth ions may be injected artificially into a crystal, which produces a field of cubic symmetry around these ions. The splitting of the energy levels in a field of cubic symmetry has been examined theoretically in [59], where only the part of the potential proportional to $\bar{r^4}$ is taken into account. Bleaney [88] has shown that the splittings in a cubic field may be calculated with the aid of a special form of the spin Hamiltonian.

Finally, we would like to mention that a number of papers [4, 6], which in their time played a great role in explaining the magnetic properties of rare earth salts, have lost significance because of their incorrect assumptions concerning the symmetry of the crystalline field.

3.8. S-State Ions

Paramagnetic ions having $3d^5$ and $4f^7$ electron configurations occur in the states

$$^6S_{5/2}\,(Mn^{2+},\ Fe^{3+}) \text{ and } {}^8S_{7/2}(Gd^{3+},\ Eu^{2+},\ Cm^{3+}).$$

The resultant orbital angular momentum of the electrons equals zero, and therefore the electric field of the crystal should not split the ground states of these ions. Actually, small splittings have been detected both in adiabatic demagnetization experiments and in observations of paramagnetic resonance.

The complexity of the processes leading to a splitting of the energy levels of ions found in the S state makes it difficult to undertake direct calculations. The spin Hamiltonian method is therefore ordinarily used. When no external magnetic field exists, the spin Hamiltonian will be an even polynomial of the fourth (for Mn^{2+}, Fe^{3+}) or sixth (Gd^{3+}, Eu^{2+}, Cm^{3+}) degree in the projection of the spin moments $\hat{S}_x$, $\hat{S}_y$, $\hat{S}_z$. The number of terms in this Hamiltonian is considerably reduced if the symmetry of the crystalline field is taken into consideration. Thus, for instance, the spin Hamiltonian for a Mn^{2+} or Fe^{3+} ion can be given the following form:

$$\mathscr{H}_{sp} = D\left(\hat{S}_z^2 - \frac{35}{12}\right) + E(\hat{S}_x^2 - \hat{S}_y^2) + \frac{a}{6}(\hat{S}_1^4 + \hat{S}_2^4 + \hat{S}_3^4) + g\beta \boldsymbol{H}_0 \hat{\boldsymbol{S}}. \quad (3.50)$$

Here the first term takes into account the effect of the trigonal or tetragonal field with axis of symmetry directed along the Z axis; the second term is related to small deviations in the direction of lower symmetry; the third term gives the effect of cubic symmetry, where S_1, S_2, S_3 are the spin components referred to the cubic axes; and the last term takes the effect of the external magnetic field into account. For ions occurring in the S state, the g factor is isotropic. In [31, 60] detailed calculations were made of the position and intensity of the paramagnetic resonance absorption lines for ions with $S = 5/2$ and $S = 7/2$ under the assumption that the crystalline field has cubic symmetry. In addition, both the cases of strong and weak magnetic fields have been examined.

We shall briefly discuss the different mechanisms capable of causing splitting of the ground levels of ions in the S state under the influence of the crystalline field. The origin of the third term of spin Hamiltonian (3.50) has been clarified by Van Vleck and Penney [61], who have shown that the fifth-order perturbation involving simultaneously the influence of the electric field of cubic symmetry and the spin-orbit coupling causes a splitting of the ground level of an ion of the configuration d^5. The constant a can be estimated from the formula

$$a \approx \frac{K\lambda^4}{E_{PS}^4}. \quad (3.51)$$

Here K denotes the matrix element of the potential of the crystal's cubic field $\langle 3d | V_{\text{cub}} | 3d \rangle$, calculated with the aid of single-electron functions; E_{PS} is the energy spacing between the ^4P and ^6S terms of the free ion. Taking $K = 10^4\ \text{cm}^{-1}$, $\lambda = 300\ \text{cm}^{-1}$, $E_{PS} = 2.5 \cdot 10^4\ \text{cm}^{-1}$, we obtain $a \approx 10^{-4}\ \text{cm}^{-1}$. It is known from experiment that the constant a in Fe^{3+} is approximately one order of magnitude greater than that in Mn^{2+}. This is explained by the fact the the ratio λ/E_{PS} for Fe^{3+} is somewhat greater than for Mn^{2+}; moreover, the magnitude of K for the trivalent ion obviously is greater than for the divalent ion.

The origin of the first (and second) term of the spin Hamiltonian may be explained in two ways. Abragam and Pryce [17] have considered the following splitting mechanism. The magnetic dipole interaction of electron spins inside the paramagnetic atom depends not only on their relative orientation but also on the electron coordinates. If the electron cloud has cubic or spherical symmetry, after averaging, the spin-spin interaction energy is independent of the relative spin orientation; consequently the ground state of the paramagnetic ion is found to be completely degenerate with respect to spin. The field of tetragonal or trigonal symmetry causes a slight distortion of the electron cloud, which thus acquires an ellipsoidal shape. In this case the spin-spin interaction energy averaged over the electron cloud will depend on the relative orientation of the spins. The splitting of the ground level of a paramagnetic ion arises as early as the second approximation and is proportional to $\hat{S}_z^2 - 35/12$. The constant D can be estimated from the formula

$$D \approx \frac{U\left(\frac{\beta^2}{r^3}\right)}{E_{DS}}. \tag{3.52}$$

Here $U = \langle 3d | U_2^0 | 4s \rangle$ and E_{DS} is the spacing between the $3d^4 4s\,{}^6D$ and $3d^5\,{}^6S$ terms. According to Watanabe [62] the $D\hat{S}_z^2$-type term arises in fourth-order perturbation calculations if one simultaneously takes into account the spin-orbit interaction and fields of cubic and axial symmetry. An estimate of the splitting can be made by means of the formula

$$D \approx \frac{\lambda^2 K U'}{E_{PS}^3}, \tag{3.53}$$

where $U' = \langle 3d | U_2^0 | 3d \rangle$. If we take $U = U' = 10^3$ cm^{-1}, $E_{DS} = 2.5 \cdot 10^4$ cm^{-1}, $\overline{r^{-3}} = 5a_0^{-3}$, both formulas (3.52) and (3.53) give $|D| \approx 0.1$ cm^{-1}, which is in good agreement with experimental data.

In the other papers of [62], devoted to calculations of the ground terms of ions in the S state, similar splitting mechanisms are considered.

If the paramagnetic resonance spectra of S-state ions reveal hyperfine structure, the latter may be computed by adding the spin Hamiltonian (3.29) to (3.50). Evidently the existence of hyperfine structure in the electron energy levels of S-state ions is explained solely by the configuration interaction.

3.9. Covalent Bonding and the 3d, 4d, and 5d Transition Groups

Ionic crystals the paramagnetism of which is due to the elements of the $3d$, $4d$ and $5d$ transition groups often contain octahedral complexes MX_6. In the center of such complexes there is the atom M with an unfilled d shell, and at the vertices of the octahedron are water molecules, CN radicals or atoms of chlorine, fluorine, etc. The bond inside the MX_6 complex is often of a covalent character, a fact which was first indicated by Pauling [63], who attempted to explain the features of the magnetic properties of potassium ferrocyanide by means of the theory of localized pairs. Van Vleck [64] showed, however, that the experimental static magnetic susceptibility data are equally well explained by an assumption of covalent forces within the $Fe(CN)_6$ complex or by the attribution of a purely ionic character to the interaction, albeit in the presence of a strong crystalline field, which disrupts the normal type of coupling between the electrons of the iron atom.

If the molecular orbital method is compared with the localized pair method, it is found that the results obtained by the first method are more general and in better agreement with experiment. Detailed calculations of the energy splittings in a strong crystalline field have been carried out for an atom with the configuration d^5 [65]. Van Vleck has extended the localized pair method to cyanides of other elements with electron configurations from d^1 to d^4 [66]. A further impetus to the development of the theory of a covalent bond inside the complex MX_6 was given by the discovery of the unusual hyperfine structure of the iridium paragmanetic resonance spectra [67]. It turns out that the absorption lines of iridium occurring in the complex ion $[IrCl_6]^{2-}$ have a structure due to the magnetic moment of the chlorine nucleus, and this fact clearly indicates the covalent nature of the bond inside the complex. Detailed examination shows that the hyperfine structure of the Ir spectrum cannot be explained by the σ bond already studied by Van Vleck, and it must therefore be assumed that the π bond between iridium and chlorine also plays a marked role. A general treatment of the theory of paramagnetic resonance in MX_6 complexes with covalent σ and π bonds has been made by Stevens [68].

A short time later, a comparison was made of data on the absorption of light by hydrated iron-group salts and experimental results on paramagnetic resonance in these substances [69].

A contradiction was noted, which could be resolved by assuming that the bonding in the octahedral complex is partially covalent. Double covalent bonds have been established in the vanadyl complex of vanadium sulfate [70] by comparing the paramagnetic resonance data with the results of optical absorption spectra and X-ray analysis. A further generalization of the theory became necessary in order to explain the paramagnetic resonance spectra of iron-group chelates [71] and fluorides [72]; in fluorides the formation of molecular orbitals, aside from $2s$ and $2p$ functions of fluorine, also necessitates the introduction of states with a principal quantum number $n = 3$. We note that the hyperfine structure of Mn^{2+} ions introduced into a ZnF_2 crystal can be explained by taking into account the covalent bonds [89].

Following Stevens [68] and Owen [69], we shall give a general treatment of the effect of covalent bonding on the paramagnetic resonance spectra of d transition group elements, using the molecular orbital method.

a) Energy levels and molecular orbitals of a complex

If the bonding is purely ionic, the atom is a positive ion with an unfilled nd shell (n = 3, 4, 5), in which the electrons are distributed over the following orbitals[1]: $d_{3z^2-r^2}$, $d_{x^2-y^2}$, d_{xy}, d_{yz}, d_{zx}. The subscripts indicate what kind of angular dependence the effective d wave functions possess. If the interelectron interactions are neglected, the ground state of atom M is split in the crystalline field of cubic symmetry into a lower triplet and an upper doublet, according to (3.11). The first two of the above-enumerated orbitals refer to a doublet and, following Bethe [1], are called $d\gamma$ orbitals. The functions d_{xy}, d_{yz}, d_{zx} refer to a triplet and are called $d\epsilon$ orbitals.

Particle X in the ionic approximation of diamagnetism is a negative ion, which as a rule, has a filled p shell; examples include $X = Cl^-$ or O^{-2}[2]. From the orbital functions of atoms M and X_6 we must compose the molecular orbitals of the entire octahedral complex.

Let us first consider the covalent σ bond, which is formed by the $nd\gamma$, $(n+1)s$ and $(n+1)p$ orbitals of the central atom and the p_σ orbitals of the neighboring atoms that overlap them appreciably. The s functions of the X atoms will also be associated with the p_σ orbit. In all, we may construct 6 [2 $(d\gamma)$ + 1 (s) + 3 (p)] bonding and six antibonding orbitals, four of which contain magnetic $d\gamma$ orbitals [64]:

$$\left.\begin{aligned}\sigma^*_{3z^2-r^2} &= \alpha d_{3z^2-r^2} - \sqrt{1-\alpha^2}\,\frac{1}{\sqrt{21}}\times\\ &\quad\times[2p_6 - 2p_3 + p_1 + p_2 - p_4 - p_5]_\sigma,\\ \sigma^*_{x^2-y^2} &= \alpha d_{x^2-y^2} - \sqrt{1-\alpha^2}\,\frac{1}{2}\,[p_2 + p_4 - p_1 - p_5]_\sigma;\end{aligned}\right\} \tag{3.54}$$

$$\left.\begin{aligned}\sigma_{3z^2-r^2} &= \sqrt{1-\alpha^2}\,d_{3z^2-r^2} + \alpha\,\frac{1}{\sqrt{21}}\times\\ &\quad\times[2p_6 - 2p_3 + p_1 + p_2 - p_4 - p_5]_\sigma,\\ \sigma_{x^2-y^2} &= \sqrt{1-\alpha^2}\,d_{x^2-y^2} + \alpha\,\frac{1}{2}\,[p_2 + p_4 - p_1 - p_5]_\sigma.\end{aligned}\right\} \tag{3.55}$$

Here σ represents the bonding orbitals, σ^* the antibonding orbitals, and the subscripts 1, 2, 3, 4, 5, 6 refer to atoms X located on the X, Y, Z, $-X$, $-Y$, $-Z$ axes, respectively. The coefficient α shows

---

[1] By orbitals, we mean, as in quantum chemistry, "orbital" wave functions of individual electrons.

[2] If the octahedral complex is formed by water molecules, the atom directed toward atom M is an oxygen atom.

how much the ψ functions of the central atom and of the surrounding atoms are mixed. If $\alpha = 1$, the bond is purely ionic; if, however, $\alpha^2 = 1 - \alpha^2 = 0.5$, electrons are split with equal probability between M and X_6.

A covalent π bond may be formed by mixing the $d\epsilon$ orbital of the central atom with the p_π orbitals of X_6. Generally speaking, this bond should be weaker, because the combining orbitals are aligned so that they have little overlap. The molecular orbitals have the following form [68, 69]:

$$\pi^*_{xy} = \beta d_{xy} - \sqrt{1-\beta^2}\,\frac{1}{2}\,[p_1 + p_2 - p_4 - p_5]_\pi, \tag{3.56}$$

$$\pi_{xy} = \sqrt{1-\beta^2}\,d_{xy} + \beta\,\frac{1}{2}\,[p_1 + p_2 - p_4 - p_5]_\pi\,. \tag{3.57}$$

The other four combinations of π_{yz}, π^*_{yz}, π_{zx}, π^*_{zx} are obtained from (3.56) and (3.57) by a circular permutation of the indices. The coefficient β shows how large is the π bond; when $\beta = 1$ the π bond does not exist. In (3.54) to (3.57) we have neglected the influence of the overlapping of the atomic orbitals of M and X_6 on the normalization of the σ and π functions.

In Figure 3.3 there is shown a possible energy level diagram of free atoms of M and X_6 and the complex MX_6. We see that the σ bond increases the splitting Δ caused by the cubic field of the crystal; the π bond decreases it somewhat. This diagram fits the cases $X = Cl^-$ and H_2O; if, however, $X = CN^-$, the formation of the π bond with M is produced by means of an orbital of the excited level of a carbon atom lying above the $d\epsilon$ level. Consequently, the sign of β in (3.56) and (3.57) must be changed, so that bonding orbitals become antibonding, and vice versa. Now the π bond also leads to an increase of Δ.

For further development of the theory, as already mentioned in Sec. 3.1, the comparative magnitude of the cubic field effect and of the interaction between electrons which leads to the formation of the term is significant. In hydrated iron-group salts, the magnitude of Δ is much less than the spacings between the different terms of a free paramagnetic ion; while in cyanides and some other iron-group salts, and in compounds of elements of the $4d$ and $5d$ transition group, the reverse relation holds. The latter is evidently explained by the fact that in heavy elements, first the Russell-Saunders coupling is weak, and second the d orbitals lie further from the nucleus and therefore greatly overlap the orbitals of the X_6 atoms.

b) Hydrated iron-group salts

The method of calculating the paramagnetic resonance spectra is the same as in Sec. 3.3 but the matrix elements of perturbation (3.12) must now be calculated with consideration of the presence of

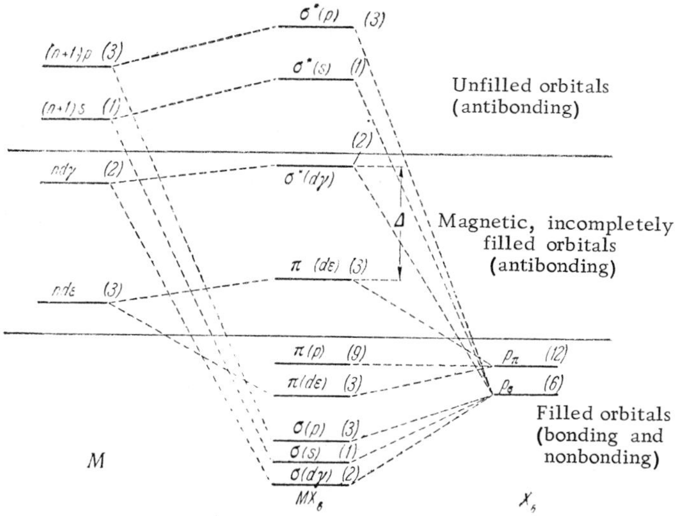

Fig. 3.3. Diagram of the transition from the orbital energy level of a paramagnetic atom M and of diamagnetic atoms X_6 to the energy levels of the complex MX_6.
The degree of orbital degeneracy of the levels is indicated in parentheses.

covalent bonds. For this purpose the wave function of the entire unfilled electron shell must be expanded in d functions of the separate electrons, and then the latter are replaced by the orbitals (3.54) to (3.57). By taking only the σ bonds into account, Owen [69] has shown that the systematic discrepancies between the optical and magnetic data concerning the interval Δ can be removed if the following values of the coefficient α are selected. Thus, for instance, according to the purely ionic theory developed previously by us, for Ni^{2+}, $g = 2.0023 - 8\,\lambda/\Delta$; if, however, the covalent σ bonds are taken into account, we obtain

$$g = 2.0023 - \alpha^2 \frac{8\lambda}{\Delta}. \tag{3.58}$$

This result may be interpreted in the following manner: each of the two unpaired electrons is found with a probability α^2 in the nickel atom and with a probability $1/6\ (1 - \alpha^2)$ in each water molecule. As a result the spin-orbit coupling diminishes and instead of λ we have $\lambda' = \alpha^2\lambda$. For the complex $[Ni(H_2O)_6]^{2+}$ experimental values of Δ and λ, taken from optical observation, and values of g, obtained from paramagnetic resonance measurements, lead according to (3.58) to $\alpha = 0.83$. The covalent bonds should also reduce the hyperfine splitting, which is actually found to be the case in copper salts [25].

c) Strong crystalline field [68]

In this case we must first consider the effect of the cubic field on each electron, and then that of the interelectron interaction. We assume that the problem of the electron motion in the complex MX_6 has been solved by the self-consistent field method and that we have obtained in general a number of degenerate energy levels. If we start to fill these levels with electrons, when their number corresponds to the closed shells of atoms M and X_6, the complex also will have a closed shell. The magnetic properties of the complex will be determined by the electrons of its unfilled shell, which correspond to the d electrons of an isolated atom. These electrons begin to fill the threefold orbital level π^* $(d\varepsilon)$, which may be characterized by the configuration $(d\varepsilon)^n$.

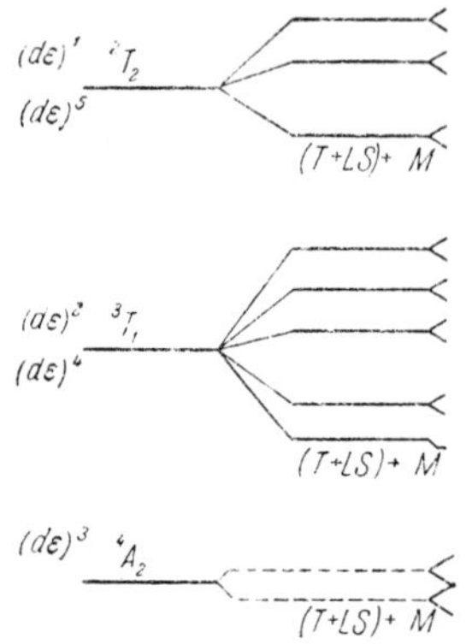

Fig. 3.4. Diagram of the splitting of the ground state of an octahedral complex under the influence of spin-orbit interaction (LS), of a tetragonal field (T) and of a magnetic field (M).
It is assumed that the tetragonal field constant $\delta > 0$; if $\delta < 0$, for the configuration $(d\epsilon)^2$ the lower level will be a doublet. The dashed line indicates the splitting which arises only in the second approximation of perturbation theory.

As in the theory of an atom, the self-consistent field method does not completely encompass the electrostatic interaction between electrons. A calculation of this interaction by perturbation theory leads to the appearance of terms (Figure 3.4), the lowest of which can be proved to exactly obey Hund's rule. This ground term can be characterized by the values of the total electron spin S and of the effective orbital angular momentum L', namely: $(d\epsilon)^1$ and $(d\epsilon)^5$ $L' = 1$, $S = 1/2$; $(d\epsilon)^2$ and $(d\epsilon)^4$ $L' = 1, S = 1$; $(d\epsilon)^3$ $L' = 0$, $S = 3/2$; $(d\epsilon)^6$ $L' = 0$, $S = 0$.

If more than six d electrons exist in the atom, it will be necessary to position the excess on the highest lying level σ^* $(d\gamma)$, which is energetically very unfavorable. As a result, such atoms do not form stable complexes MX_6 or enter into the composition of complexes which have a symmetry that is not octahedral.

We shall see that the ground states of all configurations, with the exception of $(d\epsilon)^3$, possess a threefold orbital degeneracy. Consequently, because of the Jahn-Teller effect, the octahedral symmetry must be lowered. We shall assume that a weak field of lower symmetry, such as tetragonal, is superimposed on the cubic field. The total splitting caused by this field will be represented by δ. If the spin-orbit interaction is also taken into account, the following series of values of energy E_k [1] are obtained:

$$\left.\begin{aligned}(d\varepsilon)^{1}\,{}^{2}T_{2}:\quad & E_1 = E_2 = -\frac{\delta}{3} - \frac{1}{2}\lambda,\\ & E_{3,5} = E_{4,6} = \frac{1}{2}\left[\left(\frac{\lambda}{2} + \frac{\delta}{3}\right) \pm \sqrt{\frac{9}{4}\lambda^2 - \delta\lambda + \delta^2}\right];\end{aligned}\right\} \quad (3.59)$$

$$\left.\begin{aligned}(d\varepsilon)^{2}\,{}^{3}T_{1}:\quad & E_{1,3} = E_{2,4} = \frac{1}{2}\left[-\frac{\delta}{3} \pm \sqrt{\delta^2 + \lambda^2}\right],\\ & E_5 = E_6 = \frac{\delta}{3} - \frac{\lambda}{2},\\ & E_{7,8} = \frac{1}{2}\left[-\frac{\delta}{3} + \frac{\lambda}{2} \pm \sqrt{\frac{9}{4}\lambda^2 + \delta\lambda + \delta^2}\right],\\ & E_9 = \frac{\delta}{3} + \frac{\lambda}{2}.\end{aligned}\right\} \quad (3.60)$$

The energy levels $(d\varepsilon)^{5}\,{}^{2}T_2$ are obtained from $(d\varepsilon)^1$, and $(d\varepsilon)^{4}\,{}^{3}T_1$ from $(d\varepsilon)^2$, by means of a change of sign of δ and λ. Splitting of the level $(d\varepsilon)^3$ takes place only when the higher approximations of perturbation theory are taken into account. In the case of an odd number of electrons, we shall have a Kramers doublet, and therefore it is always possible to observe paramagnetic resonance. If the number of electrons is even, however, it is impossible to observe paramagnetic resonance (ground states are singlets); the exception is the configuration $(d\varepsilon)^2$, if $\delta < 0$. Calculation of the doublet splitting in a magnetic field shows that owing to the covalent bonding the g factor decreases. Thus for $[IrCl_6]^{2-}$, for instance,

$$g = 2 - \frac{2}{3}(1 - \beta^2). \quad (3.61)$$

We have already pointed out that as a consequence of the covalent bonds, the paramagnetic resonance line exhibits hyperfine structure due not only to the moment of nucleus M, but also to the moments of the nuclei X_6. Calculation of the hyperfine structure may be performed with the aid of spin Hamiltonian (3.20), containing an additional series of terms that can take into account the spins of the X_6 nuclei. Thus, if a strong magnetic field is applied along the Z axis and only the octahedral symmetry of the crystalline field is taken into account, the spin Hamiltonian is

$$\hat{\mathscr{H}}_{\text{sp}} = g_{\parallel}\beta_0 H_0 \hat{S}'_z + A(\hat{S}'_z\hat{I}_z)_0 + A'\{(\hat{S}'_z\hat{I}_z)_3 + (\hat{S}'_z\hat{I}_z)_6\}, \quad (3.62)$$

where $A' = -{}^{32}/_{15}\,\beta^2(1-\beta^2)\,g_0\beta_0\beta_N\langle r^{-3}\rangle$. The subscript zero refers to the central atom, and the subscripts 3 and 6, to the atoms X, situated on the Z axis.

---

[1] We shall use the notation of Mulliken [73] for designation of the terms of the octahedral complex.

In conclusion it should be mentioned that the spin-orbit interaction may be described by one constant λ only in the case of octahedral symmetry. The deviations of the symmetry of the field from octahedral cause an anisotropy of the spin-orbit interaction.

3.10. Actinides

It is firmly established at present that the elements of the transition group beginning with thorium contain partially filled $5f$ shells [44]. Actinides are distinguished from the $4f$ transition group of rare earths by a tendency to form compounds containing chemically very stable complexes similar to the uranyl ion $(UO_2)^{2+}$. Systematic study of the magnetic properties of the actinides and in particular of their paramagnetic resonance phenomena has only recently begun, and until now only the compounds containing UO_2, NpO_2 and PuO_2 have been studied extensively. The experimental data concerning these complexes have found a theoretical interpretation in [74-76].

We shall begin with a consideration of the UO_2, complex, although it does not possess normal paramagnetism and consequently does not yield a paramagnetic resonance effect.

The structure of this complex is linear: O—U—O. The free uranium atom has a closed core and six valence electrons forming the configuration $5f^3 6d 7s^2$. In $(UO_2)^{2+}$ two electrons are lost, and the four remaining ones create a strong covalent bond with the oxygen atoms. In the simplest model used in [74, 75], only the σ bond is admitted. Linear combinations of the $5f_\sigma$, $6d_\sigma$ and $7s$ functions form orbitals which are greatly stretched in the direction of the oxygen atoms and strongly overlap the sp_σ orbitals of oxygen. Therefore, in the ground state of $(UO_2)^{2+}$ no unpaired electrons remain, and consequently compounds containing uranyl will be either diamagnetic or will possess a weak temperature-independent paramagnetism.

The ions $(NpO_2)^{2+}$, $(PuO_2)^{2+}$ and $(AmO_2)^{2+}$ have structure and chemical properties similar to $(UO_2)^{2+}$. It is natural to suppose that the nature of the bond is the same in all of these ions and that the additional electrons fill the $5f$ shell, just as the $4f$ electrons of the trivalent Ce, Pr, Nd ions. However, the solid salts of transuranyl compounds differ greatly from those of the lanthanides in that the crystalline field has a great influence on the magnetic properties of the lanthanides, whereas for the $5f$ electrons of the actinides, the dominant force is the axially symmetric field produced by the binding electrons of the complex. To a first approximation, the magnetic properties of compounds containing a transuranyl complex are the same as that of a linear molecule; the crystalline field introduces only a small correction.

The complex $(NpO_2)^{2+}$ contains one unpaired f electron, which moves in a strong field of axial symmetry. Therefore, the constants of motion, in the first approximation, will be the components of total (j_z), orbital (l_z) and spin (s_z) angular momenta along the axis of symmetry, which is assumed to be the Z axis. In an axial field all possible values $|l_z| = 3, 2, 1, 0$ will correspond to the different energy levels. The lowest level, located approximately 10^4 cm^{-1} from the next, corresponds to a state with $|l_z| = 3$, because in this case the charge of the unpaired electron is located in the equatorial plane, so that its repulsion from electrons forming the σ bond is at a minimum. This fourfold degenerate level ($l_z = \pm 3$, $s_z = \pm 1/2$) is split by the spin-orbit interaction into two doublets: $j_z = \pm 5/2, \pm 7/2$. The first doublet is 3000-4000 cm^{-1} below the second, and consequently the paramagnetism of neptunyl ions is due to this interaction alone.

The paramagnetic resonance spectrum can be calculated by the following simple spin Hamiltonian:

$$\hat{\mathscr{H}} = g_{\parallel}\beta H_z \hat{S}'_z + g_{\perp}\beta(H_x \hat{S}'_x + H_y \hat{S}'_y) + A\hat{I}_z\hat{S}'_z + B(\hat{I}_x\hat{S}'_x + \hat{I}_y\hat{S}'_y) + P\left[\hat{I}_z^2 - \frac{1}{3} I(I+1)\right] - \gamma\beta_N H\hat{I}. \qquad (3.63)$$

Here $g_{\parallel} = 2\langle + | \hat{l}_z + 2\hat{s}_z | + \rangle$, $g_{\perp} = 2\langle + \hat{l}_x | + 2\hat{s}_x | - \rangle$, where $|+\rangle$ and $|-\rangle$ represent the wave functions of the lower doublets and S' denotes the effective spin, which equals 1/2. In an approximation that takes only the σ bond into account, $g_{\parallel} = 4$ and $g_{\perp} = 0$. If, however, we also take into account the possibility of a π bond, the orbital angular momentum decreases, as we have seen in the preceding section, and l_z must be replaced by kl_z, where $k < 1$. Now $g_{\perp} \neq 0$, $g_{\parallel} = 6k - 2$. Comparison with experimental data shows that $k = 0.9$. It should be mentioned, of course, that due to the large gradient of the electric field caused by the electrons forming the covalent bond, the hyperfine structure due to the quadrupole moment of the Np nucleus will be strong.

The complex $(PuO_2)^{2+}$ contains two unpaired electrons, the motion of which is perturbed mainly by the axial field and their mutual electrostatic repulsion. For this reason, just as in the case of neptunyl, it would appear that unpaired electrons must occupy the state $l_z = \pm 3$. In fact, owing to the mutual electrostatic repulsion, a ground state of the configuration $5f^2$ is determined by the modified Hund rule: the projection of the spin of the electrons must be a maximum, $S_z = 1$, and the projection of the orbital angular momentum must have the maximum value compatible with $S_z = 1$, namely, $|l_{1z}| = 3$, $|l_{2z}| = 2$, and therefore $L_z = \pm 5$. The spin-orbit interaction causes further splitting of the energy level, as a result of which the lower level becomes a doublet with $j_z = \pm(5 - 1) = \pm 4$.

An elementary calculation shows that if we again introduce the effective spin $S' = 1/2$, then for this doublet, $g_{\parallel} = 6$ and $g_{\perp} = 0$. The probability of a transition between the magnetic sublevels is then equal to zero independently of the direction of the external magnetic field H. Detailed consideration shows that taking into account the different corrections does not change $g_{\perp} = 0$. As a result, the paramagnetic resonance effect is a maximum when the periodic magnetic field is located parallel to the Z axis. This is due to the fact that the low-symmetry crystalline field, which was not considered by us before, mixes the wave functions with $j_z = \pm 4$. It must be kept in mind that the doublet under consideration is not of a Kramers type, since the number of uncoupled electrons is even. The spin Hamiltonian will thus have the form

$$\mathscr{H} = g_{\parallel}\beta H_z \hat{S}'_z + A\hat{S}'_z\hat{I}_z + P\left[\hat{I}_z^2 - \frac{1}{3}I(I+1)\right] + \Delta_x\hat{S}'_x + \Delta_y\hat{S}'_y. \quad (3.64)$$

The last two terms take into account the splitting produced by the low-symmetry crystalline field.

3.11. Effect of Exchange and Dipolar Interactions on the Appearance of the Paramagnetic Resonance Spectrum

Interesting exchange effects have been discovered in certain copper salts. The temperature dependence of the static magnetic susceptibility of copper acetate is unusual [77]. Sharp anomalies in the magnetic behavior of this substance have also been detected by the paramagnetic resonance method [78]. All of these features have been explained in the following manner. The unit cell of copper acetate contains two closely positioned paramagnetic ions, which behave like a single "molecule" on account of the strong exchange bonds between them, and they may be found either in the paramagnetic state with spin $S = 1$ or in the diamagnetic state with spin $S = 0$. It is well known [10] that if there are no other forces acting on the spin, the exchange interaction is characterized by a cosinusoidal dependence on the direction of the spins; the exchange energy equals $-J\hat{S}_1\hat{S}_2$, if J denotes the exchange integral and S_1 and S_2 the spins of the interacting atoms. Moreover, it has been demonstrated that if besides the exchange forces there exist other forces which also greatly influence the direction of the spin, the cosinusoidal law is preserved, but only for the "effective" spin [21, 22]. In copper acetate these exchange interactions are much stronger than the spin-orbit interaction (which appears only in the second-order theory), and consequently the Hamiltonian for the system of two copper ions under consideration will be

$$\mathscr{H} = \hat{X}_1 + \hat{X}_2 - J\hat{S}_1\hat{S}_2 + \lambda(\hat{L}_1\hat{S}_1 + \hat{L}_2\hat{S}_2) + \\ + \beta H_0(\hat{L}_1 + 2\hat{S}_1 + \hat{L}_2 + 2\hat{S}_2). \quad (3.65)$$

Here the subscripts 1, 2 denote the copper ions in the unit cell, and the separate terms of the Hamiltonian signify: the energy in the crystalline field, the exchange interaction, the spin-orbit coupling, and the energy in the external magnetic field. The exchange interaction splits the lower orbital level of the "molecule" into spin singlets and triplets. By means of (3.65) a physical explanation can be given for all the known facts concerning the static magnetic properties of copper acetate, the paramagnetic resonance spectrum and its hyperfine structure.

Exchange interactions influence the form of the paramagnetic resonance spectrum in copper sulfates [79], but here the anomalies are of a different nature, as the exchange energy is comparable in order of magnitude with the radio-frequency quantum; it equals roughly 0.15 cm^{-1}, whereas in copper acetate $J = 300$ cm^{-1}.

The broadening of the resonance lines is usually caused by the magnetic dipolar interaction. In some cases, however, when the substance is magnetically dilute and at the same time the unpaired spins are located close to one another, these interactions may give rise to the appearance of hyperfine structure in the paramagnetic absorption spectrum. Such structure has been observed in neodymium ethylsulfate [80]. If the static magnetic field is parallel to the hexagonal axis of the crystal, the spectrum is a symmetrical triplet with a spacing of 360 gauss between the outer absorption peaks. The central peak has approximately double the intensity of the outer one. A simple calculation of the energy of the dipolar interaction between the ion and the two neighboring particles yields the value $\pm 2g\ \beta/c^3, 0, 0$; here $c = 7$A is the distance between the two neighboring particles situated along the hexagonal axis. Thus, the satellites should be at a distance of 50 $g_{\|} = 180$ gauss from the central peak. A more complex spectral structure has been established in gadolinium ethylsulfate, and it is explained by the large spin of the Gd^{3+} ion.

3.12. Forbidden Spectral Lines. Multiple Quantum Transitions

Up to this point, when we spoke of paramagnetic resonance spectra, we had in mind resonance lines arising from those spin levels between which the transition probabilities are nonvanishing in first-order perturbation theory. We shall now consider some causes of the emergence of additional "forbidden" resonance absorption lines.

a) Dipole interactions between unpaired spins

Let us assume that the crystalline field does not split the spin levels, so that each level corresponds to a definite value M of the projection of the spin angular momentum in the direction of the field H_0. By virtue of this, to a first approximation, magnetic dipole transitions are possible only between neighboring levels ($\Delta M = \pm 1$) under the influence of the component of the oscillatory magnetic field perpendicular to field H_0. Let us now consider the magnetic dipole interactions between the unpaired spins of the crystal. As a consequence of this interaction, the wave functions η_M ($M = S, S-1, \ldots, -S$) referring to different spin levels are mixed and take the form (see Sec. 5.2):

$$\eta_M + \sum_{i=M-2}^{M+2} \varepsilon_i \eta_i, \text{ where } \varepsilon_i \sim \frac{\beta^2}{a^3}(g\beta H_0)^{-1};$$

here a is the mean distance between neighboring unpaired spins. Now the off-diagonal matrix elements of the vector $\hat{S}$ will differ from zero not only in the case $\Delta M = \pm 1$, but also for the transitions $\Delta M = \pm 2, \pm 3$. If the intensity of the main resonance line ($\Delta M = \pm 1$) is taken to be 1, the intensity of the lines $\Delta M = \pm 2$ and $\Delta M = \pm 3$ will be approximately $4|\epsilon_i|^2$ and $9|\epsilon_i|^2$, respectively, if the oscillatory field is perpendicular to field H_0. For a parallel arrangement of the field, the transitions $\Delta M = \pm 1$ and $\Delta M = \pm 2$ give rise to two forbidden resonance lines, whose intensities are approximately $|\epsilon_i|^2$ and $4|\epsilon_i|^2$. The existence of forbidden lines was first established experimentally by Zavoyskiy in manganese salts [81], and was later observed by others [82].

b) Hyperfine interactions

As the concentration of the unpaired spins decreases, the intensity of the additional absorption lines due to magnetic dipole interactions between the spins is weakened. Other forbidden absorption peaks may arise, however, if the nuclei of the paramagnetic atoms possess nonzero spin. We shall assume that the paramagnetic resonance spectrum can be described by the following spin Hamiltonian:

$$\begin{aligned} \hat{\mathscr{H}}_{sp} = D\{\hat{S}_z^2 - \tfrac{1}{3}S(S+1)\} + \beta\,\{g_{\parallel}H_z\hat{S}_z + g_{\perp}(H_x\hat{S}_x + H_y\hat{S}_y)\} + \\ + A\hat{S}_z\hat{I}_z + B(\hat{S}_x\hat{I}_x + \hat{S}_y\hat{I}_y) + P\left\{\hat{I}_z^2 - \tfrac{1}{3}I(I+1)\right\}. \end{aligned} \qquad (3.66)$$

Let us first take the field H_0 parallel to the Z axis of symmetry of the crystalline field. Figure 3.5a gives a diagram of the energy levels arising under the influence of the magnetic hyperfine interaction for the special case $S = 1/2$ and $I = 3/2$. On account of the quadrupole interactions, the energy levels are no longer equally spaced (Figure 3.5b). Each level corresponds to a wave function $\eta_{M,m}$ with a definite magnetic quantum number M of electron spin and magnetic quantum number m of nuclear spin. The arrows in Figure 3.5b illustrate transitions which are allowed according to the selection rules $\Delta M = \pm 1$, $\Delta m = 0$, if the oscillatory field is perpendicular to the steady field.

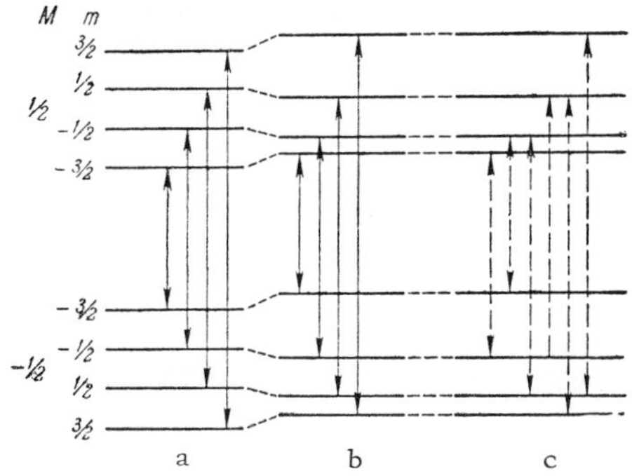

Fig. 3.5. Diagram of the energy levels and transitions in the case $S = 1/2$, $I = 3/2$. a—Quadrupole moment of the nucleus equals zero and the periodic magnetic field is perpendicular tc H_0; b—the quadrupole moment is nonzero and the periodic field is perpendicular to H_0; c—the quadrupole moment is nonzero and the periodic field is parallel to H_0 (forbidden transitions).

In second-order perturbation theory the term $B(\hat{S}_x\hat{I}_x + \hat{S}_y\hat{I}_y)$ causes the wave functions to take the form $\eta_{M,m} + \alpha\eta_{M\pm 1,\, m\mp 1}$, where $\alpha \sim B/g_{\parallel}\beta H_0$. It is now easy to convince oneself that if the magnetic oscillatory field is parallel to H_0 additional absorption peaks should arise, corresponding to the transitions $\Delta M = \pm 1$, $\Delta M = \pm 2$. These transitions are indicated in Figure 3.5 c by dashed arrows. The ratio of the intensity of the forbidden line to the intensity of the principal paramagnetic resonance lines is approximately $|\alpha^2| : 1$. Forbidden absorption lines in parallel fields have been observed experimentally in cobalt, manganese and vanadyl salts [83].

c) Multiple quantum transitions

Additional absorption lines may appear as the result of a quantum transition, related to the simultaneous absorption of several photons by the paramagnetic atoms. Such transitions are forbidden in first-order perturbation theory, but become possible at higher approximations by means of one or several intermediate states of the atom. A multiple quantum transition under the influence of a powerful radio-frequency field was first discovered in molecular beam experiments [85], and later by the method of nuclear paramagnetic resonance [86]. Electron paramagnetic resonance studies have recently established the existence of multiple quantum transitions in Mn^{2+} ions introduced into a MgO lattice [87].

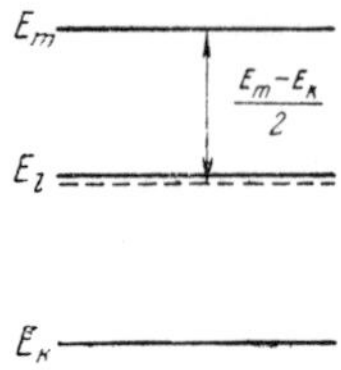

Fig. 3.6. Diagram of two-quantum transitions between levels k and m.

Let us assume that among the spin energy levels there exist three levels E_k, E_l, E_m (Figure 3.6), such that $\omega_{lk} \neq \omega_{ml}$ but $|\omega_{ml} - \omega_{lk}| \ll 1/2\, \omega_{mk}$ $[\omega_{ij} = (E_i - E_j)/\hbar]$. We also assume that in first-order perturbation theory, transitions between the neighboring levels $k \longleftrightarrow l$ and $l \longleftrightarrow m$ are allowed, but the transition $k \longleftrightarrow m$ is forbidden. The state of the unpaired spin can be described by means of the Hamiltonian

$$\hat{\mathscr{H}} = \hat{\mathscr{H}}_{sp} + \hat{\mathscr{H}}', \quad \hat{\mathscr{H}}' = g\beta \boldsymbol{H}_1 \hat{\boldsymbol{S}} = \frac{1}{2} g\beta H_1 \{\hat{S}_- e^{i\omega t} + \hat{S}_+ e^{-i\omega t}\}, \tag{3.67}$$

where $\hat{\mathscr{H}}_{sp}$ is the spin Hamiltonian which determines the system of spin energy levels of the unpaired spin, $\hat{\mathscr{H}}'$ is the time-dependent part of the Hamiltonian, depicting the interaction with the radio-frequency magnetic field, and $\hat{S}_{\pm} = \hat{S}_x \pm i\hat{S}_y$. Thus, to simplify the calculation, in place of the oscillatory magnetic field we consider a field rotating with angular velocity ω.

We assume that the atom is initially in state k. Then in first-order time-dependent perturbation theory, the probability that at moment t the atom will be in state l equals

$$|a_{kl}^{(1)}(t)|^2 = \frac{g^2\beta^2 H_1^2}{4\hbar^2} |\langle k|\hat{S}_+|l\rangle|^2 \left| \frac{e^{i(\omega_{lk}-\omega)} - 1}{\omega_{lk} - \omega} \right|^2; \tag{3.68}$$

in second-order perturbation theory it will be

$$|a_{km}^{(2)}(t)|^2 = \frac{g^4\beta^4 H_1^4 |\langle k|\hat{S}_+|l\rangle|^2 \, |\langle l|\hat{S}_+|m\rangle|^2}{16\hbar^4 (\omega_{lk} - \omega)^2} \times \\ \times \left| \frac{e^{i(\omega_{mk}-2\omega)t} - 1}{\omega_{mk} - 2\omega} \right|^2. \tag{3.69}$$

We see that the probability of the transition $k \longleftrightarrow m$ differs appreciably from zero if 1) the frequency of the variable field equals approximately $1/2\, \omega_{mk}$ and 2) the matrix elements of the perturbation connecting levels m and k with the intermediate level are not equal to zero. We shall now account for the finiteness of the absorption line width, for which we introduce the shape function $g(\omega)$ (see Sec. 1.3). Carrying out the integration in the customary manner

$$W_{ij} = \int |a_{ij}(t)|^2 g_{ij}(\omega)\, d\omega, \tag{3.70}$$

the transition probability is found to be proportional to the time t. Allowing also for the difference in population of the levels E_k, E_l, E_m and considering that the magnitude of $g_{ij}(0)$ is inversely proportional to the absorption line width $\Delta\nu_{ij}$, we obtain the following expression for the ratio of the intensity I_2 of the line due to a two-quantum transition to the intensity I_1 of an ordinary $l \longleftrightarrow k$ resonance line:

$$\frac{I_2}{I_1} = \frac{1}{2}\left(\frac{\dfrac{g\beta H_1}{\hbar}}{\omega_{lk} - \dfrac{1}{2}\omega_{mk}}\right)^2 \frac{\Delta\nu_{kl}}{\Delta\nu_{km}} |\langle l|\hat{S}_+|k\rangle|^2. \tag{3.71}$$

We see that the intensity of the lines arising due to two-quantum transitions becomes large if the frequency of Larmor precession corresponding to the magnetic field H_1 is comparable to the frequency interval between the ordinary absorption lines associated with the transitions $k \longleftrightarrow l$ and $l \longleftrightarrow m$. We note that when the radio-frequency field power is so large that $g\beta H_1/\hbar \sim (\omega_{lk} - 1/2\, \omega_{mk})$, application of perturbation theory is invalid and formula (3.71) ceases to be correct.

In addition to the two-quantum transitions which have been considered by us, transitions caused by the absorption of three or more photons are also possible. In third-order perturbation theory, the probability of a three-quantum transition is

$$|a_{kn}^{(3)}(t)|^2 = \frac{g^6\beta^6 H_1^6 |\langle k|\hat{S}_+|l\rangle|^2 \, |\langle l|\hat{S}_+|m\rangle|^2 \, |\langle m|\hat{S}_+|n\rangle|^2}{64\hbar^6(\omega_{lk} - \omega)^2(\omega_{mk} - 2\omega)^2} \times \\ \times \left|\frac{e^{i(\omega_{nk} - 3\omega)t} - 1}{\omega_{nk} - 3\omega}\right|^2. \tag{3.72}$$

Here l and m are intermediate states, by means of which the transitions under consideration become possible.

Literature for Chapter III

1. Bethe, H. A. Ann. Phys. 3, 133, 1929; Runchiman, W. A. Phil. Mag. 1, 1075, 1956.
2. Kramers, H. A. Proc. Acad. Sci. Ams. 33, 959, 1930.
3. Van Vleck, J. H. The Theory of Electric and Magnetic Susceptibilities, Oxford, 1932; Phys. Rev. 41, 208, 1932.
4. Penney, W. G., R. Schlapp. Phys. Rev. 41, 194, 1932.

5. Schlapp, R., W. G. Penney. Phys. Rev. 42, 666, 1932.
6. Kynch, G. F. Trans. Faraday Soc. 33, 1402, 1937; Penney, W. G., G. F. Kynch. Proc. Roy. Soc. A170, 112, 1939; Polder, D. Physica 9, 709, 1942.
7. Landau, L., Ye. Lifshits. Quantum Mechanics, Gostekhizdat, 1948.
8. Stevens, K. W. H. Proc Phys. Soc. A65, 209, 1952.
9. Bleaney, B., K. W. H. Stevens. Rep. Progr. Phys. 16, 108, 1953.
10. Vonsovskiy, S. V. Contemporary Studies of Magnetism, Gostekhizdat, 1952.
11. Pryce, M. H. L. Phys. Rev. 80, 1107, 1950.
12. Jahn, H. A., E. Teller. Proc. Roy. Soc. A161, 220, 1937; Jahn, H. A. Proc. Roy. Soc. A164, 117, 1938.
13. Van Vleck, J. H. J. Chem. Phys. 7, 72, 1950.
14. Öpik, U., M. H. L. Pryce. Proc. Roy. Soc. A238, 425, 1957; Lonquet, H. C., U. Öpik, M. H. L. Pryce, R. A. Sack. Proc. Roy. Soc. A244, 1, 1958.
15. Gorter, C. J. Phys. Rev. 42, 437, 1932.
16. Pryce, M. H. L. Proc. Phys. Soc. A63, 25, 1950.
17. Abragam, A., M. H. L. Pryce. Proc. Roy. Soc. A205, 135, 1951.
18. Pryce, M. H. L. Nature, London, 164, 117, 1949; Abragam, A., M. H. L. Pryce. Proc. Roy. Soc. A206, 173, 1951.
19. Kambe, K., S. Koide, T. Usui. Progr. Theor. Phys. 7, 15, 1952.
20. Ollom, J. F., J. H. Van Vleck. Physica 17, 205, 1952.
21. Stevens, K. W. H. Proc. Roy. Soc. A214, 237, 1952.
22. Ishiguro, E., K. Kambe, T. Usui. Physica 17, 310, 1951.
23. Pryce, M. H. L. Nature, London, 162, 539, 1948.
24. Abragam, A., M. H. L. Pryce. Proc. Roy. Soc. A205, 135, 1951; A206, 164, 1951.
25. Bleaney, B., K. D. Bowers, M. H. L. Pryce. Proc. Roy. Soc. A228, 166, 1955.
26. Van Vleck, J. H. J. Chem. Phys. 7, 61, 1939.
27. Becquerel, J., W. Opechowski. Physica 6, 1039, 1939.
28. Finkelstein, R., J. H. Van Vleck. J. Chem. Phys. 8, 790, 1940.
29. Broer, L. J. F. Physica 9, 547, 1942.
30. Weiss, P. R. Phys. Rev. 73, 470, 1948; 74, 1478, 1948.
31. Kittel, C., J. M. Luttinger. Phys. Rev. 73, 162, 1948.
32. Brovetto, P., S. Ferroni. Nuovo Cimento 9, 628, 1952.
33. Mejer, P. H. E., H. J. Gerritsen. Phys. Rev. 100, 742, 1955.
34. Davis, C. F., M. W. P. Strandberg. Phys. Rev. 105, 446, 1957.
35. Abragam, A., M. H. L. Pryce. Nature, London, 163, 992, 1949.
36. Abragam, A., M. H. L. Pryce. Proc. Phys. Soc. A63, 409, 1950.
37. Abragam, A. Phys. Rev. 79, 534, 1950; Physica 17, 209, 1951.
38. Fermi, E. Z. Phys. 60, 320, 1930.
39. Bleaney, B. Phil. Mag. 42, 441, 1951; Physica 17, 441, 175, 1951.
40. Abragam, A., J. Horowitz, M. H. L. Pryce. Proc. Roy. Soc. A230, 169, 1955.

41. Lipson, H., C. A. Beevers. Proc. Roy. Soc. A148, 664, 1935; Lipson, H. Proc. Roy. Soc. A151, 347, 1935.
42. Kleiner, W. H. J. Chem. Phys. 20, 1784, 1952.
43. Tanabe, Y., S. Sugano. J. Phys. Soc. Japan 9, 753, 766, 1954; 11, 864, 1956.
44. Yel'yushevich, M. A. Spectra of Rare Earths, Gostekhizdat, 1953.
45. Elliott, R. J., K. W. H. Stevens. Proc. Roy. Soc. A218, 553, 1953.
46. Lang, R. Canad. J. Res. 14, 127, 1936.
47. Hellwege, K. H., H. C. Kahle. Z. Phys. 129, 62, 1950.
48. Gobrecht, H. Ann. Phys. 31, 300, 1938.
49. Bethe, H. A., F. H. Spedding. Phys. Rev. 52, 454, 1937.
50. Elliott, R. J., K. W. H. Stevens. Proc. Roy. Soc. A215, 437, 1952; Elliott, R. J. Rev. Mod. Phys. 25, 167, 1953.
51. Judd, B. R. Proc. Roy. Soc. A227, 552, 1955.
52. Elliott, R. J., B. R. Judd, W. A. Runchiman. Proc. Roy. Soc. A240, 509, 1957.
53. Elliott, R. J., K. W. H. Stevens. Proc. Phys. Soc. A64, 932, 1951.
54. Elliott, R. J., K. W. H. Stevens. Proc. Roy. Soc. A219, 387, 1953.
55. Elliott, R. J., K. W. H. Stevens. Proc. Phys. Soc. A64, 205, 1951; A65, 370, 1952.
56. Judd, B. R. Proc. Roy. Soc. A232, 458, 1955.
57. Judd, B. R. Proc. Roy. Soc. A241, 122, 1957.
58. Judd, B. R. Proc. Phys. Soc. B70, 880, 1957.
59. Afanas'yeva, N. V. Dissertation, Leningrad, GPI, 1955.
60. Boer, J., R. Lieshout. Physica 15, 569, 1949; Debye, P. Ann. Phys. 32, 85, 1937; Kronig, R. de L., C. J. Bouwkamp. Physica 6, 290, 1939; Lacroix, R. Helv. Phys. Acta 30, 374, 1957.
61. Van Vleck, J. H., W. G. Penney. Phil. Mag. 17, 961, 1934.
62. Watanabe, H. Progr. Theor. Phys. 18, 405, 1957; Hutchison, C. A., B. R. Judd, D. F. D. Pope. Proc. Phys. Soc. B70, 514, 1957; Lacroix, R. Helv. Phys. Acta 30, 478, 1957.
63. Pauling, L. J. Amer. Chem. Soc. 53, 1367, 1931.
64. Van Vleck, J. H. J. Chem. Phys. 3, 807, 1935.
65. Howard, J. B. J. Chem. Phys. 3, 207, 1935.
66. Kotani, M. J. Phys. Soc. Japan 4, 293, 1949; Kamimura, H. J. Phys. Soc. Japan 11, 1171, 1956.
67. Owen, J., K. W. H. Stevens. Nature, London, 171, 836, 1953.
68. Stevens, K. W. H. Proc. Roy. Soc. A219, 542, 1953.
69. Owen, J. Proc. Roy. Soc. A227, 183, 1955; Disc. Faraday Soc. 19, 127, 1955.
70. Palma-Vittorelli, M. B., M. U. Palma, D. Palumbo, F. Sgarlata. Nuovo Cimento 3, 718, 1956.
71. Maki, A. H., B. R. McGarvey. J. Chem. Phys. 29, 31, 35, 1958.

72. Tinkham, M. Proc. Roy. Soc. A236, 549, 1956.
73. Mulliken, K. Phys. Rev. 43, 279, 1933; J. Chem. Phys. 3, 375, 1935.
74. Elliott, R. J. Phys. Rev. 89, 659, 1953.
75. Eisenstein, J. C., M. H. L. Pryce. Proc. Roy. Soc. A229, 20, 1955.
76. Eisenstein, J. C., M. H. L. Pryce. Proc. Roy. Soc. A238, 31, 1956.
77. Guha, B. C. Proc. Roy. Soc. A206, 353, 1951.
78. Bleaney, B., K. D. Bowers. Phil. Mag. 43, 372, 1952.
79. Bagguley, D. M. S., J. H. E. Griffiths. Proc. Roy. Soc. A201, 366, 1950.
80. Bleaney, B., R. J. Elliott, H. E. D. Scovil. Proc. Phys. Soc. A64, 933, 1951.
81. Zavoyskiy, Ye. K. Doklady Akad. Nauk SSSR 57, 887, 1947.
82. Buckmaster, H. A. Canad. J. Phys. 34, 150, 341, 1956; Gorter, C. J. Uspekhi Fiz. Nauk 53, 545, 1954.
83. Jeffries, C. D. Phys. Rev. 106, 164, 1957; Abragam, M., R. W. Kedzie, C. D. Jeffries. Phys. Rev. 106, 165, 1957; Jeffries, C. D. Low Temperature Phys. and Chem., Madison, Univ. Wisconsin Press, 634, 1958; Anderson, W. A., L. H. Piette. J. Chem. Phys. 30, 591, 1959.
84. Bleaney, B. Phil. Mag. 42, 441, 1951.
85. Hughes, V., L. Grabner. Phys. Rev. 79, 314, 1950; Kusch, P. Phys. Rev. 93, 1022, 1954; Besset, C., J. Horowitz, A. Messiah, J. Winter. J. Phys. Radium 15, 251, 1954; Brossel, J., B. Cagnac, A. Kastler. J. Phys. Radium 15, 6, 1954; Hughes, V., J. S. Geiger. Phys. Rev. 99, 1842, 1955.
86. Anderson, W. Phys. Rev. 104, 850, 1956; Kaplan, J. I., S. Meiboom. Phys. Rev. 106, 499, 1957; Bloembergen, N., P. Sorokin. Phys. Rev. 110, 865, 1958; Salwen, H. Phys. Rev. 101, 623, 1956; Yatsiv, S. Bull. Am. Phys. Soc., ser. II, 3, 144, 1958.
87. Sorokin, P. P., I. L. Gelles, W. V. Smith. Phys. Rev. 112, 1513, 1958.
88. Bleaney, B. Proc. Phys. Soc. 73, 937, 939, 1959.
89. Mukherji, A., T. P. Das. Phys. Rev. 111, 1479, 1958.
90. Low, W. Paramagnetic Resonance, Academic Press, New York, 1960.

CHAPTER IV

Spectra of Ionic Crystals. Experimental Data

4.1. Introduction. Crystallographic Data

Experimental data on paramagnetic resonance spectra in solids are presented in Section 4.2 in the form of tables. Spectral data for liquid solutions of salts are contained in Section 4.3. Finally, Section 4.4 gives information on nuclear spins which have been detected by means of paramagnetic resonance. In addition to the chemical formula of the paramagnetic substance the first column of the tables in Section 4.2 gives its degree of dilution by a diamagnetic substance (usually in atomic percent) and crystal structure data. If the crystal structure is identical with one of the ten most important types considered in this section (see below, pp. 93-95), the corresponding number is cited in the first column. For example, cr. st. 1 means "crystal structure 1" and the compound is an alum. For the other crystalline structures a reference to the appropriate crystallographic literature is given; the number of this reference and the letter "K" are given in brackets. A list of this literature for all the ions is given at the end of the chapter. In the adjoining columns are given the temperature of the experiment and the fundamental constants of the spin Hamiltonian[1] in cm^{-1}, determined from the form of the spectrum.

The arrangement of the material is similar to that adopted in the preceding chapter. First we consider ions of the iron group whose lower orbital levels in the octahedral magnetic complexes are singlets (V^{2+}, Cr^{3+}, Ni^{2+}), and the adjacent ions Cr^{2+}, Mn^{3+} and Cu^{2+}, which also have lower orbital singlets in a crystalline field with a tetragonal component. Finally it is necessary to include in this section such compounds as $CsCoCl_3$, in which the magnetic ion Co^{2+} is surrounded by a distorted tetrahedron of Cl^-. In a tetrahedral magnetic complex, the sign of the cubic field is opposite to that in an octahedral complex. The orbital levels are therefore reversed, and the Co^{2+} ion in these compounds gives a spectrum similar to the spectra of compounds of trivalent chromium or divalent vanadium.

---

[1]The hyperfine interval factor is sometimes given with a superscript indicating the mass number of the isotope referred to.

The next series of tables contains data on the ions Ti^{3+}, V^{4+}, V^{3+}, Fe^{2+} and Co^{2+} (Table 4.2). Then follow the rare earths. First, data are given for rare earth ions with odd numbers of electrons (Table 4.3) and then the same with even numbers of electrons (Table 4.4).

In a special section we separately list ions of all groups of the periodic system which occur in S states (Mn^{2+}, Fe^{3+}, Gd^{3+}, Eu^{2+} and Cm^{3+}, Table 4.5).

The next part of the tables is devoted to compounds having strong covalent bonds between paramagnetic ions and their environment (individual compounds of the iron group, and also compounds of the palladium, platinum and finally actinide groups (see Table 4.6).

Table 4.7 contains some data on compounds containing atoms of metals in anomalous valence states.

The sequence of ions inside each section of the table corresponds to the increasing atomic numbers of the elements in the periodic system of Mendeleyev.

For convenient use of the literature, the references are given for each ion individually. Some special information concerning the structure of a given compound and its other properties is cited in the remarks. An explanation of the notation used in the tables is given in the glossary, p. 3.

For each ion after the data obtained in diluted single crystals, a list is given of substances studied either in the form of powders or of magnetically concentrated single crystals along with the constants found in these investigations.

To explain the form of the paramagnetic resonance spectra of ionic crystals, certain crystallographic data are required; these were obtained by ordinary X-ray analysis. The paramagnetic properties of salts are determined mainly by the magnetic complexes they contain. It is very important to know the number of such complexes existing in each crystal cell and their arrangement. We shall therefore assign an orthogonal coordinate system X, Y, Z to each magnetic complex. If only one magnetic complex occurs in a unit cell, or even if several exist but they are all equivalent and have the same orientation, the X, Y, Z axes coincide with the principal axes K_1, K_2, K_3 of the paramagnetic susceptibility tensor. In the general case, however, the axes K_1, K_2, K_3 arise due to an averaging of the X, Y, Z axes of the different magnetic complexes. It must be kept in mind that the K_1, K_2, K_3 axes in most cases do not coincide with the crystallographic axes a, b, c.

Magnetic complexes of the compounds of $3d$, $4d$ and $5d$ transition groups often are octahedra whose centers are occupied by the paramagnetic ion M, and whose vertices, located at a distance R from the center, are occupied by identical particles X. Such particles may be water molecules (the spacing between M and the oxygen atoms is approximately 2 Å), halide ions ($R \approx 2.5$ Å), CN radicals (distance from M to C ≈ 1.8 Å, and from M to N ≈ 3 Å). Owing to 1) the Jahn-Teller effect and 2) the influence of the neighboring magnetic complex of particles, the octahedron is distorted so that the electric field acting on ion M acquires either trigonal, tetragonal or even lower symmetry. The first reason explains why the crystalline field can be appreciably altered by replacing the particle M by another, even if the environment is completely unaltered. The second reason explains why the perfectly identical complexes MX_6 in different salts may have a different symmetry.

We shall first consider the most thoroughly studied hydrated iron-group salts, whose octahedral complexes contain six water molecules.

1) Alums [1-3]: $M'M'''(S^*O_4)_2 \cdot 6H_2O$, where $M' = $ K, Na, Rb, Cs, NH_4, ... ; $M''' = $ Al, Gd, La, ... or a trivalent ion of the $3d$ group; $S^* = $ S, Se. The crystal symmetry is cubic. Each cell contains four complexes, whose positions change in different allotropic modifications. Existence of the α, β, γ modifications is evidently related to the difference in the dimensions of the monovalent ions M'. In the α modification, the octahedral complexes are distorted somewhat along the trigonal axes of the crystal: [111], $[1\bar{1}1]$, $[1\bar{1}\bar{1}]$, $[11\bar{1}]$; the cubic axes of the octahedron turn around the crystalline axis [111]. All four complexes of the unit cell of the β modification are completely equivalent; the cubic axes of the octahedra coincide with the cubic axes of the crystal. The paramagnetic resonance in the γ modification of the crystals has not been studied. At temperatures of 80 - 160°K, phase transitions, which change the symmetry of the magnetic complexes, are observed. The α structure of alums usually occurs in salts with $M' = $ K, Rb, Tl, NH_4; in β alums, $M' = $ Cs, (NH_3CH_3); and in γ alums, $M' = $ Na.

2) Tutton salts [1, 4, 5]: $M'_2M''(S^*O_4)_2 \cdot 6H_2O$, where $M' = $ Rb, NH_4, K, ... ; $M'' = $ Mg, Zn, or a divalent ion of the $3d$ group. The monoclinic crystal contains two complexes $M''(H_2O)_6$ in each cell. Four water molecules are located at distances of 1.9 Å from M'', nearly forming a square, and two other molecules are at distances of 2.15 Å from M''. Thus the symmetry of the complex is nearly tetragonal. The Z axis may be taken as the tetragonal symmetry axis.

If a reflection is made through the ac plane, the X, Y, Z axes of one of the complexes change into axes of another complex. The angle of inclination of the Z axis to the ac plane is denoted by α; ψ denotes the angle between c and the projection of Z on the ac plane.

3) Double nitrates [1]: $M''_3M'''_2(NO_3)_{12} \cdot 24H_2O$, where $M'' = $ Mg, Zn, or a divalent ion of the $3d$ group; $M''' = $ Bi ..., or a trivalent ion of the $4f$ group. The crystal is trigonal and each unit cell

contains one trivalent and two divalent ions.[a] Two $3d$ magnetic complexes $M''(H_2O)_6$ have trigonal distortions that are somewhat different in magnitude.

4) Fluosilicates [1, 6, 7]: $M''SiF_6 \cdot 6H_2O$, where $M'' = Zn$, Mg, or a divalent ion of the $3d$ group. The crystal is trigonal; it is assumed that each unit cell contains one molecule and that the magnetic complex is slightly distorted along the trigonal axis. Paramagnetic resonance studies show that a single unit cell contains six magnetic complexes, differing only in the orientation of the axes of deformation.

5) Bromates [1, 8]: $M''(BrO_3)_2 \cdot 6H_2O$, where $M'' = Zn$ or a divalent ion of the $3d$ group. The crystal has cubic symmetry. The four complexes $M''(H_2O)_6$ existing in a unit cell are octahedra which are distorted along the trigonal axes, as in a similar complex of α alums.

6) Sulfates [1, 9]: $M''SO_4 \cdot 7H_2O$. The structure of crystals in which $M'' = Ni$, Zn, Mg; has been studied; the symmetry is orthorhombic. The unit cell of the crystal contains four complexes, whose axes are interchanged during a reflection in the symmetry planes (100), (010), (001).

Apart from hydrated $3d$ group salts, the most carefully investigated compounds are cyanides, in which the octahedral complexes contain six CN radicals. Two isomorphic series of cyanides have been studied;

7a) $K_3M'''(CN)_6$, $M''' = Cr$, Mn, Fe, Co. The crystal has a symmetry which is nearly orthorhombic [1, 10-12].

7b) $K_4M''(CN)_6 \cdot 3H_2O$, $M'' = V$, Mn, Fe. The symmetry of the crystal is monoclinic, very close to tetragonal [1, 13].

A unit cell of the crystal, just as for the other series, contains four magnetic complexes, which are pairwise equivalent.

The X, Y, Z axes of one pair may be obtained by a reflection of the axes of the other pair of complexes through three mutually perpendicular planes of the crystal. Of the $4d$ and $5d$ group compounds, the most thoroughly studied crystals contain octahedral complexes formed by halides, namely:

8a) $M'_2M^{IV}X_6$, $M' = K$, NH_4, ...; $M^{IV} = Pt$, Ir, Mo, ...; $X = Cl$, Br [1, 14]. The crystals have cubic symmetry. In the case $X = Cl$, all the magnetic complexes of the unit cell are entirely equivalent to one another. If, however, $X = Br$, then in three of the complexes contained in the unit cell, the octahedra are somewhat distorted along the three different cubic axes.

8b) $Na_2M^{IV}X_6 \cdot 6H_2O$, $M^{IV} = Ir$, Pt, $X = Cl$, Br [1]. The crystal is triclinic; the number of complexes per unit cell is unknown, but they are all entirely magnetically equivalent. There exists

[a] [Erroneous, ed.]

a small rhombic, chiefly tetragonal distortion of the symmetry of the octahedral complex.

In rare earth salts evidently no octahedral complexes exist. The following compounds have been studied in detail:

9) Ethylsulfates [1, 15]: $M'''(C_2H_5SO_4)_3 \cdot 9H_2O$, where M''' is a trivalent $4f$ group ion. The crystals are trigonal; the unit cell contains two entirely equivalent complexes. Nine water molecules occur at the corners of three identical and mutually parallel equilateral triangles, whose planes are perpendicular to the trigonal axis of the crystal. A rare earth ion is located at the center of the middle triangle; the outer triangles are turned by an angle of $\pi/3$ with respect to the central triangle.

The double nitrates $(M'_3M'''_2(NO_3)_{12} \cdot 24H_2O)$ have been considered above (see 3). We note that the rare earth ion is surrounded by NO_3 groups, which produce a field of trigonal symmetry.

10) Nitrates. Of the $5f$ group compounds, detailed investigations have been made of rubidium nitrates containing groups such as uranyl [16] $(M^{IV}O_2Rb(NO_3)_3$, where $M^{IV} = U, Np, Pu, \ldots)$. The symmetry of the crystal is rhombohedral; a unit cell contains two equivalent complexes. Each complex contains the linear group $O - M^{IV} - O$ parallel to the hexagonal axis of the crystal. Three groups of nitrates are positioned around it in a plane perpendicular to the hexagonal axis.

Literature for Section 4.1

1. Bowers, K. D., J. Owen. Rep. Progr. Phys. 18, 304, 1955.
2. Lipson, H. Proc. Roy Soc. A151, 347, 1935; Lipson, H., C. A. Beevers. Proc. Roy. Soc. A148, 664, 1935.
3. Wells, A. F. Structural Inorganic Chemistry, Clarendon Press, Oxford, 1950.
4. Tutton, A. E. H. Phil. Trans. Roy. Soc. A216, 1, 1916.
5. Hofmann, W. Z. Kristall. 78, 279, 1931.
6. Pauling, L. Z. Kristall. 72, 482, 1930.
7. Wyckoff, R. W. Crystal Structures, New York, Interscience Publishers Inc., 2, chap. 10, 1951.
8. Yu, S. H., C. A. Beevers. Z. Kristall. 95, 426, 1936.
9. Beevers, C. A., C. M. Schwartz. Z. Kristall. 91, 157, 1935.
10. Gottfried, C., J. G. Nagelschmidt. Z. Kristall. 73, 357, 1930.
11. Barkhatov, V. Acta Phys.-chim. URSS 16, 123, 1942.
12. Barkhatov, V., G. Zhdanov. Acta Phys.-chim. URSS 16, 43, 1942.
13. Pospelov, V. A., G. S. Zhdanov. Zh. Fiz. Khim. 21, 405, 1947.
14. Bokiy, G. B., P. I. Usikov. Doklady Adad. Nauk SSSR 26, 782, 1940.
15. Ketelaar, J. A. A. Physica 4, 619, 1937.

16. Dieke, G. H., A. B. F. Duncan. Spectroscopic Properties of Uranium Compounds, National Nuclear Energy Series, III, 2, New York, McGraw-Hill, 1949.

4.2. Constants of the Spin Hamiltonian for Solid Paramagnetic Substances

1. Iron-group ions ($L \neq 0$) with a lower orbital singlet (see Table 4.1, pp. 102-119)

$3d^3$ (V^{2+}, Cr^{3+})

In the lower orbital singlet, arising under the action of the octahedral field, there is a fourfold spin degeneracy, which splits in fields of lower symmetry to two Kramers doublets. The spin Hamiltonian is

$$\mathscr{H} = g\beta(H_z\hat{S}_z + H_x\hat{S}_x + H_y\hat{S}_y) + D\left(\hat{S}_z^2 - \frac{5}{4}\right) + E(\hat{S}_x^2 - \hat{S}_y^2) + $$
$$+ A(\hat{S}_z\hat{I}_z + \hat{S}_x\hat{I}_x + \hat{S}_y\hat{I}_y);$$

thus, $s = 3/2$, $I = 0$ for even isotopes of Cr^{3+}, 3/2 for Cr^{53}, 7/2 for V^{51} and 6 for V^{50}. The value of I for V^{50} was determined from paramagnetic resonance experiments.

Neglecting the hyperfine structure of the level in a field $H_0 \parallel Z$ we write the formula

$$\frac{1}{2}g\beta H_0 \pm \{(D + g\beta H_0)^2 + 3E^2\}^{\frac{1}{2}},$$
$$-\frac{1}{2}g\beta H_0 \pm \{(D - g\beta H_0)^2 + 3E^2\}^{\frac{1}{2}}.$$

The hyperfine structure in Cr^{3+} salts is often not resolved because of the small value of the constant A and the appreciable width of the absorption line.

In the V^{51} salts with the field $H_0 \parallel Z$ and $g\beta H_0 \gg E$ and A allowing for the hyperfine structure the levels are

$$\pm\frac{3}{2}g\beta H_0 + D \pm \frac{3}{2}Am, \quad \pm\frac{1}{2}g\beta H_0 - D \pm \frac{1}{2}Am$$
$$\left(m = \frac{7}{2}, \frac{5}{2}, \ldots, -\frac{7}{2}\right).$$

Analogous to V^{2+} and Cr^{3+} ions in an octahedral environment, the Co^{2+} ion in a tetrahedral complex has a lowest orbital singlet with a fourfold spin degeneracy. The only such compound studied, Cs_3CoCl_5, gave a spectrum described by the spin Hamiltonian

$$\mathscr{H} = g_{\parallel}\beta H_z\hat{S}_z + g_{\perp}\beta(H_x\hat{S}_x + H_y\hat{S}_y) + D\left(\hat{S}_z^2 - \frac{5}{4}\right)$$

with $S = 3/2$, overlooking the hyperfine structure, which is unresolved because of the large width.

$3d^4$ (Cr^{2+}, Mn^{3+})

The cubic field of the octahedron and the trigonal field leaves the lowest orbital doublet degenerate. The orbital degeneracy is removed by the tetragonal field; the lowest orbital level retains a fivefold spin degeneracy, which is removable by a rhombic field.

Only divalent chromium sulfate has been studied. The hyperfine structure due to Cr^{51} is not resolved. The spin Hamiltonian is ($S = 2$)

$$\mathscr{H} = \beta g_{\parallel} H_z\hat{S}_z + \beta g_{\perp}(H_x\hat{S}_x + H_y\hat{S}_y) + D(\hat{S}_z^2 - 2) + E(\hat{S}_x^2 - \hat{S}_y^2).$$

The levels in the field $H_0 \parallel Z$ lie at

$$-2D; \quad -D \pm (g_{\parallel}^2\beta^2H^2 + 9E^2)^{\frac{1}{2}}; \qquad 2D \pm 2g_{\parallel}\beta H.$$

As yet, Mn^{3+} compounds have not been investigated.

$3d^8$ (Ni^{2+})

In an octahedral field the lower orbital level is a singlet which is triply degenerate with respect to spin; a trigonal and a tetragonal field split it into a doublet and singlet, but a rhombic field splits it into three singlets. The experimental results are described by the spin Hamiltonian

$$\mathscr{H} = g\beta(H_z\hat{S}_z + H_x\hat{S}_x + H_y\hat{S}_y) + D\left(\hat{S}_z^2 - \frac{2}{3}\right) + E(\hat{S}_x^2 - \hat{S}_y^2)$$

with $S = 1$ and an isotropic g; no hyperfine structure has been observed. For the field $H_0 \parallel Z$ the levels correspond to

$$-\frac{2}{3}D, \ \frac{1}{3}D \pm (E^2 + g^2\beta^2H^2)^{\frac{1}{2}}.$$

$3d^9$ (Cu^{2+})

In an octahedral field the lower orbital level is a "nonmagnetic" doublet. A field of rhombic or tetragonal symmetry splits it into two Kramers doublets. A trigonal field does not split the lower orbital doublet; in this case the orbital degeneracy is removed by the Jahn-Teller effect or by the spin-orbit coupling. The experimental results are described by the spin Hamiltonian

$$\hat{\mathscr{H}} = \beta(g_z H_z \hat{S}_z + g_x H_x \hat{S}_x + g_y H_y \hat{S}_y) + A_z \hat{S}_z \hat{I}_z + A_x \hat{S}_x I_x + A_y \hat{S}_y \hat{I}_y + P\left(\hat{I}_z^2 - \frac{5}{4}\right) + P'(\hat{I}_x^2 - \hat{I}_y^2) + g_n \beta_n \hat{H}\hat{I}$$

with $S = 1/2$ and $I = 3/2$.

For $H_0 \parallel Z$ and $g\beta H_0 \gg A \gg P'$ the levels lie at $\pm \frac{1}{2} g_z \beta H_0 \pm \frac{1}{2} A_z m + P(m^2 - 5/4)$, where $m = 3/2, 1/2, -1/2, -3/2$. Copper acetate is a special case, which was considered above in Chapter III.

The behavior of a Ti^{3+} ion located in a tetragonal environment must be similar to that of a copper ion.

2. Iron-group ions ($L \neq 0$) with a lower orbital triplet (see Table 4.2, pp. 120-125)

$3d^1$ (Ti^{3+}, V^{4+}, Mn^{6+})

In an octahedral field the lower level is an orbital triplet; it is split into three Kramers doublets by fields of lower symmetry. When the octahedral complex is slightly distorted the spin-lattice relaxation time is very short and the effect is observed only at very low temperatures. In cases of great distortion (VO^{2+}, ion, MnO_3) the relaxation time is sufficiently long for observation of the effect at room temperature. In Ti^{3+} salts the results are described by the following Hamiltonian ($S = 1/2$):

$$\hat{\mathscr{H}} = g_{\parallel} \beta H_z \hat{S}_z + g_{\perp} \beta (H_x \hat{S}_x + H_y \hat{S}_y).$$

The hyperfine structure for Ti^{3+} is not resolved. It is observed in diluted vanadyl salts ($I = 7/2$ for V^{51}).

$3d^2$ (V^{3+}, Fe^{2+})

In an octahedral field the lower level is an orbital triplet with a fivefold spin degeneracy. A rhombic field removes the degeneracy completely. In $(Fe, Zn)F_2$ a weak splitting of the lower doublet is observed. The spectrum is described by the Hamiltonian ($S = 1/2$, $g_{\perp} = 0$)

$$\mathscr{H} = g_{\parallel}\beta H_z\hat{S}_z + \Delta\hat{S}_x,$$

where Δ characterizes the weak splitting of the doublets by low symmetry components of the crystalline field.

$3d^7$ (Co^{2+})

In an octahedral field the lower orbital triplet is degenerate. Fields of lower symmetry and spin-orbit coupling split it into Kramers doublets. The experimental results are described by the Hamiltonian ($S = 1/2$, $I = 7/2$)

$$\mathscr{H} = \beta(g_z H_z\hat{S}_z + g_x H_x\hat{S}_x + g_y H_y\hat{S}_y) + A_z\hat{S}_z\hat{I}_z + A_x\hat{S}_x\hat{I}_x + A_y\hat{S}_y\hat{I}_y.$$

The following equalities sometimes hold: $g_x = g_y = g_{\perp}$; $A_x = A_y = A_{\perp}$ (axial symmetry).

3. Rare earth ions ($L \neq 0$) with an odd number of electrons (see Table 4.3, pp. 125-130)

$4f^1$ (Ce^{3+}), $4f^3$ (Nd^{3+}), $4f^5$ (Sm^{3+}),
$4f^9$ (Dy^{3+}), $4f^{11}$ (Er^{3+}), $4f^{13}$ (Yb^{3+})

In the cases investigated, the experimental data are described by the Hamiltonian ($S' = 1/2$)

$$\mathscr{H} = g_{\parallel}\beta H_z\hat{S}_z + g_{\perp}\beta(H_x\hat{S}_x + H_y\hat{S}_y),$$

which is augmented in the case of odd isotopes by the additional fine structure interaction terms $A\hat{S}_z\hat{I}_z + B(\hat{S}_x\hat{I}_x + \hat{S}_y\hat{I}_y)$. Sometimes (in Ce^{3+} ethylsulfates) a second (Kramers) doublet is observed, which is describable by the same Hamiltonian and is located at a distance of several cm^{-1} above the lower doublet.

4. Rare earth ions with an even number of electrons (see Table 4.4, pp. 131-132)

$4f^2$ (Pr^{3+}), $4f^4$ (Pm^{3+}), $4f^6$ (Eu^{3+}), $4f^8$ (Tb^{3+}),
$4f^{10}$ (Ho^{3+}), $4f^{12}$ (Tm^{3+})

Since the number of electrons in these ions is even, the lower spin doublet can be nondegenerate. A trigonal field does not remove the degeneracy, however, and the lower symmetry components in crystals of ethylsulfates and double nitrates are small. Consequently, paramagnetic resonance is observed; the existing experimental data are described by the Hamiltonian

$$\mathscr{H} = g_{\parallel}\beta H_z\hat{S}_z + \Delta_x\hat{S}_x + \Delta_y\hat{S}_y + A\hat{S}_z\hat{I}_z.$$

Thus, $g_\perp$ is taken to be zero; the term Δ represents small splittings due to distortion from a field having a symmetry lower than trigonal.

5. Ions in S states (see Table 4.5, pp. 133-144)

$3d^5$ (Mn^{2+}, Fe^{3+})

The lowest orbital level is a singlet with a sixfold spin degeneracy. The electric field of an octahedron of water molecules splits the singlet into three Kramers doublets with a spacing which is usually less than 1 cm^{-1}. The spin Hamiltonian (for odd isotopes) is

$$\mathscr{H} = g\beta(H_z\hat{S}_z + H_x\hat{S}_x + H_y\hat{S}_y) + \frac{1}{6}a\left(\hat{S}_\xi^4 + \hat{S}_\eta^4 + \hat{S}_\zeta^4 - \frac{707}{16}\right) + \\ + D\left(\hat{S}_z^2 - \frac{35}{12}\right) + \frac{7}{36}F\left(\hat{S}_z^4 - \frac{95}{14}\hat{S}_z^2 + \frac{81}{16}\right) + A(\hat{S}_z\hat{I}_z + \hat{S}_x\hat{I}_x + \hat{S}_y\hat{I}_y).$$

Here a is the splitting by the cubic field; ξ, η, ζ are mutually perpendicular axes, with respect to which the Z axis is positioned in the [111] direction.

If the symmetry of the magnetic complex is no higher than orthorhombic (for instance, in Mn^{2+} Tutton salts), the term $E(\hat{S}_x^2 - \hat{S}_y^2)$ is added to the Hamiltonian.

$4f^7$ (Gd^{3+}, Eu^{2+})

On account of the large value of $S = 7/2$, the spin Hamiltonian is very complicated, and is not given here in detail. It may be written (neglecting hyperfine structure) in the form

$$\mathscr{H} = g\beta(H_z\hat{S}_z + H_x\hat{S}_x + H_y\hat{S}_y) + \\ + B_2^0\hat{U}_2^0 + B_2^2\hat{U}_2^2 + B_4^0\hat{U}_4^0 + B_6^0\hat{U}_6^0 + B_6^6\hat{U}_6^6.$$

Here each $\hat{U}_n^m$ is an operator, and the coefficients B_n^m are determined from experiment. The following notation is customarily used for convenience:

$$b_2^0 = 3B_2^0,\ b_2^2 = 3B_2^2,\ b_4^0 = 60B_4^0,\ b_6^0 = 1260B_6^0,\ b_6^6 = 1260B_6^6;$$

thus $b_2^0 = D$, $b_2^2 = 3E$, and $3b_4^0 = F$.

For Eu^{2+}, studied in a field of cubic symmetry, g and A are isotropic, but the total spin Hamiltonian has not been established.

6. Compounds with strong covalent bonding (see Table 4.6, pp. 145-151)

Among such substances are cyanides of trivalent iron and divalent manganese from the $3d$ group and also all the previously studied paramagnetic substances of the $4d$ and $5d$ group compounds.

For Fe^{III}, Mn^{II}, Mo^{V}, Ru^{III}, Ag^{II} and Ir^{IV} the effective spin has the value $S' = 1/2$ and the spectrum is described by the spin Hamiltonian

$$\mathscr{H} = \beta (g_z H_z \hat{S}_z + g_x H_x \hat{S}_x + g_y H_y \hat{S}_y),$$

which for odd isotopes is augmented by the appropriate term, which takes the hyperfine structure into account. In some cases we must also allow for the hyperfine structure arising due to interactions of an uncompensated electron with the nuclear spins of the atom covalently bonded with the central atom (for instance, in the case of $(NH_4)_2[IrCl_6]$, diluted by the corresponding platinum salt).

For Mo^{III} and Re^{IV} the spin Hamiltonian is

$$\mathscr{H} = \beta (g_z H_z \hat{S}_z + g_x H_x \hat{S}_x + g_y H_y \hat{S}_y) + \\ + D\left\{\hat{S}_z^2 - \frac{1}{3} S(S+1)\right\} + E(\hat{S}_x^2 - \hat{S}_y^2)$$

with an effective spin $S' = 3/2$. For odd isotopes the Hamiltonian must be supplemented by terms characterizing the hyperfine structure of the spectrum.

The number of $4d$ and $5d$ group compounds whose paramagnetic resonance spectra have been studied is very small; one of the experimental difficulties is the selection of isomorphous diamagnetic salts which are required to lessen the magnetic dipole interactions, because the latter are very significant in these particular compounds in the undiluted state. Actinide compounds constitute the last group of the class of substances with strong covalent bonding which are under investigation. Only in a very small number of actinide compounds has paramagnetic resonance been studied. In neptunyl double nitrate the spectrum is described by the spin Hamiltonian

$$\mathscr{H} = g_{\parallel} \beta H_z \hat{S}_z + g_{\perp} \beta (H_x \hat{S}_x + H_y \hat{S}_y) + A \hat{S}_z \hat{I}_z + \\ + B(\hat{S}_x \hat{I}_x + \hat{S}_y \hat{I}_y) + P\left(\hat{I}_z^2 - \frac{35}{12}\right)$$

with an effective spin $S' = 1/2$ and $I = 5/2$ (for the odd isotope Np^{237}).

For plutonium $g_{\perp} = 0$ and the spin Hamiltonian is

$$\mathscr{H} = g_{\parallel} \beta H_z \hat{S}_z + A \hat{S}_z \hat{I}_z + \Delta_x \hat{S}_x + \Delta_y \hat{S}_y.$$

The effective spin $S' = 1/2$; $I = 1/2$ for Pu^{239} and $5/2$ for Pu^{247}. The last two terms of the Hamiltonian describe small splittings due to distortions of the crystal and thermal fluctuations.

Table 4.1

V^{2+}

Formula	T, °K	g	D	E	A	Reference	Note
$(NH_4)_2V(SO_4)_2 \cdot 6H_2O$ (cr. st. 2) $V:Zn = 1:3$	290		0.155 ± 0.005			[1]	$\psi = +4°$, $\alpha = 23.5°$
$V:Zn = 10^{-3}$	20	1.951 ± 0.002	0.158 ± 0.010	0.049 ± 0.005	^{51}A 0.0088 ± 0.0002	[2, 3]	$\psi = +2°$, $\alpha = 22°$
$K_4V(CN)_6 \cdot 3H_2O$ (cr. st. 7) $V:Fe = 0.1—5 \cdot 10^{-2}$	90, 20	g_x 1.9919 ± 0.0006; g_y 1.9920 ± 0.0006; g_z 1.9920 ± 0.0006	-0.0264 ± 0.0004	-0.0072 ± 0.0004	^{50}A -0.00211 ± 0.00003; ^{51}A -0.00555 ± 0.00003	[4, 5]	$\frac{^{50}A}{^{51}A} = 0.3792 \pm 0.0008$; a)
V^{2+} in Al_2O_3	290	~ 1.98	~ 0.31		$A \approx B = 0.0091$	[9]	
V^{2+} in MgO $V:Mg \sim 2 \cdot 10^{-7}$	290	1.9803 ± 0.0005			$^{51}A = 0.00740 \pm 0.00002$	[6]	
V^{2+} in $ZnSiF_6$ $6H_2O$	20	$g_\parallel$ 1.970; $g_\perp$ 1.976	0.0804		-0.00839	[10]	

Paramagnetic resonance also observed in VSO_4 ($T = 290°$ K) [7]; $V(C_6H_4)_4(CN)_8$ ($T =$ 270 to 20° K, $g = 2.0$) 8]; V^{2+} in phthalocyanine ($T = 290$, 20° K, $g = 2.0$) [11].

Note: a) Direction cosines:

	a	b	c
X	0.707	0	—0.707
Y	0.523	± 0.676	—0.523
Z	0.470	∓ 0.737	—0.470

Table 4.1 (Cont'd)

Cr^{3+}

Formula	T, °K	g	D	E	A	Reference	Note
$CsCr(SO_4)_2 \cdot 12H_2O$ (cr. st. 1)	290	1.98	0.072_5 ± 0.003			[1—3]	
	193	1.98 ± 0.02	— 0.067				
	90, 20	1.98 ± 0.02	— 0.066_5 ± 0.001				
$KCr(SO_4)_2 \cdot 12H_2O$ (cr. st. 1)	290	1.98	0.060 ± 0.003			[1—6]	a)
	193	1.98 ± 0.02	0.027 ± 0.003				
	160	1.98 ± 0.02	0.017_5				
	90	1.98 ± 0.02	I : 0.130 II : 0.075 ± 0.005				
	20	1.98 ± 0.02	I : 0.135 ± 0.002 II : 0.075 ± 0.005				
Cr : Al = 2 : 17	290	1.98	0.045_5			[4]	
$(NH_3CH_3)Cr(SO_4)_2 \cdot 12H_2O$ (cr. st. 1)	290	1.98	0.082_5 ± 0.003			[1, 2, 7, 8]	b)
	90	1.97_5 ± 0.01	0.087 ± 0.002	0.009 ± 0.001			
	20	1.976 ± 0.007	— 0.0871 ± 0.0007	— 0.0092 ± 0.0008			
Cr : Al = 10^{-2}	90	1.97_5 ± 0.01	0.095_9 ± 0.002	0.009 ± 0.001		[7]	c)
	20	1.977 ± 0.003	— 0.0958 ± 0.0004	— 0.0092 ± 0.0008		[8]	

Table 4.1 (Cont'd)

Formula	T, °K	g	D	E	A	Reference	Note
$(NH_4)Cr(SO_4)_2 \cdot 12H_2O$ (cr. st. 1)	290	1.98	0.067_5 ± 0.003			[1—5, 9, 10]	d)
	193	1,98 ± 0.02	0.042_5				
	90	1,98 ± 0,02	0.017_5				
	80	1.98 ± 0,02	I : 0.157 ± 0.002 II : 0.121 ± 0.002				
	20	1,98 ± 0,02	I : 0.158 ± 0.002 II : 0.120 ± 0.002				
Cr : Al = 2 : 17	290	1,97	0.050			[4]	
Cr : Al = 1 : 0	295	1,988 ± 0.001	0.0675 ± 0.0010			[11]	e)
Cr : Al = 1 : 17		1,9771 ± 0.0010	0.0492 ± 0.0005				
Cr : Al = 1 : 47		1,9772 + 0.0010	0.0490 ± 0.0005				
Cr : Al = 1 : 47	77	1,9765 ± 0,0010					
$[(NH_2)_3C]Cr(SO_4)_2 \cdot 6H_2O$ (cr. st. 1) Cr : Al = 1 : 20	373	I : 1,980 ± 0.005 II : 1,980 ± 0,002	I : 0.0610 ± 0.0004 II : 0.0488 ± 0.0004			[12]	f)
	290	I : 1,980 ± 0.003	I : 0.0750 ± 0.0002				

Table 4.1 (Cont'd)

Formula	T, °K	g	D	E	A	Reference	Note
Cr : Al = 1 : 50	295	II : 1.977 ± 0.001 1.975 ± 0.005	II : 0.0590 ± 0.0002 I : 0.0576 ± 0.0005			[13]	
	195	1.975 ± 0.005	II : 0.0730 ± 0.0005 I : 0.0696 ± 0.0006				
	77	1.975 ± 0.005	II : 0.0882 ± 0.0010 I : 0.0822 ± 0.0010				
	35	1.975 ± 0.005	II : 0.105 ± 0.003 I : 0.085 ± 0.003				
			II : 0.109 ± 0.005				
Rb Cr $(SO_4)_2 \cdot 12H_2O$ (cr. st. 1)	290	1.98	0.082_5 ± 0.003			[1—3]	
	193	1.98 ± 0.02	0.063				
	90, 20	1.98 ± 0.02	0.054 ± 0.001				
KCr $(SeO_4)_2 \cdot 12H_2O$ (cr. st. 1)	90		0.064 ± 0.002			[7]	
	20		0.070 ± 0.002				
Cr : Al = 1 : 10	90		0.089_5 ± 0.001				
	20		0.098 ± 0.001				

Table 4.1 (Cont'd)

Formula	T, °K	g	D	E	A	Reference	Note
Cr : Al $= 10^{-2}$	90	1.976 $\pm$ 0.002	0.0900 $+$ 0.0003			[14]	
	20	1.976 $\pm$ 0.002	0.0983 $\pm$ 0.0003				
$KCr(SeO_4)_2 \cdot 12D_2O$ (cr. st. 1) Al : Cr	90, 20	1.976 $\pm$ 0.002	0.10_5		0.0018_5 $\pm$ 0.0001	[14]	
$K_3Cr(CN)_6$ (cr. st. 7)	90, 20 4.2	1.998 $\pm$ 0.008	$\sim$0.045	$\sim$0.013		[39, 15, 16]	g)
Cr : Co $= 0.1$—10^{-4}	90, 20	g_x 1.993 $\pm$ 0.001; g_y 1.991_4 $\pm$ 0.001; g_z 1.991 $\pm$ 0.001	$+$0.0831 $\pm$ 0.0010	$+$0.0108 $\pm$ 0.0010	$+$0.00147 $\pm$ 0.00005	[15, 16]	h)
	4.2	g 1.992 $\pm$ 0.0002				[39]	
Cr : Mn $= 0.1$—10^{-4} $Cr[(CH_3CO)_2CH]_3$ [к. 1]	90, 20	g_x 1.992 $\pm$ 0.002; g_y 1.995 $\pm$ 0.002; g_z 1.993 $\pm$ 0.002	$+$0.0538 $\pm$ 0.0010	$+$0.0120 $\pm$ 0.0010	$+$0.00147 $\pm$ 0.00010		i)
Cr : Al $= 1 : 50$	290	1.983 $\pm$ 0.002	0.592 $\pm$ 0.002	0.052 $\pm$ 0.002		[17]	j) $M_m = 2$
$Cr[CH_3CF_3(CO)_2CH]_3$ Cr : Al	290	$\sim$1.98	0.59			[18]	$M_m = 2$, orthorhomb.
$Cr[(CF_3CO)_2CH]_3$	290	$\sim$1.98	0.70			[18]	$M_m = 1$,
Cr^{3+} in TiO_2 Cr : Ti $= 10^{-3}$	290	1.97	0.55	0.27	0.0017	[35]	hexag.

Table 4.1 (Cont'd)

Formula	T, °K	$g_{\parallel}$	$g_{\perp}$	D	E	A	Reference	Note
Cr^{3+} in Al_2O_3 Cr : Al $= 10^{-2}$—10^{-4} (enriched in odd isotope)	290 4.2	1.982 ± 0.002	1.979 ± 0.009	— 0.1912 ± 0.0010			[19—21, 23]	
Cr : Al $= 10^{-4}$	290					A 0.001680 ± 0.000004 B 0.001680 ± 0.000006	[22, 23]	
Cr^{3+} in $Al_2Be_3(SiO_3)_6$	78 1.6	1.973 ± 0.002	1.97 ± 0.01	— 0.893 ± 0.002			[34]	$M = 2$, $M_m = 1$, hexag.
Cr^{3+} in CaF_2 Cr : Ca $= 10^{-6}$	90, 20	g				∼ 0.0010	[40]	o)
Cr^{3+} in MgO Cr : Mg $= 10^{-3}$—10^{-4}	290, 77	1.9800 ± 0.0006				0.00160 ± 0.00003	[24, 36]	k)
	290, 77	1.980 ± 0.001	1.986 ± 0.001	0.0819		$A = B$ 0.00162 ± 0.00004	[24]	$M_m = 3$, l)
	90, 20	g 1.98		0.031 ± 0.002	0.22 ± 0.01		[36, 37]	$M_m = 6$, m)
Cr^{3+} in ZnF_2 Cr : Zn $= 10^{-5}$	290	I : 1.976 ± 0.007 II : 1.975 ± 0.007	I : 1.958 ± 0.004 II : 1.959 ± 0.006	D_{max} I : 0.602 ± 0.008 II : 0.581 ± 0.008			[25]	$M_m = 2$ n)

Paramagnetic resonance absorption also observed at room temperature for $CrBr_3$ ($g = 1.99$) [6]; $Cr(C_2H_3O_2)_3 \cdot H_2O$ [26]; $Cr(C_5H_5N)_2(OH)_2(H_2O)Cl$ ($g = 1.99$) [27]; $Cr(C_7H_5O_3)_3H_2O$ ($g = 2.07$) [27]; $Cr[(CH_3)_3(CH)_2CH_2(CO)_2]_3$ ($g \approx 2$, $D > \approx 0.5$) [17]; $Cr[(C_6H_5)(CO)_2CHCH_3]_3$ ($g \approx 2$, $D > \approx 0.5$) [17]; $CrCl_3$ ($g = 1.99 - 2.37$) [28, 41, 42]; CrF_3 ($g = 2.00$) [6]; $[Cr(H_2O)_4Cl_2]Cl$ ($g = 1.95$) [27]; $[Cr(H_2O)_4Cl_2]Cl \cdot 2H_2O$ [28]; $[Cr(H_2O)_5Cl]Cl_2 \cdot H_2O$ [28]; $[Cr(NH_3)_5Cl]Cl_2$ ($g = 1.97$) [27]; $[Cr(NH_3)_6]Cl_3 \cdot H_2O$ ($g = 1.97$) [27]; $[Cr(NH_3)_6](NO_3)_3 \cdot H_2O$ ($g = 1.95$) [27]; $[Cr(NH_2CH_3)_6]_2 \cdot (SO_4)_3$ ($g \approx 2$, $D \approx 0.15$) [17]; $Cr(NO_3)_3 \cdot 9H_2O$ ($g = 2.26$) [27, 29]; $Cr(OH)_3$ [28]; $Cr(OH)_3 \cdot 2H_2O$ ($g = 2.00$) [27]; $[Cr(SCN)_2\{C_2H_4(NH_2)_2\}_2](SCN)$ ($g = 1.98$) [27, 30]; Cr_2O_3 [28]; $Cr_2(SO_3)_3$ ($g = 2.00$) [6]; $Cr_2(SO_4)_3$ ($g = 1.98$) [6]; $Cr_2(SO_4)_3 \cdot 5H_2O$ [26]; $Cr_2(SO_4)_3 \cdot 15H_2O$ [26]; $Cr_2(SO_4)_3 \cdot 18H_2O$ ($g = 2.00$) [27]; $K_3Cr(C_2O_4)_3 \cdot 3H_2O$ ($g \approx 2$, $D \approx 0.4$) [17]; $Cr_2(CH_3NH_3)_2(SO_4)_2 \cdot 24H_2O$ ($T = 0.06 - 1$ °K) [31]; $CrPO_4 \cdot 3H_2O$ [26]; $CrCl_3$ ($g = 1.997 \pm 0.003$) [32]; $K_2Cr_2(SO_4)_4 \cdot 24H_2O$ [33]; Cr in CaF_2 [38].

Notes:

a) Below 160°K two different magnetic complexes exist.

b) The temperature of the crystalline transition is 157 ± 2°K. Below this point the spectrum corresponds to rhombic symmetry; the direction cosines of the rhombic axes with respect to the tetragonal axes a, b, c are:

	a	b	c
X	−0.35 ± 0.05	−0.35 ± 0.05	+0.87 ± 0.03
Y	+0.71 ± 0.04	−0.71 ± 0.04	0 ± 0.05
Z	+0.61 ± 0.04	+0.61 ± 0.04	+0.50 ± 0.04

The direction for the other three ions are obtained by rotating the XYZ system by an angle of $\pi/2$ about the c axis. D and E do not change between 90°K and 13°K.

c) The temperature of the crystalline transition is 170 ± 2°K. Below this point the spectrum corresponds to rhombic symmetry.

d) The crystalline transition is at about 80°K. Below this temperature two different magnetic complexes exist.

e) δ decreases at a rate of about 0.0005 cm^{-1} deg^{-1} over the temperature range 295 to 77°K; i.e., the trigonal component of the crystalline field decreases as the temperature is reduced.

f) The crystal has three Al atoms per unit cell situated on the C_3 axis, but only two of them are equivalent. This explains the observed intensities of spectra I and II: spectrum II is double in intensity.

g) Only one line.

h) Directional cosines of the angles at T = 20°K:

	a	b	c
X	0.104	± 0.994	0
Y	0	0	1
Z	0.994	± 0.104	0

i) Directional cosines of the angle at T = 90°K:

	a	b	c
X	0	± 0.996	0.087
Y	0	± 0.087	0.996
Z	1	0	0

j) The immediate environment of Cr^{3+} in chromic acetylacetonate and its fluorine derivatives is a distorted octahedron of six O; the local field is mainly axial. In chromic acetylacetonate a gradual transition is observed between 290 and 90°K: at 90°K the complex divides into three types with slightly different orientations of the Z axis or having somewhat different splittings; $\psi = +22.5°$, $\alpha = 59°$.

k) The spectrum consisting of one isotropic line shows that Cr^{3+} is located in a strictly cubic crystalline field.

l) The spectrum belongs to the Cr^{3+} ion in an axial crystalline field. The axes of the nonequivalent ions are directed along the cubic axes. The spectrum arises in the case of large Cr^{3+} concentrations.

m) The spectrum belongs to the Cr^{3+} ion in a rhombic crystalline field. The direction of the field of the X, Y, Z axes: X = (110), Y = $(1\bar{1}0)$, Z = (001). The number of Cr^{3+} ions in a rhombic field is 1/2 to 1/4 of the number of Cr^{3+} ions in a cubic field. The spectrum arises in the case of large Cr^{3+} concentrations.

n) The existence of two spectra is explained by the different relative positions of the Cr^{3+} ions and of the compensating F^- ions; the hyperfine interaction with the F nuclei causes only a broadening of the line. The constant of this interaction is ≈ 3-5 gauss. The constant of the hyperfine interaction with the F^{19} nuclei is ≈ 20 gauss. Zero field absorption occurs at the frequency ν = (2847 ± 2) · 10^{-4} sec^{-1}.

Table 4.1 (Cont'd)

Co^{2+}

Formula	T, °K	$g_{\parallel}$	$g_{\perp}$	D	E	Reference	Note
Cs_3CoCl_5 [к 2]	90, 20	2.32 ± 0.04	2.27 ± 0.04	~ —4.5	0	[1]	M=4. Each ion surrounded by a distorted tetrahedron of 4 Cl. M_m = 1; the spectrum corresponds to axial symmetry with an axis parallel to c.

Cr^{2+}

Formula	T, °K	$g_{\parallel}$	$g_{\perp}$	D	E	Reference	Note
$CrSO_4 \cdot 5H_2O$	290	1.95	1.99	2.24	0.10	[1]	M_m = 2; angle between the z axes equals 86°

Ni^{2+}

Formula	T, °K	g	D	E	ψ°	θ°	α°	Reference	Note
$K_2Ni(SO_4)_2 \cdot 6H_2O$ (cr. st. 2)	290	2.25 ± 0.05	— 3.30	— 0.51_7	— 12.5	11	45	[1]	
			— 3.50 ± 0.01	— 0.55 ± 0.01				[2]	
$(NH_4)_2Ni(SO_4)_2 \cdot 6H_2O$ (cr. st. 2)	290	2.25 ± 0.05	— 2.24 ± 0.01	— 0.38_7 ± 0.01	— 14	3.5	45	[1, 2]	a)
	90	2.25 ± 0.05	— 1.99	— 0.48_6	— 14	3.5	45	[1]	
$Tl_2Ni(SO_4)_2 \cdot 6H_2O$ (cr. st. 2)	290	2.25 ± 0.05	— 2.65	— 0.10	— 11	11	45	[1]	
$K_2Ni(SeO_4)_2 \cdot 6H_2O$ (cr. st. 2)	290	2.25 ± 0.05	— 3	— 1	— 13	0	45	[1]	
$(NH_4)_2Ni(SeO_4)_2 \cdot 6H_2O$ (cr. st. 2)	290	2.25 ± 0.05	— 1.89	— 0.79	— 28	0	50	[1]	
	90	2.25 ± 0.05	— 1.73	— 0.82	— 28	0	50	[1]	
$Ni_3La_2(NO_3)_{12} \cdot 24H_2O$ (cr. st. 3) Ni : Mg = 1 : 800	90	2.24	0.177 ± 0.002	0				[3]	

Table 4.1 (Cont'd)

Formula	T, °K	g	D	E	$\psi°$	$\theta°$	$\alpha°$	Reference	Note
$NiSiF_6 \cdot 6H_2O$ (cr. st.4)	290	2.3	−0.50	0				[4, 5]	b)
	195	2.29	−0.32	0					
	90	2.26	−0.17	0					
	60		−0.14	0					
	20	2.29	−0.12	0					
	14		−0.12	0					
	290	2.34 ± 0.02	−0.6					[6]	c)
$Ni(BrO_3)_2 \cdot 6H_2O$ (cr. st. 5)	290	2.29 ± 0.04	1.93 ± 0.04	0				[7]	
$NiSO_4 \cdot 7H_2O$ (cr. st. 6)	290	2.2_0	-3.5_6	-1.5_0				[8]	d)
Ni^{2+} in MgO (powder)	290	2.225 ± 0.005						[9, 10]	e)
	77	2.227 ± 0.005							
	4	2.234 ± 0.004							
Ni^{2+} in $CdCl_2$	20	2.28	1.4100					[16]	f)
$NiCl_2$ (powder)	290	2.25						[17]	g)
	90	2.24							
	50.2	2.27							
	40.6	2.46							
	20.4	2.30							

Paramagnetic resonance absorption was also observed at room temperature in $NiBr_2$ (g = 2.27) [11]; $NiBr_2(NH_3)_6$ (g = 2.14 and 2.16) [12, 13]; $NiCl_2$ (g = 2.21) [11]; $NiCl_2 \cdot 6H_2O$ [14]; NiI_2 $(NH_3)_6$ (g = 2.14) [13, 7]; $Ni(C_6H_4)_4$ $(CN)_8$ (g = 2.20; T = 270 - 20°K) [15]; Ni $(NH_3)_6$ ClO_4 (g = 2.17) [13].

NOTES:

a) For Zn : Ni = 50, the parameters and axes are virtually unchanged.

b) For Zn : Ni = 4.16, D is ~ 20% greater than in undiluted salts at all temperatures.

c) The dependence of D and g on the hydrostatic pressure p has been studied; g does not depend on p, $\partial D/\partial p = 0.834 \cdot 10^{-4}$ cm^{-1}/kg$\cdot$cm^{-2}; D = 0 with p = 6200 kg/cm^2.

d) For one complex the directional cosines of the axes equal: Z (0.95; 0.31; 0), Y (- 0.31; 0.95; 0.09). The axes of the other complexes are obtained by a mirror reflection.

e) A single line whose width is almost unchanged with temperature.

f) A trigonal distortion of the cubic field occurs.

g) The low temperature measurement may not be accurate (see Orton, J. W. Rep. Progr. Phys. 22, 204, 1959). The Z_1 and Z_2 axes of the two ions lie in the K_1OK_3 plane where the angle Z_1OK_1 and the angle $Z_2OK_1 = \pm\theta$, and where the angle $K_1Oc = \psi$. X_1 is approximately parallel to Y_2; both axes lie in the K_2OK_3 plane with the angle $X_1OK_2 = \alpha$, and with the angle $Y_2OK_2 = 90° - \alpha$.

Table 4.1 (Cont'd)

Cu^{2+}

Tutton salts (cr. st. 2)

Formula	T, °K	g			A		P	$\psi°$	$\alpha°$	Reference	Note
$Cs_2Cu(SO_4)_2 \cdot 6H_2O$	90	g_{min} (K_1K_3) 2,08 ± 0,02	g_2 2,06 ± 0,02	g_z 2,43 ± 0,02				+ 114	40	[1]	
$K_2Cu(SO_4)_2 \cdot 6H_2O$	290	g_1 2,31 ± 0,03	g_2 2,07 ± 0,03	g_3 2,25 ± 0,03				+ 105		[2]	
	90	g_x 2,14 ± 0,02	g_y 2,04 ± 0,02	g_z 2,36 ± 0,02				+ 105	42	[1]	
Cu : Zn = = $2 \cdot 10^{-2} - 5 \cdot 10^{-4}$	290	g_z 2,05 ± 0,03	g_{max} (K_2K_3) 2,25 ± 0,03	g_1 2,26 ± 0,03				+ 15	32	[2]	
	20	g_z 2,44 ± 0,02	g_{min} (K_1K_3) 2,13 ± 0,02		A_z 0.0103 ± 0.0005	$A_{min}(K_1K_3)$ 0,0034 ± 0,0005	0,0011 ±0,0001	≈+ 105	42 ± 2	[3]	

Table 4.1 (Cont'd)

Formula	T, °K	g			A			P	ψ°	α°	Reference	Note
$Cu : Zn = 5 : 10^{-3}$	77	$g_{\parallel}$ 2.47 ± 0.05	$g_{\perp}$ 2.08 ± 0.04		A − 0.0083	B 0.0045		0.001			[42]	a)
$K_2Cu(SO_4)_2 \cdot 6D_2O$ $Zn : Cu = 200 - 1000$	20	g_x 2.16 ± 0.02	g_y 2.04 ± 0.02	g_z 2.42 ± 0.02	A_x < 0.0017	A_y + 0.0061 ± 0.0003	A_z − 0.0099 ± 0.0001	+ 0.00110 ± 0.00005 P' 0.00013 ± 0.00006	≈ + 105	43	[3]	$\frac{^{65}A}{^{63}A} = 1.069 \pm 0.003$ $\frac{^{63}P}{^{65}P} = 1.08 \pm 0.02$
$K_2Cu(SO_4)_2 \cdot 6H_2O$	90	g_z 2.38 ± 0.02	$g_{min}(K_1K_3)$ 2.07 ± 0.02	g_2 2.04_5 ± 0.02					+ 73	37	[1]	
$(NH_4)_2Cu(SO_4)_2 \cdot 6H_2O$	290	g_1 2.32 ± 0.03	g_2 2.09 ± 0.03	g_3 2.25 ± 0.03					+ 77		[2], [45, 49]	
	90	g_z 2.45 ± 0.02	$g_{min}(K_1K_3)$ 2.12 ± 0.02	g_2 2.06 ± 0.02					+ 65	39	[1]	
$Zn : Cu = 50 - 2000$	290	g_z 2.04 ± 0.03	g_{max} 2.26 ± 0.03	g_1 2.28 ± 0.03					+ 167	32	[2]	
	20	g_x 2.12 ± 0.02	g_y 2.05 ± 0.02	g_z 2.46 ± 0.02	A_x 0.0025 ± 0.0005	A_y 0.0035 ± 0.0005	A_z 0.0130 ± 0.0005	0.0011 ± 0.0001	+ 65	38	[3]	

Table 4.1 (Cont'd)

Formula	T, °K	g			A			P	ψ °	α °	Reference	Note
		g_z	$g_{min}(K_1K_3)$	g_y								
$(NH_4)_2Cu(SeO_4)_2 \cdot 6H_2O$	90	2.39 $\pm$ 0.02	2.075 $\pm$ 0.02	2.06_5 $\pm$ 0.02					+ 72	37.5	[1]	
		g_1	g_3									
$Rb_2Cu(SO_4)_2 \cdot 6H_2O$	290	2.28 $\pm$ 0.03	2.24 $\pm$ 0.03						+ 105		[2]	
		g_z	$g_{min}(K_1K_3)$	g_2								
	90	2.45 $\pm$ 0.02	2.11 $\pm$ 0.02	2.07 $\pm$ 0.02					+ 105	40	[1]	
		g_z	$g_{max}(K_2K_3)$	g_1								
Zn : Cu = 50 — 2000	290	2.08 $\pm$ 0.03	2.27 $\pm$ 0.03	2.25 $\pm$ 0.03					+ 15	33	[2]	
		g_z	$g_{min}(K_1K_3)$		A_z	$A_{min}(K_1K_3)$						
	20	2.44 $\pm$ 0.02	2.12 $\pm$ 0.02		0.0116 $\pm$ 0.0005	0.0030 $\pm$ 0.0005		0.0011 $\pm$ 0.0001	~ + 105	42 $\pm$ 2	[3]	b)
		g_x	g_y	g_z	A_x	A_y	A_z					
$Rb_2Cu(SO_4)_2 \cdot 6D_2O$ Zn : Cu = 200 — 1000	20	2.15 $\pm$ 0.02	2.04 $\pm$ 0.02	2.43 $\pm$ 0.02	< 0.0020	+ 0.0059 $\pm$ 0.0004	— 0.0110 $\pm$ 0.0002	+ 0.0012 $\pm$ 0.0001	~ + 105	42 $\pm$ 2	[3]	b)
		g_z	$g_{min}(K_1K_3)$	g_3								
$Tl_2Cu(SO_4)_2 \cdot 6H_2O$	90	2.40 $\pm$ 0.02	2.08 $\pm$ 0.02	2.06 $\pm$ 0.02					+ 112	39.5	[1]	

Table 4.1 (Cont'd)

Other copper compounds

Formula	T, °K	g			A			Reference	Note
$Cu_3Bi_2(NO_3)_{12} \cdot 24H_2O$ (cr.st.3) Cu : Mg = 1 : 100	90	$g_{\parallel}$ 2.219 ± 0.003	$g_{\perp}$ 2.217 ± 0.003		A 0.0027 ± 0.0001	B 0.0026 ± 0.0001		[4]	
	20	$g_x = g_y$ 2.096 ± 0,003	g_z 2.454 ± 0.003		$A_x = A_y$ 0.0017 ± 0.0002	A_z 0.0110 ± 0.0002			
$Cu_3La_2(NO_3)_{12} \cdot 24H_2O$ (cr. st. 3)	290		2.22						
	90, 20	$g_x = g_y$ 2.10	g_z 2.41					[5]	c)
$Cu_3La_2(NO_3)_{12} \cdot 24D_2O$ Cu : Mg = 1 : 500 (cr.st.3)	90	$g_{\parallel}$ 2.219 ± 0,003	$g_{\perp}$ 2.218 ± 0.003		A 0.00290 ± 0.00005	B 0.00275 ± 0.00005		[4, 5]	d)
	45		2.235 ± 0.005						
	20	$g_x = g_y$ 2.097 ± 0.002	g_z 2.470 ± 0.002		A_x + 0.00190 ± 0.00005	A_y + 0.00123 ± 0,00005	A_z − 0.0113 ± 0,00005	[4]	P = 0.00111 ± 0.00005 P' = 0.00004 ± 0.00001
$CuSiF_6 \cdot 6H_2O$ (cr.st.4)	290		2.20					[6]	
Cu : Zn	90	$g_{\parallel}$ 2.221 ± 0.005	$g_{\perp}$ 2.230 ± 0,005		A 0.0021 ± 0.0005	B 0.0028 ± 0.0005		[4]	e)
	20, 12	$g_x = g_y$ 2.10 ± 0.01	g_z 2.46 ± 0,01		$A_x = A_y$ < 0.0030	A_z 0.0110 ± 0.0003			

Table 4.1 (Cont'd)

Formula	T, °K	g			A			Reference	Note
$Cu(BrO_3)_2 \cdot 6H_2O$ (cr. st. 5) $Cu : Zn = 1 : 100$	90	2.21_7 $\pm$ 0.01					0.0028 $\pm$ 0.0005	[4]	f)
$CuSO_4 \cdot 5H_2O$ [к3]	290	$g_{\parallel}$ 2.08	$g_{\perp}$ 2.27					[10, 25, 28, 39, 40, 41, 45]	g)
		$g_x = g_y$ 2.08	g_z 2.46						
		g_1 2.267	g_2 2.236	g_3 2.086					
	77	g_1 2.264	g_2 2.233	g_3 2.083					
$Cu(NH_3)_4SO_4 \cdot H_2O$ [к4]	290	g_1 2.054 $\pm$ 0.003	g_2 2.104 $\pm$ 0.006	g_3 2.181 $\pm$ 0.005				[7, 24, 35, 36]	orthorhomb., h)
		$g_{\parallel}$ 2.22 $\pm$ 0.02	$g_{\perp}$ 2.05 $\pm$ 0.02					[33]	
$[Cu(C_5H_5N)_m] SO_4 \cdot nH_2O$	290	g_1 2.072 $\pm$ 0.004	g_2 2.081 $\pm$ 0.006	g_3 2.314 $\pm$ 0.010				[24]	
$Cu(NH_3)_4(NO_3)_2$ [к4]	290	g_a 2.07 $\pm$ 0.02	g_b 2.14 $\pm$ 0.02	g_c 2.02 $\pm$ 0.02				[7, 35, 36]	orthorhomb.

Table 4.1 (Cont'd)

Formula	T, °K	g			A		Reference	Note
Cu $(C_5H_5N)_6(NO_3)_2$ [K4]	290	$g_{\parallel}$ 2.25 ± 0.02	$g_{\perp}$ 2.05 ± 0.02		A 0.0199 ± 0.0007	B < 0.0014	[23]	$M_m = 1$, rhombic, i)
$[Cu(C_5H_5N)_m](NO_3)_2 \cdot nH_2O$	290	g_1 2.056 ± 0.004	g_2 2.124 ± 0.015	g_3 2.161 ± 0.008			[24]	
$CuCl_2 \cdot 2H_2O$ [K5]	290 to 15	g_a 2.187 ± 0.005	g_b 2.037 ± 0.005	g_c 2.252 ± 0.005			[9, 45, 49]	$M_m = 2$, orthorhomb., j)
$K_2CuCl_4 \cdot 2H_2O$ [K6]	290	g_x 2.06	g_z 2.38				[11, 25, 45]	$M_m = 2$, tetrag., k)
$(NH_4)_2CuCl_4 \cdot 2H_2O$ [K6]	290	$g_{\parallel}$ 2.06	$g_{\perp}$ 2.22				[11]	k)
Cu $(C_6H_4)_4(CN)_8$ [K7]	290 to 20	g_x $< 2.10_5$ $g_{\parallel}$ 2.165 ± 0.004	g_y 2.06 $g_{\perp}$ 2.045 ± 0.003	g_z > 2.30	A 0.0208 ± 0.0010	B 0.0031 ± 0.0010	[15, 16]	$M = 2$, monoclinic, l)
Cu $[C_2H_2(NH_2)_2]_2Cl_2 \cdot H_2O$ [K8]	290	g_1 2.050 ± 0.004	g_2 2.057 ± 0.010	g_3 2.244 ± 0.010			[24]	$x = 1$ or 2 $M_m = 2$, monoclinic, m)

Table 4.1 (Cont'd)

Formula	T, °K	g			D	E	Reference	Note
		$g_{\parallel}$	$g_{\perp}$					
Cu $(HCOO)_2 \cdot 4H_2O$ [к9]	290	2.35	2.06				[26, 31]	$M_m = 2$, monoclinic, n)
		g_{max}	g_{min}					
Cu $(HCOO)_2 \cdot 2H_2O$ [к9]	290	2.24	2.10				[26]	$M_m = 4$, n)
		g_x	g_y	g_z				
Cu $(CH_3COO)_2 \cdot H_2O$ [к10]	290, 90	$2.05_8 \pm 0.005$	$2.09_3 \pm 0.005$	$2.34_4 \pm 0.01$			[12, 13]	$S = 1$
	90	2.08 ± 0.03	2.08 ± 0.03	2.42 ± 0.03	0.345 ± 0.005	0.007 ± 0.003	[27]	$M=4$, $M_m=2$, monoclinic, o)
Cu $(CH_3CH_2COO)_2 \cdot H_2O$	290	I: $2.36_8 \pm 0.015$	$2.11_1 + 0.015$	$2.09_8 \pm 0.015$	0.344 ± 0.007	0.004	[50]	S = 1, 3 different magnetic complexes, see Sec. 3.11, p)
		II: $2.36_0 \pm 0.015$	$2.10_0 \pm 0.015$	$2.08_2 \pm 0.015$	0.341 ± 0.007	0.004		
		III: $2.36_8 \pm 0.015$	$2.10_2 \pm 0.015$	$2.10_0 \pm 0.015$	0.345 ± 0.007	0.002		
		2.09	-2.10	2.35	0.38	≈ 0	[14]	$S = 1$
		$g_{\parallel}$	$g_{\perp}$					
Cu $[(CH_3CO)_2CH]_2$	290 90	2.254 ± 0.001	2.075 ± 0.0008				[8], [32]	q)
		$g_{\parallel}$	g_1	g_2				
Cu : Pd = 1 : 200	77	2.266_1	2.055_1	2.051_9			[37]	$A = -0.0160$, $Q' = 0.0007$, $B = -0.0195$ r)
		$g_{\parallel}$	$g_{\perp}$	A	B	Q		
Cu^{2+} in AgCl	290 77	A: 2.00 ± 0.02	2.28 ± 0.02	0.00093 ± 0.00093	0.0090 ± 0.0006	0.0019 ± 0.0005	[51]	
		B: 2.26 ± 0.02	2.07 ± 0.02	0.0100 ± 0.0006	0.0043 ± 0.0005	0.0021 ± 0.0005		
		C: 2.30 ± 0.02	2.07 ± 0.02	0.0112 ± 0.0001	0.0044 ± 0.0005	0.0021 ± 0.0005		

Table 4.1 (Cont'd)

Formula	T, °K	g			A			Reference	Note
Cu^{2+} in MgO (powder)		2.190 ± 0.002			0.0019 ± 0.0001			[52]	Field of cubic symmetry
Cu^{2+} in NaCl	290	a) 2.07 b) 2.06 c) 2.16						[53]	s)
Cu^{2+} in KCl	290	2.180 ± 0.009						[53]	
Dimethylglyoxime Cu^{2+}		g_x 2.065	g_y 2.033	g_z 2.136				[54]	
Cu^{2+} in $CdCl_2$	290	$g_{\parallel}$ 2.205 ± 0.010	$g_{\perp}$ 2.19 ± 0.01					[55]	t)
	90 20	2.34 ±0.01	2.07 ± 0.01		0.0120 ± 0.0010				$M_m = 3$

Paramagnetic resonance also observed in the following compounds at room temperature: $CuBr_2$ ($g = 2.23$) [17]; $Cu(C_2O_4)$ ($g = 2.12$) [31]; $CuC_4H_4O_6 \cdot 3H_2O$ ($g = 1.97$) [17]; $Cu[C_2H_2(NH_2)_2]_2SO_4 \cdot 2H_2O$ ($g_{max} = 2.25$, $g_{min} = 2.05$) [36]; $Cu[C_2H_2(NH_2)_2]_2(NO_3)_2 \cdot 2H_2O$ ($g_{max} = 2.25$, $g_{min} = 2.05$) [36]; $Cu(C_3H_5O_3)_2 \cdot 2H_2O$ ($g = 2.09$) [17]; $Cu(C_5H_5N)_4(NO_3)_2 \cdot H_2O$ ($g = 2.04$) [17]; $Cu[(CH_3)_3C(CO)_2CH_2C_5H_{11}]_2$ ($g = 2.04$) [17]; $Cu[C_6H_5(CH_2)_3(CO)_2CH_3]_2$ ($g = 2.02$) [17]; $Cu(C_7H_5O_2)_2 \cdot 2H_2O$ ($g = 1.97$) [17]; CuF_2 ($g = 2.15$) [17]; CuF_2 basic ($g = 2.08$) [18]; $Cu(NH_4)_2(C_2O_4)_2 \cdot 2H_2O$ ($g(010) = 2.1 - 2.28$, $g(100) = 2.05 - 2.23$, $M_m = 2$) [29, 31]; $CuK_2(C_2O_4)_2$ ($g = 2.13$) [31]; $CuNa_2(C_2O_4)_2$ ($g = 2.07$) [31]; $Cu(NH_3)_4Cl_2 \cdot H_2O$ [19, 35]; $Cu(NH_3)_4SO_4 \cdot H_2O$ ($g = 2.09$; $T = 300$, 90, 4° K) [34, 35] [33]; $CuSO_4$ [19]; $CuSO_4 \cdot 3H_2O$ ($g = 2.19$) [34]; $CuSO_4 \cdot 5H_2O$ [$T = 300°$ K; $g = 2.20$; $T = 90°$ K; $g = 2.22$) [29, 34, 43, 46, 49] $CuSO_4 \cdot 4NH_3 \cdot H_2O$ ($g = 2.04 - 2.19$) [45, 49]; $CuSiF_6 \cdot 4H_2O$ ($g_{\parallel} = 2.40$; $g_{\perp} = 2.10$) [6]; $CuWO_4 \cdot 2H_2O$ ($g = 2.17$) [17]; $2CuC_2O_4 \cdot H_2O$ ($g = 2.07$) [17]; $Cu_3CO_2(CN)_{12}$ ($g = 2.17$; $T = 290 - 12°$ K) [21]; Cu chlorophyllate ($T = 270$, 90° K; $g = 2.05 \pm 0.01$; Mg : Cu, $g = 2.06$) [15, 44]; silicate glass ($g_{\parallel} = 2{,}32$ $g_{\perp} = 2{,}06$) [38]; persulfate of copper di-o-phenanthrolinate ($T = 290$, 90, 20°K, $g_{\parallel} = 2.3_0$, $g_{\perp} = 2.05$) [22]; copper derivative of salicylaldimine (Cu : Ni = 1 : 200) [47]; CuS [20]; chlorinated and nonchlorinated tetraphenylporphine Cu^{2+} ($g = 2.18$, $A_{Cu} = 0.0250$, $A_{Cl} = 0.0120$) [30].

Notes:

a) The measurements were conducted at $\nu \approx 5 \cdot 10^8$ cps.

b) For T > 20°K a second anomalous spectrum appears; the g factors of both spectra differ by less than 1%.

c) Transition temperature from 173 to 273°K.

d) Transition temperature from 33 to 45°K.

e) Transition temperature from 12 to 50°K.

f) Transition temperature from < 7 to 35°K.

g) Each Cu^{2+} is surrounded by a distorted octahedron of four H_2O and two oxygens; the Cu^{2+} ion may be assumed to be in a tetragonal field (the rhombic field is very small); the angle between the tetragonal axes is 86 ± 2°; g_{max} and g_{min} are determined in the planes of the tetragonal axes of the nonequivalent ions.

h) The ratio of the spin-orbit coupling constant λ' of the Cu^{2+} ion in the crystal to the constant λ for the free ion $\lambda'/\lambda = 0.55$.

i) The sharp anisotropic exchange leads to the removal of the hyperfine structure in the direction perpendicular to the Z axis; it is resolved in the direction of the Z axis.

j) Each Cu^{2+} has a two-dimensional environment of two H_2O and two Cl; an extended octahedron results from two more remote Cl belonging to the other Cu^{2+} ion. Only a single line was observed. Below 4.3°K the material is antiferromagnetic.

k) Each Cu^{2+} is surrounded by four Cl, forming a rhombus in the aa plane, and by two H_2O molecules on the normal to this plane. The two rhombi of nonequivalent ions are turned by 90° with respect to one another around the c axis—the H_2O - H_2O line (Y axis); thus, Cu is located in a field of rhombic symmetry. The spectrum was measured at wavelengths 5.4 and 6.6 mm; the exchange frequency is $1.1 \cdot 10^{10}$ cps.

l) Each Cu^{2+} is surrounded by a square of four N.

m) Cu^{2+} is surrounded by four N; O is located perpendicular to the plane of N opposite Cu (at a distance of 2.68 A) and on the other side we find Cl (at a distance of 2.89 A).

n) Each Cu^{2+} is surrounded by four O and two H_2O, which form a distorted octahedron.

o) Bimolecular cells; each Cu^{2+} is surrounded by a distorted octahedron of four O, H_2O and a neighboring Cu^{2+}; the distance between the Cu neighbors is 2.6 A. D = 0.345 ± 0.005, E = 0.007 ± 0.003, $A_z = 0.008$, A_x, $A_y < 0.0010$. (See Section 3.11.)

p) It is apparent from the paramagnetic resonance spectrum that the cell contains six magnetic complexes, each with two Cu^{2+} ions; three complexes are derived from the remaining three by reflection in the ac plane. Each complex is approximately tetragonal.

q) Each Cu^{2+} is surrounded by four O in a single plane. The hyperfine structure is described by the relation

$$K^2g^2 = A^2g_{\|}^2 \cos^2\vartheta + B^2g_{\perp}^2 \sin^2\vartheta + 2C^2g_{\|}g_{\perp} \sin\vartheta \cos\vartheta \; ;$$

C = ± 0.0062 cm^{-1} at T = 77°K and C = ± 0.0043 cm^{-1} at T = 290°K.

r) Type A: Axial distortion of the crystalline field is due to the interaction of the Cu^{2+} with a positive lattice site vacancy in the (110) direction; type B: the same, but the vacancy is located in the (100) direction; type C: axial distortion of the field of cubic symmetry due to the Jahn-Teller effect directed along (100). The effect was observed only in halogenated crystals.

s) Spectra (a) and (b) were obtained from crystals drawn from the melt; spectrum (c) was obtained from aqueous solution.

t) Trigonal distortions of the cubic field occur.

Table 4.2

Ti^{3+}

Formula	T, °K	$g_{\parallel}$	$g_{\perp}$	Reference	Note
$CsTi(SO_4)_2 \cdot 12H_2O$ (cr. st. 1)	4.2—2.5	1.25 ± 0.02	1.14 ± 0.02	[1]	$M_m = 2$
$KTi(C_2O_4)_2 \cdot 2H_2O$	90—20	1.86	1.96	[2]	$M_m = 2$. The immediate environment of the Ti^{3+} is an octahedron of 6 O; the local field is axially symmetric.
$Ti[(CH_3CO)_2CH]_3$ [κ1] Ti : Al = 10^{-2} (powder)	290	2.00	1.93	[3]	
$CsTi(SO_4)_2 \cdot 12H_2O$ (powder)	7.88 6.33	1.53 1.35		[4]	The g factor depends on temperature; the line width is very broad and is determined by the relaxation time

V^{4+}

Formula	T, °K	g			Reference	Note
$K_2V_2O_2(C_2O_4)_3 \cdot 4H_2O$	290. 90	g_1 1.95_4	g_2 1.98_5	g_3 1.96_7	[1]	In the powder diluted with a Ti^{3+} salt, one can observe a hyperfine structure due to $^{51}V\left(I=\frac{7}{2}\right)$; $^{51}A = 0.010 \pm 0.001$
$VOCl_2$	290	2.00			[2]	
$VO_3(C_6H_4)_3N_2(CH)_2$	290	2.02			[2]	

Table 4.2 (Cont'd)

Formula	T, °K	g			Reference	Note
$VOSO_4 \cdot 2H_2O$	290	1.96			[3]	
$VOSO_4 \cdot 5H_2O$ (powder)	300	$1.990_1 \pm 0.002$			[4]	
	70	$1.998_7 \pm 0.002$				
	4	1.994 ± 0.004				

Mn^{6+}

Formula	T, °K	g	Reference	Note
MnO_3	290	1.96	[1]	

V^{3+}

Formula	T, °K	$g_{\parallel}$	D	A	Reference	Note
V^{3+} in Al_2O_3	4.2 2 90	1.92 ± 0.01	$\sim +10$	0.0193 ± 0.0002 350 gauss	[1] [2]	The transition $\Delta M = 2$ was observed

Table 4.2 (Cont'd)

Co^{2+}

Formula	T, °K	g			A			Reference	Note
$K_2Co(SO_4)_2 \cdot 6H_2O$ (cr. st. 2) Co : Zn = 1 : 500 — 10^{-5}	20	g_z 6.56 ± 0.13	g_{min} 2.50 ± 0.05	g_2 3.35 ± 0.07	A_z 0.0286 ± 0.0006	A_{min} 0.0065 ± 0.0003	A_2 0.0080 ± 0.0004	[1]	$\psi = +163°$, $\alpha = 35°$
$(NH_4)_2Co(SO_4)_2 \cdot 6H_2O$ (cr. st. 2) Co : Zn = 1 : 500 — 10^{-5}	20	g_z 6.45 ± 0.13	g_{min} 3.06 ± 0.06	g_2 3.06 ± 0.06	A_z 0.0245 ± 0.0005	A_{min} 0.0020 ± 0.0001	A_2 0.0020 ± 0.0001	[1]	$\psi = +130°$, $\alpha = 34°$
$(NH_4)_2Co(SO_4)_2 \cdot 6D_2O$ (cr. st. 2) $Co^{60}:Co^{59}:Zn = 1:50:10\,000$	20	g 6.41				^{59}A 0.0251	^{60}A 0.0144	[2]	$\frac{\mu(Co^{60})}{\mu(Co^{59})} = 0.8191 \pm 0.0016$
$Rb_2Co(SO_4)_2 \cdot 6H_2O$ (cr. st. 2) Co : Zn	20	g_z 6.65	g_{min} 2.7	g_2 3.3	A_z 0.0293 ± 0.0003	A_{min} 0.0049 ± 0.0005		[3]	$\psi = +157°$, $\alpha = 37°$
$Co_3Bi_2(NO_3)_{12} \cdot 24H_2O$ (cr. st. 3) Co : Mg = 10^{-2}	20	$g_{\parallel}$ I: 7.29 ± 0.01 $g_{\parallel}$ II: 4.108 ± 0.003	$g_{\perp}$ 2.338 ± 0.004 $g_{\perp}$ 4.385 ± 0.003		A 0.0283 ± 0.0001 A 0.0085 ± 0.0001	$B \leqslant$ 0.0001 B 0.0103 ± 0.0001		[4]	Two different magnetic complexes
$(Ce + Bi)_2Co_3(NO_3)_{12} \cdot 24H_2O$ (cr. st. 3) Co : Mg = 1 : 200 Ce — 0%, Bi — 100% Ce — 10%	4	$g_{\parallel}$ I: 4.145 ± 0.002 4.12 ± 0.01	$g_{\perp}$ 4.415 ± 0.002 4.45 ± 0.01		A 0.0095 ± 0.0003 0.0082 ± 0.0009	B 0.0103 ± 0.0003 0.0114 ± 0.0009		[5]	Two different magnetic complexes

Table 4.2 (Cont'd)

Formula	T, °K	g		A		Reference	Note
		$g_{\parallel}$	$g_{\perp}$				
Ce — 20%		4.22 ± 0.01	4.22 ± 0.01	0.0090 ± 0.0009	0.0090 ± 0.0009		
Ce — 50%		4.30 ± 0.01	4.31 ± 0.01	0.00897 ± 0.0009	0.0107 ± 0.0009		
Ce — 80%		4.02 ± 0.01	4.45 ± 0.01				
Ce — 100%		4.14 ± 0.01					
Ce — 0%, Bi — 100%		II : 7.20 ± 0.01	2.39 ± 0.02	0.0302 ± 0.0006	⩽0.0001		
Ce — 10%			2.37 ± 0.01				
Ce — 20%		7.41	2.36 ± 0.01				
Ce — 50%		10.55					
Ce — 80%		7.33	2.36 ± 0.01				
Ce — 100%		7.3					
$La_2Co_3(NO_3)_{12} \cdot 24H_2O$	4	I : 4.050 ± 0.002 II : 7.23 ± 0.01	4.430 ± 0.002 2.310 ± 0.002	0.00807 ± 0.00030 0.02788 ± 0.00060	0.01033 ± 0.00030 ⩽0.0001	[5]	Two different magnetic complexes
$CoSiF_6 \cdot 6H_2O$ (cr. st. 4) Co : Zn = 1 : 500 — 10^{-5}	20	5.82 ± 0.12	3.44 ± 0.07	0.0184 ± 0.0004	0.0047 ± 0.0002	[1]	a)
		6.6 ± 0.1	2.62 ± 0.05	0.023	0.0009		
		6.6 ± 0.2	2.82 ± 0.06	0.025	0.0013		b)

Table 4.2 (Cont'd)

Formula	T, °K	g			A			Reference	Note
		3.58 $\pm$ 0.05	4.09 $\pm$ 0.05		0.01	0.01			b)
$CoSO_4 \cdot 7H_2O$ (cr. st. 6)	20	g_x 2.30 $\pm$ 0.05	g_y 3.30 $\pm$ 0.07	g_z 6.90 $\pm$ 0.014	A_x 0.0028 $\pm$ 0.0001		A_z 0.0254 $\pm$ 0,0005	[1]	c)
Co : Zn $= 10^{-2}$ Co^{2+} in ZnF_2	20	g_x 2,6	g_y 6,05 $\pm$ 0.01	g_z 4.1 $\pm$ 0.1	A_x — 0.0043	A_y 0.0217 $\pm$ 0.0002	A_z 0.0067	[6]	$M_m = 2$, d)
Co^{2+} in NaF; $8 \cdot 10^{15}$ centers in a 0.05-cm^3 crystal after irradiation	20	g_x 4.3	g_y 3,3	g_z 5,7		A_y 0.0082	A_z 0,0250	[7]	e)
Co^{2+} in MgO Co : Mg $= 10^{-2} — 2 \cdot 10^{-3}$	20 4	g ~ 4.5 4.2785 $\pm$ 0.0001			A 0.00977_9 $\pm$ 0.00002			[8]	
Co^{2+} in Al_2O_3	1.6	$g_{\parallel}$ 2.316 $\pm$ 0.005		$g_{\perp}$ 4.98 $\pm$ 0.01	A 0.00334 $\pm$ 0.00005		B 0.00974 $\pm$ 0,00013	[13]	
Co^{2+} in CaF_2 Co : Ca $\approx 10^{-3}$	4.2 20	2.27 ~ 6.6		4.95 3.40 $\pm$ 0.05			0.0170 $\pm$ 0,0004	[15] [14]	f)
Co^{2+} in $CdCl_2$	20	3.06 $\pm$ 0,02		4.98 $\pm$ 0,02	0.0035		0.0170	[17]	g)

Paramagnetic resonance was also observed in: Co $(C_6H_4)_4(CN)_8$ (T = 270 - 20°K, two complexes I: g = 2.9; II: g = 2.4 - 1.98) [9] (T = 290°K, g = 1.98; T = 20°K, g = 2.90) [10]; $K_2Co(SO_4)_2 \cdot 6D_2O$ (T = 20°K, Co : Zn; the sample contained 4mC Co^{56}, $\frac{\mu^{56}}{\mu^{56}} = 0.829 \pm 0.002$; the sample contained 4mC Co^{58}, $\frac{\mu^{58}}{\mu^{59}} = 0.8374 \pm 0.0024$ [11, 12, 16].

Notes: a) Principal line; $g_{\parallel}$ corresponds to the c axis of the crystal.
b) Much weaker lines (lattice defects).

c) For one complex the Z axis lies in the (110) plane with $\angle$ ZOc = 13° and the X axis in the (110) plane with $\angle$ XOc = 103°, and the Y axis is parallel to the (110) plane. The axes of the other complexes have a regular reflection. For the undiluted salt, g is anisotropic in the ab plane and varies from 1.4 to 5.8.

d) A hyperfine structure due to F nuclei was observed: $A_y^N = (32 \pm 1) \cdot 10^{-4}\ cm^{-1}$, $A_z^N = (21 \pm 5) \cdot 10^{-4}\ cm^{-1}$.

e) There are six types of magnetic ions with similar spectra. A well-resolved structure was observed which was due to interaction both of Co and F nuclei. This spectrum disappears after irradiation, and two isotropic lines appear. One of these has an unresolved structure and possibly belongs to Co^{2+} in a slightly distorted cubic environment, while the other belongs to Co^{+}. All irradiated centers disappear on heating to 150°C.

f) A hyperfine structure was observed from the interaction with F nuclei: $A_F \approx 0.00030\ cm^{-1}$.

g) There are trigonal distortions of the cubic field.

Table 4.2 (Cont'd)

Formula	T, °K	g_z	Δ	Reference	Note
FeF_2 [K13] Fe : Zn = 1 : 3000	90	8.97 ± 0.05	0.224 ± 0.010	[1]	M = 2, M_m = 1; each Fe is surrounded by a distorted octahedron of six F. A hyperfine structure was observed due to F nuclei (the constants were determined at T = 12°K):
	20	8.97 ± 0.02	0.203 ± 0.004	[1, 2]	$A_z^{I} = (9.98 \pm 0.52) \cdot 10^{-3}\ cm^{-1}$, $A_z^{II} = (6.39 \pm 0.43) \cdot 10^{-3}\ cm^{-1}$
Fe^{2+} in ZnS		2.26		[3]	
Fe^{2+} in MgO		3.428; 6.9		[3]	
Fe^{2+} in $CdCl_2$	20	$g_{\parallel}$ 7.4		[6]	The line is asymmetrical

Paramagnetic resonance was also observed at $T = 20°$ K in $K_2Fe(SO_4)_2 \cdot 6H_2O$, $(NH_4)_2Fe(SO_4)_2 \cdot 6H_2O$, $FeSiF_6 \cdot 6H_2O$ [4]; $(C_8H_4N_2)_4Fe$ ($T = 290.20°$ K, $g = 3.8$; 2.0) [5].

Table 4.3

Ce^{3+}

Formula	T, °K	$g^a_{\parallel}$	$g^a_{\perp}$	$g^b_{\parallel}$	$g^b_{\perp}$	Reference	Note
$Mg_3Ce_2(NO_3)_{12} \cdot 24H_2O$ (cr. st. 3) Ce : La = 1 : 20	4.2	0.25 ±0.05	1.84 ±0.02			[1]	
Ce^{141} : La = 10^{-5}	4.2		1.84			[2]	$A^{141} = 0{,}002$ $B^{141} = 0{,}0126 \pm 0{,}0001$
$Ce(C_2H_5SO_4)_3 \cdot 9H_2O$ (cr. st. 9) Ce : La = 1 : 200	2.5	1.0 ±0.2	2.25 ±0.2	3.80 ±0.04	⩽0.4	[3]	Doublet b is lower
	4.2	0.955 ±0.005	2.185 ±0.01	3.72 ±0.01	0.20 ±0.005	[3, 4]	Doublet b is $(3 \pm 1)\,cm^{-1}$ above doublet a
		$g_{\parallel}$	$g_{\perp}$				
Ce^{3+} in CaF_2 Ce : Ca ≈ 10^{-4}	20	3.030 ±0.003	1.396 ±0.002			[5]	$M_m = 3$, the crystal axes of the nonequivalent ions are directed along the edges of the cube
Ce^{3+} in $LaCl_3$ Ce : La = 2 : 100	4	4.0366 ±0.0015	0.17 ±0.08			[6]	

Table 4.3 (Cont'd)

Nd^{3+}

Formula	T, °K	$g_{\parallel}$	$g_{\perp}$	Isotope	A	B	Reference	Note
$Mg_3Nd_2(NO_3)_{12} \cdot 24H_2O$ (cr. st. 3) Nd : La = 10^{-2}	4.2	0.45 ±0.05	2.72 ±0.02	143	0.0052 ±0.0005	0.0312 ±0.0001	[1]	
				145	0.0032 ±0.0003	0.0194 ±0.0001		
Nd : La = 10^{-6}	4.2		2.72	147	≈0.004	0.0237 ±0.0001	[7]	
$Nd(C_2H_5SO_4)_3 \cdot 9H_2O$ (cr. st. 9)	20	3.535 ±0.001	2.072 ±0.001	143	0.03803 ±0.00001	0.01989 ±0.00005	[2]	$\frac{^{143}A}{^{145}A} = 1.6083 \pm 0.0012$
Nd : La = 1 : 200				145	0.02364 ±0.00001	0.01237 ±0.00005		
$Nd(NO_3)_3 \cdot 6H_2O$ Nd : La = 1 : 200	20—13	g_x 3.88 ±0.01	g_z 0.74 ±0.01	143	A_x 0.0432 ±0.0002	A_z 0.0082 ±0.0010	[6]	For both isotopes
		g_y 1.72 ±0.01			A_y 0.0193 ±0.0002			$\lvert P_x - P_z \rvert < 0.005$, $\lvert P_y - P_z \rvert < 0.005$
				145	A_x 0.0270 ±0.0002	A_z 0.0051 ±0.0010		
					A_y 0.0119 ±0.0002			
		$g_{\parallel}$	$g_{\perp}$					
Nd^{3+} in CaF_2 Nd : Ca = 10^{-3}	20	4.412 ±0.008	1.301 ±0.002				[5]	a)
Nd^{3+} in SrF_2 Nd : Sr = 10^{-2}	20	4.289 ±0.008	1.505 ±0.002				[5]	a)

Table 4.3 (Cont'd)

Formula	T, °K	$g_{\parallel}$	$g_{\perp}$	Isotope	A	B	Reference	Note
Nd^{3+} in $LaCl_3$ $Nd:La = 2:10^3$	4	3.996 ±0.001	1.763 ±0.001	143	0.0425 ±0.0002	0.0167 ±0.0001	[8]	$^{143}P < 1 \cdot 10^{-4}$
				145	0.0264 ±0.0002	0.0104 ±0.0001		$^{145}P < 1 \cdot 10^{-4}$

Paramagnetic resonance was also observed in $Nd_2(SO_4)_3$ ($T = 90°$ K) [3]; $Nd_2(SO_4)_3 \cdot 8H_2O$ ($T = 90°$ K) [3]; Nd_2O_3 ($T = 290°$ K, $g = 3.2$) [4].
Note: a) $M_m = 3$. There is an axial electric field around each ion; the crystal axes of the nonequivalent ions are the axes of the cube.

Sm^{3+}

Formula	T, °K	$g_{\parallel}$	$g_{\perp}$	Isotope	A	B	Reference	Note
$Mg_3Sm_2(NO_3)_{12} \cdot 24H_2O$ (cr. st. 3)	4.2	0.76 ±0.01	0.40 ±0.05	147	0.0346 ±0.0005	<0.010	[1]	
				149	0.0287 ±0.0005	<0.010		
$Sm(C_2H_5SO_4)_3 \cdot 9H_2O$ (cr. st. 9)	4.2	0.596 ±0.002	0.604 ±0.002	147	0.0060 ±0.0001	0.0251 ±0.0001	[2]	$P < 0.0004$
$Sm:La = 10^{-2}$				149	0.0049 ±0.0001	0.0205 ±0.0001		$\frac{^{147}A}{^{149}A} = 1.222 \pm 0.008$
Sm^{3+} in $LaCl_3$ $Sm:La = 1:50$	4	0.5841 ±0.0003	0.6127 ±0.0006	147	0.00607 ±0.00002	0.0245 ±0.0001	[4]	
				149	0.00499 ±0.00002	0.0202 ±0.0001		

Paramagnetic resonance was also observed in Sm; in SrS ($T = 77–20°$ K); Sm in SrS · SrSe [3].

Table 4.3 (Cont'd)

Dy^{3+}

Formula	T, °K	g		Isotope	A_x		Reference	Note
$Dy(CH_3COO)_3 \cdot 4H_2O$ Dy : Y = 1 : 150	4.2	g_x 13.60 ±0.06		161 163	0.0381 ±0.0005 0.0540 ±0.0005		[1]	a)
		$g_{\parallel}$	$g_{\perp}$		A	B		
$Dy_2Mg_3(NO_3)_{12} \cdot 24H_2O$ Dy : La = $2 \cdot 10^{-3}$		4.281 ±0.006	8.923 ±0.160	161	0.01161 ±0.00007	0.02463 ±0.00015	[2]	$^{161}P =$ 0.00142 ± 0.00010 $^{163}P = -$0.00168 ± 0.00010
				163	0.01622 ±0.00007	0.03415 ±0.00015		$\frac{^{163}Q}{^{161}Q} = 1.18 \pm 0.15$

Note: a) $M_m = 1$, triclinic crystal. All principal values of the g factor are different; the direction of the magnetic field corresponds to the maximum value of the g factor.

Er^{3+}

Formula	T, °K	$g_{\parallel}$	$g_{\perp}$	A	B	Reference	Note
$Er(C_2H_5SO_4)_3 \cdot 9H_2O$ Er : La = 1 : 200	4	1.47 ±0.03	8.85 ±0.2	0.0052 ±0.0001	0.0314 ±0.0001	[1]	$P = 0.0030 \pm 0.0003$
Er^{3+} in CaF_2 Er : Ca = 10^{-5}	20, 14	g 6.78 ±0.01				[2]	a)

Table 4.3 (Cont'd)

Formula	T, °K	$g_{\|}$	$g_{\perp}$	A	B	Reference	Note
		$g_{\|}$	$g_{\perp}$				
		7.76 ±0.02	6.253 ±0.006	0.0261 ±0.0003	0.0219 ±0.0003		b)
		6.76 ±0.02	9.11 ±0.01				c)
$Er_2Mg_3(NO_3)_{12} \cdot 24H_2O$	4.2	4.21 ±0.01	7.990 ±0.010	0.0142 ±0.0001	0.0274 ±0.0001	[3]	$P \approx 0.0013$
Er^{3+} in $LaCl_3$ Er : La $= 5 \cdot 10^{-3}$		1.989 ±0.001	8.757 ±0.002	0.00664 ±0.00003		[4]	$P = 0.00086$

Notes:
a) Isotropic line.
b) Line from the main doublet.
c) Line from the excited doublet.

Yb^{3+}

Formula	T, °K	g_x	Isotope	A_x	Reference	Note
$Yb(CH_3COO)_3 \cdot 4H_2O$	4.2	4.57 ±0.02	171	0.122 ±0.001	[1]	a)
Yb : Y $= 10^{-2}$			173	0.0341 ±0.0003		

Note: a) $M_m = 1$, triclinic crystal. All principal values of the g factor are different; the direction of the magnetic field corresponds to the maximum value of the g factor.

Table 4.4

Pr^{3+}

Formula	T, °K	$g_{\parallel}$	$g_{\perp}$	Δ	A	Reference	Note
$Mg_3Pr_2(NO_3)_{12} \cdot 24H_2O$ (cr. st. 3) Pr : La = 10^{-2}	4,2	1.55 ±0,02			0.077 ±0.002	[1]	
$Pr(C_2H_5SO_4)_3 \cdot 9H_2O$ (cr. st. 9)	20	1,69 ±0.01	<0.03	~0.19	0.083 ±0.001	[2, 5]	
Pr : La = 1 : 200 Pr : Y		g_z 1.52_5 ±0.02		0.11 ±0.04	A_z 0.0755 ±0.0020	[5, 7, 3]	$V_2^0 = 50$ cm^{-1}, $V_4^0 = -100$ cm^{-1} $V_6^0 = -48$ cm^{-1}, $V_6^6 = 660$ cm^{-1}
$PrCl_3 \cdot 7H_2O$	4	3.02	2.23			[3]	$M_m = 2$, triclinic crystal
$PrCl_3$ Pr : La = 0,11	4,2	1.791	3.975			[4]	One line was observed
$PrCl_3$ Pr : La = 1 : 50	4	1.035 ±0.005	0.10 ±0.15		0.0502 ±0.0003	[8]	
Pr^{3+} in $LaAlO_3$ Pr : La = 10^{-3}	4,2	2.67 ±0,02			0.119 ±0.003	[6]	Crystal of the perovskite type

Table 4.4 (Cont'd)

Tb^{3+}

Formula	T, °K	$g_{\parallel}$	$g_{\perp}$	Δ	A	Reference	Note
$Tb(C_2H_5SO_4)_3 \cdot 9H_2O$ (cr. st. 9) $Tb : Y = 10^{-3}$	20	17.72 ±0.02	<0.3	0.387 ±0.001	0.209 ±0.002	[1, 4]	$V_6^0 = (220 \pm 30)\ cm^{-1}$, $V_2^0 = 37\ cm^{-1}$
$Tb(NO_3)_3 \cdot 6H_2O$ $Tb : La = 10^{-3}$	13	g_x, $g_y < 1$	g_z 18.0 ±0.4	0.210 ±0.007	A_z 0.212 ±0.005	[2]	
Tb^{3+} in CaF_2 $Tb : Ca = 10^{-4}$	20—10	17.8 ±0.1		0.173 ±0.001	0.209 ±0.001	[5]	HFS from F^+ was observed; even number of components; the spacing between them is on the order of 5 gauss
Tb^{3+} in $LaCl_3$ $Tb : La = 5 \cdot 10^{-3} - 2 \cdot 10^{-2}$	4	17.78 ±0.01	<0.1	0,2010	0.2120 ±0.0030	[6]	

Paramagnetic resonance was also observed in Tb^{3+} in SrS ($T = 290°$ K) [3].

Ho^{3+}

Formula	T, °K	g_z	Δ	A	B	P	Reference	Note
$Ho(C_2H_5SO_4)_3 \cdot 9H_2O$ $Ho : Y = 10^{-2}$	13	15.410 ±0.010	0,065 ±0.015	0.3340 ±0.0010	0.0200 ±0.0040	0.0003 ±0.0003	[1]	
		$g_{\parallel}$ 7.705 ±0.005 $g_{\perp}$ 3.86			0.083		[2]	$D = (-5.8 \pm 0.2)\ cm^{-1}$ a)
Ho^{3+} in $LaCl_3$ $Ho : La = 5 \cdot 10^{-3}$		$g_{\parallel}$ 16.010 ±0.018	$g_{\perp}$ ≈0	0.3510 ±0.0070			[3]	

Note: Detailed study showed that the best explanation for the experimental data can be obtained if $S = 1$ is assigned to the ground level.

Table 4.5

Mn^{2+}

Formula	T, °K	g	D	E	a	A	Reference	Note
$(NH_4)_2Mn(SO_4)_2 \cdot 6H_2O$ (cr.st.2)	290		0.0231 ±0.0002	0.006	0.0003	0.0090 ±0.0002	[1]	$\psi = +60°$, $\alpha = 30°$
Mn : Mg = 1 : 250	290		0.022_0	0.004_1		0.0095	[2]	$\psi = +59°$, $\alpha = 30{,}5°$
Mn : Zn	290	2,000 ±0.005	0.0238	0.007_5	0.0005	0.0091	[3]	
Mn : Zn = 10^{-3}	230		+0.0243 ±0.0005	0.010 ±0.002	+0.0005 ±0.0001	-0.0091_1 ±0.0001	[4]	$\psi = +58°$, $\alpha = 32°$
	195		+0.0258 ±0.0005	0.008 $\pm0.001_0$	+0.0007 ±0.0001	-0.0089_0 ±0.0001		
	90		+0.0275 ±0.0005	0.007 ±0.001	+0.0007 ±0.0001	-0.0089_9 ±0.0001		
	20		+0.0277 ±0.0005	0.005 ±0.001	+0.0008 ±0.0002	−0.0093		
$Mn_3Bi_2(NO_3)_{12} \cdot 24H_2O$ (cr.st.3)	90	I:1.99 ±0.02	−0.0211 ±0.0001	0	+0.0008 ±0.0001	−0.0090	[5]	Two different magnetic complexes
Mn : Mg = 1 : 200	20	1.997 ±0.003	−0.0215 ±0.0001	0	+0.0008 ±0.0001	−0.0090		
	90	II:1.99 ±0.02	−0.0064 ±0.0001	0	+0.0010 ±0.0001	−0.0089		
	20	1.997 ±0.003	−0.0080 ±0.0001	0	+0.0010 ±0.0001	−0.0090		
$MnSiF_6 \cdot 6H_2O$ (cr.st.4)								
Mn : Mg = 1 : 20 — 1 : 150	290		−0.0274	0.0030	+0.0007	−0.0092	[6]	$M_m = 6$
Mn : Zn	290	2,000 ±0.005	0.0171	0	0.0007_5	0.0090	[3]	
Mn : Zn = 10^{-3}	290		−0.0179 ±0.0003	0	+0.0007 ±0.0001	−0.0095	[4]	

Table 4.5 (Cont'd)

Formula	T, °K	g	D	E	a	A	Reference	Note
	195		—0.0161 ±0.0003	0	+0.0010 ±0.0002	—0.0092		
	90	2.000 ±0.001	—0.0141 ±0.0003	0	+0.0011 ±0.0002	—0.0092		
	20		—0.0134 ±0.0003	0	+0.0009 ±0.0002	—0.0091		
$MnSO_4 \cdot 7H_2O$ (cr.st.6) Mn : Mg	290	2.000 ±0.005	0.040_0	~0		0.0088	[3]	a)
$MnCO_3$ [κ14] Mn : Ca = 1 : 2000	290	2.002	0.0075	0		0.00878	[7]	$F = 0.0058$, c)
Mn^{2+} in ZnS	290	2.0016 ±0.0001	—0.0105			—0.0065	[33]	$M_m = 2$, $F = -0.00076$, hexagon.
Mn^{2+} in ZnS	290, 90, 4	2.0025 ±0.0002	0		—0.000781 ±0.000006	—0.00637 ±0.00001	[34, 35, 38, 53]	Cubic
Mn^{2+} in ZnF_2 Mn : Zn = $5 \cdot 10^{-6}$	290	2.002 ±0.005	—0.0186 ±0.0008	—0.0041 ±0.0008		—0.0096 ±0.0003	[21]	$M_m = 2$, b)
$Mn(HCOO)_2 \cdot 2H_2O$ Mn : Zn	290	1.999 $\pm 0.001_5$	0.0485 ±0.0005	0.011	0.0009_5	0.0091 ±0.0001	[10]	d)
$Mn(CH_3COO)_2 \cdot 3H_2O$ Mn : Zn	290		0.0235	0.002_5		0.0084	[3, 11]	e)
$Mn(CH_3COO)_2 \cdot 4H_2O$ Mn : Zn = 1 : 100	290	2.00 ±0.01	0.0412	0.006_3	0.0008	0.0087	[1]	f)
Mn^{2+} in NaCl Mn^{2+}: $Na^{+1} = 10^{-2}$—$4 \cdot 10^{-6}$	290	2.0011 ±0.0005				0.00829 ±0.00005	[52]	
(on slow cooling from a melt)	290	2.004					[40]	g)
(on rapid cooling from a melt)	290	2.015						

Table 4.5 (Cont'd)

Formula	T, °K	g	D	E	a	A	Reference	Note
(from an aqueous solution)	290	2.020 ±0.005						h)
the same	290	2.018						
" "	290	2.0012 ±0.0008	0.01285 ±0.00010	0.00479 ±0.00004		—0.00827 ±0.00008	[47]	o)
Mn^{2+} 0.001—0.02% by weight	290	2.010 ±0.005					[28, 29]	h)
		2.0022 ±0.0008				0.00807 ±0.00002		i)
Mn^{2+} in KCl	290	2.0041				0.00886	[30]	i)
Mn^{2+} 10^{-2} — 10^{-6} (from a melt)	290, 80	2.002					[28]	h)
Mn^{2+} in KCl, KBr, KI (from a solution)	290 80	2.0047				0.00887	[28] [52]	i)
Mn^{2+} in KBr Mn^{2+} 0.001—0.02% by weight		2.0043 ±0.0005				0.00886 ±0.00002	[29]	
Mn^{2+} in NaF $4 \cdot 10^{6}$ Mn^{2+} in 0.05 cm^3 crystal	90	I : 1.996 ±0.006 II : 2.00 ±0.01	I : 0.0089 ±0.0005 II : 0.0225 ±0.0008			I : 0.0091 ±0.0004 II : 0.0092 ±0.0004	[20]	j)
Mn^{2+} in MgO 0.001—0.1% Mn^{2+} by wt.	290 70, 4	2.0015 ±0.0001			+0.00186 ±0.00003	—0.00812 ±0.00005	[22, 23, 29]	
Mn^{2+} in CaF_2 0.04%—0.5% Mn^{2+} by weight	290	2.0013 ±0.001				0.00954 ±0.00001	[23]	
	4	2.0012 ±0.001				0.00945 ±0.00001	[23]	
Mn : Ca = 10^{-4} (from a melt)	90	1.998 ±0.003			+0.00006 ±0.00004	—0.00978 ±0.00010	[48]	m)
Mn^{2+} in ZnO Mn : Zn = 10^{-3}	77	2.0016 ±0.0006	—0.02169 ±0.00022		—0.00020 ±0.00005	—0.00760 ±0.00004	[49]	Hexagon.
Mn^{2+} in CdS Mn : Cd = 10^{-3}	300	2.0029 ±0.0006	+0.00082 ±0.00022		—0.00014 ±0.00005	—0.00653 ±0.00004	[49]	Hexagon., n)

Table 4.5 (Cont'd)

Formula	T, °K	g	D	E	a	A	Reference	Note
Mn^{2+} in AgCl Mn : Ag = 10^{-4} — 10^{-2} (from a melt)	290 290	I: 2.006 ±0.003 II: 2.000 +0.003				I: 0.0081 ±0.0004	[18]	k)
Mn^{2+} in AgBr Mn : Ag = 10^{-4} — 10^{-2} (from a melt)	290	—2.006 ±0.010				0.0077 ±0.0004	[18]	
Mn^{2+} in Ge	77 1.5	2.0061 ±0.0002			+0.00088 ±0.00005	—0.00425 ±0.00003	[19]	
$MnCl_2$ (powder) Mn : Sr = 1 : 1000	20	2.00				^{53}A = 0.00907 ^{55}A = 0.00871	[32]	l)
Mn^{2+} in phosphors 0.1—0.005% Mn^{2+} (powders)	290							
$KMgF_3$		2.004 ±0.0025				0.00918	[37]	
CaF_2		2.004 ±0.0025				0.00922	[37, 50]	
$CsCaF_3$		2.004 ±0.0025				0.00908	[37]	
CaO		2.004 ±0.0025				0.00849	[37, 50]	
$MgAl_2O_4$, $4MgO \cdot 3Al_2O_3$, $6MgO \cdot As_2O_5$		1.999 2.004 ±0.0025				0.00877 0.00811	[37]	
CdS		2.006 ±0.0025				0.00607	[37, 50]	
CdTe		2.002 2.008 ±0.0025				0.00648 0.00551	[37, 50]	
$ZnO \cdot Al_2O_3$		2.004 ±0.0025				0.00756	[37]	

ZnS		2.004 ±0.0025				0.00644 0.00638	[37] [9, 25, 50]	
MnS (powder)	290	2.001 2.0024 ±0.0004	0.002			0.0063	[8, 37]	Hexagon.
Mn : Zn = 10^{-3} — 10^{-5}	290		0.001			0.0065		
Mn^{2+} in NaBr (from a melt)	290	2.07 ±0.01				±0.0001	[9]	
Mn^{2+} in $SrCl_2$ (powder)	20	2				$^{55}A = 0.00974$	[52]	
Mn : Sr = 10^{-3}						$^{53}A = 0.00910$	[54]	
Mn^{2+} in SrS — SrSe (powder)	290	2.00				$A_1 = 0.0089$ $A_2 = 0.0086$	[55]	Two types of spectra apparently depending on the surroundings of S or Se
Mn^{2+} in $CdCl_2$	290, 90, 20	2.00	0.0015 ±0.0005			0.0082 ±0.0005	[56]	Trigonal distortion of the cubic field
Mn^{2+} in LiCl (from a melt)		2.003 ±0.001				0.0076 ±0.0005	[57]	
Mn—Au couples in Si	20	$g_{\parallel}$ 2.0	$g_{\perp}$ 4.0			$A = 0.0060$ $B = 0.0096$	[51]	$P = 0.00009$, p)

Paramagnetic resonance was also observed at room temperature in: a) phosphors containing small concentrations of Mn^{2+}: $ZnAl_2O_4$ ($g \approx 2.0$, $A = 0.00765$) [9]; MgO ($g = 2.001$, $A = 0.00812$; 0.0072) [9, 50]; $CdSiO_3$ ($g \approx 2.0$) [9]; Mg_2GeO_4 ($g \approx 2.0$) [9]; ZnF_2 ($g \approx 2.0$) [9]; ZnS Tb ($g \approx 2.0$) [9]; Zn_2SiO_4 ($g \approx 2.0$) [9]; $8ZnO \cdot BeO \cdot 5SiO_2$ ($g \approx 2.0$) [9]; Zn_2GeO_4 ($g \approx 2.0$) [9]; $Zn_3(PO_4)_2$ ($g \approx 2.0$) [9]; MgF_2 ($g = 2.001$, $A = 0.00906$) [50]; CdF_2 ($g = 2.001$, $A = 0.00906$) [50]; SrF_2 ($g = 2.002$, $A = 0.0093$) [50]; **BaF_2** ($g = 2.004$, $A = 0.0091$) [50]; CdO ($g = 2.001$, $A = 0.00873$) [50]; MgS ($g = 2.001$, $A = 0.00719$) [50]; CaS ($g = 2.001$, $A = 0.00757$) [50]; SrS ($g = 2.000$, $A = 0.00750$) [50]; MgSe ($g = 2.004$, $A = 0.00712$) [50]; CaSe ($g = 2.004$, $A = 0.00729$) [50]; CaTl ($g = 2.003$, $A = 0.00672$] [50]; ZnO ($A = 0.0079$) [50]; CdSe ($g = 2.003$, $A = 0.00615$) [50]; CdTl ($g = 2.013$, $A = 0.00581$) [50]; ZnSe ($g = 2.01$, $A = 0.0060$) [50]; ZnTl ($A = 0.0056$) [50]; **b) undiluted compounds:** $Mn(BO_2)_2$ ($g = 2.01$) [12]; MnB_4O_7 [42]; $Mn(CH_3COO)_2 \cdot 2H_2O$ ($g = 2.00$) [13]; $Mn(C_3H_5O_3)_2 \cdot 3H_2O$ [14]; $Mn(C_6H_4)_4(CN)_8$ ($g = 2.0$, T to 20° K) [15]; $Mn(C_{15}H_{31}COO)_2$ ($g = 2.00$) [16]; $Mn(C_{17}H_{35}COO)_2$ ($g = 2.00$) [16]; **$MnCO_3$** ($g = 2.00$) [12, 36, 42, 47]; $MnC_2O_4 \cdot 2H_2O$ ($g = 2.00$) [16]; $MnCl_2$ [42, 45]; $MnCl_2 \cdot 2H_2O$ [45]; $MnCl_2 \cdot 4H_2O$ ($g = 2.00$; 2.09) [12, 13, 26, 31, 42, 45]; MnF_2 [14, 42]; $Mn(H_2PO_2)_2 \cdot H_2O$ [14, 42]; $MnK_2(SO_4)_2 \cdot 6H_2O$ [14]; $Mn(NH_4)_2(SO_4)_2 \cdot 6H_2O$ [24]; $Mn(NO_3)_2 \cdot 6H_2O$ [24, 44]; MnS ($g = 2.0$) [42]; $MnSO_4$ ($g = 2.00$) [13, 17, 42, 45, 46]; $MnSO_4 \cdot H_2O$ ($g = 2.00$) [13, 17, 42, 45, 46]; $MnSO_4 \cdot 4H_2O$ ($g = 2.00$—2.07) [17, 25, 42, 45, 46]; $MnSO_4 \cdot 5H_2O$ ($g = 2.06$) [17, 45, 46]; $Mn_2Fe(CN)_6 \cdot 7H_2O$ [14]; $Mn_2(P_2O_7) \cdot 3H_2O$ [14, 42]; $Mn_3(AsO_4)_2$ [14]; $Mn_3(C_6H_5O_7)_2$ [14]; $Mn_3(PO_4)_2 \cdot 3H_2O$ [42]; $Mn_3(PO_4)_2 \cdot 7H_2O$ [14]; $MnCl_2 \cdot 4H_2O$ ($T = 1.6$—2.3° K) [31].

In addition, a study has been made of the Mn^{2+} absorption line in paramagnetic Tutton salts $M(NH_4)_2(SO_4)_2\,6H_2O$ ($M = Ni^{2+}, Co^{2+}, Fe^{2+}, Cu^{2+}$), and also in $CuSO_4 \cdot 5H_2O$ [44]). The intermetallic compound $MnAu_2$ (polycrystal) has been studied; at $T > 90°$ C $g \approx 2.0$; below 90° C, $MnAu_2$ is antiferromagnetic [43]. Finally, the paramagnetic resonance of Mn^{2+} was measured in amorphous phthalocyanine ($g = 2.0$) [41].

Notes:

a) The directional cosines of the Z axis (0.282, ± 0.952, 0.122).

b) Zn in ZnF_2 is surrounded by a distorted octahedron of six F ions, four of which (type I) form a rectangle with sides 2.59 and 3.13 A; the two other F (type II) lie on a perpendicular to the plane of the rectangle at a distance of 2.04 A. The Z axis is chosen along the long side of the rectangle (c axis); the X axis passes through the type II F ion and is parallel to the short side of the rectangle. Hyperfine structure due to F nuclei is observed:

$$A_y^{I} = (16.5 \pm 0.7) \cdot 10^{-4}\text{cm}^{-1}, \quad A_y^{II} = (14.6 \pm 1.2) \cdot 10^{-4}\text{cm}^{-1},$$
$$A_z^{I} = (18.2 \pm 0.2) \cdot 10^{-4}\text{cm}^{-1}, \quad A_z^{II} = (12.5 \pm 0.2) \cdot 10^{-4}\text{cm}^{-1}.$$

c) Calcite $CaCo_3$, M = 2. The nearest neighbors of Ca are six O with trigonal symmetry. The magnetic complexes with Mn are equivalent. The structure of the crystal is hexagonal.

d) $M_m = 2$, $\psi = +97°$, $\alpha = 62°$, monoclinic structure.

e) $M_m = 1$, Z ≡ c, X ≡ c, X ≡ b, monoclinic structure.

f) $M_m = 2$, $\psi = +47°$, $\alpha = 29°$.

g) If the sample obtained from the melt is heated and maintained for some time at the temperature T, and then quickly cooled to room temperature: 1) if $T < 300$ °C, the resonance curves do not change; 2) if the temperature $T > 500$ °C, curve I changes into II. At intermediate temperatures a superposition of curves I and II is observed. There probably exist two different states of Mn^{2+} in NaCl, one of which is stable above 500° C, and the other below it. The first exists in rapidly cooled samples, the second in slowly cooled ones.

h) Lines without structure.

i) A line with Mn^{55} hyperfine structure.

j) There exist two types of centers, each composed of three nonequivalent magnetic ions. Because of the complexity of the spectrum, D, g, A are determined only along the axes of the crystalline field. The intensity of the second spectrum is 1/100 as strong as the first. Each of the Mn hyperfine structure lines has a resolved structure caused by interaction with the F nuclei. The constants of this interaction are: $A_s = 0.00144 \pm 0.00003$, $A_p = 0.00028 \pm 0.00007$. The intensity of the Mn^{2+} spectrum decreases greatly after irradiation.

k) Spectrum I of six peaks corresponds to an isolated Mn^{2+} ion. Spectrum II consisting of a single peak is observed only in samples with a higher concentration of Mn^{2+}, and probably is caused by aggregates of Mn^{2+} ions.

l) $\mu^{53}/\mu^{55} = 1.455 \pm 0.002$.

m) $a = (+0.6 \pm 0.4)\ 10^{-4}$ cm^{-1}, $A_s = (9.5 \pm 0.3)\ 10^{-4}$ cm^{-1}, $A_p = (2.7 \pm$ $\pm\, 0.5)\ 10^{-4}$ cm^{-1}. A_s, A_p are constants of the hyperfine structure, due to the interaction of the spin of the F nucleus with the s and p_σ orbitals, respectively.

n) In addition to the ordinary hyperfine structure, we also observed hyperfine structure due to magnetic interaction of the Mn^{2+} electrons with the neighboring Cd nuclei.

o) Spectrum due to the complex Mn^{2+} - Na vacancy; Z axis is directed along the bond Mn^{2+}- Na^+ vacancy; y axis is parallel to the cubic axis. The complexes are unstable.

p) At 20° K each Mn^{2+} line is split by the interaction with the Au nuclei; the quadrupole interaction with Au is assumed to be stronger than the magnetic interaction.

Table 4.5 (Cont'd)

Fe^{3+}

Formula	T, °K	g	D	a	F	Reference	Note
$KFe(SeO_4)_2 \cdot 12H_2O$ (cr. st. 1)	90	2.003 ±0.003	−0.0103 ±0.0001	−0.0127 ±0.0002	−0.0002 ±0.0002	[1]	$\varphi = (10.5 \pm 0.5)°$
Al : Fe = 1 : 300	20	2.003 ±0.001	−0.0115 ±0.0001	−0.0127 ±0.0001	−0.0002 ±0.0001		
$(NH_3CH_3)Fe(SO_4)_2 \cdot 12H_2O$ (cr. st. 1) Fe : Al = 1 : 200	90		(−)0.188 ±0.014	(−)0.010 ±0.004		[1]	
$NH_4Fe(SO_4)_2 \cdot 12H_2O$ Fe : Al = 1 : 80	4		0.016 ±0.001	(−)0.0128 ±0.0004		[23]	
$RbFe(SO_4)_2 \cdot 12H_2O$ (cr. st. 1)	90	2.003 ±0.003	+0.0022 ±0.0002	−0.0134 ±0.0002	−0.0003 ±0.0002	[1]	$\varphi = (7.5 \pm 0.5)°$
Fe : Al = 1 : 300	20	2.003 ±0.001	+0.0031 ±0.0001	−0.0134 ±0.0001	−0.00033 ±0.0001		
Fe^{3+} in $Al_2Be_3(SiO_3)_6$	290	2.00	0.01658	0.01445	0.00045	[15]	$\delta_1 = 0.058$ cm^{-1}, $\delta_2 = 0.050_5$ cm^{-1}.
Fe^{3+} in MgO	290	2.0037 ±0.0007		+0.0205		[16]	
Fe^{3+} in $SrTiO_3$ $Fe^{3+} : Ti^{4+} = 10^{-4}$	290	2.004 ±0.001	0	0.0198 ±0.0010		[11, 17]	b)
	77		0.00077 ±0.00003	0.02201 ±0.0011			
Fe^{3+} in Si (enriched and not enriched)	10	2.0699		+0.00373		[19, 21]	$A^{57} = 7.0 \cdot 10^{-4}$ cm^{-1}, d)
$Fe[(CH_3CO)_2CH]_3$ Fe : Co = 10^{-2}	290		0.07			[10]	c)
Fe^{3+} in $MgWO_4$ [κ18]	78	2.0	−0.687			[23]	$E = +0.174$ cm^{-1}, e)
Fe^{3+} in Al_2O_3 Fe : Al = 10^{-3}	290	2.003 ±0.001	+0.1679 ±0.0001	0.0241 ±0.0004	+0.0329 ±0.0002	[12, 22]	a)

Table 4.5 (Cont'd)

Formula	T, °K	g	D	a	F	Reference	Note
	77	2.003 ±0.001	+0.1716 ±0.0001	0.0236 ±0.0004	+0.0337 ±0.0002		
	4.2	2.003 ±0.001	+0.1719 ±0.0001	0.0224 ±0.0004	+0.0339 ±0.0002		
Fe^{3+} in $BaTiO_3$ Fe : Ti $= 10^{-4} - 4 \cdot 10^{-4}$	290	2.00	~0.0830	0.0094		[20]	

Paramagnetic resonance was also observed at room temperature in $Fe[CH_3CF_3(CO)_2CH]_3$ (Fe : Al) [10]; $Fe(C_5H_7O_2)_3$ ($g \approx 1.95$) [4]; $Fe(C_7H_5O_2)_3$ [5]; $Fe(C_{17}H_{35}COO)_3$ ($g \sim 2.00$) [6]; $FeCl(C_6H_4)_4(CN)_8$ ($T = 270 - 20°$ K, $g = 3.8$; 2.0) [7]; $FeCl_3$ [5]; $FeF_3 \cdot 4.5 \cdot H_2O$ [13]; $FeK(SO_4)_2 \cdot 12H_2O$ (Fe : Al $= 1 : 385$, $\delta = 0.03\,cm^{-1}$) [14]; $FeNH_4(SO_4)_2 \cdot 12H_2O$ ($g = 2$, $\delta = 0.032\ cm^{-1}$) [14]; $Fe(NH_4)(SO_4)_2 \cdot 12H_2O$ ($g = 1.97$) [13]; $Fe(NH_4)_3(C_6H_5O_7)_2 \cdot 24H_2O$ ($g \approx 1.98$) [4]; $Fe_4[Fe(CN)_6]_3$ [5]; $FeOH(C_2H_3O_2)_2$ (5); $FePO_4 \cdot 4H_2O$ [5]; $(FeF_3)_2 \cdot 9H_2O$ ($g = 2.02$) [4]; $Fe_2(SO_4)_3 \cdot 3H_2O$ ($g \approx 2.01$) [8]; $Fe_2(C_2O_4)_3$ [5]; $Fe_2(SO_4)_3 \cdot 9H_2O$ ($g \approx 2.01$) [4]; $Fe_3(CH_3COO)_6(OH)_2NO_3 \cdot 6H_2O$ ($T = 15°$ K, $g = 2.0$) [9]; $Fe_2[C_3H_5(OH)_2OPO_3]_3$ [5]; Fe^{3+} in $3Y_2O_3 \cdot 5Ga_2O_3$ [24].

Notes:

a) $M_m = 2$; the nonequivalence results from the difference in the directions of the axes of the cubic field.

b) Below the transition point (about 100°K) a single crystal consists of tetragonal domains.

c) $M_m = 2$, orthorhombic crystal. Dilution with Al yielded a similar but not identical spectrum. Thus, the crystal field acting on Fe^{3+} may change from diluent to diluent.

d) Isotropic line.

e) The Y axis is parallel to the b axis; the Z axis lies on the ac plane and forms a 41.5° angle with the a axis. The signs of D and E were determined from a comparison of intensities at 2 and 4°K.

Table 4.5 (Cont'd)

Gd^{3+}

Formula	T, °K	g	b_2^0	b_2^2	b_4^0	b_6^0	b_6^6	Reference	Note
$Mg_3Gd_2(NO_3)_{12} \cdot 24H_2O$ (cr. st. 3) Gd : Bi = 1 : 5000	290, 77	1.991						[15]	$^{155}A = (3.7 \pm 0.3) \times 10^{-4}$ cm^{-1}, $^{157}A = (4.95 \pm 0.16) \times 10^{-4}$ cm^{-1}
Gd : Bi = 10^{-2}	90, 20	1.992 ±0.003	0.0124 ±0.0001		+0.00009 ±0.00001	+0.00006 ±0.00001	+0.0012 ±0.0001	[1]	
$Gd(C_2H_5SO_4)_3 \cdot 9H_2O$ (cr. st. 9)	90	1.990 ±0.002	+0.0204$_7$ ±0.0002		−0.00039$_6$ ±0.00003	+0.00006$_3$ ±0.00001	+0.00035 ±0.00005	[2]	
Gd : La = 1 : 200 $Gd_2(SO_4)_3 \cdot 8H_2O$ [k 16]	20	1.990 ±0.002	+0.0199$_8$ ±0.0001		−0.000391 ±0.000015	+0.000053 ±0.000005	+0.00040 ±0.00005	[13]	
Gd : Sm = 1 : 200	300		(+)0.0633 ±0.0005	(+)0.038 ±0.005	(−)0.0013 ±0.0003			[12] [3]	a, b)
Gd Cl_3 [k 15]	290	1.991 ±0.001	+0.000836 ±0.000010		+0.000168 ±0.000004	+0.000064 ±0.000015		[7]	c)
Gd : (La, Ce) = 10^{-4}	90	1.991 ±0.001	+0.001600 ±0.000002		+0.000213 ±0.000005	+0.000025 ±0.000005	+0.000140 ±0.00003	[7]	d)
Gd : La = $5 \cdot 10^{-2}$	4	1.991 ±0.001						[21]	$^{155}A = (3.8 \pm 0.2) \times 10^{-4}$ cm^{-1}, $^{157}A = (5.0 \pm 0.2) \times 10^{-4}$ cm^{-1}
$GdCl_3 \cdot 7H_2O$ Gd : La	290	g_x 1.998 ±0.003 g_y 2.000 ±0.003	+0.01313 ±0.00005	−0.00752 ±0.00020	+0.0002 ±0.0001			[19]	

Table 4.5 (Cont'd)

Formula	T, °K	g	b_2^0	b_2^2	b_4^0	b_6^0	b_6^6	Reference	Note
$GdCl_3 \cdot 7D_2O$ Gd : La $= 2 \cdot 10^{-4}$	99—77 290 77	g_z 1.989 ±0.003 1.99	+0.0099 ±0.0030	—0.0115 ±0.0007				[15]	$\frac{\mu^{155}}{\mu^{157}} = 0.75 \pm 0.07$ $^{157}A = (5{,}3 \pm 0{,}3) \times 10^{-4}$ cm^{-1}
Gd^{3+} in LaF_3 Gd : La $= 10^{-4}$	90	1.990 ±0.001	+0.0239 ±0.0001	—0.0005 ±0.0002	—0.00056 ±0.00002	+0.000014 ±0.000020		[22]	f)

Formula	T, °K	g	ΔE, e)	Reference	Note
Gd in ThO_2 Gd : Th $= 10^{-5}$	290	1.9913 ±0.0005	0.1755 ±0.0003	[16]	$c = (219.9 \pm 0.3) \cdot 10^{-4}$ cm^{-1}, $d = (1.0 \pm 0.3) \cdot 10^{-4}$ cm^{-1},
	90	1,991 ±0.001	0.1796 ±0.0008	[16]	$c = (225.0 \pm 0.8) \cdot 10^{-4}$ cm^{-1}, $d = (1.7 \pm 0.8) \cdot 10^{-4}$ cm^{-1}, $M_m = 1$, $\frac{\mu^{155}}{\mu^{157}} = 0.744 \pm 0.007$
Gd^{3+} in CaF_2	290. 4	1.9918 ±0.0010	0.1491 ±0.0008	[8, 9, 10, 14]	$M_m = 3$ The principal axes of the tetragonal field are parallel to the edges of the cube,
	90		~2.1	[20]	$a = +0.0175$

Paramagnetic resonance was also observed in: Gd^{3+} in $LaAlO_3$ ($T = 4.2$; 295; 195; 83° K, structureless line with $g = 1.992 \pm 0.002$, six peaks of fine structure with $g = 1.55 - 2.7$) [18]; $Gd(NO_3)_3 \cdot 6H_2O$ (Gd : La $= 10^{-1}$) [4]; $GdCl_3 \cdot 6H_2O$ [6]; $Gd(BrO_3)_3 \cdot 9H_2O$ [5]; Gd^{3+} in SrS ($T = 290°$ K, Gd : Sr $= 10^{-4}$, $\frac{\mu^{155}}{\mu^{157}} = 0.73 \pm 0.03$) [11, 17].

Notes: a) The magnitude of b_2^0 may not be accurate (see Bowers, K. D. and J. Owen. Rep. Progr. Phys. 18, 304, 1955). b) Monoclinic. $M = 8$; $M_m = 2$. The axes are given by the angles $\psi_z = 28^\circ$, $\alpha_z = \pm 35^\circ$, $\psi_y = 0^\circ$, $\alpha_y = \pm 52^\circ$, where ψ_i is the angle between c and the plane containing the Z axis; α_i is the angle between the i-th axis and the ac plane $(i = z, y)$. c) Hexagonal. The crystal field in Gd has a C_{3h} symmetry. d) The sign of the coefficients b_n^m was determined from measurements of the relative intensities in parallel fields at 20°K. e) $\Delta E = 8c - 2d$ is the total splitting in the cubic field. f) $M_m = 3$. The ion is acted on by a rhombic crystal field; $b_4^2 = 60B_4^2 = +0.0027 \pm 0.0003$; $b_4^4 = 60B_4^4 = -0.0043 \pm 0.0003$; $b_6^2 + b_6^6 = 1260\,(B_6^2 + B_6^6) = +0.00085 \pm 0.00030$; $b_6^4 = 1260\,B_6^4 = -0.0001 \pm 0.0005$.

Table 4.5 (Cont'd)

Eu^{2+}

Formula	T, °K	g	ΔE	Isotope	A	Reference	Note
Eu^{2+} in CaF_2	290	1.971 ±0.001		151	0.00346 ±0.00001	[4]	Magnetic moments Eu^{151} and Eu^{153} have the same sign
				153	0.00154 ±0.00001		
	290	1.9927 ±0.0010	0.1784 ±0.0009	151	0.00303 ±0.00001	[2, 3, 5, 6, 9]	$R = 0.612 \pm 0.003$ $\frac{\mu^{151}}{\mu^{153}} = 2.26 \pm 0.02$
				153	0.00151 ±0.00001		
(natural) (from a melt) Eu : Ca = 10^{-4}	290 90	1.993 1.989 ±0.002	0.1810 ±0.0050	151	0.00345 ±0.00002	[12] [11, 14]	$a = 0.0186$ cm^{-1} $b_4^0 = (57.9 \pm 0.2) \cdot 10^{-4}$ cm^{-1} $b_6^0 = (0.5 \pm 0.2) \cdot 10^{-4}$ cm^{-1}
				153	0.00153 ±0.00004		
Eu^{2+} in $SrCl_2$	290	1.995 ±0.005		151	0.00322 ±0.00003	[7]	
				153	0.00144 ±0.00003		

Table 4.5 (Cont'd)

Formula	T, °K	g	ΔE	Isotope	A	Reference	Note
Eu^{2+} in SrS (powder) Eu : Sr ~ 10^{-4}	290	1.992 ±0.001		151 153 152	0.00300 ±0.00001 0.00134 ±0.00001 0.00139 ±0.00001	[1, 4, 13]	$\frac{\mu^{151}}{\mu^{153}} = 2.24 \pm 0.03$
	90—20	2.0	0.18			[8, 9]	
Eu^{2+} in SrS — SrSe	90—20	2.0	0.18			[8]	

Paramagnetic resonance observed in Eu^{2+} in KCl $\left(\frac{\mu^{154}}{\mu^{153}} = 1.308 \pm 0.004,\ \frac{\mu^{152}}{\mu^{151}} = 0.5574 \pm 0.006,\ \frac{\mu^{151}}{\mu^{153}} = 2.264 \pm 0.006,\ T = 77^\circ K,\ g = 2,\ {}^{151}A = (32.56 \pm 0.06) \cdot 10^{-4}\ cm^{-1}\ {}^{152}A = (15.12 \pm 0.15) \cdot 10^{-4}\ cm^{-1},\ {}^{153}A = (14.38 \pm 0.03) \cdot 10^{-4}\ cm^{-1},\ {}^{154}A = (15.67 \pm 0.06) \cdot 10^{-4} cm^{-1}\right)$ [9].

Cm^{3+}

Formula	T, °K	g	b_2^0	Reference	Note
Cm^{3+} in $LaCl_3$ Cm : La = 1 : 2000	290, 77	1.9914 ±0.0008	0.00076 ±0.00002	[1, 2]	$(b_6^6 - 5b_6^0) \geq 0.00034 \pm 0.00005$
$Mg_2Cm_2(NO_3)_{12} \cdot 24H_2O$ Cm : Bi	290	2.003	0.00020 ±0.00002	[1]	$b_4^0 = 0.00020 \pm 0.00002$

Paramagnetic resonance observed in Cm^{3+}, in ThO_2 and $CaCl_2$ [1].

Table 4.6

Fe^{III}

Formula	T, °K	g			Reference	Note
$K_3[Fe(CN)_6]$ (cr. st. 7)	20	g_a 2.30 ±0.03	g_b 2.18 ±0.03	g_c 0.94 ±0.03	[1]	Direction cosines of the axes a b c Z 0 0 1 X ±0.866 0.500 0 Y ±0.500 0.866 0
Fe : Co = 10^{-2}	20	2.35 ±0.02	2.10 ±0.02	0.91_5 ±0.01	[2]	
Fe^{III} in myoglobin single crystals obtained from whale muscle	20	g_1 6	g_2 2.00 ±0.01	g_3 6.00 ±0.05	[3]	$\Delta > 2\ cm^{-1}$
Fe^{III} in hemoglobin single crystals	20	$g_\parallel$ 2.00 ±0.01	$g_\perp$ 5.95 ±0.05		[4]	$\Delta > 2\ cm^{-1}$
$ClFe(C_6H_4)_4(CN)_8$	290—20	3.8			[5]	
Fe^{III} in ferrimyoglobin and ferrihemoglobin azides	290, 20	g_x 1.72	g_y 2.22	g_z 2.80	[4—6]	The Z axis is normal to the hemin plane
in borax pearl	77	4			[7]	The distance between the peaks of hyperfine structures due to the Fe nucleus is~10 gauss
in polycrystalline hemin		$g_\parallel$ 6.0			[5]	
in acid metaferrihemoglobin in acid metaferrimyoglobin in ferrihemoglobin fluoride in ferrimyoglobin fluoride		$g_\parallel$ 5.90 ±0.05			[5]	The line is asymmetric

Table 4.6 (Cont'd)

Formula	T, °K	g			Reference	Note
$K_4[Mn(CN)_6] \cdot 3H_2O$ (cr. st. 7) $Mn : Fe = 10^{-2}$	12	g_x 2.624 ±0.008 A_x 0.00845 ±0.00005	g_y 2.182 ±0.008 A_y 0.00465 ±0.00005	g_z 0.72 ±0.05 A_z 0.0083 ±0.0013	[1]	*a* *b* *c* Z 0.295 ±0.899 —0.322 X 0.864 ±0.105 —0.495 Y 0.410 ±0.423 —0.807

Mo^{V}, Mo^{III}, Tc^{IV}

Formula	T, °K	$g_{\parallel}$	$g_{\perp}$	A	B	Reference	Note
Mo^{V} **in the form of an impurity in** $K_3[InCl_6] \cdot 2H_2O$ $Mo : In = 10^{-2}$	290, 20	I: 1.951 ±0.005 II: 1.959 ±0.004	1.939 ±0.006 1.939 ±0.006	0.0079 ±0.0002 0.0077 ±0.0002	0.00385 ±0.0002 0.00385 ±0.0002	[1]	Two magnetically nonequivalent complexes in a unit cell; hyperfine structure due to Cl nuclei was observed.
$K_3[Mo(CN)_8]$ **(powder)**	290, 20	g: 2.005 ±0.005				[2]	
$K_2[MoCl_6] \cdot 2H_2O$ $Mo^{III} : In = 1 : 200$	90, 20	g I: 1.93 ±0.06 II: 1,93 ±0.06	$D \gg 1$ $\frac{E}{D} = 0.08$ $D \gg 1$ $\frac{E}{D} = 0.15$	A_z 0.0039 ±0.0005 0.0039 ±0.0005		[1]	Several magnetically nonequivalent complexes in a unit cell; only two were measured
K_2MoCl_5 **(powder)**	290	1.76				[2]	
$K_3MoCl_5 \cdot H_2O$ **(powder)**	290—20	1.96				[3]	
$KMoF_4$ **(powder)**	14	1.95				[3]	
Tc^{4+} **in** K_2PtCl_6 (cr. st. 8) $Tc : Pt = 10^{-4}$	4.2	1.9896 ±0.0005		A_{max} 0.01378 ±0.00004	A_{min} 0.01334 ±0.00004	[1]	

Table 4.6 (Cont'd)

Ru^{III}

Formula	T, °K	g_x	g_y	g_z	A_x	A_y	A_z	Reference	Note
$[Ru(NH_3)_6]Cl_3$ Ru : Co = 1 : 200	20	I: 2.06	2.02	1.72	0.0048	0.0048	0.0049	[1—3]	a)
		±0.01	±0.01	±0.01	±0.0002	±0.0002	±0.0002		
		II: 1.80	1.90	2.06	0.0048	0.0048	0.0050		
		±0.01	±0.01	±0.01	±0.0002	±0.0002	±0.0002		
		III: 1.15	1.84	2.66	0.0045	0.0041	0.0054		$\frac{^{101}A}{^{99}A} = 1.09 \pm 0.03$
		±0.01	±0.01	±0.01	±0.0002	±0.0002	±0.0002		
$K_3[RuCl_6] \cdot 2H_2O$	20	1.0	1.22	3.24				[4]	
Ru : In = 10^{-2}		±0.01	±0.02	±0.02					
$[Ru(NH_3)_6]Cl_3$	20	2.21	2.05	1.5				[1]	
3HgCl				±0.1					

Paramagnetic resonance has been observed in undiluted crystals of $[Ru(NH_3)_6]Cl_3$, $[Ru(NH_3)_5Cl]Cl_2$ at $T = 20°$ K [1].

Note: a) Three pairs of magnetically nonequivalent complexes of type I, II, III in a unit cell. The *ac* plane is a mirror-symmetry plane for the ions of each pair.

Table 4.6 (Cont'd)

Ag^{II}, Re^{IV}

Formula	T, °K	$g_{\parallel}$	$g_{\perp}$	Reference	Note
$Ag(C_5H_5N)_4S_2O_8$ (powder)	297, 20	2.18	2.04	[1]	
Ag : Cd = 1 : 20 (powder)	4.2	g=2.06		[1]	
Silver di-o-phenanthroline persulfate	290, 90, 20	2.18	2.04	[2]	
$K_2[ReCl_6]$ (cr. st. 8) Re : Pt = 1 : 200	90, 20	g=1.8		[1]	Six lines are observed (possibly hyperfine structure from Re^{185}, Re^{187})

Ir^{IV}

Formula	T, °K	g	HFS of Ir	HFS of Cl or Br	Reference	Note
$K_2[IrBr_6]$ (cr. st. 8) Ir : Pt = 1 : 200	20	$g_{\parallel}$ 1.60 ±0.10; $g_{\perp}$ 1.87 ±0.04			[1]	M_m = 3; the axes of the nonequivalent complexes are parallel to the edges of the unit cubic cell.
$K_2[IrCl_6]$ (cr. st. 8) Ir : Pt = 1 : 200	20	$g_x = g_y = g_z$ 1.78 ±0.02			[2]	All complexes are equivalent

Table 4.6 (Cont'd)

Formula	T, °K	g	HFS of Ir	HFS of Cl or Br	Reference	Note
$(NH_4)_2[IrCl_6]$ (cr. st. 8) Ir : Pt = 1 : 200	20	$g_x = g_y = g_z$ 1.775 ±0.001	$A_x = A_y = A_z$ 0.00265 ±0.00010	$A'_1 = A'_2 = A'_3$ 0.00088 ±0.00004	[1]	All the complexes are equivalent; the X, Y and Z axes are parallel to the edges of the cubic unit cell and to the axes of the Cl_6 octahedron. The value of A' is for Cl^{35}.
$Na_2[IrBr_6] \cdot 6H_2O$ (cr. st. 8) Ir : Pt = 1 : 200	20	g_x 2.25 ±0.02	$A_x = A_y$ 0.00255 ±0.00010	$A'_1 = A'_2$ 0.0057 ±0.0002	[1]	All the complexes are equivalent; the X, Y and Z axes are parallel to axes of the Br_6 octahedron. The value of A' is for Br^{81}.
		g_y 2.21 ±0.02				
		g_z 0.75 ±0.10				
$Na_2[IrCl_6] \cdot 6H_2O$ (cr. st. 8)	20	g_x 2.20 ±0.02	A_x 0.00255 ±0.00010	A'_1 0.00116 ±0.00004	[1]	All the complexes are equivalent; the X, Y and Z axes are parallel to axes of the Cl_6 octahedron. The value of A' is for Cl^{35}.
Ir : Pt = 1 : 200		g_y 2.07 ±0.02	A_y 0.00255 ±0.00010	A'_2 0.00107 ±0.00004		
		g_z 1.05 ±0.02	A_z 0.0024 ±0.0001	$A'_3 < 0.0005$		

Paramagnetic resonance observed in $(NH_4)_2IrCl_6$ at $T = 20 - 2°$ K and dilution Ir : Pt = 1 : 10, 1 : 100 [3].

Table 4.6 (Cont'd)

U^{III}

Formula	T, °K	$g_{\parallel}$	$g_{\perp}$	A	B	P	Reference	Note
U^{III} in CaF_2 $U:Ca = 10^{-3}$	20	3.501 ±0.008	1.866 ±0.002				[1]	a) ; $M_m = 3$; the ions are acted on by the axial field; the crystal axes of the nonequivalent ions are directed along the edges of the cube
U^{III} in SrF_2 $U:Sr = 10^{-2}$	20	3.433 ±0.008	1.971 ±0.002					
U^{III} in BaF_2 $U:Ba = 10^{-4}$	20—10	3.337 ±0.002	2.115 ±0.001				[6]	
UCl_3				A^{235}	B^{235}	P^{235}	[2, 3]	
$U:La = 10^{-3}$ (enriched in U^{235})	20, 4	4.153 ±0.005	1.520 ±0.002	0.0176 ±0.001	0.00575 ±0.00005	0.00055 ±0.00005		
$U:Nd$	20, 4	3.991	1.769	A^{233}	B^{233}	P^{233}	[3]	
$U^{233}:La = 10^{-5}$ (enriched sample)	4, 2	4.149	1.520	0.03786 ±0.00012	0.01236 ±0.00010	0.00099 ±0.00010	[4]	
UF_3 (powder)	290, 90	2.8—2.9	2.1—2.2				[5]	
UF_4 (powder)	290	$g = 2.1_5$					[5]	

Note: a) A complex hyperfine structure due to F^- nuclei was observed in CaF_2, SrF_2. In some directions it was clearly resolved into an even number of components.

Table 4.6 (Cont'd)

NpO_2^{II}, PuO_2^{II}

Formula	T, °K	$g_{\parallel}$	$g_{\perp}$	A	B	P	Reference	Note
$(NpO_2)Rb(NO_3)_3$ (cr. st. 10) $NpO_2 : UO_2$	20—12, 4.3	3.40 ±0.01	0.20_5 ±0.02	A^{237} $(+)0.1654_5$ ±0.0002	B^{237} 0.0178_2 ±0.0002	P^{237} $(-)0.0301_5$ ±0.0003	[1—3]	The relative signs of A and P are determined directly
$(PuO_2)Rb(NO_3)_3$ (cr. st. 10) $PuO_2 : UO_2 = 1:17—1:200$	20—12	5.32 ±0.02	$\leqslant 0.4$	^{239}A 0.0862 ±0.0005	^{241}A 0.0609 ±0.0004		[1]	Δ small; $\frac{^{241}A}{^{239}A} = 0.706 \pm 0.004$
$Na(PuO_2)(CH_3COO)_3$ [к17]	4	5.92	~0				[2]	a)
$(Pu, U)O_2Rb(NO_3)_3$	7—1.5	3.18 ±0.01	~0	0.0504 ±0.001	~0		[3]	b)

Notes:

a) Cubic, $M = 4$. Linear O—U—O groups lie along the body diagonals of the cube; there are also six O from the acetate groups around each U. The eight O form a distorted cube.

b) The spectrum is apparently due to Pu oxides whose composition has not been determined as yet.

7. Compounds with anomalous valence

Table 4.7

Formula	T, °K	g	A	Reference	Note
Cr^+ in NaF $6 \cdot 10^{15}$ Cr^+ in 0.05 cm³ crystal	90	2.000 ±0.002	0.00140 ±0.00005	[1]	Before irradiation the Cr^{3+} in NaF fails to give a spectrum down to 20°K; after irradiation there appears a spectrum which is assumed to arise from Cr^+. The magnitude of the cubic splitting parameter is $a = 0.00036 \pm 0.00004$. The constants of interaction with the fluorine nuclei are $A_s = 0.00128 \pm 0.00002$, $A_\sigma = 0.00009 \pm 0.00007$. Upon heating up to 150°C the irradiation effects disappear.
Co^+ in NaF	90	2.31 ±0.02		[1]	The line appears at 90°K after irradiation and has a flat apex approximately 200 gauss wide; we assume that it is due to Co^+. After heating up to 150°C the irradiation effects disappear.
Ni^+ in NaF $5 \cdot 10^{15}$ Ni^+ in 0.05 cm³ crystal	20	$g_\parallel$ 2.766 ±0.002 $g_\perp$ 2.114 ±0.002		[1]	Before irradiation no spectrum was observed to 20°K. After irradiation there appears a spectrum attributed to Ni^+, $M_m = 3$; the spectra of nonequivalent ions are similar and correspond to axial symmetry; the symmetry axes of the nonequivalent ion are located along the edges of the cube. The constants of interaction with the F nuclei are $A_s^I = 0.0041 \pm 0.0002$, $A_\sigma^I = 0.0016 \pm 0.0003$,

Table 4.7 (Cont'd)

Formula	T, °K	g	A	Reference	Note
					$A_s^{II} = 0.0010 \pm 0.0001$, A_σ^{II} very small. Index I refers to 4F which are located in a plane normal to the axis of symmetry; index II refers to 2F on the axis of symmetry. The effects of irradiation disappear upon heating to 150°C.
Fe^+ in MgO $Fe : Mg \approx 10^{-3}$	20	4.15 ±0.01		[2]	
Fe^+ in NaF $Fe : Na \approx 10^{-4}$	20,4	4.344 +0.002		[3]	Constants of hyperfine structure from the interaction with F^-: $A_s = 0.00283$, $A_\sigma = 0.0010 \pm 0.00010$ ± 0.0001 $a = 0.00088 \pm 0.00005$
Mn^{2-} in Ge		2.0061 ±0.0002	A —0.00424 ±0.00003	[4]	
solutions:					
$(C_6H_6)_2 CrI$	290	1.986_3 ±0.002	3.6 * ±0.5 3	[6,7]	
$(C_6H_5 \cdot C_6H_{11})_2CrI$	290	1.986_8 ±0.002	3.7 * ±0.5	[6]	
$(C_6H_5 \cdot C_6H_5)(C_6H_5)$ CrI	290	1.986_8 ±0.002	3.6 * ±0.3	[6]	
$(C_6H_5 \cdot C_6H_5)_2$ CrI	290	1.986_0 ±0.002	3.6 * ±0.3	[6, 8]	
$(C_6H_5 \cdot C_6H_5)OC_6H_5Cr$	290	1.993 ±0.007		[8]	
Chromium dipyridyl (*I*)		1.993		[5]	
Vanadyl dipyridyl (0)		1.980		[5]	
Titanium dipyridyl (−*I*)		2.007		[5]	

* A_s is determined by the contact interaction of s electrons; A_σ includes dipole interactions and the relationship through p_σ orbits. It is assumed that A_s and A_σ are the same for all six F.

Literature for Section 4.2

For Table 4.1

V^{2+}

1. Hutchison, C. A., L. S. Singer. Phys. Rev. 89, 256, 1953.
2. Bleaney, B., D. J. E. Ingram, H. E. D. Scovil. Proc. Phys. Soc. A64, 601, 1951.
3. Kikuchi, C., H. M. Sirvetz, V. W. Cohen. Phys. Rev. 92, 109, 1953.
4. Baker, J. M., B. Bleaney. Proc. Phys. Soc. A65, 952, 1952.
5. Baker, J. M., B. Bleaney, K. D. Bowers. Proc. Phys. Soc. B69, 1205, 1956.
6. Low, W. Phys. Rev. 101, 1827, 1956.
7. Bagguley, D. M. S., B. Bleaney, J. H. E. Griffiths, R. P. Penrose, B. I. Plumpton. Proc. Phys. Soc. 61, 551, 1948.
8. Ingram, D. J. E., J. E. Bennett. J. Chem. Phys. 22, 1136, 1954.
9. Lambe, J., R. Ager, C. Kikuchi. Bull. Am. Phys. Soc., ser. II, 4, 261, 1959.
10. Baker, J. M. (see J. W. Orton, Rep. Progr. Phys. 22, 204, 1959).
11. Ingram, D. J. E., J. E. Bennett. J. Chem. Phys. 22, 1136, 1954.

Cr^{3+}

1. Bagguley, D. M. S., J. H. E. Griffiths. Proc. Roy. Soc. A204, 188, 1950.
2. Bleaney, B. Proc. Roy. Soc. A204, 203, 1950.
3. Kip, A. F., S. F. Davis, L. Jennings, D. Reiner, R. Malvano. Nuovo Cimento 8, 683, 1951.
4. Whitmer, C. A., R. T. Weidner, J. S. Hsiang, P. R. Weiss. Phys. Rev. 74, 1478, 1948.
5. Halliday, D., J. Wheatley. Phys. Rev. 74, 1712, 1948.
6. Ting, Y., D. Williams. Phys. Rev. 82, 507, 1951.
7. Baker, J. M., B. Bleaney. International low temperature conference, Paris (Paris: Institute International du Froid), 1955.
8. Baker, J. M., Proc. Phys. Soc. B69, 633, 1956.
9. Bleaney, B., R. P. Penrose. Proc. Phys. Soc. 60, 395, 1948.
10. Yager, W. A., F. R. Merritt, A. N. Holden, C. Kittel. Phys. Rev. 75, 1630, 1949.
11. Davis, C. F., M. W. P. Strandberg. Phys. Rev. 105, 447, 1957.
12. Bogle, G. C., J. R. Gabrill, G. A. Botomley. Trans. Faraday Soc. 53, 1058, 1957.
13. Daniels, J. M., H. Wesemeyer. Canad. J. Phys. 36, 144, 1958.
14. Bleaney, B., K. D. Bowers. Proc. Phys. Soc. A64, 1135, 1951.
15. Bowers, K. D., Proc. Phys. Soc. A65, 860, 1952.
16. Baker, J. M., B. Bleaney, K. D. Bowers. Proc. Phys. Soc. B69, 1205, 1956.

17. Singer, L. S. J. Chem. Phys. 23, 379, 1955.
18. Jarrett, H. S. J. Chem. Phys. 27, 1298, 1957.
19. Manenkov, A. A., A. M. Prokhorov. Zh. Eksp. Teoret. Fiz. 28, 762, 1955.
20. Zaripov, M. M., Yu. Ya. Shamonin. Zh. Eksp. Teoret. Fiz. 30, 291, 1956.
21. Geusic, J. E. Phys. Rev. 102, 252, 1956.
22. Manenkov, A. A., A. M. Prokhorov. Zh. Eksp. Teoret. Fiz. 31, 346, 1956.
23. Zverev, G. M., A. M. Prokhorov. Zh. Eksp. Teoret. Fiz. 34, 513, 1958.
24. Low, W. Phys. Rev. 105, 801, 1957.
25. Tinkham, M. Proc. Roy. Soc. A236, 535, 1956.
26. Bagguley, D. M. S., B. Bleaney, J. H. E. Griffiths, R. P. Penrose, B. J. Plumpton. Proc. Phys. Soc. 61, 551, 1948.
27. Lancaster, F. W., W. Gordy. J. Chem. Phys. 19, 1181, 1951.
28. Kozyrev, B. M., S. G. Salikhov, Yu. Ya. Shamonin. Zh. Eksp. Teoret. Fiz. 22, 56, 1952.
29. Tishkov, P. G. Zh. Eksp. Teoret. Fiz. 32, 620, 1957.
30. Lancaster, F. W., W. Gordy. J. Chem. Phys. 20, 740, 1952.
31. Ambler, E., R. P. Hudson. Physica 22, 866, 1956.
32. Ting, Y., L. D. Farringer, D. Williams. Phys. Rev. 97, 1037, 1955.
33. Sundaramma, K. Proc. Indian Acad. Sci. A44, 345, 1956.
34. Geusic, J. E., M. Peter, E. O. Schultz-Du Bois. Bull. Am. Phys. Soc., ser. II, 4, 21, 1959; Bell Syst. Techn. J. 38, 291, 1959.
35. Gerritsen, H. J., S. E. Harrison, H. R. Lewis, J. R. Wittke. Bull. Am. Phys. Soc., ser. II, 4, 165, 1959.
36. Wertz, J. E., P. Auzins. Phys. Rev. 106, 484, 1957.
37. Griffiths, J. H. E., J. W. Orton. Proc. Phys. Soc. 73, 948, 1959.
38. Baker, J. M., W. Hayes, D. A. Jones. Proc. Phys. Soc. 73, 942, 1959.
39. Swarup, P. Canad. J. Phys. 37, 848, 1959.
40. Baker, J. M. (see J. W. Orton. Rep. Progr. Phys. 22, 204, 1959).
41. Ting, Y., L. D. Farringer, D. Williams. Phys. Rev. 97, 1037, 1955.
42. Leech, J. W., A. J. Manuel. Proc. Phys. Soc. B69, 210, 1956.
43. Sierro, J., R. Lacroix, K. A. Muller. Helv. Phys. Acta 32, 286, 1959.

Co^{2+}

1. Owen, J. (see K. D. Bowers, J. Owen. Rep. Progr. Phys. 18, 304, 1955).

Cr^{2+}

1. Ono, K., S. Koide, H. Sekiyama, H. Abe. Phys. Rev. 96, 38, 1954; K. Ono. J. Phys. Soc. Japan 12, 1231, 1957.

Ni^{2+}

1. Griffiths, J. H. E., J. Owen. Proc. Roy. Soc. A213, 459, 1952.
2. Date, M. Sci. Repts. Res. Inst., Tohoku Univ. A6, 390, 1954.
3. Trenam, R. S. (see K. D. Bowers, J. Owen. Rep. Progr. Phys. 18, 304, 1955).
4. Holden, A. N., C. Kittel, W. A. Yager. Phys. Rev. 75, 1443, 1949.
5. Penrose, R. P., K. W. H. Stevens. Proc. Phys. Soc. A63, 29, 1950.
6. Walsh, W. M., N. Bloembergen. Phys. Rev. 107, 904, 1957.
7. Owen, J. (see K. D. Bowers, J. Owen. Rep. Progr. Phys. 18, 304, 1955).
8. Ono, K. J. Phys. Soc. Japan 8, 802, 1953.
9. Low, W. Phys. Rev. 109, 247, 1958.
10. Low, W. Phys. Rev. 101, 1827, 1956.
11. Ting, Y., D. Williams. Phys. Rev. 82, 507, 1951.
12. Lancaster, F. W., W. Gordy. J. Chem. Phys. 19, 1181, 1951.
13. Lütze, E. Z. phys. Chem. 8, 32, 1956.
14. Bagguley, D. M. S., B. Bleaney, J. H. E. Griffiths, R. P. Penrose, B. I. Plumpton. Proc. Phys. Soc. 61, 551, 1948.
15. Ingram, D. J. E., J. E. Bennett. J. Chem. Phys. 22, 1136, 1954.
16. Partridge, M. F. (see J. W. Orton. Rep. Progr. Phys. 22, 204, 1959).
17. Leech, J. W., A. J. Manuel. Proc. Phys. Soc. B69, 210, 1956.

Cu^{2+}

1. Bleaney, B., R. P. Penrose, B. I. Plumpton. Proc. Roy. Soc. A198, 406, 1949.
2. Bagguley, D. M. S., J. H. E. Griffiths. Proc. Phys. Soc. A65, 594, 1952.
3. Bleaney, B., K. D. Bowers, D. J. E. Ingram. Proc. Roy. Soc. A228, 147, 1955.
4. Bleaney, B., K. D. Bowers, R. S. Trenam. Proc. Roy. Soc. A228, 157, 1955.
5. Bijl, D., A. C. Rose-Innes. Proc. Phys. Soc. A66, 954, 1953.
6. Yokozawa, Y. Monogr. Res. Inst. Appl. Elect. Hokkaido Univ. 4, 95, 1954.
7. Okamura, T., M. Date. Phys. Rev. 94, 314, 1954.
8. Bagguley, D. M. S., J. H. E. Griffiths, J. Owen (see K. D. Bowers, J. Owen. Rep. Progr. Phys. 18, 304, 1955).

9. Gerritsen, H. J., B. Bolger, R. F. Okkes (see K. D. Bowers, J. Owen. Rep. Progr. Phys. 18, 304, 1955).
10. Bagguley, D. M. S., J. H. E. Griffiths. Proc. Roy. Soc. A201, 366, 1950.
11. Abe, H., K. Ono, I. Hayashi, J. Shimada, K. Iwanaga. J. Phys. Soc. Japan 9, 814, 1954.
12. Abe, H., J. Shimada. Phys. Rev. 90, 316, 1953.
13. Bleaney, B., K. D. Bowers. Proc. Roy. Soc. A214, 451, 1952.
14. Abe, H. Phys. Rev. 92, 1572, 1953.
15. Ingram, D. J. E., J. E. Bennett. J. Chem. Phys. 22, 1136, 1954.
16. Bennett, J. E., D. J. E. Ingram. Nature, London, 175, 130, 1955.
17. Lancaster, F. W., W. Gordy. J. Chem. Phys. 19, 1181, 1951.
18. Ramaseshan, S., G. Suryan. Proc. Ind. Acad. Sci. A36, 211, 1952.
19. Bagguley, D. M. S., B. Bleaney, J. H. E. Griffiths, R. P. Penrose, B. I. Plumpton. Proc. Phys. Soc. 61, 551, 1948.
20. Kozyrev, B. M., S. G. Salikhov, Yu. Ya. Shamonin. Zh. Eksp. Teoret. Fiz. 22, 56, 1952.
21. Perakis, N., J. Wucher, H. M. Gijsman. Compt. Rend. 239, 243, 1954.
22. Bowers, K. D. Proc. Phys. Soc. A66, 666, 1953.
23. Abe, H., M. Ohtusuka. J. Phys. Soc. Japan 11, 896, 1956.
24. Abe, H., K. Ono. J. Phys. Soc. Japan 11, 947, 1956.
25. Ono, K., M. Ohtsuka. J. Phys. Soc. Japan 13, 206, 1958.
26. Shimoda, J., H. Abe, K. Ono. J. Phys. Soc. Japan 11, 1956, 137, 1956.
27. Abe, H., J. Shimoda. J. Phys. Soc. Japan 12, 1255, 1957.
28. Sundaramma, K. Proc. Indian Acad. Sci. A46, 232, 1957.
29. Sundaramma, K. Proc. Indian Acad. Sci. A44, 345, 1956.
30. Bennett, J. E., D. J. E. Ingram. Phil. Mag. 1, 970, 1956.
31. Sundaramma, K. Proc. Indian Acad. Sci. A42, 292, 1955.
32. McGarvey, B. R. J. Phys. Chem. 60, 71, 1956.
33. Karlson, E. H., R. D. Spence. J. Chem. Phys. 24, 471, 1956.
34. Lütze, E. Z. phys. Chem. 8, 32, 1956.
35. Date, M. J. Phys. Soc. Japan 11, 1016, 1956.
36. Miduno, Z., O. Matumura, K. Hukuda, K. Horai. Mem. Fac. Sci. Kuysyu Univ. B2, 13, 1956.
37. Maki, A. H., B. R. McGarvey. J. Chem. Phys. 29, 31, 1958.
38. Sands, R. H. Phys. Rev. 99, 1222, 1955.
39. Sundaramma, K., S. Suryan. Current Sci. 26, 80, 1957.
40. Palma-Vittorelli, M. B., M. U. Palma, D. Palumbo, M. Santangelo. Ricerca Sci. 25, 2364, 1955.
41. Palma-Vittorelli, M. B., M. U. Palma, D. Palumbo, M. Santangelo. Nuovo Cimento 2, 811, 1955.
42. Garif'yanov, N. S., M. M. Zaripov. Zh. Eksp. Teoret. Fiz. 28, 629, 1955.
43. Lütze, E. Naturwiss. 41, 279, 1954.

44. Ingram, D. J. E., J. E. Bennett. Disc. Faraday Soc. 19, 140, 173, 1955.
45. Kumagai, H., K. Ono, I. Hayashi, H. Abe, J. Shimoda, H. Shono, H. Ibamoto, J. Tachimori. J. Phys. Soc. Japan 9, 369, 1954.
46. Kumagai, H., I. Hayashi, K. Ono, H. Abe, J. Shimoda, H. Shono. J. Phys. Soc. Japan 9, 376, 1954.
47. Maki, A. H., B. R. McGarvey. J. Chem. Phys. 29, 35, 1958.
48. Vittorelli, M. P. P., M. U. Palma, D. Palumbo, M. Santangelo. Ricerca Sci. 23, 1423, 1953.
49. Ubbink, J., J. A. Poulis, H. J. Gerritsen, C. J. Gorter. Physica 18, 361, 1952.
50. Abe, H. J. Phys. Soc. Japan 13, 987, 1958.
51. Tucker, R. F., Jr. Phys. Rev. 112, 725, 1958.
52. Hayes, W. (see J. W. Orton. Rep. Progr. Phys. 22, 204, 1959).
53. Abe, H., H. Nagano, M. Nagusa, K. Oshima. J. Chem. Phys. 25, 378, 1956.
54. Jarrett, H. S. J. Chem. Phys. 28, 1260, 1958.
55. Partridge, M. F. (see J. W. Orton. Rep. Progr. Phys. 22, 204, 1959).

For Table 4.2

Ti^{3+}

1. Bleaney, B., G. S. Bogle, A. H. Cooke, R. J. Duffus, M. C. M. O'Brien, K. W. H. Stevens. Proc. Phys. Soc. A68, 57, 1955.
2. Bogle, G. S., J. Owen (see K. D. Bowers, J. Owen. Rep. Progr. Phys. 18, 304, 1955).
3. Jarrett, H. S. J. Chem. Phys. 27, 1298, 1957.
4. Bijl, D. Proc. Phys. Soc. A63, 405, 1950.

V^{4+}

1. Griffiths, J. H. E., I. M. Ward (see K. D. Bowers, J. Owen. Rep. Progr. Phys. 18, 304, 1955).
2. Lancaster, F. W., W. Gordy. J. Chem. Phys. 19, 1181, 1951.
3. Hutchinson, C. A., L. S. Singer. Phys. Rev. 89, 256, 1953.
4. Palma-Vittorelli, M. B., M. U. Palma, D. Palumbo, F. Sgarlata. Nuovo Cimento 3, 718, 1956.
5. Ingram, D. J. E., J. E. Bennett. Disc. Faraday Soc. 19, 140, 173, 1955.

Mn^{6+}

1. Lancaster F. W., W. Gordy. J. Chem. Phys. 19, 1181, 1951.

V^{3+}

1. Zverev, G. M., A. M. Prokhorov. Zh. Eksp. Teoret. Fiz. 34, 1023, 1958.
2. Lambe, J., R. Ager, C. Kikuchi. Bull. Am. Phys. Soc., ser. II, 4, 261, 1959.

Co^{2+}

1. Bleaney, B., D. J. E. Ingram. Proc. Roy. Soc. A208, 143, 1951.
2. Dobrowolsky, W., R. V. Jones, C. D. Jeffries. Phys. Rev. 101, 1001, 1956.
3. Bowers, K. D. (see K. D. Bowers, J. Owen. Rep. Progr. Phys. 18, 304, 1955).
4. Trenam, R. S. Proc. Phys. Soc. A66, 118, 1953.
5. Gager, W. B., P. S. Jastram, J. G. Daunt. Phys. Rev. 111, 803, 1958.
6. Tinkham, M. Proc. Roy. Soc. A236, 535, 1956.
7. Hayes, W., D. A. Jones. Proc. Phys. Soc. 71, 459, 1958.
8. Low, W. Phys. Rev. 109, 256, 1958.
9. Ingram, D. J. E., J. E. Bennett. J. Chem. Phys. 22, 1136, 1954.
10. Ingram, D. J. E., J. E. Bennett. Disc. Faraday Soc. 19, 140, 173, 1955.
11. Jones, R. V., W. Dobrowolsky, C. D. Jeffries. Phys. Rev. 102, 738, 1956.
12. Dobrowolsky, W., C. D. Jeffries. Phys. Rev. 108, 60, 1957.
13. Geusic, J. E. Bull. Am. Phys. Soc., ser. II, 4, 261, 1959.
14. Baker, J. M., W. Hayes, D. A. Jones. Proc. Phys. Soc. 73, 942, 1959.
15. Zverev, G. M., A. M. Prokhorov. Zh. Eksp. Teoret. Fiz. 36, 647, 1959.
16. Baker, J. M., B. Bleaney, P. M. Llewellyn, P. F. D. Shaw. Proc. Phys. Soc. A69, 353, 1956.
17. Partridge, M. F. (see J. W. Orton. Rep. Progr. Phys. 22, 204, 1959).

Fe^{2+}

1. Tinkham, M. Proc. Phys. Soc. A68, 258, 1955.
2. Tinkham, M. Proc. Roy. Soc. A236, 535, 1956.
3. Low, W. Phys. Rev. 101, 1827, 1956.
4. Bleaney, B., K. W. H. Stevens. Rep. Progr. Phys. 16, 108, 1953.
5. Ingram, D. J. E., J. E. Bennett. J. Chem. Phys. 22, 1136, 1954.
6. Partridge, M. F. (see J. W. Orton. Rep. Progr. Phys. 22, 204, 1959).

For Table 4.3

Ce^{3+}

1. Cooke, A. H., H. J. Duffus, W. P. Wolf. Phil. Mag. 44, 623, 1953.
2. Kedzie, R. W., M. Abraham, C. D. Jeffries. Phys. Rev. 108, 54, 1957.
3. Bogle, G. S., A. H. Cooke, S. Whitley. Proc. Phys. Soc. A64, 931, 1951.
4. Bogle, G. S., A. H. Cooke (see K. D. Bowers, J. Owen. Rep. Progr. Phys. 18, 304, 1955).
5. Baker, J. M., W. Hayes, D. A. Jones. Proc. Phys. Soc. 73, 942, 1959.
6. Hutchison, C. A., E. Wong. J. Chem. Phys. 29, 754, 1958.

Nd^{3+}

1. Cooke, A. H., H. J. Duffus. Proc. Roy. Soc. A229, 407, 1955.
2. Bleaney, B., H. E. D. Scovil, R. S. Trenam. Proc. Roy. Soc. A223, 15, 1954.
3. Kurenev, V. Ya., S. G. Salikhov. Zh. Eksp. Teoret. Fiz. 21, 864, 1951.
4. Garif'yanov, N. S. Dissertation, Kazan, 1952.
5. Bleaney, B., P. M. Llewellyn, D. A. Jones, Proc. Phys. Soc. B69, 858, 1956.
6. Sanadze, T. I. Zh. Eksp. Teoret. Fiz. 33, 1042, 1957; Trudy Gruz. Politekh. Inst. No. 4, 177, 1957.
7. Kedzie, R. W., M. Abraham, C. D. Jeffries. Phys. Rev. 108, 54, 1957.
8. Hutchison, C. A., E. Wong. J. Chem. Phys. 29, 754, 1958.

Sm^{3+}

1. Cooke, A. H., H. J. Duffus. Proc. Roy. Soc. A229, 407, 1955.
2. Bogle, G. S., H. E. D. Scovil. Proc. Phys. Soc. A65, 368, 1952.
3. Low, W. Phys. Rev. 98, 426, 1955.
4. Hutchison, C. A., E. Wong. J. Chem. Phys. 29, 754, 1958.

Dy^{3+}

1. Cooke, A. H., J. G. Park. Proc. Phys. Soc. A69, 282, 1956.
2. Park, J. G. Proc. Roy. Soc. A245, 118, 1958.

Er^{3+}

1. Bogle, G. S., H. J. Duffus, H. E. D. Scovil. Proc. Phys. Soc. A65, 760, 1952.

2. Baker, J. M., W. Hayes, D. A. Jones. Proc. Phys. Soc. 73, 942, 1959.
3. Judd, B. R., E. Wong. J. Chem. Phys. 28, 1097, 1958.
4. Hutchison, C. A., E. Wong. J. Chem. Phys. 29, 754, 1958.

Yb^{3+}

1. Cooke, A. H., J. G. Park. Proc. Phys. Soc. A69, 282, 1956.

For Table 4.4

Pr^{3+}

1. Cooke, A. H., H. J. Duffus. Proc. Roy. Soc. A229, 407, 1955.
2. Bleaney, B., H. E. D. Scovil. Phil. Mag. 43, 999, 1952.
3. Davis, C. F., A. F. Kip, R. Malvano. R. C. Acad. Lincei 11, 77, 1951.
4. Anderson, J. H. C. A. Hutchison. Phys. Rev. 97, 76, 1955.
5. Baker, J. M., B. Bleaney. Proc. Phys. Soc. A68, 936, 1955.
6. Gränischer, H., K. Hubner, K. A. Müller. Helv. phys. Acta 30 480, 1957.
7. Baker, J. M., B. Bleaney. Proc. Roy. Soc. A245, 156, 1958.
8. Hutchison, C. A., E. Wong. J. Chem. Phys. 29, 754, 1958.

Tb^{3+}

1. Baker, J. M., B. Bleaney. Proc. Phys. Soc. A68, 257, 1955.
2. Sanadze, T. I., M. Kalach, G. A. Tsintsadze. Trudy Inst. Fiz. AN Gruz. SSR 5, 271, 1957.
3. Manenkov, A. A., A. M. Prokhorov, Z. A. Trapeznikova, M. V. Fok. Izvest. Akad. Nauk SSSR, Ser. Fiz., 21, 779, 1957; Optika i Spektroskopiya 2, 470, 1957.
4. Baker, J. M., B. Bleaney. Proc. Roy. Soc. A245, 156, 1958.
5. Berulava, B. G., T. I. Sanadze. Conference on Paramagnetic Resonance, Kazan, 1959.
6. Hutchison, C. A., E. Wong. J. Chem. Phys. 29, 754, 1958.

Ho^{3+}

1. Baker, J. M., B. Bleaney. Proc. Phys. Soc. A68, 1090, 1955.
2. Baker, J. M., B. Bleaney. Proc. Roy. Soc. A245, 156, 1958.
3. Hutchison, C. A., E. Wong. J. Chem. Phys. 29, 754, 1958.

For Table 4.5

Mn^{2+}

1. Ingram, D. J. E. Proc. Phys. Soc. A66, 412, 1953.
2. Brovetto, P., G. Cini, S. Ferroni. Nuovo Cimento 10, 1325, 1953.

3. Hayashi, I., K. Ono. J. Phys. Soc. Japan 8, 270, 1953.
4. Bleaney, B., D. J. E. Ingram. Proc. Roy. Soc. A205, 336, 1951.
5. Trenam, R. S. Proc. Phys. Soc. A66, 118, 1953.
6. Arakawa, T. J. Phys. Soc. Japan 9, 790, 1954.
7. Hurd, F. K., M. Sachs, W. D. Herschberger. Phys. Rev. 93, 373, 1954.
8. Schneider, E. E., T. S. England. Physica 17, 221, 1951.
9. Herschberger, W. D., H. N. Leifer. Phys. Rev. 88, 714, 1952.
10. Ingram, D. J. E. Phys. Rev. 90, 711, 1953.
11. Kumagai, H., K. Ono, I. Hayashi, K. Kambe. Phys. Rev. 87, 374, 1952.
12. Lancaster, F. W., W. Gordy. J. Chem. Phys. 19, 1181, 1951.
13. Kozyrev, B. M., S. G. Salikhov, Yu. Ya. Shamonin. Zh. Eksp. Teoret. Fiz. 22, 56, 1952.
14. Bagguley, D. M. S., B. Bleaney, J. H. E. Griffiths, R. P. Penrose, B. I. Plumpton. Proc. Phys. Soc. 61, 551, 1948.
15. Ingram, D. J. E., J. E. Bennett. J. Chem. Phys. 22, 1136, 1954.
16. Abe, H., J. Shimoda. National Science Report, Ochanomizu University 4, 77, 1953.
17. Kumagai, H., K. Ono, I. Hayashi, H. Abe, J. Shimoda, H. Shono, H. Ibamoto. Phys. Rev. 83, 1077, 1951.
18. Abe, H. J. Phys. Soc. Japan 12, 435, 1957.
19. Watkins, G. D. Bull. Am. Phys. Soc., ser. II, 2, 345, 1957.
20. Hayes, W., D. A. Jones. Proc. Phys. Soc. 71, 459, 1958.
21. Tinkham, M., Proc. Roy. Soc. A236, 535, 1956.
22. Low, W. Phys. Rev. 105, 792, 1957.
23. Low, W. Phys. Rev. 105, 793, 1957.
24. Kurushin, A. I. Zh. Eksp. Teoret. Fiz. 32, 938, 1957.
25. Sundaramma, K. Proc. Indian Acad. Sci. A44, 345, 1956.
26. Kurushin, A. I. Izvest. Akad. Nauk SSSR, Ser. Fiz., 20, 1232, 1956.
27. Lütze, E. Z. phys. Chem. 8, 32, 1956.
28. Forrester, P. A., E. E. Schneider. Proc. Phys. Soc. B69, 833, 1956.
29. Low, W. Proc. Phys. Soc. B69, 837, 1956.
30. Low, W. Phys. Rev. 101, 1827, 1956.
31. Ambler, E., R. P. Hudson. Physica 22, 866, 1956.
32. Dobrowolsky, W., R. V. Jones, C. D. Jeffries. Phys. Rev. 104, 1378, 1956.
33. Keller, S. P., I. L. Gelles, W. V. Smith. Phys. Rev. 110, 850, 1958.
34. Matarese, L. M., C. Kikuchi. J. Phys. Chem. Solids 1, 117, 1956.
35. Watkins, G. D. Phys. Rev. 110, 986, 1958.
36. Hurd, F. K., M. Sachs, W. D. Herschberger. Phys. Rev. 93, 373, 1954.

37. Van Wieringen, I. S. Disc. Faraday Soc. 19, 118, 173, 1955.
38. Müller, K. A. Helv. phys. Acta 28, 450, 1955.
39. Lütze, E. Naturwiss. 41, 279, 1954.
40. Oshima, K., H. Abe, H. Nagano, M. Nagusa. J. Chem. Phys. 23, 1721, 1955.
41. Ingram, D. J. E., J. E. Bennett. Disc. Faraday Soc. 19, 140, 173, 1955.
42. McLean, C., G. J. W. Kor. Appl. Sci. Res. B4, 425, 1955.
43. Asch, G., A. J. P. Meyer. Compt. Rend. 246, 1180, 1958.
44. Ono, K., I. Hayashi. J. Phys. Soc. Japan 8, 561, 1953.
45. Kumagai, H., K. Ono, I. Hayashi, H. Abe, J. Shimada, H. Shono, H. Ibamoto, S. Tachimori. J. Phys. Soc. Japan 9, 369, 1954.
46. Kumagai, H., I. Hayashi, K. Ono, H. Abe, J. Shimada, H. Shono. J. Phys. Soc. Japan 9, 376, 1954.
47. Morigaki, K., M. Fujimoto, J. Iton. J. Phys. Soc. Japan 13, 1174, 1958.
48. Baker, J. M., B. Bleaney, W. Hayes. Proc. Roy. Soc. A247, 141, 1958.
49. Dorain, P. Phys. Rev. 112, 1058, 1958.
50. Matumura O. J. Phys. Soc. Japan 14, 108, 1959.
51. Ludwig, G. W., R. O. Carlson, H. H. Woodbury. Bull. Am. Phys. Soc., ser. II, 4, 22, 1959.
52. Abe, H., H. Nagano, M. Nagusa, K. Oshima. J. Chem. Phys. 25, 378, 1956.
53. Matarese, L. M., C. Kikuchi. Phys. Rev. 100, 1243, 1955.
54. Dobrowolsky, W., R. V. Jones, C. D. Jeffries. Phys. Rev. 104, 1378, 1956.
55. Low, W. Phys. Rev. 98, 426, 1955.
56. Partridge, M. F. (see J. W. Orton. Rep. Progr. Phys. 22, 204, 1959.
57. Fukuda, K., J. Uchida, H. Joshimura. Phys. Soc. Japan 13, 971, 1958.

Fe^{3+}

1. Bleaney, B., R. S. Trenam. Proc. Roy. Soc. A223, 1, 1954.
2. Ubbink, J., J. A. Poulis, C. J. Gorter. Physica 17, 213, 1951.
3. Meijer, P. H. E. Physica 17, 899, 1951.
4. Lancaster, F. W., W. Gordy. J. Chem. Phys. 19, 1181, 1951.
5. Bagguley, D. M. S., B. Bleaney, J. H. E. Griffiths, R. P. Penrose, B. I. Plumpton. Proc. Phys. Soc. 61, 551, 1948.
6. Abe, H., J. Shimoda. National Science Report, Ochanomizu University 4, 77, 1953.
7. Ingram, D. J. E., J. E. Bennett. J. Chem. Phys. 22, 1136, 1954.
8. Ting, Y., D. Williams. Phys. Rev. 82, 507, 1951.
9. Gerritsen, H. J., B. Bolger, R. F. Okkes (see K. D. Bowers, J. Owen. Rep. Progr. Phys. 18, 304, 1955).

10. Jarrett, H. S. J. Chem. Phys. 27, 1298, 1957.
11. Müller, K. A. Arch. Sci. 10, fasc. spec., 130, 1957.
12. Korniyenko, L. S., A. M. Prokhorov. Zh. Eksp. Teoret. Fiz. 33, 805, 1957.
13. Lütze, E. Z. phys. Chem. 8, 32, 1956.
14. Date, M. Sci. Repts. Res. Insts., Tohoku Univ. A6, 497, 1954.
15. Zaripov, M. M., Yu. Ya. Shamonin. Izvest. Akad. Nauk SSSR, Ser. Fiz., 20, 1224, 1956.
16. Low, W. Phys. Rev. 105, 792, 1957.
17. Müller, K. A. Helv. phys. Acta 31, 173, 1958.
18. Kumagai, H., K. Ono, I. Hayashi, H. Abe, J. Shimoda, H. Shono, H. Ibamoto, S. Tachimori. J. Phys. Soc. Japan 9, 369, 1954.
19. Ludwig, G. W., H. H. Woodbury, R. O. Carlson. Phys. Rev. Letters 1, 295, 1958.
20. Low, W., D. Shaltiel. Phys. Rev. Letters 1, 51, 286, 1958; A. W. Hornig, R. C. Rempel, H. E. Weaver. Phys. Rev. Letters 1, 284, 1958; A. W. Hornig, O. O. Jaynes, H. E. Weaver. Phys. Rev. 96, 1703, 1954.
21. Ludwig, G. W., R. O. Carlson, H. H. Woodbury. Bull. Am. Phys. Soc., ser. II, 4, 22, 1959.
22. Bogle, G. S., H. F. Symmons. Proc. Phys. Soc. 73, 531, 1959.
23. Peter, M. Phys. Rev. 113, 801, 1959.
24. Geschwind, S., D. F. Linn. Bull. Am. Phys. Soc., ser. II, 4, 261, 1959.

Gd^{3+}

1. Trenam, R. S. Proc. Phys. Soc. A66, 118, 1953.
2. Bleaney, B., H. E. D. Scovil, R. S. Trenam. Proc. Roy. Soc. A223, 15, 1954.
3. Bogle, G. S., V. Heine. Proc. Phys. Soc. A67, 734, 1954.
4. Garif'yanov, N. S. Doklady Akad. Nauk SSSR 84, 923, 1952.
5. Bleaney, B., R. J. Elliott, H. E. D. Scovil, R. S. Trenam. Phil. Mag. 42, 1062, 1951.
6. Lancaster, F. W., W. Gordy. J. Chem. Phys. 19, 1181, 1951.
7. Hutchison, C. A., B. R. Judd, D. E. D. Pope. Proc. Phys. Soc. B70, 514, 1957.
8. Low, W. Phys. Rev. 109, 265, 1958.
9. Ryter, C. Helv. Phys. Acta 30, 353, 1957.
10. Low, W. Phys. Rev. 105, 792, 1957.
11. Manenkov, A. A., A. M. Prokhorov. Zh. Eksp. Teoret. Fiz. 33, 1116, 1957.
12. Kurushin, A. I. Izvest. Akad. Nauk SSSR, Ser. Fiz., 20, 1232, 1956.
13. Buckmaster, H. A. Canad. J. Phys. 34, 341, 1956.
14. Ryter, C., R. Lacroix. Compt. Rend. 242, 2812, 1956.

15. Low, W. Phys. Rev. 103, 1309, 1956.
16. Low, W., D. Shaltiel. J. Phys. Chem. Solids 6, 315, 1958.
17. Manenkov, A. A., A. M. Prokhorov, Z. A. Trapeznikova, M. V. Fok, Izvest. Akad. Nauk SSSR, Ser. Fiz., 21, 779, 1957.
18. Granisher, H., K. A. Müller. Nuovo Cimento 6, suppl. N 3, 1217, 1957.
19. Weger, W., W. Low. Phys. Rev. 111, 1526, 1958.
20. Baker, J. M., B. Bleaney, W. Hayes. Proc. Roy. Soc. A247, 141, 1958.
21. Hutchison, C. A., E. Wong. J. Chem. Phys. 29, 754, 1958.
22. Jones, D. A., J. M. Baker, D. F. D. Pope. Proc. Phys. Soc. 74, 249, 1959.

Eu^{2+}

1. Bleaney, B., W. Low. Proc. Phys. Soc. A68, 55, 1955.
2. Ryter, C. Helv. phys. Acta 30, 353, 1957.
3. Lacroix, R., C. Ryter. Arch. Sci. 10, fasc. spec., 132, 1957.
4. Manenkov, A. A., A. M. Prokhorov, Doklady Akad. Nauk SSSR 107, 402, 1956.
5. Ryter, C., R. Lacroix. Compt. Rend. 242, 2812, 1956.
6. Lacroix, R., C. Ryter. Colloq. AMPERE, Inst. Phys., Univ. Geneve, 55, 1956.
7. Low, W. Phys. Rev. 101, 1827, 1956.
8. Low, W. Phys. Rev. 98, 426, 1955.
9. Abraham, M., R. Kedzie, C. D. Jeffries. Phys. Rev. 108, 57, 1957.
10. Manenkov, A. A., A. M. Prokhorov, Z. A. Trapeznikova, M. V. Fok, Izvest. Akad. Nauk SSSR, Ser. Fiz., 21, 779, 1957; Optika i Spektroskopiya 2, 470, 1957.
11. Baker, J. M., B. Bleaney, W. Hayes. Proc. Roy. Soc. A247, 141, 1958.
12. Matumura, O., K. Horai, J. Miduno. J. Phys. Soc. Japan 13, 768, 1958.
13. Manenkov, A. A., A. M. Prokhorov, N. S. Trukhlyayev, G. N. Yakovlev, Doklady Akad. Nauk SSSR 112, 623, 1955.
14. Ryter, C., R. Lacroix. Compt. Rend. 242, 2812, 1956.

Cm^{3+}

1. Fields, P., A. Friedman, B. Smaller, W. Low. Phys. Rev. 105, 757, 1957.
2. Abraham, M., B. B. Cunningham, C. D. Jeffries, R. W. Kedzie. Bull. Am. Phys. Soc. 1, 396, 1956.

For Table 4.6

Fe^{III}

1. Bleaney, B., D. J. E. Ingram. Proc. Phys. Soc. A65, 953, 1952.
2. Baker, J. M., B. Bleaney, K. D. Bowers. Proc. Phys. Soc. B69, 1205, 1956.
3. George, P., J. E. Bennett, D. J. E. Ingram. J. Chem. Phys. 24, 627, 1956.
4. Bennett, J. E., D. J. E. Ingram. Nature, London 177, 275, 1956.
5. Ingram, D. J. E., J. E. Bennett. Disc. Faraday Soc. 19, 140, 173, 1955.
6. Gibson, J. F., D. J. E. Ingram. Nature, London 180, 29, 1957.
7. Garif'yanov, N. S., M. M. Zaripov, B. M. Kozyrev, Doklady Akad. Nauk SSSR 113, 1243, 1957.

Mn^{II}

1. Baker, J. M., B. Bleaney, K. D. Bowers. Proc. Phys. Soc. B69, 1205, 1956.

Mo^{V}

1. Owen, J., I. M. Ward. Phys. Rev. 102, 591, 1956.
2. Griffiths, J. H. E., J. Owen, I. M. Ward. Proc. Roy. Soc. A219, 526, 1953.

Mo^{III}

1. Owen, J., I. M. Ward (see K. D. Bowers, J. Owen. Rep. Progr. Phys. 18, 304, 1955).
2. Ramaseschan S., G. Suryan. Phys. Rev. 84, 593, 1951.
3. Griffiths, J. H. E., J. Owen, I. M. Ward. Proc. Roy. Soc. A219, 526, 1953.

Tc^{IV}

1. Low, W., P. M. Llewellyn. Phys. Rev. 110, 842, 1958.

Ru^{III}

1. Griffiths, J. H. E., J. Owen, I. M. Ward. Proc. Roy. Soc. A219, 526, 1953.
2. Griffiths, J. H. E., M. C. M. O'Brien, J. Owen, I. M. Ward (see K. D. Bowers, J. Owen, Rep. Progr. Phys. 18, 304, 1955).

3. Griffiths, J. H. E., J. Owen. Proc. Phys. Soc. A65, 951, 1952.
4. Owen, J., I. M. Ward (see K. D. Bowers, J. Owen. Rep. Progr. Phys. 18, 304, 1955).

Ag^{II}

1. Gijsman, H. M., H. J. Gerritsen, J. van den Handel. Physica 20, 15, 1954.
2. Bowers, K. D. Proc. Phys. Soc. A66, 666, 1953.

Re^{IV}

1. Owen, J., I. M. Ward. Phys. Rev. 102, 591, 1956.

Ir^{IV}

1. Griffiths, J. H. E., J. Owen. Proc. Roy. Soc. A226, 96, 1954.
2. Griffiths, J. H. E., J. Owen, I. M. Ward. Proc. Roy. Soc. A219, 526, 1953.
3. Griffiths, J. H. E., J. Owen, J. G. Park, M. F. Partridge. Phys. Rev. 108, 1345, 1957.

U^{III}

1. Bleaney, B., P. M. Llewellyn, D. A. Jones. Proc Phys. Soc. B69, 858, 1956.
2. Bleaney, B., C. A. Hutchison, P. M. Llewellyn, D. F. D. Pope. Proc. Phys. Soc. B69, 1167, 1956.
3. Hutchison, C. A., P. M. Llewellyn, E. Wong, P. B. Dorain. Phys. Rev. 102, 292, 1956.
4. Dorain, P. B., C. A. Hutchison, E. Wong. Phys. Rev. 105, 1307, 1957.
5. Ghosh, S. N., W. Gordy, D. G. Hill. Phys. Rev. 96, 36, 1954.
6. Berulava, B. G., T. I. Sanadze. Conference on Paramagnetic Resonance, Kazan, 1959.

Np^{II}

1. Bleaney, B., P. M. Llewellyn, M. H. L. Pryce, G. R. Hall. Phil. Mag. 45, 992, 1954.
2. Abraham, M., C. D. Jeffries, R. W. Kedzie, J. C. Wallmann. Phys. Rev. 106, 1357, 1957.
3. Abraham, M., C. D. Jeffries, R. W. Kedzie, J. C. Wallmann. Phys. Rev. 112, 553, 1958.

Pu II

1. Bleaney, B., P. M. Llewellyn, M. H. L. Pryce, G. R. Hall. Phil. Mag. 45, 991, 1954.
2. Hutchison, C. A., W. B. Lewis. Phys. Rev. 95, 1096, 1954.
3. Abraham, M., C. D. Jeffries, R. W. Kedzie, J. C. Wallmann. Phys. Rev. 112, 553, 1958.

For Table 4.7

1. Hayes, W., D. A. Jones. Proc. Phys. Soc. 71, 503, 1958.
2. Orton, J. W. (see J. W. Orton. Rep. Progr. Phys. 22, 204, 1959).
3. Bleaney, B., W. Hayes. Proc. Phys. Soc. B70, 626, 1957.
4. Watkins, G. D. Bull. Amer. Phys. Soc. 2, 345, 1957.
5. Elschner, Herzog. VII Colloq. AMPERE, Paris, July 1958.
6. Voevodskiy, V. V., Yu. N. Molin, V. M. Chibrikin. Optika i Spektroskopiya 5, 90, 1958.
7. Feltham, R. D., P. Sogo, M. Calvin. J. Chem. Phys. 26, 1354, 1957.
8. Tsvetkov, Yu. D., V. V. Voevodskiy, G. A. Razyvayev, Yu. V. Sorokin, G. A. Domrachev. Doklady Akad. Nauk SSSR 115, 118, 1957.

4.3. Paramagnetic Resonance Spectra in Electrolyte Solutions

Paramagnetic absorption in liquid salt solutions was first observed by Zavoyskiy [1] in 1944.

Up to the present time the inorganic compounds in solution that have been most studied are iron-group salts. The principal solvent has been water; in addition, various mono- and diatomic alcohols, glycerol, acetone, dioxane and other organic liquids have been used as solvents.

A measurable resonance effect was found in solutions containing VO^{2+}, Cr^{3+}, Mn^{2+}, Fe^{3+}, Cu^{2+} ions. There exist data on the observation of paramagnetic resonance in solutions of Gd^{3+} and $[W(CN)_8]^{3-}$ salts.

The absorption lines investigated are either singlets or else they exhibit hyperfine structure. The fine-structure peaks are not resolved, although, as is known, they can be observed in several polycrystals (for example, in chrome alum powder). In solutions, however, fine structure is manifested only in the line width.

The values of the effective g factors lie near 2, but for a number of ions, in particular for Cu^{2+}, their exact magnitude depends significantly on the immediate environment of the ion. In particular, a replacement of the solvent or the formation of the complex leads to a change in g.

The hyperfine structure of the paramagnetic absorption line is observed in aqueous solutions of simple salts of $^{55}Mn^{2+}$ [2-4], $^{51}VO^{2+}$ [4, 5], and also in solutions of complex salts of $^{63,65}Cu^{2+}$ [6] and $^{183}W^{5+}$ [7].

The spectrum is described by the spin Hamiltonian

$$\hat{\mathscr{H}} = g\beta H_0 \hat{S} + A\hat{I}\hat{S}.$$

The resonance values of the field $H_0 = H_0^*$ for the transitions $(M, m) \to (M - 1, m)$ are given by the expression

$$H_0^* = H - Am - \frac{A^2}{2H}[I(I+1) - m^2],$$

where $H = h\nu/g\beta$, which is in good agreement with experiment for aqueous solutions of Mn^{2+} and VO^{2+}.

At low oscillatory field frequencies ($\nu \approx 100$ Mc) (i.e., under conditions corresponding to the Zeeman effect with hyperfine structure in weak fields), in aqueous solutions of Mn^{2+} salts a single peak with $g = 1.00$ is observed. The position of this peak is described by the formula

$$h\nu = g_F \beta H, \quad \text{(a)}$$

where F is the quantum number of the resultant angular momentum of the electron shell and nucleus, and $g_F = \frac{F(F+1) + J(J+1) - I(I+1)}{2F(F+1)}$.

Actually, for $J = I = 5/2$ for Mn^{2+} we obtain $g_F = 1$. This effect, discovered by Al'tshuler, Kozyrev and Salikhov [2], was the first evidence of the influence of nuclear spin on an electron paramagnetic resonance line. The applicability of formula (a) to the description of the effect in aqueous Mn^{2+} salt solutions shows that the fine splittings are in that case very small compared with the hyperfine splittings. Measurements in solutions of other ions (for instance, VO^{2+}) under weak field conditions have showed that there is no agreement with formula (a).

In solutions containing $^{57}Fe^{3+}$, $^{53}Cr^{3+}$ and hydrated $^{63,65}Cu^{2+}$ ions, no hyperfine structure is observed as a consequence of the smallness of its constants compared with the line width. For $^{57}Fe^{3+}$ and $^{53}Cr^{3+}$ the hyperfine structure constants are also very small in all solids of their compounds. For $^{63,65}Cu_{aq}^{2+}$ ions the situation is to a certain extent close to that observed in solid copper salts, which have trigonal symmetry; in the latter the hyperfine structure constant at sufficiently high temperatures is small and is close to being isotropic; the g factor is also close to being isotropic (see tables for solid Cu^{2+} salts).

In aqueous solution, the copper ion is surrounded by a distorted octahedron of water molecules; one of its axes is extended on account of the Jahn-Teller effect. We have evidently three possible deformation types corresponding to the same energy. Transitions may occur between them, and these in each case give the Jahn-Teller effect a dynamic character. Calculation [8] shows

Table 4.8

g Factors and Hyperfine Structure Constants in Liquid Solutions of Paramagnetic Salts at Room Temperature

Formula	Ion concentration, moles/liter	Diluent	g	A, gauss	Reference
1) VO^{2+} $VOCl_2$; $VOSO_4$	0.5—0,1	Water	1.962±0.002	116	[4]
	0.3	Water:acetone = 1 : 19	1.962 ±0.002	110	[4]
2) Cr^{2+} $Cr(NO_3)_3$	3—0.25	Water	1.972 ±0.008		[9]
3) Mn^{2+} $MnCl_2$; $MnSO_4$;	0.2—0.01	Water	2.000 ±0.002	95.6	[4]
$Mn(NO_3)_2$	0,3	Water	(~2)		[6]
4) Fe^{3+} $[FeF_2]^{1+}$ $[FeF_3]$	0.3	Water	(~2)		[6]
5) Cu^{2+}	4—0.01	Water	2.184 ±0.004		[9]
$Cu(NO_3)_2 \cdot 3H_2O$	2.5	Ethyl alcohol	2.184 ±0.004		[9]
"	2	Acetone	2.156 ±0.004		[9]
"	2—1	Glycerol	2.088* ±0.004		[9]
Cu acetylacetonate	1	Dioxane + toluene	2.138*	~70*	[10]
"	0.08	The same	2.130*	~73*	[10]
"	1	Chloroform + toluene	2.127*	~79*	[10]
"	0,14	Chloroform + toluene	2.124*	~79*	[10]
"	0.19	Chloroform + carbon tetrachloride	1.126*	~77*	[10]
Cu 3-ethylacetonate	1	Dioxane + toluene	2.134*	~73*	[10]
"	0.27	The same	2.129*	~75*	[10]
"	0.15	Dioxane	~2.2*	~36*	[11]
Cu ethanolamine	0.15	Water	2,11*	~75*	[11]
Cu diethanolamine	0.15	Water	2.12*	~75*	[11]

Note to Table 4.8. The values for the g factors and hyperfine structure constants denoted by an asterisk were obtained without consideration of the second approximation.

the possibility of explaining on this basis the single line which is observable in aqueous solutions of copper salts. The existence of resolved hyperfine structure lines in the solution of a number of complex copper salts is due to the fact that the large bulk of the ligands and their greater strength of bonding to the Cu^{2+} ions cause the Jahn-Teller effect to lose in some degree its dynamic character. Accordingly, the hyperfine structure constants increase and evidently become, like the g factor, less isotropic. Values of the g factors and the hyperfine structure constants of ions studied in solution are given in Table 4.8.

We note in conclusion that paramagnetic resonance was also studied in several supercooled solutions (glasses) [12-14]. Thus, for $^{51}VO^{2+}$, $^{53}Cr^{3+}$, $^{55}Mn^{2+}$, and $^{63,65}Cu^{2+}$, ions, hyperfine structure of absorption lines has been observed, and it is anisotropic for VO^{2+} and Cu^{2+}. In the case of Mn^{2+} it is isotropic, a single peak being detected at low frequencies. Just as in aqueous solutions of this ion, $g = 1$, but the peak is broader. One of the results of this work was the establishment of the values of spin $I = 1/2$ for the Fe^{57} nucleus [15]. Experiments have been performed in fused, solidified borax containing Fe^{57}.

Literature for Section 4.3

1. Zavoyskiy, Ye. K. Doctoral Dissertation, Moscow, Phys. Inst. Acad. Sci., 1944.
2. Al'tshuler, S. A., B. M. Kozyrev, S. G. Salikhov. Doklady Akad. Nauk SSSR 71, 855, 1950. (Presented to the Academy March 7, 1948.)
3. Tinkham, M., R. Weinstein, A. F. Kip. Phys. Rev. 84, 848, 1951.
4. Garif'yanov, N. S., B. M. Kozyrev. Doklady Akad. Nauk SSSR 98, 929, 1954.
5. Pake, G. E. Disc. Faraday Soc. 19, 184, 1955.
6. McGarvey, B. R. J. Phys. Chem. 61, 1232, 1957.
7. Weissman, S. I., Clifford S. Garner. J. Am. Chem. Soc. 78, 1072, 1956.
8. Avvakumov, B. I. Zh. Eksp. Teoret. Fiz. (in press).
9. Kozyrev, B. M. Doctoral Dissertation, Moscow, Phys. Inst. Acad. Sci., 1957.
10. McGarvey, B. R. J. Phys. Chem. 60, 71, 1956.
11. Kozyrev, B. M., A. I. Rivkind. Doklady Akad. Nauk SSSR 127, 1044, 1959.
12. Garif'yanov, N. S. Doklady Akad. Nauk SSSR 103, 41, 1955.
13. Sands, K. H. Phys. Rev. 99, 1222, 1955.
14. Garif'yanov, N. S. Izvest. Akad. Nauk SSSR, Ser. Fiz., 21, 824, 1957.
15. Garif'yanov, N. S., M. M. Zaripov, B. M. Kozyrev. Doklady Akad. Nauk SSSR 113, 1243, 1957.

4.4. Application of Electron Paramagnetic Resonance to the Determination of Spins of Atomic Nuclei

One of the important accomplishments of paramagnetic resonance spectra studies has been the determination of the nuclear spins of atomic nuclei. Table 4.9 gives the pertinent data. It must be noted that this table does not indicate the numerous cases in which values of the nuclear spin determined previously by other methods (and sometimes unreliably) have been confirmed by the electron paramagnetic resonance method. We shall not give a special table of the values of the magnetic moments of nuclei obtained by this method, since they cannot compete in accuracy with the data obtained by the nuclear paramagnetic resonance method. Some information regarding magnetic moments are given in the notes to Tables 4.1 - 4.6.

Table 4.9

Values of Nuclear Spins Determined by the Electron Paramagnetic Resonance Method

Isotope	Nuclear spin	Reference	Isotope	Nuclear spin	Reference	Isotope	Nuclear spin	Reference
V^{50}	6	[1]	Mo^{97}	$\frac{5}{2}$	[9]	Sm^{149}	$\frac{7}{2}$	[13]
Cr^{53}	$\frac{3}{2}$	[2]	Ru^{99}	$\frac{5}{2}$	[10]	*Eu^{153}	3	[14]
Mn^{53}	$\frac{7}{2}$	[3]	Ru^{101}	$\frac{5}{2}$	[10]	*Eu^{154}	3	[15]
Fe^{57}	$\frac{1}{2}$	[4]	*Ce^{141}	$\frac{7}{2}$	[11]	Dy^{161}	$\frac{5}{2}$	[16]
*Co^{56}	4	[5]	Nd^{143}	$\frac{7}{2}$	[12]	Dy^{163}	$\frac{5}{2}$	[16]
*Co^{57}	$\frac{7}{2}$	[6]	Nd^{145}	$\frac{7}{2}$	[12]	Er^{167}	$\frac{7}{2}$	[17]
*Co^{60}	5	[7]	Nd^{147}	$\frac{5}{2}$	[11]	*Pu^{239}	$\frac{1}{2}$	[18]
Ni^{61}	$\frac{3}{2}$	[8]	Sm^{147}	$\frac{7}{2}$	[13]	*Pu^{241}	$\frac{5}{2}$	[19]
Mo^{95}	$\frac{5}{2}$	[9]						

Literature for Section 4.4

1. Baker, J. M., B. Bleaney. Proc. Phys. Soc. A65, 952, 1952.
2. Bleaney, B., K. D. Bowers. Proc. Phys. Soc. A64, 1135, 1951.

3. Dobrowolsky, W., R. V. Jones, C. D. Jeffries. Phys. Rev. 104, 1378, 1956.
4. Garif'yanov, N. S., M. M. Zaripov, B. M. Kozyrev. Doklady Akad. Nauk SSSR 113, 1243, 1957.
5. Baker, J. M., B. Bleaney, P. M. Llewellyn, P. F. D. Shaw. Proc. Phys. Soc. A69, 353, 1956.
6. Baker, J. M., B. Bleaney, K. D. Bowers, P. F. D. Shaw, R. S. Trenam. Proc. Phys. Soc. A66, 305, 1953.
7. Dobrowolsky, W., R. V. Jones, C. D. Jeffries. Phys. Rev. 101, 1001, 1956.
8. Woodbury, H. H., S. W. Ludwig. Phys. Rev. Letters 1, 16, 1958.
9. Owen, J., I. M. Ward. Phys. Rev. 102, 591, 1956.
10. Griffiths, J. H. E., J. Owen. Proc. Phys. Soc. A65, 951, 1952.
11. Kedzie, R. W., M. Abragam, C. D. Jeffries. Phys. Rev. 108, 58, 1956.
12. Bleaney, B., H. E. D. Scovil. Proc. Phys. Soc. A63, 1369, 1950.
13. Bogle, G. S., H. E. D. Scovil. Proc. Phys. Soc. A65, 368, 1952.
14. Manenkov, A. A., A. M. Prokhorov, P. S. Trukhlyayev, G. N. Yakovlev, Doklady Akad. Nauk SSSR 112, 623, 1955.
15. Abragam, M., R. W. Kedzie, C. D. Jeffries. Phys. Rev. 108, 58, 1956.
16. Cooke, A. H., J. G. Park. Proc. Phys. Soc. A69, 282, 1956.
17. Bleaney, B., H. E. D. Scovil. Proc. Phys. Soc. A64, 204, 1951.
18. Bleaney, B., P. M. Llewellyn, M. H. L. Pryce, G. R. Hall. Phil. Mag. 54, 773, 1954.
19. Bleaney, B., P. M. Llewellyn, M. H. L. Pryce, G. R. Hall. Phil. Mag. 45, 991, 1954.

Literature on Crystallography

1. Astbury, W. F. Proc. Roy. Soc. A112, 448, 1926; G. F. Morgan, H.D.H. Drew. J. Chem. Phys. 119, 1059, 1921; R. B. Roof. Acta Cryst. 9, 791, 1956.
2. Powell, H. M., A. F. Wells. J. Chem. Phys. 359, 1935.
3. Beevers, C. A., H. Lipson. Proc. Roy. Soc. A146, 570, 1934.
4. Groth, P. Chem. Kristall. 2, 438, 1908.
5. Harker, D. Z. Kristall. 93, 136, 1936.
6. Chrobak, L. Z. Kristall. 88, 35, 1934; R. W. Wyckoff. Crystal Structures, New York, Interscience Publishers, Inc., v. 2, chap. 10, 1951.
7. Robertson, J. M. J. Chem. Soc., 615, 1935.
8. Mazzi, F. Rend. Soc. Mineral Italiana 9, 148, 1953.
9. Kiriyama, R., H. Ibamoto, K. Matsuo. Acta Cryst. 7, 482, 1954.
10. Van Niekerk, J. N., F. R. L. Schoening. Acta Cryst. 6, 227, 1953; P. Groth. Chem. Kristall. 3, 66, 1918.
11. Groth, P. Chem. Kristall. 3, 341, 1916.

12. Cox, E. G., K. C. Webster. J. Chem. Soc., 731, 1935.
13. Ferrari, A. R. C. Accad. Lincei 3, 224, 1926.
14. Wyckoff, R. W. Am. J. Sci. 50, 317, 1920.
15. Zachariasen, W. H. J. Chem. Phys. 3, 197, 1935.
16. Zachariasen, W. H. J. Chem. Phys. 16, 254, 1948.
17. Fankuchen, I. Z. Kristall. 91, 473, 1935.
18. Keeling, R. O. Acta Cryst. 10, 209, 1957.

Chapter V

Shape of a Paramagnetic Resonance Absorption Line in Ionic Crystals and Acoustic Paramagnetic Resonance

5.1. Introduction

The construction of a theory of the shape of a paramagnetic resonance line is a much more complicated problem than the theoretical interpretation of paramagnetic spectra. This subject has been studied very little experimentally. Hence, in spite of the existence of a number of experimental investigations, many problems still remain unsolved.

The deep-rooted analogy existing between electron and nuclear resonance frequently makes it possible to carry over the results obtained in one realm to the other. In studies of the shape of nuclear resonance lines the Bloch phenomenological equation [1] plays a prominent role

$$\left.\begin{aligned} \frac{d\boldsymbol{M}}{dt} &= \gamma[\boldsymbol{M}, \boldsymbol{H}] - \boldsymbol{i}\frac{M_x}{T_2} - \boldsymbol{j}\frac{M_y}{T_2} - \boldsymbol{k}\frac{M_z - M_0}{T_1}, \\ \boldsymbol{H} &= \boldsymbol{k}H_0 + \boldsymbol{i}H_r \cos 2\pi\nu t, \end{aligned}\right\} \tag{5.1}$$

where $\boldsymbol{M}$ is the magnetization at time t, M_0 is the equilibrium value of the magnetization corresponding to the static magnetic field H_0, γ is the gyromagnetic ratio, T_1 and T_2 are the longitudinal and transverse relaxation times, respectively; $\boldsymbol{i}$, $\boldsymbol{j}$ and $\boldsymbol{k}$ are unit vectors along the coordinate axes. If the interaction of the magnetic moment of the particle with the environment under the conditions of an immobile lattice (spin-spin interaction) is much stronger than the interactions with the lattice vibrations (spin-lattice interactions), the longitudinal relaxation time T_1 may be identified with the spin-lattice relaxation time τ, and the transverse relaxation time T_2 may be called the spin-spin relaxation time. If the spin-lattice interactions are stronger than the spin-spin interactions, both the longitudinal and the transverse relaxation times are determined by the spin-lattice interactions, and consequently $T_1 = T_2 = \tau$.

The steady-state solution of (5.1) gives the real and imaginary parts of the paramagnetic susceptibility:

$$\left.\begin{aligned}\chi' &= \frac{1}{2}\chi_0\nu_0 T_2 \frac{\pi^2 T_2(\nu_0-\nu)}{1+4\pi^2T_2^2(\nu_0-\nu)^2+\frac{1}{4}\gamma^2H_r^2T_1T_2},\\ \chi'' &= \frac{1}{2}\chi_0\nu_0 T_2 \frac{2\pi}{1+4\pi^2T_2^2(\nu_0-\nu)^2+\frac{1}{4}\gamma^2H_r^2T_1T_2}.\end{aligned}\right\} \quad (5.2)$$

In most cases electron paramagnetic resonance is observed under conditions in which the saturation factor is small ($1/4\,\gamma^2 H_r^2 T_1 \; T_2 \ll 1$) and may be neglected. It should be kept in mind that in formulas (5.2) only the component of the periodic magnetic field that is polarized in the direction of the Larmor precession is taken into account. The magnitudes of χ' and χ'' therefore depend on the sign of the static magnetic field, and hence on the sign of ν_0. If $\nu_0 = 0$, it also follows from (5.2) that $\chi'' = 0$. This of course is incorrect, since absorption also occurs when no static magnetic field is present. This shortcoming has been eliminated by Garstens [2], who obtained the following formulas for a linearly polarized wave:

$$\left.\begin{aligned}\chi' &= \frac{1}{2}\chi_0\left[\frac{1+4\pi^2\nu_0(\nu-\nu_0)T_2^2}{1+4\pi^2(\nu-\nu_0)^2T_2^2}+\frac{1-4\pi^2\nu_0(\nu+\nu_0)T_2^2}{1+4\pi^2(\nu+\nu_0)^2T_2^2}\right],\\ \chi'' &= \frac{1}{2}\chi_0\nu T_2\left[\frac{4\pi^2}{1+4\pi^2(\nu-\nu_0)^2T_2^2}+\frac{4\pi^2}{1+4\pi^2(\nu+\nu_0)^2T_2^2}\right].\end{aligned}\right\} \quad (5.3)$$

Note that these expressions agree with the well-known dispersion formulas of Van Vleck and Weisskopf [3].

Shaposhnikov [4] developed a thermodynamical method for the study of relaxation phenomena. Taking up the problem of paramagnetic resonance [5], he arrived at the Van Vleck-Weisskopf formula after solving differential equations for the magnetization of a paramagnetic substance, obtained by means of thermodynamics under the assumption of the existence of a spin system interacting weakly with the lattice vibrations. Skrotskiy and Kurbatov [6], using Shaposhnikov's method, have produced a general thermodynamic theory of relaxation and resonance phenomena in two spin systems. These types of systems are often encountered among paramagnetic substances, since many substances contain two species of paramagnetic particles.

Wangsness and Bloch [7] have developed a statistical quantum theory of dynamical phenomena in paramagnetic substances, starting with the equation of motion of an appropriate statistical operator. It has been shown that Bloch's phenomenological equation (5.1) is correct if no spin-spin interactions exist and if the paramagnetism is of the pure spin type (no splitting of the spin energy levels by electric fields). Thus, the Bloch phenomenological equation (or any of its various modifications) is applicable over a very limited domain. It is rather extensively used, however, since it gives a qualitative explanation of the different aspects of paramagnetic resonance phenomena: 1) it follows from the equation that the shape of a resonance line is determined by the time $T_2 = \tau'$ and is independent of $T_1 = \tau$ if the spin-spin interactions are stronger than the spin-lattice interactions; and contrariwise, the line shape is determined by the time $T_2 = T_1 = \tau$ and is independent of the spin-spin interactions if they are weaker than the spin-lattice interactions; 2) the equation enables us to take into account the dependence of the line shape on the intensity of the periodic magnetic field which is capable of causing a "saturation" effect; 3) the equation makes it possible to quantitatively evaluate various transient processes in radio engineering equipment containing paramagnetic substances.

The difficulties of constructing a microscopic quantum theory of processes determining the shape of a paramagnetic resonance line compel us to consider two extreme cases: either the spin-spin interactions are much stronger than, or much weaker than, the spin-lattice interactions. As a result, we may assume that in the first case we are dealing with interactions of the system of paramagnetic particles which exist under adiabatic conditions when no exchange of energy with lattice vibrations occurs (or with the Brownian motion of the particles in the liquid). In the second case, it is customarily assumed that the paramagnetic particles are isolated from one another and that each individually interacts with the lattice vibrations. In the following sections we shall devote ourselves to a theoretical and experimental investigation of spin-spin and spin-lattice interactions in ionic crystals and their liquid solutions. In addition, we shall examine the theory of acoustic paramagnetic resonance — a phenomenon whose study may give valuable information concerning spin-lattice interactions.

5.2. Spin-Spin Interactions

1. If two neighboring paramagnetic atoms are located at a distance r from one another, each Zeeman energy level is broadened by the value $\sim h/\beta^2 r^{-3}$ as a result of the dipole interaction. This may be intuitively visualized in the following manner. Besides the external magnetic field H_0, a local field H_{loc} created by the neighboring particles also acts on each atom. The resonance condition therefore takes the form $h\nu = g\beta_0(H_0 + H_{loc})$. Since the mean spread of possible values of H_{loc} is of the order β/r^3, it is clear that for $\Delta\nu$ one obtains the value given above for the width of the resonance line.

If all the paramagnetic particles are identical then, besides the magnetostatic broadening mechanism considered by us, another broadening mechanism — the dynamic one — will act. Let us consider two precessing dipoles with oppositely directed moments. Each of them will create at the other's location a periodic field of the resonance frequency, under whose influence an exchange of orientations of the moments is possible, since the total energy is conserved in this case. The limitation on the lifetime of each particle in a given Zeeman energy level leads to a broadening which according to the uncertainty principle has the value $\sim h/\beta^2 r^{-3}$.

The methods of calculation developed up to the present time make possible a calculation of the moments of the resonance absorption curves. By the k-th moment of the absorption line we mean the following quantity:

$$M_k = \int (\nu - \nu_0)^k g(\nu)\, d\nu. \tag{5.4}$$

If the paramagnetic resonance line is Gaussian in shape (1.20), $M_2 = \sigma^2$, $M_4 = 3\sigma^4$. If the line shape is Lorentzian (1.21), in order that the integrals M_k for $k > 0$ might converge, it is necessary to cut the curve $g(\nu)$. If we assume that when $|\nu - \nu_0| \geq \alpha$ the function $g(\nu) = 0$, then $M_2 = \alpha\Delta\nu/\pi$, $M_4 = \alpha^3\Delta\nu/3\pi$.

This method was first used by Waller and later by Broer [9] to evaluate the magnitude of the spin-spin interaction. The first analysis of the shape of the paramagnetic resonance absorption line by the method of moments was made by Van Vleck [10]. The Van Vleck theory is based on the following assumptions: a) the magnetism of the particle is purely spin; b) no ferromagnetism exists; c) the frequency of the oscillating field is so high that the Zeeman energy is much greater than the mean energy of the spin-spin interaction between neighboring particles; d) the exchange forces are isotropic; e) the temperature is so high that all Zeeman levels are equally populated.

The Hamiltonian of the spin system contains a Zeeman energy, dipolar and exchange interactions:

$$\hat{\mathcal{H}} = \hat{\mathcal{H}}_{\text{Zee}} + \hat{\mathcal{H}}_{\text{dip}} + \hat{\mathcal{H}}_{\text{exc}} \tag{5.5}$$

where

$$\hat{\mathcal{H}}_{\text{Zee}} = g\beta H_0 \sum_j \hat{S}_{zj}, \tag{5.6}$$

$$\hat{\mathcal{H}}_{\text{dip}} = g^2\beta^2 \sum_{j<k} [r_{jk}^{-3} (\hat{\boldsymbol{S}}_j \hat{\boldsymbol{S}}_k) - 3r_{jk}^{-5} (\boldsymbol{r}_{jk}\hat{\boldsymbol{S}}_j)(\boldsymbol{r}_{jk}\hat{\boldsymbol{S}}_k)], \tag{5.7}$$

$$\hat{\mathcal{H}}_{\text{exc}} = \sum_{j<k} \tilde{A}_{jk} \hat{\boldsymbol{S}}_j \hat{\boldsymbol{S}}_k. \tag{5.8}$$

Here $\hat{S}_{zj}$ denotes the z-th component of the vector matrix of the spin angular momentum of the j-th atom; r_{jk} is the distance between the j-th and k-th atoms; $\tilde{A}_{jk} = 2Z^2 I_{jk}$, where Z is the number of electrons in an unfilled atomic shell; and I_{jk} is the ordinary exchange integral. The dipole interaction matrix is conveniently represented in the following form:

$$\left.\begin{aligned}
&\mathscr{H}_{\text{dip}} = \hat{A} + \hat{B} + \hat{C} + \hat{D} + \hat{E} + \hat{F} = g^2\beta^2 \sum r_{jk}^{-3} \times \\
&\qquad \times (\hat{a}_{jk} + \hat{b}_{jk} + \hat{c}_{jk} + \hat{d}_{jk} + \hat{e}_{jk} + \hat{f}_{jk}), \\
&\hat{a}_{jk} = (1 - 3\cos^2\vartheta_{jk})\,\hat{S}_{zj}\hat{S}_{zk}, \\
&\hat{b}_{jk} = \frac{1}{4}(1 - 3\cos^2\vartheta_{jk})\,(\hat{S}_{k+}\hat{S}_{j-} + \hat{S}_{k-}\hat{S}_{j+}), \\
&\hat{c}_{jk} = \hat{d}^*_{jk} = -\frac{3}{2}\sin\vartheta_{jk}\cos\vartheta_{jk}\,e^{-i\varphi_{jk}}(\hat{S}_{j+}\hat{S}_{zk} + \hat{S}_{jz}\hat{S}_{k+}), \\
&\hat{e}_{jk} = \hat{f}^*_{jk} = -\frac{3}{4}\sin^2\vartheta_{jk}\,e^{-2i\varphi_{jk}}\hat{S}_{j+}\hat{S}_{k+},
\end{aligned}\right\} \tag{5.9}$$

where $\hat{S}_{\pm} = \hat{S}_x \pm i\hat{S}_y$, and ϑ_{jk} is the angle between H_0 and r_{jk}.

Let us choose a representation in which the matrices S_{zj} are diagonal; their eigenvalues are denoted by m_j. The magnetic quantum number of the entire spin system will equal $M = \sum m_j$. If we neglect the interactions between spins, we obtain a system of equally spaced energy levels $E_M = g\beta H_0 M$, which will be strongly degenerate, since there exists an enormous number of combinations of values m_j which can give the same value of M. The eigenfunctions of $\mathscr{H}_{\text{Zee}}$ are denoted by $\psi_{M;\, m_1,\, m_2,\, \ldots}$. If $\mathscr{H}_{\text{dip}} + \mathscr{H}_{\text{exc}}$ is considered as a perturbation and the usual perturbation theory for a degenerate case is employed to solve the problem in the first approximation, it is necessary to calculate the matrix elements of the perturbation by means of the ψ functions referring only to the one energy level E_M under consideration. It is easy to see that application of the separate parts of the perturbation operator to $\psi_{M,\, m_1,\, m_2,\, \ldots}$ gives new ψ functions, whose values of M, m_j, m_k are changed in the following manner:

$$\left.\begin{aligned}
&\hat{a}_{jk}: \quad \Delta M = 0,\ \Delta m_j = 0,\ \Delta m_k = 0; \\
&\hat{d}_{jk}: \quad \Delta M = -1,\ \Delta m_j = \begin{cases} 0 \\ -1 \end{cases},\ \Delta m_k = \begin{cases} -1 \\ 0 \end{cases}; \\
&\hat{b}_{jk}: \quad \Delta M = 0,\ \Delta m_j = \pm 1,\ \Delta m_k = \mp 1; \\
&\hat{e}_{jk}: \quad \Delta M = 2,\ \Delta m_j = 1,\ \Delta m_k = 1; \\
&\hat{c}_{jk}: \quad \Delta M = 1,\ \Delta m_j = \begin{cases} 0 \\ 1 \end{cases},\ \Delta m_k = \begin{cases} 1 \\ 0 \end{cases}; \\
&\hat{f}_{jk}: \ \Delta M = -2,\ \Delta m_j = -1,\ \Delta m_k = -1.
\end{aligned}\right\} \tag{5.10}$$

The operator $\mathscr{H}_{\text{exc}}$ acts similarly on $\hat{b}_{jk}$. It is apparent from (5.10) and (5.8) that the nonvanishing matrix elements belonging to the level E_M, contain only the matrices $\hat{A}$, $\hat{B}$ and $\mathscr{H}_{\text{exc}}$.

The probability of a transition between the two Zeeman levels E_M and $E_{M'}$ under the influence of a radio-frequency field directed along the x axis will evidently be proportional to $|\langle M|\hat{S}_x|M'\rangle|^2$. Since the matrix element of operator $\hat{S}_x = \Sigma \hat{S}_{xj}$ in the first order differs from zero only if $M' = M \pm 1$, only one clear absorption line of the Larmor frequency ν_0 can possibly appear. In the next order for calculation of the perturbation energy we also take into account the operators $\hat{C}$, $\hat{D}$, $\hat{E}$ and $\hat{F}$, and as a result the wave functions corresponding to the energy level E_M, take the form $\psi_M + \varepsilon_1\psi_{M-1} + \varepsilon_2\psi_{M+1} + \varepsilon_3\psi_{M+2} + \varepsilon_4\psi_{M-2}$, where ϵ_i are of the order $\beta^2 r^{-3} / g\beta H_0$. It is clear that, in the second order, transitions are also possible from level M to levels $M' = M$, $M \pm 2$, $M \pm 3$. Thus, near the main line of frequency ν_0 satellites appear at the frequencies 0, $2\nu_0$, and $3\nu_0$. The intensity of the satellites will be related to the intensity of the main line approximately as $\epsilon^2 : 1$. If we take into account a still higher-order approximation, the appearance of weak satellites at still higher frequencies is possible.

2. In a treatment of the main resonance line one must truncate the Hamiltonian (5.5) by omitting the terms $\hat{C}$, $\hat{D}$, $\hat{E}$, $\hat{F}$, which do not commute with the principal part of the Hamiltonian $\mathscr{H}_{\text{Zee}}$. The eigenvalues of the truncated Hamiltonian $\hat{\mathscr{H}}^+$ are denoted by $\mathscr{H}_n$, and the transition frequencies by $\nu_{nn'}$. Then, by definition, the mean square frequency of the absorption line is

$$\langle \nu^2 \rangle = \frac{\sum\limits_{n,\,n'} \{\nu^2_{nn'}\, |\langle n' | \hat{S}_x | n \rangle|^2\}}{\sum\limits_{n,\,n'} |\langle n' | \hat{S}_x | n \rangle|^2}. \tag{5.11}$$

This expression can be represented in the form

$$\langle \nu^2 \rangle = -\frac{Sp\,(\hat{\mathscr{H}}^+ \hat{S}_x - \hat{S}_x \hat{\mathscr{H}}^+)^2}{h^2 Sp\,(\hat{S}_x)^2}. \tag{5.12}$$

It would be quite hopeless to attempt to calculate the eigenvalues of $\mathscr{H}_n$, because their number is comparable with the number of atoms in the crystal. The great advantage of formula (5.12) is that it includes only diagonal sums, whose invariance enables us to make calculations in an arbitrary representation. The simplest representation evidently will be one in which the spatial quantization is accomplished for each spin individually. After calculating the matrix traces occurring in (5.12), the second moment of the absorption line is found to be equal to

$$M_2 = \left\langle \left(\nu - \frac{g\beta H_0}{h} \right)^2 \right\rangle = \frac{3}{4} g^4 \beta^4 h^{-2} S(S+1) \sum_k r_{1k}^{-6} \cdot (3\cos^2\vartheta_{1k} - 1)^2, \quad (5.13)$$

where k enumerates all the magnetic particles of the lattice, and the subscript 1 refers to some atom taken as the origin. For a crystalline powder

$$M_2 = \frac{3}{5} g^4 \beta^4 h^{-2} S(S+1) \sum_k r_{1k}^{-6}. \quad (5.14)$$

For a simple cubic lattice whose constant is d, we obtain

$$\sum_k r_{1k}^{-6} = 8.5\, d^{-6}. \quad (5.15)$$

If the quantum-mechanical calculations are replaced by magnetostatic calculations and in this way we discard the influence of the "dynamic" broadening mechanism, for M_2 we obtain the same expression (5.13), multiplied by 4/9. This reduced magnitude must occur when one speaks of broadening produced by interactions of different kinds of dipoles, for instance, interactions between paramagnetic atoms and nuclear spins of the neighboring diamagnetic particles. Thus, if there exist two species of magnetic particles with spins S and S' and with spectroscopic splitting factors g and g', the second moment of the resonance line arising from particles of the first type will be formed from (5.13) and the following expression:

$$M_2' = \frac{1}{3} g'^4 \beta^4 h^{-2} S'(S'+1) \sum r_{1j}^{-6} (3\cos^2\vartheta_{1j} - 1)^2, \quad (5.16)$$

where the subscript 1 refers to a particle of the first type taken as the origin of the calculations, and j enumerates particles of the second type. If $g' = g$, these formulas are not valid, because the resonance lines given by particles of various types now coalesce into one line. This case has been considered in [11].

Van Vleck has also made a calculation of the second moment $\tilde{M}_2$ of the absorption curve, which embraces not only the main line, but also additional lines at the frequencies $0,\ 2g\beta H_0,\ 3g\beta H_0$. . It was found that $\tilde{M}_2 = 10/3\ M_2$, this relation, which Broer [9] again examined, being independent of H_0, since although the heights of the additional absorption curves are inversely proportional to H_0, the frequencies are approximately linear with respect to H_0.

Let us return to a consideration of the main paramagnetic resonance line. It is apparent from (5.13) that the isotropic exchange forces do not influence at all the magnitude of the second moment of the absorption line. In order to determine the influence of exchange forces on the line shape, it is therefore necessary to consider higher moments. In the same paper Van Vleck calculated the fourth moments; later Glebashev calculated the sixth moment [12]. We note that the odd moments equal zero, and consequently the absorption line is symmetrical. Calculations have shown that in the case of pure dipolar interactions the ratios of the moments are close to the values obtained for Gaussian functions, namely; $M_6^{1/6} : M_4^{1/4} : M_2^{1/2} = 1.57:1.32:1$. If exchange interactions are stronger than the dipole interactions, then $M_4^{1/4} : M_2^{1/2} \gg 1$, and consequently the line acquires a Lorentzian shape. Since the area of the absorption curve and its second moment do not contain exchange integrals, one may conclude that the absorption becomes narrower at the center and correspondingly less step at the edges.

This narrowing of the lines under the influence of exchange forces, mentioned before in [13, 14], is a result of the basic assumptions of Van Vleck's theory, which in many cases are unacceptable for real crystals.

Van Vleck's theory of dipolar broadening has been extended by Kittel and Abrahams [15] to the case of solid paramagnetic solutions. If the concentration of paramagnetic atoms $f > 0.1$, the line is found to retain its Gaussian shape and its width is proportional to $\sqrt{f}$; if, however, $f < 0.01$, the line shape becomes Lorentzian, and the width $\sim f$. Glebashev [16] has generalized these calculations, taking into account also the influence of exchange isotropic forces.

3. The assumption of the purely spin nature of paramagnetism greatly limits the range of applicability of Van Vleck's theory. If the effective spin $S' > 1/2$, however, the electric field of the crystal always causes small splittings of the spin levels. If $S' = 1/2$, the effect of the crystalline field is still manifest, and the g factor becomes anisotropic.

Pryce and Stevens [17] have generalized the Van Vleck theory and have indicated a method of calculating the moments of a curve which is applicable to the most diverse cases. The general method of calculation consists of the following. The Hamiltonian of the spin system is represented as

$$\hat{\mathscr{H}} = \hat{\mathscr{H}}_0 + \hat{W}, \tag{5.17}$$

where the main part of the Hamiltonian $\hat{\mathscr{H}}_0$ determines the energy levels, transitions between which produce the individual lines of the paramagnetic resonance spectrum, while the perturbation $\hat{W}$ causes the line broadening. Furthermore, expressions of type

(5.12) are used to calculate the moments of the line. To isolate the one absorption line under consideration, the operators $\tilde{W}$ and $\tilde{S}_x$ are truncated so that the truncated operator $\hat{\tilde{W}}$ commutes with $\mathscr{H}_0$, and the truncated operator $\hat{\tilde{S}}_x$ contains only off-diagonal matrix elements, guaranteeing the required quantum transitions. Truncation of the matrix W and $\tilde{S}_X$ is performed either by means of appropriate projection matrices, as proposed by Pryce and Stevens [17], or by direct cancelling of the unwanted matrix elements.

The following cases were considered in [17]: 1) one type of particle exists, all of whose energy spacings in the unperturbed state are different; 2) the particles in the unperturbed state have coincident or nearly degenerate levels; 3) two types of particles exist; 4) there exists hyperfine structure of the energy levels of the particles. In addition, Pryce and Stevens have examined the subject of the dependence of the absorption line width on temperature and crystal shape. The perturbation is of the customary two-particle nature and may be represented in the form $\hat{W} = \Sigma_{ij} \hat{W}_{ij}$. If the second moment is expanded in a series in $1/kT$, it becomes

$$M_2 = a_0 \sum_{i,j} |\langle W_{ij}\rangle|^2 + \frac{a_1}{kT} \sum_{i,j} |\langle W_{ij}\rangle| + \dots, \tag{5.18}$$

where a_0, a_1 are certain quantities which are independent of W and T Since W_{jk}^2 decreases no slower than $1/r_{jk}^6$, for the temperature-independent part of the moment M_2 one may perform the transformation

$$\sum_{i,j}{}' |\langle W_{ij}\rangle|^2 = N \sum_{j} |\langle W_{ij}\rangle|^2.\,^{1)} \tag{5.19}$$

It makes no difference whether the origin of a chosen particle i is located at the center of the crystal or near its boundary. Transformation (5.19) is not valid for the part of the moment proportional to $1/kT$, since W_{ij} increases slowly as r_{ij} increases. As a result, a displacement of the paramagnetic resonance line must occur near the Curie point, and the line width will depend on temperature and crystal shape. From the microscopic point of view, one may say that near the Curie point the demagnetization of the investigated sample becomes a significant factor. Glebashev [18] has made detailed calculations of the temperature dependence of the moments of the resonance line. At sufficiently high temperatures paramagnetic resonance lines will become asymmetric and their widths will change.

---

[1] A prime over the sign $\sum$ means that $j \neq k$.

4. Ishiguro, Kambe and Usui [19] have calculated M_2 for nickel fluosilicate, in which there is only one magnetic ion per unit cell. The main Hamiltonian is

$$\hat{\mathscr{H}}'_0 = \sum_i (g\beta H_0 \hat{S}_i + D\hat{S}^2_{zi}). \qquad (5.20)$$

A diagram of the spin levels of the individual particle is given in Figure 3.2. If the field H_0 is parallel to the hexagonal axis of the crystal (Z axis) for both line $-1 \to 0$ and $0 \to 1$ we have

$$h^2 M_2 = \sum' \left[\tilde{A}^2_{ik} + \frac{5}{4}\frac{g^4\beta^4}{r^6_{ik}}(3\cos^2\vartheta_{ik} - 1)^2\right]. \qquad (5.21)$$

For the case $H_0 \perp Z$, if we assume $g\beta H_0 \gg D$, this formula will be correct. Calculation of the lattice sums gives

$$h^2 M_2 = 6\tilde{A}^2 + \frac{3.13 g^4\beta^4}{d^6}, \ H_0 \parallel Z; \ h^2 M_2 = 6\tilde{A}^2 + \frac{6.50 g^4\beta^4}{d^6}, \ H_0 \perp Z. \qquad (5.22)$$

From a comparison with experiment [20] one may estimate the magnitude of the exchange coefficient $|\tilde{A}| = 0.027\ \text{cm}^{-1}$.

Griffith and Owen [21] have discovered a discrepancy between their measurements of the line shape of nickel Tutton salts and the theory of Ishiguro, Kambe and Usui. Stevens [22] has made detailed calculations and shown that the discrepancies are explained first by the presence in Tutton salts of two nonequivalent paramagnetic ions per unit cell, and second, a more complex form of the spin Hamiltonian containing the additional term $E(\hat{S}^2_x - \hat{S}^2_y)$. From a comparison with experimental data, Stevens evaluated the exchange coefficient $\tilde{A} = -0.026\ \text{cm}^{-1}$.

Kambe and Ollom [23] have calculated the second moment for the central line (transition $-1/2 \to 1/2$) of the paramagnetic resonance, if the spin of the particles S is a half-integer. Due to the action of the crystalline field, the other transitions gives lines at different frequencies and will not be considered in this book. a) If all the particles are equivalent, then

$$h^2 M_2 = \left[\frac{S(S+1)}{3} + \frac{2S^2(S+1)^2 - 3S(S+1) + \frac{1}{8}}{2(2S+1)}\right]\sum_k{}' \tilde{A}^2_{jk} +$$
$$+ \left[-\frac{2}{3}S(S+1) + \frac{2S^2(S+1)^2 + \frac{7}{8}}{2(2S+1)}\right]\sum_k{}' \tilde{A}_{jk}\frac{g^2\beta^2}{r^3_{jk}} \times$$
$$\times (3\cos^2\vartheta_{jk} - 1) + \left[\frac{S(S+1)}{3} + \frac{\frac{1}{2}S^2(S+1)^2 + \frac{3}{4}S(S+1) + \frac{13}{32}}{2(2S+1)}\right] \times$$
$$\times \sum_k{}' \frac{g^4\beta^4}{r^6_{jk}}(3\cos^2\vartheta_{jk} - 1)^2. \qquad (5.23)$$

b) If there exist particles of another species with a g factor g' and spin S', they contribute an additional term:

$$h^2 M_2' = \frac{1}{3} S'(S'+1) \sum_{k'}{}' \left[\tilde{A}_{jk'} + \frac{gg'\beta^2}{r_{jk'}^3} (1 - 3\cos^2\vartheta_{jk'})\right]^2. \qquad (5.24)$$

c) If there exist several nonequivalent particles of the same species in a crystalline lattice, the spin-spin interaction of the particles with the other nonequivalent particles gives an additional contribution to the second moment:

$$\begin{aligned} h^2 M_2'' = & \left[\frac{1}{3} S(S+1) - \frac{1}{4}(2S+1) + \frac{(2S+1)^3}{32}\right] \sum_{k'} \tilde{A}_{jk'}^2 + \\ & + \left[-\frac{2}{3} S(S+1) + \frac{1}{8}(2S+1) + \frac{(2S+1)^3}{32}\right] \sum_{k'} \tilde{A}_{jk'} \frac{g^2\beta^2}{r_{jk'}^3} \times \\ & \times (3\cos^2\vartheta_{jk'} - 1) + \left[\frac{1}{3} S(S+1) + \frac{1}{8}(2S+1) + \frac{(2S+1)^3}{128}\right] \times \\ & \times \sum_{k'} \frac{g^4\beta^4}{r_{jk'}^6} (3\cos^2\vartheta_{jk'} - 1)^2. \end{aligned} \qquad (5.25)$$

If M_2^* denotes the second moment calculated from formula (5.13), which is valid when no crystalline splitting exists, for purely dipole interactions we obtain

Spin	$\frac{M_2}{M_2^*}$	$\frac{M_2''}{M_2^*}$
$\frac{1}{2}$	1	1
$\frac{3}{2}$	$\frac{9}{10}$	$\frac{4}{5}$
$\frac{5}{2}$	$\frac{107}{105}$	$\frac{257}{315}$
$\frac{7}{2}$	$\frac{881}{756}$	$\frac{164}{189}$

Abragam and Kambe [24] have calculated the dipolar broadening of a resonance line due to transitions between the energy sublevels arising in an electric field of the crystal when external magnetic field equals zero. In this case the following assumptions were made: a) spin $S = 1$ or $3/2$; b) the crystalline field has axial symmetry; c) the axis of symmetry is the same for all particles. The following expressions are obtained for the second moment of a resonance line:

$$
\left.
\begin{array}{l}
S=1:\quad M_2=\dfrac{g^4\beta^4}{4h^2}\sum_k{}' r_{jk}^{-6}\times \\
\quad\times[5(1-3\gamma_{jk}^2)^2+9(1-\gamma_{jk}^2)^2-2(1-3\gamma_{jk}^2)(\alpha_{jk}^2-\beta_{jk}^2)], \\
S=\dfrac{3}{2}:\quad M_2=\dfrac{g^4\beta^4}{96h^2}\sum_k{}' r_{jk}^{-6}\times \\
\times[207(1-3\gamma_{jk}^2)^2+1512\gamma_{jk}^2(1-3\gamma_{jk}^2)+459(1-\gamma_{jk}^2)^2- \\
\qquad -108(1-3\gamma_{jk}^2)(\alpha_{jk}^2-\beta_{jk}^2)],
\end{array}
\right\} \quad (5.26)
$$

where α_{jk}, β_{jk}, γ_{jk} are the direction cosines of the radium vector r_{jk}; the Z axis is taken as the axis of symmetry of the crystalline field. For a cubic lattice with an electric field parallel to one of the axes,

$$
S=1:\quad M_2=28.4\frac{g^4\beta^4}{h^2d^6};\quad S=\frac{3}{2}:\quad M_2=60.0\frac{g^4\beta^4}{h^2d^6}. \qquad (5.27)
$$

The broadening caused by the existence of "nonresonant" particles (particles that do not participate in the establishment of the resonance line) has also been calculated.

5. In all the papers we have been examining which take into account the existence of energy splitting produced by the electric field of the crystal, the influence of the crystalline field has been assumed to be much stronger than the dipolar or exchange interaction. When this is not the case, resonance lines will appear when the external field causes a splitting that is much greater than that of the crystalline field. Hence the term of the Hamiltonian which takes into account the effect of the crystalline field must be transferred from the main part $\hat{\mathscr{H}}_0$ to the perturbation part $\hat{W}$. The crystalline field together with the dipolar and exchange interactions will participate in the broadening of the resonance line. This case has been considered by Bersohn [25] who proposed that the effect of the crystalline field may be transmitted to an axially symmetric Hamiltonian $ES_z^2+FS_z^4$. Calculations give the second moment as

$$
\begin{aligned}
h^2M_2 &= \frac{3}{4}g^4\beta^4S(S+1)\sum r_{1k}^{-6}(3\cos^2\vartheta_{1k}-1)+ \\
&+\frac{1}{5}[4S(S+1)-3]E^2+\frac{1}{35}[48S^2(S+1)^2-76S(S+1)+30]EF+ \qquad (5.28)\\
&+\frac{1}{105}[80S^3(S+1)^3-268S^2(S+1)^2+336S(S+1)-135]F^2.
\end{aligned}
$$

Here, just as in the case considered by Van Vleck, the second moment is independent of the isotropic exchange interactions.

6. In all crystals whose paramagnetic ions contain an odd number of electrons, the ground state of these ions is found to be a Kramers doublet. Such a class of substances includes the previously mentioned rare earth salts, many iron group salts, etc. Although the ground state in all these cases may be characterized by the effective spin $S' = 1/2$, still the Van Vleck theory is usually not valid here. The electric field ofthe crystal cannot split a level with $S' = 1/2$, but it can cause a very anisotropic g factor.

Kopvillem [26] has made a calculation of the second moment of the resonance line for this case under the following assumptions: a) the crystal temperature is so low that only the lowest Kramers doublet is populated; b) all the paramagnetic ions are equivalent, and hence have the same g tensor. Since in the type of paramagnetic substances under consideration the spin-lattice interactions are for the most part very strong, and since observations of the paramagnetic resonance must be made at low temperatures, the temperature dependence of the line shape, which was adopted in calculations of the moment M_2, may turn out to be significant.

Calculations have shown that: a) the line width depends on the direction of the static magnetic field; b) isotropic exchange forces affect the magnitude of M_2; hence the exchange interactions in general increase the width of the resonance line; this broadening is different for different directions of the magnetic field; c) the width of the line caused by dipole interactions decreases with a reduction of temperature. The magnitude of the second moment due to dipolar interactions is found to equal

$$\left.\begin{aligned} M_2 = \frac{\beta^4}{8(1+e^m)h^2} \sum_j{}' \Big\{ & (B_{1j}^{(x)} + B_{1j}^{(y)})^2 e^m + B_{1j}^{(z)2} \times \\ & \times \left(\frac{3}{2} + 2e^m + \frac{1}{2} e^{2m}\right) - B_{1j}^{(z)}(B_{1j}^{(x)} + B_{1j}^{(y)})(1+3e^m)\Big\}, \\ m = -\frac{g_{zz}\beta H_0}{kT}, \quad B_{1j}^{(\alpha)} & = g_{\alpha\alpha}^2 r_{1j}^{-3}(1 - 3\cos^2\vartheta_{1j}^{(\alpha)}), \quad \alpha = x, y, z, \end{aligned}\right\} \qquad (5.29)$$

where x, y, z are the principal axes of the g tensor, $\vartheta_{1j}^{(\alpha)}$ are the angles between r_{1j} and the α axis. When the field H_0 is parallel to the axis of symmetry of the crystal, calculation of the lattice sums (e.g., for rare earth ethylsulfates) gives

$$\left.\begin{aligned} M_2 = 66{,}73\, g_{\parallel}^2 \beta^2 [(1+e^m) a^6]^{-1} [e^m (\varkappa^4 + 3\varkappa^2 + 2) + \\ + 0{,}5\, e^{2m} + 1{,}5 + \varkappa^2], \\ \varkappa = \frac{g_{\perp}}{g_{\parallel}}, \end{aligned}\right\} \qquad (5.30)$$

where a is the larger side of the unit cell of the ethylsulfate. These calculations are further developed in the papers by Kopvillem and others [114].

7. Exchange interactions, if they are sufficiently strong, not only affect the width of the paramagnetic resonance line but can also alter its position. One such case was experimentally investigated by Bagguley and Griffiths [27] in the salt $CuSO_4 \cdot 5H_2O$. A unit cell of this substance contains two ions with different magnetic axes. Therefore, with the aid of a radio-frequency field of wavelength $\lambda = 0.85$ cm, two resonance lines of width equal to about 115 gauss were observed. If $\lambda = 3$ cm, these lines must be separated by about 500 gauss, but experiment shows that they merge into a single line. A theoretical explanation of this fact was given by Pryce [28]. The Hamiltonian of the spin system is

$$\hat{\mathcal{H}} = \beta \hat{S}' g' H_0 + \beta \hat{S}'' g'' H_0 + \hat{\mathcal{H}}_{\text{exc}}, \tag{5.31}$$

where S' and S'' are the total spins of all particles of the first and second type; g' and g'' are the corresponding g tensors. Here for simplicity the dipolar interactions are neglected. Formula (5.31) may be represented in the form

$$\left.\begin{aligned} \hat{\mathcal{H}} &= \hat{\mathcal{H}}_0 + \hat{W}, \\ \hat{\mathcal{H}}_0 &= \frac{\beta}{2}(\hat{S}' + \hat{S}'')(g' + g'')H_0 + \hat{\mathcal{H}}_{\text{exc}}, \\ \hat{W} &= \frac{\beta}{2}(S' - S'')(g' - g'')H_0. \end{aligned}\right\} \tag{5.31a}$$

If the "perturbation" $\hat{W}$ does not exist, since both terms of $\hat{\mathcal{H}}_0$ commute with one another, the transverse radio-frequency field must cause transitions between states for which the components of the total spin $S' + S''$ in the direction of $(g' + g'')H_0$ differ by unity, and the exchange interaction is conserved. As a result a single sharp absorption line should arise. The perturbation $\hat{W}$ changes the spacings between the energy levels, transitions between them following the selection rules. The line becomes broader. In addition, the perturbation mixes the wave function belonging to different levels of the exchange energy, as a consequence of which the selection rules change and the line shape changes. At high frequencies and at large fields H_0 the magnitude $\hat{W}$ can no longer be considered as a perturbation; it becomes comparable to the exchange energy. It is easily seen that under these conditions two absorption peaks appear.

Another example of the influence of exchange interactions on the appearance of the spectrum is the decrease under the action of exchange forces of the hyperfine splittings of the resonance line. Let the interaction of the magnetic moments of the nucleus with the electron shell be characterized by an isotropic hyperfine structure constant A. If we do not take the spin of the nucleus into consideration, we may for simplicity assume that all the paramagnetic atoms precess around the external magnetic field with the same Larmor frequency. On account of the interaction between the electronic and nuclear moments, the various atoms will precess with equal probability at one of $2I+1$ frequencies that differ from each other by small magnitudes of the order of A/h. Let the exchange period equal $\tau = h/J$ (J is the exchange integral). If $\tau \gg h/A$, during the exchange, the precession frequency will change by a magnitude $\sim A/h$; if however, $\tau \leq h/A$, all these changes are averaged and the individual hyperfine structure peaks merge into a single line. Consequently, a decrease in the hyperfine splittings can be expected when $J \geqslant A$. These arguments may be quantitatively confirmed by the method of moments. The Hamiltonian of the spin system may be written in the form

$$\hat{\mathscr{H}} = g\beta H_0 \sum_j \hat{S}_{zj} + \sum_{j,k} \tilde{A}_{jk} \hat{\boldsymbol{S}}_j \hat{\boldsymbol{S}}_k + A \sum_j \hat{\boldsymbol{S}}_j \hat{\boldsymbol{I}}_j.$$

Here the first term denotes the Zeeman energy, the second the exchange interactions, and the third the magnetic interactions between the nuclei and electrons. Calculations of Van Wieringen [29] led to the following expressions for the second and fourth moments of a resonance line

$$\left.\begin{aligned} M_2 &= \frac{1}{3} h^{-2} A^2 I(I+1), \\ M_4 &= h^{-4} I(I+1)\left\{\frac{1}{5}\left[I(I+1) - \frac{1}{3}\right] A^4 + \right. \\ &\left. \qquad + \frac{2}{9} S(S+1) A^2 \sum \tilde{A}_{jk}^2 \right\}. \end{aligned}\right\} \tag{5.32}$$

Exchange forces do not enter into M_2, but enhance M_4. From this it may be concluded that exchange interactions shift the absorption from the center of the spectrum to the edges. This redistribution of the intensities of the individual parts of the spectrum may be accomplished in two ways: 1) the spacings between the hyperfine components decrease; absorption increases at the sides of the entire spectrum; 2) the intervals between the hyperfine components do not change, but each line is narrowed at the center and is broadened at the sides. The method of random functions has shown that the first possibility is realized.

8. In the majority of cases only the second moment of the absorption line has been successfully calculated. Calculations of the higher moments are extremely difficult. Therefore the information which is obtainable concerning the shape of a paramagnetic resonance line by the method of moments is inadequate.

Anderson and Weiss [30] have suggested the use of the method of random functions in order to obtain detailed information regarding the shape of absorption lines, and in particular regarding exchange narrowing of these lines. This idea has been developed in the work of Anderson [31], Kubo and Tomita, and others [32]. It is impossible to discuss in detail the results of all these investigations, so we shall dwell only on the main idea and the most important applications.

The narrowing of the resonance line under the influence of exchange forces may be visualized as a consequence of frequency modulation of the precessional motion of the separate magnetic dipoles. How the frequency modulation acts on the width of the resonance line may be best understood from the following example, investigated in [33] and [31]. Let us consider an oscillator undergoing random collisions. Let the mean time interval between two collisions be taken to be τ. We shall assume that the oscillator has two different eigenfrequencies of oscillation ν_1 and ν_2. Let the oscillator undergo a change in frequency of oscillation after each collision, changing from ν_1 to ν_2 and the reverse. If the oscillator "suffers a complete absence of memory" and its state before collision in no way influences its subsequent motion, the shape function is

$$g(\nu)=\frac{1}{2\pi}\left\{\frac{\frac{1}{2\pi\tau}}{(\nu-\nu_1)^2+\frac{1}{(2\pi\tau)^2}}+\frac{\frac{1}{2\pi\tau}}{(\nu-\nu_2)^2+\frac{1}{(2\pi\tau)^2}}\right\}. \tag{5.33a}$$

A more complex form of the shape function is obtained in the case of "good memory." If merely the frequency of the oscillator is changed after the collision, but its position and velocity are preserved:

$$g(\nu)=\frac{2}{\pi}\frac{\frac{\nu_m^2}{2\pi\tau}}{(\nu-\nu_c)^4+\nu_m^4+(\nu-\nu_c)^2\left(\frac{1}{\pi^2\tau^2}-2\nu_m^2\right)}, \tag{5.33b}$$

where

$$\nu_c=\frac{1}{2}(\nu_1+\nu_2),\qquad \nu_m=\frac{1}{2}(\nu_1-\nu_2).$$

In the case of (5.33a) the intensity under resonance conditions is proportional to τ, and consequently with a decrease in τ, both resonance lines spread out, and finally when $\tau \leq 1/2\pi\nu_m$ they merge into a single broad line with the resonance frequency ν_c. In the case of (5.33b), if $\nu = \nu_c$, the intensity is proportional to $1/\tau$, and therefore at sufficiently small τ both resonance peaks merge into a single line, which grows narrower with a decrease in τ. Figure 5.1 may serve as an illustration of these statements.

In a paramagnetic crystal the frequency of precession of the magnetic moments equals $\nu_0 + \nu'$, where ν_0 is determined by the externally applied static magnetic field, and ν' by internal, local fields. It may be assumed that the distribution law of the frequencies ν' is Gaussian. We denote the mean value $(\nu')^2$ by ν_p^2. On account of the exchange interaction, neighboring particles will on the average interchange frequencies during a time interval $1/\nu_l \approx h/J_{ik}$. If we fix our attention on a single particle, we see that its frequency of precession is constantly subjected to random changes. In the case $\nu_l >> \nu_p$, this modulation of frequency can substantially narrow the resonance absorption line. Calculation shows that the shape functions of the lines may be given in the following form:

$$g(\nu) = \frac{1}{2\pi} \operatorname{Re} \int_0^\infty \exp\left[-2\pi i (\nu - \nu_0) t - \nu_p^2 u\right] dt, \tag{5.34}$$

where

$$u = \int_0^t (t - t') \exp\left(-\pi^3 \nu_l^2 t'^2\right) dt'. \tag{5.34a}$$

The frequencies ν_p and ν_l may be determined from the following equations:

$$\nu_p^2 = M_2, \quad 3\nu_p^4 + \frac{1}{2} \pi \nu_p^2 \nu_l^2 = M_4. \tag{5.35}$$

For a simple cubic lattice

$$\nu_l^2 = \frac{8{,}48}{3} \left(\frac{J_{ik}}{h}\right)^2 S(S+1). \tag{5.36}$$

Insofar as $\nu_l >> \nu_p$, it follows from (5.34a) that

$$u = \frac{1}{2} t^2, \text{ when } \nu - \nu_0 \gg \nu_l,$$
$$u = \frac{t}{\nu_l}, \quad \text{when } \nu - \nu_0 \ll \nu_l.$$

Substituting into (5.34) we obtain in the first case

$$g(\nu) = \frac{1}{\sqrt{2\pi}\,\nu_p} e^{-\frac{(\nu - \nu_0)^2}{2\nu_p^2}}, \tag{5.37a}$$

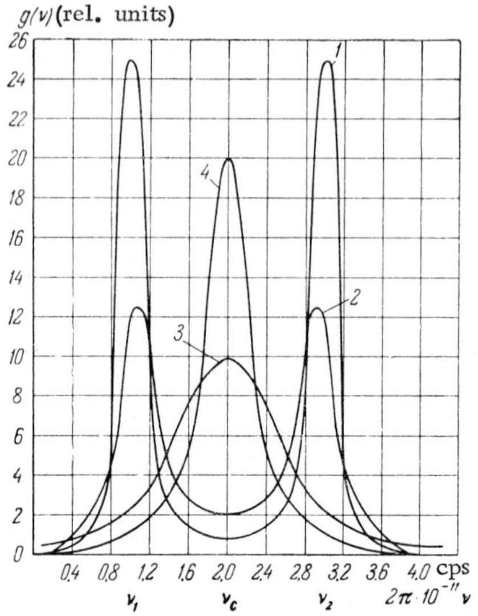

Fig. 5.1. Narrowing of the shape function of an oscillator as the collision time τ is shortened. It is assumed that the oscillator oscillates alternately with the frequencies ν_1 and ν_2, conserving velocity and position after a collision. The curves are given for different values of τ: 1) $\tau = 10^{-10}$ sec; 2) $\tau = 0.5 \cdot 10^{-10}$ sec; 3) $\tau = 10^{-11}$ sec; 4) $\tau = 0.5 \cdot 10^{-11}$ sec.

and in the second case

$$g(\nu) = \frac{1}{\pi} \frac{\frac{\nu_p^2}{\nu_l}}{(\nu - \nu_0)^2 + (\nu_p^2/\nu_l)^2}. \tag{5.37b}$$

Thus, in the case of strong exchange interaction, the absorption line, being Lorentzian at the center, acquires a Gaussian shape at the edges, which ensures the finiteness of its second and higher moments. In place of the formula $\Delta\nu = 2.35\,\nu_p$ [see (1.21)], which is valid in the case of pure dipolar interactions, we now have

$$\Delta\nu = 2\frac{\nu_p^2}{\nu_l}. \tag{5.37c}$$

It should be noted that if the exchange energy is very great, so that $\nu \gg \nu_0$, the magnitude of $\Delta\nu$ given by this formula must be multiplied by 10/3. This is explained by the fact that truncation of the Hamiltonian, performed in the calculation of (5.13), is no longer justifiable, since the difference in energy $h\nu_0$ between the two neighboring Zeeman levels may be greatly altered by the exchange energy. Because of this, the effect of the periodic magnetic field of frequency $\nu = \nu_0$ is not only to make possible the transitions $\Delta M = \pm 1$, but also others, such as $\Delta M = 0, \pm 2, \pm 3$. Thus, in equating $\nu_p{}^2$ to the second moment of the absorption curve, one must take into account the fact that the main resonance line merges with its satellites. Consequently,

$$\nu_p^2 = \tilde{M}_2 = \frac{10}{3} M_2.$$

If the resonance frequency ν_0 is increased so much that $\nu_0 \gg \nu_l$, observation of satellites becomes possible, and the factor 10/3 in the formula for the width of the main line must be discarded.

5.3. Spin-Lattice Interaction

Before we begin to consider the results of the theory of spin-lattice interaction in various types of ionic paramagnetic crystals, we shall discuss several general questions.

1. Let us consider a certain pair of energy levels of a spin system E_k and E_l $(E_k > E_l)$, whose populations are set equal to N_k and N_l. Let us denote the transition probability of the spin system per second under the influence of the lattice oscillations from level E_k to level E_l by A_{kl}. The condition of static equilibrium is

$$N_k A_{kl} = N_l A_{lk}.$$

If the distribution law can be assumed to be a Boltzmann distribution, it follows that

$$A_{lk} = A_{kl} e^{-\frac{(E_k - E_l)}{kT}}. \tag{5.38}$$

We see that $A_{kl} > A_{lk}$. This fact plays an important role in paramagnetic resonance phenomena. Let the magnetic field oscillating at the resonance frequency cause transitions between the levels E_k and E_l; the probability of such transitions per second is denoted by p_{kl} [see formulas (1.3) and (1.4)]. Under steady-state conditions

$$N_k \left(\sum_j{}' A_{kj} + p_{kl} \right) = \sum_j{}' N_j A_{jk} + N_l p_{lk}.^1 \tag{5.39}$$

One may assume with a certain degree of accuracy that $p_{kl} = p_{lk}$. If, however, $A_{kl} = A_{lk}$, then $N_k = N_l$ and paramagnetic resonance would

[1] A prime on the Σ indicates that $j \neq k$.

be impossible. The difference $A_{kl} - A_{lk}$ diminishes with an increase in temperature of the paramagnetic substance, and as a result the paramganetic resonance absorption also decreases.

In Section 5.1 we have seen that under certain conditions the width of a paramagnetic resonance line is determined by the spin-lattice paramagnetic relaxation time τ. If the energy levels E_k and the transition probabilities A_{kl} are known, this time may be calculated from the following formula [34]:

$$\tau = \frac{\sum\limits_{k>l} (E_k - E_l)^2}{\eta \sum\limits_{k>l} A_{kl} (E_k - E_l)^2}, \tag{5.40}$$

where η is the number of all possible states of the spin system. Formula (5.40) was derived under the assumption that $|E_l - E_k| \ll kT$ for any l and k. It follows from (5.40) that if for a spin system we take an individual particle of spin $S = 1/2$, then $\tau = 1/2A_{kl}$.

Paramagnetic resonance makes it possible to determine the transition probabilities A_{lk} by the saturation method. From experiments of this type we determine saturation factors $q_{lk} = n_{lk} / n_{lk}^0$ (compare Section 1.3), where n_{lk}^0 is the difference in population of the energy levels E_l and E_k if the paramagnetic substance is in a state of thermodynamic equilibrium, and n_{lk} is the same quantity under saturation conditions. The saturation factors q_{lk} may be easily expressed in terms of the transition probabilities A_{lk} and p_{lk} if we set up an equation of type (5.39) for each spin level of the paramagnetic particle.

If all the spacings between these levels are different and resonance is observed as a result of transitions under the influence of the radio-frequency field between levels E_1 and E_2, it is not difficult to show that [35]

$$q_{12} = \left(1 + \frac{p_{12}}{W_R}\right)^{-1}, \tag{5.41}$$

where the magnitude W_R, which Lloyd and Pake call the "relaxation probability," equals

$$W_R = A_{21} + \frac{1}{C_{21}} \sum_{k=3}^{\eta} A_{2k} C_{2k}. \tag{5.41a}$$

Here C_{2k} is the adjoint of the element of the second row and k-th column of the following matrix:

$$\left.\begin{array}{ll}
A_{21}-\sum\limits_{k=3}^{\eta} A_{1k}, & A_{21},\ A_{31},\ldots,\ A_{\eta 1} \\
A_{12}-\sum\limits_{k=3}^{\eta} A_{2k}, & -\sum\limits_{k=3}^{\eta} A_{2k},\ A_{32},\ldots,\ A_{\eta 2} \\
\cdots & \cdots \\
A_{1m}+A_{2m}, & A_{2m},\ A_{3m},\ldots,\ A_{\eta m} \\
\cdots & \cdots \\
A_{1\eta}+A_{2\eta}, & A_{2\eta},\ A_{3\eta},\ldots,-\sum\limits_{k=3}^{\eta} A_{\eta k}.
\end{array}\right\} \quad (5.41b)$$

The experimental conditions are often chosen so that $q_{12} = 1/2$. It is immediately apparent from (5.41) that in this case $W_R = p_{12}$.

2. For reasons mentioned in Section 5.1, the theory of spin-lattice relaxation usually singles out a particular particle in interaction with lattice vibrations, instead of the entire spin system. A perturbation theory calculation is made of the transition probabilities A_{lk} between the energy levels of an individual magnetic particle as a result of the exchange of energy with the lattice. In the unperturbed state the system under consideration consists of two noninteracting parts: a paramagnetic ion and a set of oscillators which represent the elastic vibrations of the crystal. Of all the interactions between the paramagnetic ion and the neighboring particles, we shall be interested in those which depend on the magnitude of the ion's magnetic moment. Under the influence of lattice vibrations the magnitude of these interactions will be changed. The variable part of the energy interaction between the paramagnetic ion and its surroundings is given by the spin-lattice interaction operator $\hat{\mathscr{H}}'$. One may then use the perturbation theory developed in the theory of radiation [36].

The exchange of energy between the paramagnetic ion and the lattice vibrations under the action of the perturbation $\hat{\mathscr{H}}'$ is possible by various means, the most important of which are direct (one-phonon) processes and Raman phonon (two-phonon) scattering processes. Let us denote the energy difference of any two states of a paramagnetic ion by E_{lk}. The direct processes consist of an increase (or decrease) of the energy of the ion by the magnitude E_{lk} due to the destruction (or creation) of a single quantum of the elastic lattice vibrations (single phonon). Only those lattice oscillators whose frequencies ν satisfy the following condition may participate in these processes

$$E_{lk} = h\nu. \qquad (5.42)$$

The transition probability of a paramagnetic ion as a result of the direct processes from level E_l to level E_k equals

$$A_{lk}^{(1)}=\frac{4\pi^2}{h^2}\rho_\nu\,|\mathscr{H}'_{lk}|^2. \tag{5.43}$$

Here ρ_ν is the spectral density of the oscillator frequency ν, and $\mathscr{H}'_{lk}$ is the matrix element of the spin-lattice interaction, averaged over the various states of the oscillators, which satisfy condition (5.42). Often the matrix element $\mathscr{H}'_{lk}$ which connects energy levels E_l and E_k is equal to zero in the first approximation. We then use higher approximations and calculate $\mathscr{H}'_{lk}$ in terms of intermediate states of the paramagnetic particle.

Raman phonon scattering processes consist of an increase (or decrease) of the ion energy by the magnitude E_{lk} due to the destruction of quanta of the elastic vibrations of frequency ν and the creation of quanta of frequency ν'; in addition it is obvious that the following condition must be fulfilled:

$$E_{lk}=h\nu-h\nu'. \tag{5.44}$$

For the probability of a transition under the influence of a Raman phonon scattering process, we have

$$A_{lk}^{(2)}=\frac{4\pi^2}{h^2}\int|\mathscr{H}'_{lk}|^2\rho_\nu\rho_{\nu'}d\nu'. \tag{5.45}$$

It is apparent from (5.44) and (5.45) that in Raman scattering phonon processes, elastic lattice vibrations of all frequencies participate. Therefore, in spite of the fact that Raman phonon scattering processes are of the second order, they play a prominent role in the relaxation mechanism if the temperature of the paramagnetic substance is relatively high. At low temperatures, the direct processes play the main role.

Let us denote the magnitude $A_{lk}^{(1)}$, averaged over the various values of l and k, by A_1, and the average magnitude $A_{lk}^{(2)}$ by A_2. From (5.43) and (5.45) if we assume that $E_{lk}\ll kT$, we may obtain

$$A_1=K_1\frac{kT}{\rho v^5},\qquad A_2=K_2\frac{J_n}{\rho^2 v^{10}}. \tag{5.46}$$

Here ρ is the density of the crystal, T is its temperature, v is the mean velocity of sound, K_1 and K_2 are quantities depending on the nature of the relaxation mechanism and on the structure of the energy levels of the magnetic particles, and hence also on the applied magnetic field H_0; J_n denotes

$$J_n = \int_0^{\frac{k\theta}{h}} \frac{\nu^n \exp \frac{h\nu}{kT}}{\left[\exp \frac{h\nu}{kT} - 1\right]^2} d\nu, \tag{5.47}$$

where θ is the Debye temperature. This integral may be calculated from the following approximate formulas [37]

$$J_n = n! \left(\frac{kT}{h}\right)^{n+1} \quad (T \ll \theta), \tag{5.48}$$

$$J_n = \left(\frac{k\theta}{h}\right)^{n+1} \left[\frac{e^{\frac{\theta}{T}}}{(n+1)(e^{\theta/T}-1)^2} + \right.$$
$$\left. + \frac{\theta}{(n+1)(n+2)T} \frac{(e^{\frac{\theta}{T}}+1)e^{\frac{\theta}{T}}}{(e^{\theta/T}-1)^3} - \ldots \right] (T \sim \theta), \tag{5.49}$$

$$J_n = \frac{1}{n-1} \left(\frac{k}{h}\right)^{n+1} \theta^{n-1} T^2 \quad (T \gg \theta). \tag{5.50}$$

The value of n usually equals 6 or 8. The comparatively weak temperature dependence of the relaxation time at $T \gg \theta$ therefore becomes very strong at $T \ll \theta$.

3. In the first theory of paramagnetic spin relaxation given by Waller [8], it was assumed that the reorientation of the spin of an atom with respect to the external magnetic field H_0 under the influence of lattice vibrations occurs as a result of a change in the magnetic interactions of the spin caused by these vibrations. The calculations of Waller led, however, to values of the relaxation time which are several orders of magnitude greater than those obtained experimentally. A particularly sharp discrepancy between theory and experiment was detected in titanium cesium alums. Kronig [38] and Van Vleck [37] therefore proposed a different relaxation mechanism. However, in a number of cases, as Al'tshuler [39] has shown, the Waller mechanism plays a fundamental role.

Waller's calculations were carried out for a paramagnetic substance with particles having spins $S = 1/2$. The probability of a change in orientation of the spin of these particles under the influence of the vibrations of the magnetic forces acting on it is proportional to the fourth power of the magnetic moment of the particle. Moreover, this probability is inversely proportional to R^6, if R denotes the equilibrium distance between two neighboring atoms of the crystal possessing magnetic moments. A single unit cell often contains several such atoms. It is easy to see that in such a case a more accurate result would be obtained if R denoted not the average but the shortest distance between neighboring particles with magnetic moments. From this it is clear that magnetic forces may determine the spin-lattice interaction in substances with large magnetic moments of atoms and with a large density of magnetic particles. Calculations have shown that

$$K_1 = \frac{4\pi^3 Z}{3h^4}\left(\frac{g^2\beta^2}{R^3}\right)^2 (g\beta H_0)^2 S(2S+1)(S+1)^2, \tag{5.51}$$

$$K_2 = \frac{2\pi^3 Z}{3}\left(\frac{g^2\beta^2}{R^3}\right)^2 S(2S+1)(S+1)^2, \quad n=6. \tag{5.52}$$

Here Z is the number of nearest-neighbor particles. It should be noted that Waller only considered relaxation due to a change in the spin orientation of one particle under the influence of lattice vibrations, while the direction of the other spins remained constant. However, it is apparent from (5.10) that the matrix elements of the spin-lattice perturbation differ from zero also in the case of a simultaneous reorientation of the spins of two neighboring particles. For this case it follows from the calculations that

$$K_1' = \frac{16\pi^3 Z}{3h^4}\left(\frac{g^2\beta^2}{R^3}\right)^2 (g\beta H_0)^2 (2S+1)^2 (S+1)^2, \tag{5.53}$$

$$K_2' = 3.16\pi^3 Z\left(\frac{g^2\beta^2}{R^3}\right)^2 (2S+1)^2 (S+1)^2, \quad n=6. \tag{5.54}$$

We see that a simultaneous change in orientation of the spins of two interacting particles is much more probable than a change in spin orientation of only one particle.

In substances with a large density of magnetic ions, exchange forces acquire an appreciable magnitude. The energy of the exchange interaction generally has an isotropic form $A_{12}(r)\mathbf{S}_1\mathbf{S}_2$; it is an intergral of motion, and therefore, to a first approximation, exchange forces cannot cause a transfer of energy from spins to lattice vibrations. If, however, the exchange forces are anisotropic, the magnitude of the spin lattice interactions created by them has the same order of magnitude as in the case of magnetic dipole forces.

4. In order to explain why spin-lattice interactions in titanium-cesium alums are so very large, Kronig [38] proposed the following relaxation mechansim. The elastic lattice vibrations modulate the electric field of the crystal, which in turn changes the orbital motion of the electrons of the paramagnetic ion. Through the orbital magnetic moment, the electrical field of the crystal in turn acts on the electron spin. This mechanism of spin-lattice interaction is the main one for the majority of the salts of the iron-group elements, in spite of the fact that orbital motion in these salts is "frozen." Calculations have shown that

$$\left.\begin{aligned} K_1&=\left(\frac{\lambda}{\Delta}\right)^2\left(\frac{r_0}{a}\right)^4\left(\frac{ee'}{a\Delta}\right)^2\left(\frac{g\beta H_0}{h}\right)^4,\\ K_2&=h^2\left(\frac{\lambda}{\Delta}\right)^2\left(\frac{r_0}{a}\right)^8\left(\frac{ee'}{a\Delta}\right)^4, \quad n=8.\end{aligned}\right\} \tag{5.55}$$

Here Δ is the spacing between the two lower orbital sublevels arising in the electric field of the crystal, r_0 is the mean distance of the $3d$ electron from the nucleus, a is the equilibrium distance from the center of the magnetic particle to the nearest diamagnetic ion, e' is the effective charge of this ion. The factor $(\lambda/\Delta)^2$ appears in (5.55) as a result of the fact that changes in the electric field of the crystal cannot directly produce a reorientation of the electron spin, but act instead through the orbital angular momentum. As the orbital motion is "frozen," the matrix element of spin-lattice interaction differs from zero only in high-order perturbation theory approximations.

From this it is clear that in ionic crystals containing elements of the iron group, the probabilities of relaxation transition will always be inversely proportional to a large power of the spacing Δ. It is well known from experiment that the spin-lattice relaxation time can differ by several orders of magnitude in different elements. This is explained mainly by the fact that the spacing Δ may vary with a change from one ion to another from $\sim 10^2$ cm^{-1} to $\sim 10^4$ cm^{-1}. In particular, for the titanium ion (see Section 4.2) $\Delta \approx 500$ cm^{-1}.

Van Vleck [37] has developed a theory of spin-lattice relaxation which is independent of and more complete than the analogous Kronig theory. In addition to titanium salts, he also considered salts containing Cr^{3+}. In contrast with the titanium ion, whose nondegenerate orbital levels are Kramers doublets, the chromium ion has $S = 3/2$, and as a result the nondegenerate orbital level decomposes into two close-lying Kramers doublets, whose space interval is denoted by δ. The expressions for τ obtained by Van Vleck are very cumbersome. They differ from (5.55) mainly because: in the case of direct processes, instead of $(g\beta H_0)^4$ the expression $\lambda^2\sqrt{g^4\beta^4H_0^4+c_1\delta g^2\beta^2H_0^2+c_2\delta^2}$, was obtained, where c_1 and c_2 are certain numbers on the order of unity. In the expression for K_2 there occurred $\lambda^2 J_6$ instead of $h^2 J_8$.

Bashkirov [40] has made a calculation of the spin-lattice relaxation time for copper salts whose electric fields have tetragonal symmetry. The Cu^{2+} ion, just as the Ti^{3+} ion, has $S = 1/2$. In this case, however, in contrast to titanium salts the matrix element of the spin-orbit interaction connecting the two lowest orbital states equals zero. Therefore, instead of one spacing Δ in the formula for the relaxation time there occur two spacings Δ_0 and Δ; Δ_0 is the splitting in the field created by the octahedron of water molecules surrounding the Cu^{2+} ion and Δ is the spacing between the lowest orbital sublevels arising in a field of tetragonal symmetry. In formulas (5.55) Δ^{-6} should be replaced by $\Delta_0^{-2}\Delta^{-4}$.

In many copper salts the following features have been detected experimentally: 1) the spin-lattice relaxation time at room temperature depends strongly on the angle ϑ between the field H_0 and the tetragonal axis of the crystal [41]; 2) the paramagnetic resonance spectrum in $CuSO_4 \cdot 5H_2O$ may be explained by assuming the spin-orbit coupling constant λ to be appreciably anisotropic [42]. If the constant λ is replaced by the tensor with principal values $\lambda_{\parallel}, \lambda_{\perp}, \lambda_{\perp}$, then in formula (5.55) $\frac{1}{2}[\lambda_{\parallel}^2 \sin^2\vartheta + \lambda_{\perp}^2 (1 + \cos^2\vartheta)]$ must be introduced instead of λ^2. If for $\lambda_{\parallel}$ and $\lambda_{\perp}$ we take the values adopted in [42], we obtain good agreement with the measurement [41].

Kramers' theorem shows that the spectra of ions with an even number of electrons possess a number of peculiar properties. Avvakumov [43] undertook detailed theoretical calculations for crystals with such ions as V^{3+}, Cr^{2+}, Mn^{3+}, Fe^{2+}, and Ni^{2+}. In Ni^{2+}, the lower orbital level after interaction with a field of cubic symmetry is found to be nondegenerate as was the case in Cr^{3+}, which was studied by Van Vleck. The spacing Δ ($\approx 10^4$ cm^{-1}) and the relaxation time are therefore relatively large. In the remaining ions considered by Avvakumov, the lower orbital levels after the action of the cubic field are found to be degenerate, and consequently Δ means the spacing between sublevels arising in a weak field of low symmetry. As a result the relaxation time in salts containing these ions is relatively short and observation of paramagnetic resonance at room temperature is impossible.

If relaxation arises from a Raman phonon scattering process, the temperature dependence of τ is determined by the integral J_n, in which $n = 6$ for Cr^{2+}, Mn^{3+}, and Ni^{2+} and $n = 8$ for Fe^{2+} and V^{3+} ions. Calculations have revealed a strong dependence of the relaxation time on the magnitude of the spin S; at low temperatures $\tau \sim S^{-12}$; at high temperatures $\tau \sim S^8$. For all ions except Ni^{2+} there was also established a noticeable dependence of relaxation time on the inclination of the field H_0 to the axes of the crystal. The dependence of τ on the magnitude of the field H_0 becomes appreciable if $g\beta H_0 > \delta$.

5. Ions in the S state require a special treatment. Al'tshuler [39] has considered the relaxation due to direct processes in trivalent iron salts. Bashkirov [44] also made detailed calculations of the relaxation due to second-order processes for Mn^{2+}, Fe^{3+}, Eu^{2+}, Gd^{3+} ions. If δ denotes the magnitude of the over-all splitting of the spin levels by the crystalline field, the main results of the calculation are

$$K_1 = \frac{\delta^2}{h^4}(g\beta H_0)^2, \quad K_2 = \delta^2, \quad n = 6. \tag{5.56}$$

A comparison of these formulas with (5.52) and (5.53) shows that the Waller mechanism can play a leading role when

$$\delta < \frac{g^2\beta^2}{R^3}(2S+1)(S+1). \tag{5.57}$$

Such a case apparently occurs in manganese salts in which the splitting δ is relatively small.

6. The theory of spin-lattice relaxation for rare earth salts has been given by Al'tshuler [45] using the cerium ion as an example; the crystalline field of the cerium ion was assumed to consist of two parts: a strong field of cubic symmetry and a weak field of lower symmetry. Shekun [46] carried out a theoretical treatment of relaxation in ethylsulfates of various rare earth elements. Let us remember that the crystalline field in ethylsulfates has trigonal symmetry.

In compounds of rare earth elements, the lattice vibrations, by changing the crystalline field, can directly alter the direction of the moment of the paramagnetic ion, because the coupling between the spin and orbital angular momenta in this case is stronger than the effect of the crystalline electric field. We therefore obtain expressions (5.55) for K_1 and K_2, but without the factor $(\lambda/\Delta)^2$. As the interval Δ in rare earth ions is relatively small, of the order 10-100 cm^{-1}, the spin-lattice interaction turns out to be very strong, in spite of the fact that, for $4f$ electrons, r_0 is slightly less than in valence electrons of the iron group. In ions with an even number of f electrons, the spin-lattice interaction determined by direct processes turns out to be particularly large, if the ground state has a non-Kramers degeneracy. In this case we have

$$K_1 = \frac{1}{h^4}\left(\frac{ee'}{a}\right)^2\left(\frac{r_0}{a}\right)^4(g\beta H_0)^2. \tag{5.58}$$

Here the matrix element of the spin-lattice interaction is different from zero in first-order perturbation theory.

7. It is of great interest to explain how the spin-lattice interaction changes when the concentration of the paramagnetic particles is diminished by isomorphic substitution of diamagnetic ions. This subject has been examined theoretically by Kochelayev [112].

At first glance it appears that relaxation determined by the Kronig-Van Vleck mechanism should not depend on the concentration of paramagnetic particles, since the forces which cause the spin-lattice coupling are determined by the relative displacement of the paramagnetic ions and their surrounding diamagnetic atoms. In reality, however, the following circumstance may play a significant role: any sample in practice contains crystalline lattice defects, which scatter plane Debye waves.

Under the influence of a standing plane Debye wave, vibrations of two neighboring atoms are realized with amplitudes whose differences are proportional to the frequency ν of the elastic vibrations. Since the probability of a relaxation transition is proportional to the square of the relative displacement of the paramagnetic ion and the neighboring diamagnetic particle, in the case of direct processes we obtain, in accordance with (5.45), $A_1 \sim E_{kl}^2$. After the Debye wave is scattered by a randomly positioned unpaired spin, there forms around it a spherical wave, whose intensity, of course, decreases rapidly as it is propagated. As a consequence two neighboring atoms at distances r_1 and r_2 from the scattering center will vibrate with amplitudes whose difference is proportional to $1/r_1 - 1/r_2$. In spite of the fact that the intensity of the scattered waves is far less than the intensity of the plane Debye waves, a simple calculation shows that over a broad range of paramagnetic particle concentrations and for reasonable values of defect concentration, the relaxation determined by the scattered spherical waves plays a leading role, if the amplitude of the scattered wave is frequency independent. Thus, if according to the ordinary theory of spin-lattice relaxation $A_1 \sim E_{kl}^n$, by virtue of the frequency independence of the relative displacement of neighboring particles, the relaxation probability will now be $A_1 \sim E_{kl}^{n-2}$. As has been seen above, in many cases $n = 2$ and consequently the dependence of the probability of a relaxation transition between spin levels E_k and E_l on the magnitude of the spacing E_{kl} must vanish. For a small number of crystal defects and with a sufficiently strong dilution by diamagnetic ions, the Kronig-Van Vleck relaxation mechanism will again predominate.

According to the viewpoint developed here, such crystal lattice defects, the dimensions of which are comparable to the wavelength of the incident wave, must have a substantial effect on the magnitude of the spin-lattice interaction.

The theory expounded here is applicable at low temperatures, when the relaxation is determined by one-phonon processes. At high temperatures, when the relaxation is determined by two-phonon processes, phonons of high frequencies ν play the main role, and consequently the spin-lattice interaction determined by waves scattered at the defect cease to be predominant.

8. Akhiyezer and Pomeranchuk [47] have treated the subject of paramagnetic relaxation at very low temperatures by the method of elementary excitation. They suggested that a paramagnetic substance is a nonconducting crystal containing ions with an odd number of electrons. The spin system of a paramagnetic crystal has a spectrum, whose form is determined by the crystalline electric field, the magnetic interactions, and the exchange interactions between the individual lattice ions. The deviations from the ground state of the spin system, realized at $T = 0$, are considered as a set of elementary excitations, which are propagated throughout the entire crystal as in the Bloch model of a ferromagnet. Each

elementary excitation is a quasi-particle, which can be assigned a definite energy and a certain quasi-momentum. Calculations were carried out under the assumption that the quasi-particles obey Fermi-Dirac statistics. Interactions between the elementary excitations and the lattice vibrations give rise to an energy exchange between the spin system and the lattice. From a calculation of the possibility of collision of the quasi-particles with phonons and with each other, we determine the amount of heat Q, transferred per unit time from the lattice to the spin system. It was found that $Q = \text{const}\ T_s^8 q\ (T_s / T_l)$, where the function $q(T_s / T_l)$ for $T_s \ll T_l$ is inversely proportional to $(T_s / T_l)^6$ and for $T_s \approx T_l$ is proportional to $1 - (T_s / T_l)$. If initially $T_l \gg T_s$, and $T_s \sim 10^{-4}$ °K as calculations have shown, the time during which T_l and T_s differ by 1% does not exceed 1 sec.

9. If the exchange interactions are very large (anhydrous paramagnetic salts, free radicals, ferrites), as Bloembergen and Wang [48] have shown, it is expedient to divide the spin system into two parts: Zeeman and exchange.

Figure 5.2 is a schematic diagram of the energy transfer from the Z system to the lattice. Each of the subsystems may be characterized by a particular temperature. Let us denote the temperature of the Z system by T_Z, the temperature of the Ex system by T_e, and the lattice temperature as before by T_l. It is possible to introduce separate concepts of Zeeman and exchange temperatures because the Zeeman energy operator (5.6) and the exchange energy (5.8) operator commute. The variation of the Zeeman energy may therefore occur without consumption of exchange energy. The transfer of energy from the Z system to the Ex system is possible on account of the existence of relatively weak magnetic dipolar interactions which do not commute with $\mathscr{H}_{\text{Zee}}$ and $\mathscr{H}_{\text{exc}}$.

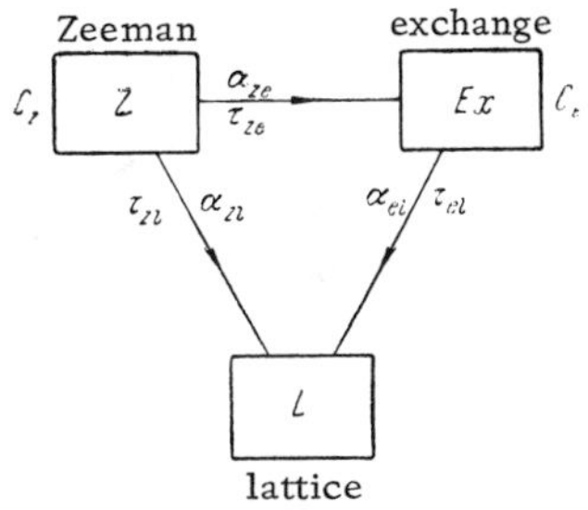

Fig. 5.2. Schematic diagram of the energy transfer via lattice vibrations in the case of strong exchange interactions.

A direct transfer of energy from the Z system to the lattice is believed unlikely, and consequently the relaxation time τ_{zl} is regarded as large compared with the times τ_{ze} and τ_{el}. Let α_{ze} and α_{el} denote the corresponding coefficients of thermal conductivity, and C_z and C_e the specific heat of the Z and Ex systems. To explain the experimental data we must assume that $\alpha_{ze} < \alpha_{el}$, and $C_z \ll C_e$.

Inasmuch as the relaxation time is determined by the ratio of the specific heat to the corresponding coefficient of thermal conductivity, it turns out that $\tau_{ze} < \tau_{el}$. Therefore τ_{ze} plays the role of the spin-lattice relaxation time for ordinary paramagnetic substances. It is noteworthy that the independence of τ_{ze} on the lattice temperature finds confirmation in saturation experiments. Under steady-state conditions the amount of heat transferred from the Z system to the Ex system equals the heat transferred from the Ex system to the lattice, i.e., $\alpha_{ze}(T_z - T_e) = \alpha_{el}(T_e - T_l)$. From this it follows that T_e is much closer to T_l, than to T_z.

5.4. Longitudinal Relaxation at Low Temperatures

1. From the theory of spin-lattice relaxation due to one-phonon processes (Sec. 5.3), it follows that the relaxation time τ, which is inversely proportional to the temperature T, decreases as the applied field H_0 increases, and in general is independent of both the concentration of unpaired spins and the dimensions of the crystal. Meanwhile a number of experimental investigations [49-53] have established facts which are in direct contraction to all these theoretical conclusions. Moreover, it was discovered that we must sometimes introduce a multiplicity of relaxation times instead of a single time. In spite of all these contradictions, there is no basis for doubting the correctness of the choice of the theory for the mechanism of the spin-lattice interaction. In some cases at least the indicated features of relaxation at liquid helium temperatures find the following explanations.

In a treatment of relaxation processes, one always assumes that the lattice vibrations may be considered as a thermostat in which the spin system is immersed. The specific heat of the spin system is always assumed to be small compared with the specific heat of the lattice. Meanwhile, if the spin system temperature is higher than the lattice temperature, equilibrium will be restored by means of one-phonon processes via excitation of vibrations over a narrow range of frequencies, which satisfy condition (5.44) approximately. The specfic heat of these low-frequency lattice oscillators, which are in direct heat contact with the spin system, is not large. It is of importance, therefore, to know how rapidly the excess energy acquired by these effective oscillators will be transported either to oscillators of other frequencies or to the helium bath surrounding the crystal. Let us denote the temperature of the spin system by T_s, the temperature of the effective oscillators by T_Z, the temperature of the lattice thermostat by T_0. If the energy transferred to the effective oscillators is drawn off so quickly that the relation $T_s - T_Z \ll T_Z - T_0$, holds for the temperature differences, the contact between the spin system and the lattice will be a bottleneck in the chain connecting the spin system with the lattice thermostat, and hence the longitudinal relaxation time T_1 will equal the time τ. Indeed, if the establishment of equilibrium between the spin system and the thermostat is a steady-state process such that $T_s - T_Z \gg T_Z - T_0$, besides the spin-lattice relaxation time τ, it is necessary to introduce a time which will characterize the exchange of energy between the effective oscillators and the helium bath (or oscillators of other frequencies). This time is denoted by T_1, because it will now determine the longitudinal relaxation, since $T_1 \gg \tau$.

2. For further discussion it is necessary to compute the number N_f of effective oscillators per unit volume. If the energy spectrum of the spin and lattice oscillators is discrete, the number of oscillators participating in the exchange of energy between the spin and lattice would be infinitely small. In fact, however, the spin-spin interaction, on the one hand, and the finiteness of the lifetime of the oscillators in the excited state, on the other, cause a broadening of the energy levels. It will be seen that broadening of the vibrational levels is of greatest significance. Let $2\Delta\nu_L$ denote the spacing of frequencies of the oscillators which bring about strong interactions with the spins. In accordance with the usual distribution law of frequencies of elastic lattice vibrations, one may assume that

$$N_f = \frac{12\pi\nu^2}{v^3}(2\Delta\nu_L). \tag{5.59}$$

The value of $\Delta\nu_L$ may be evaluated in the following manner. For simplicity we assume that the effect spin of the paramagnetic particles equals 1/2. Then, according to (5.40), the probability A_1 per unit time of a transition between the spin energy levels under the action of lattice vibrations is related to the time τ by the equation $A_1 = 1/2\,\tau^{-1}$. Each of the N_0 spins located in a unit volume may exchange one phonon with each of the N_f oscillators during a time 2τ. Consequently, the vibrations of the oscillators will be interrupted on the average after a time interval

$$\Delta t = 2\frac{N_f}{N_0}\tau.$$

Since $\Delta\nu_L = 1/(2\pi\Delta t)$, it follows from (5.59) that

$$\Delta\nu_L = \left(\frac{N_0 v^3}{96\pi^2\nu^2\tau}\right)^{\frac{1}{2}}. \tag{5.60}$$

As an example we take $N_0 = 10^{19}\,\text{cm}^{-3}$, $v = 2\cdot 10^5$ cm/sec, $\nu = 10^{10}$ cps, $2\tau = 10^{-5}$ sec; then $\Delta\nu_L = 4\cdot 10^8$ cps, which is much greater than the frequency interval $4N_0\beta^2/h$, related to the spin-spin interaction. The number of effective oscillators in our example, according to (5.59), equals $N_f \approx 5\cdot 10^{14}\,\text{cm}^{-3}$. We shall see that each effective oscillator accounts for approximately 10^4 spins. Clearly, the specific heat of the effective oscillators is negligible in comparison with that of the spin system. Therefore, if $T_1 \gg \tau$, the process of establishment of thermal equilibrium between the spin system and the assemblage of effective oscillators involves the effective oscillators taking the spin temperature, $T_Z \to T_s$. One may say simply that the effective oscillators in this case are coupled to the spin system.

We note that the formulas obtained are valid if $kT_s \ll h\nu$. If, however, $kT_s \gg h\nu$, one must introduce the population difference of two neighboring spin levels in place of N_0, i.e.,

$$\frac{N_0 h\nu}{2kT_s}.$$

3. What is the mechanism determining longitudinal relaxation if $T_1 > \tau$? Equilibrium between the spin system and the helium bath can be established by various means. Frohlich and Heitler [54] have shown that the thermal conductivity of the spin system is very small. The direct transport of energy from the spin system to the helium bath is therefore not very effective. This is easily understood when it is considered that the rate of propagation of excitations of the spin system (magnons) in substances with not too high a concentration of unpaired spins is much slower than the velocity of sound: $v \gg \beta^2/hr^3$ (see Sec. 5.1).

Two possible mechanisms remain: a) transport of energy of the effective oscillators to all other lattice vibrations; b) direct transfer of the energy of effective vibrations to the helium bath. Van Vleck [55] has considered mechanism (a), taking into account the anharmonicity of the lattice vibrations. Let dQ/dt be the amount of heat transported per second from the effective oscillators to the remaining lattice vibrations. Then

$$\frac{dQ}{dt} = b\,(T_Z - T_0), \tag{5.61}$$

where b is the thermal conductivity, equal to

$$b = \left(\frac{36}{35}\right)^2 \pi^3 \frac{k^5 T_0^4 V N_f \nu}{h^3 \rho^3 v^9} \left[\left(\frac{18}{A} - \frac{15B}{A^3}\right)^2 + 2\left(\frac{5}{A} - \frac{3B}{A^3}\right)^2\right]. \tag{5.62}$$

If ΔV denotes the change in volume V of the crystal under the action of a pressure p, the meaning of coefficients A and B becomes clear from the following formula:

$$\frac{\Delta V}{V} = Ap - Bp^2. \tag{5.62a}$$

For chrome potassium alums [56] $A = 6.3 \cdot 10^{-12}$ cm^2/dyne, $B = 1.08 \cdot 10^{-22}$ cm^4/dyne^2. Returning to the numerical example considered in this section and assuming the sample to be spherical with radius R, by means of (5.62) we obtain $b \approx 2 \cdot 10^{-4} \cdot R^3$ w/deg.

To evaluate the effectiveness of mechanism (b) we assume first that the elastic waves experience no perturbation, except for the interaction with the spin system and the walls of the crystal [57]. The case considered by us is most favorable for the penetration of heat from the thermostat into the sample. Let us visualize a spherical cavity, in which elastic waves that strike the wall have temperature T_Z and the waves radiated by the wall have the temperature T_0. If $u(T)$ denotes the energy density of the effective vibrations of temperature T, a unit surface of the wall absorbs energy $\frac{1}{4}\, vu(T_Z)$ and radiates energy $\frac{1}{4}\, vu(T_0)$ per sec. If the difference $T_Z - T_0$ is small,

$$u(T_Z) - u(T_0) = N_f k (T_Z - T_0),$$

and hence the heat transported per second by the effective vibrations to the helium bath equals $a(T_Z - T_0)$, where the thermal conductivity is

$$a = \pi R^3 N_f k v. \tag{5.63}$$

Substituting the above values of N_f and v, we obtain $a \approx 4 \cdot 10^{-3} \cdot R^2$ w/deg.

The longitudinal relaxation time T_1 can be determined as the ratio of the specific heat of the spin system C_s to the coefficient of thermal conductivity of the channel connecting the spin system with the lattice thermostat. If we take both mechanisms (a) and (b) into account we obtain

$$T_1 = C_s \left(\frac{1}{a} + \frac{1}{b}\right). \tag{5.64}$$

If $S' = 1/2$, then [34]

$$C_s = \frac{N_0 V h^2 \nu^2}{k T_s^2}. \tag{5.65}$$

In the example considered by us $a/b \gg 1$, and consequently mechanism (a) is much more effective than mechanism (b). In this case with the aid of (5.63)-(5.65) we obtain

$$T_1 = \left(\frac{1}{6} N_0 v \tau\right)^{\frac{1}{2}} \left(\frac{h}{kT_s}\right)^2 \nu R. \tag{5.66}$$

If $kT_s \ll h\nu$, obviously,

$$T_1 = \left(\frac{1}{12} N_0 v \tau\right)^{\frac{1}{2}} \left(\frac{h}{kT_s}\right)^{\frac{5}{2}} \nu^{\frac{3}{2}} R. \tag{5.66a}$$

Substituting again the values used in our example, we obtain $T_1 \approx 10^{-2}$ sec.

If the mean free path of the effective phonons is small in comparison with the linear dimensions of the crystal, the mechanism we have described for the transport of energy of the effective vibrations to the thermostat will be disrupted by diffusion processes. The mean free path of a phonon whose path is interrupted by a collision with a magnon is of the order $\sim v\tau$. Consequently, if $R \gg v\tau$, phonon diffusion processes begin to play a predominant role in the transport of energy from the spin system to the lattice thermostat. An estimate of the magnitude of the longitudinal relaxation time for this case [58] gives, for $h\nu \ll kT_s$ the approximate expression:

$$T_1 = \frac{R^2 h^2 N_0 v}{18\pi^2 (kT_s)^2}. \tag{5.67}$$

We note that in this case it is impossible, strictly speaking, to define a single relaxation time. The temperature of the spin system and of the assemblage of effective oscillators will vary from the center of the crystal to its edge. As a result there arises a certain distribution of relaxation times.

The formulas obtained by us for the longitudinal relaxation time evidently make possible an explanation of the experimental facts concerning the character of the dependence of T_1 on the concentration of unpaired spins N_0, the temperature T_s, the dimensions R of the crystal, and the intensity of the applied field H_0 (of frequency ν).

The longitudinal relaxation at low temperatures has not been adequately studied experimentally. Discussions of this subject [59, 60] in connection with the creation of masers (see Chapter VIII), hitherto have not led to a definite result (see Sec. 5.9).

5.5. Experimental Data on Ionic Crystals

1. Line width in solid paramagnetic substances

The various types of interactions in paramagnetic substances are studied experimentally both by a determination of the width and shape of the paramagnetic resonance line, and by a method which uses the phenomenon of saturation of these lines. In addition, information concerning the spin-spin and spin-lattice relaxation times is obtained from measurements of the paramagnetic absorption and dispersion susceptibilities in the case of a mutually parallel arrangement of the static and high-frequency magnetic fields.

By the line width ΔH we will mean the distance, expressed in gauss, between the points of the curve $\chi''(H_0)$, at which χ'' has a value equal to one half the maximum value. In some papers an alternate definition of line width is used: the distance in gauss between the inflection points of the curve $\chi''(H_0)$. Such a definition is advantageous when the result of the measurement is a differential curve $(d\chi''/dH)(H_0)$. We shall denote this width by δH. For Lorentzian shaped curves $\Delta H = 1.73\delta H$ and for Gaussian curves $\Delta H = 1.26\delta H$. We note that in low-frequency measurements one must use the definition of the "right half-width," i.e., the distance in gauss between the point corresponding to the position of the absorption maximum and the point where $\chi'' = \frac{1}{2}\chi''_{max}$, lying in regions of the field H_0 greater than the maximum. The right half-width will be denoted by ΔH_{rh}.

Besides the measurements of $\chi''(H_0)$, to evaluate the resonance line width we also use a measurement of the dependence of χ' and $d\chi'/dH$ on the field intensity H_0. In the last case the difference between the Lorentzian and Gaussian line shapes is easily established by means of the determination of the ratio of the quantity $d\chi'/dH$ at the maximum and at the minima of the curve $(d\chi'/dH)(H_0)$. For a Lorentzian line shape this ratio equals 8 : 1, and for the Gaussian 3.5 : 1 [61].

Measurement of the magnitude of ΔH (or δH) gives appreciably less accurate results than does the determination of the position of lines in the spectrum. The inadequacy of the assignment of the shape and width of the line to some extent is inherent in most paramagnetic resonance measurement methods and is related mainly to the impossibility of completely separating the effects arising from the real and imaginary parts of the high-frequency susceptibility.

We shall initially focus our attention on data concerning pure paramagnetic salts that are not diluted with the appropriate diamagnetic ions. Their line widths have values from tens to thousands of gauss. Sometimes the lines are not completely observable. If we exclude the case of ions with an even number of electrons (paramagnetic resonance may not occur in them because of the smallness of the radio-frequency quantum compared with the zero-field splitting of the spin sublevels), the absence of the signal may be related only to very strong spin-lattice interactions. A sufficient lowering of the temperature diminishes these interactions and makes the effect observable. In general, the narrowing of the lines during cooling is the most convincing proof that spin-lattice interactions determine their width.

Another means of explaining the nature of the observed width is the study of the dependence of ΔH on the frequency of the absorbed radiation. If the width increases considerably with an increase of frequency, it is natural to relate this increase to the influence of the anisotropy of the g factor; in such a case, to determine the actual relaxation line width, measurements must be conducted at the lowest frequencies. Lastly, the effect of anisotropy is exerted most strongly in investigations of polycrystalline samples; it is not eliminated, however, in single crystals, inasmuch as in the majority of cases a unit cell contains several nonequivalent magnetic ions.

One of the most important methods for the study of the internal interactions in paramagnetic substances is the analysis of the absorption line shape. Until now, however, this has been done mainly by a calculation of the second and fourth moments of experimental curves of $\chi''(H)$ and by comparison of the results with the Van Vleck line width theory [10]. The limited applicability of this theory to a large number of real crystals has already been mentioned above.

Some typical results of measurements of the width and shape of absorption lines in undiluted paramagnetic salts of Mn^{2+} are given in Table 5.1 [62].

Table 5.1

Substance	$(\Delta H_{\frac{1}{2}})_{exp}$, gauss	$(\Delta H_{\frac{1}{2}})_{theor}$, gauss	$\frac{\langle \Delta H^4 \rangle^{\frac{1}{4}}}{\langle \Delta H^2 \rangle^{\frac{1}{2}}}$
$MnCl_2 \cdot 4H_2O$	1410	1530	1.23
$MnCl_2$	750	2950	1.40
$MnSO_4 \cdot 4H_2O$	1150	1560	1.28
$MnSO_4 \cdot H_2O$	320	2870	1.46
$MnSO_4$	665	3520	1.35
$MnCO_3$(cryst.)	460	4460	1.43
$Mn_3(PO_4)_2 \cdot 3H_2O$	465	1246	1.38
$Mn_2P_2O_7 \cdot 3H_2O$	1070	1250	1.32
$Mn(NO_3)_2 \cdot 6H_2O$	1210	1033	1.31
MnF_2	470	7020	1.39
MnS	780	7520	1.40

From an examination of the data in this table one may conclude that:

1) In magnetically concentrated salts the line width is much less than what would be expected when only magnetic dipolar interactions are taken into account; and the line shape is Lorentzian or nearly Lorentzian. From this it follows that appreciable exchange interactions exist in such salts.

2) In salts with a smaller magnetic ion concentration (for example, in Tutton salts of Mn^{2+} and Cu^{2+} and in chrome alums) the

line shape is almost Gaussian, and the width differs little from the dipolar interaction width, since here the effect of exchange is already small.

It should be mentioned, however, that the study of the dependence of exchange interaction on the mean distances between the magnetic particles in highly concentrated paramagnetic substances is possible only in a comparison of substances possessing identical types of crystalline lattices. Otherwise, it is easy to reach erroneous conclusions, because in a region of high magnetic concentrations, it is meaningless to deal with mean interionic distances without taking into account the specific details of the actual lattices. In particular, Kashayev [63] has shown, for instance, that the absorption line in $CuF_2 \cdot 2H_2O$ is considerably narrower than in CuF_2 in spite of the fact that the mean distances between the Cu^{2+} ions are smaller than those in the first salt, and hence the exchange narrowing of the line in the second salt should effect the CuF_2 more strongly. According to crystallographic data, we are here dealing with distances between neighboring ions Cu^{2+} in CuF_2 which are greater than those found in $CuF_2 \cdot 2H_2O$.

Among the substances with strong exchange interactions, we shall discuss $CrCl_3$, polycrystalline samples of which were investigated repeatedly under different conditions. The form of the absorption line is shown in Figure 1.2 (p. 10). The magnitude of ΔH was determined over the frequency range from 10^{10} to 10^7 cps and was found to be constant within the limits of experimental error and equal to 140 ± 5 gauss [64] (if at low frequencies we define it as double the "right half-width"). The temperature variation over the range from 290 to 77°K did not effect ΔH. The value of ΔH which was calculated by Van Vleck from magnetic dipolar interactions alone is greater than the observed value of 1000 gauss. The ratio $\Delta H/\delta H$ corresponds to the Lorentzian shape.

A good example of the Gaussian shape is the line observed by Bleaney [65], which corresponds to the $1/2 \rightleftarrows 3/2$ transition in the spectrum of chrome cesium alums $CrCs(SO_4)_2 \cdot 12H_2O$ for the orientation of the crystalline optical axis along the field. The width of this line is $\Delta H = 280$ gauss, and it is illustrated in Figure 5.3. The experimental data are shown in the figure by points and the curve is drawn, according to the Gaussian law, with a mean square width $\sigma_{\parallel} = 118$ gauss. This latter magnitude was calculated by Bleaney according to the Van Vleck theory, taking into account the existence of nonequivalent Cr^{3+} ions in the unit cell. The good agreement with experiment leads to the conclusion that the role of exchange interactions in chrome cesium alums is not large.

Sometimes the line corresponds to neither a Lorentzian nor a Gaussian shape. In particular, an intermediate shape was found by Japanese investigators [66] for $MnSO_4 \cdot 4H_2O$ and $MnSO_4 \cdot 5H_2O$. Deviations from the shape expected according to the Van Vleck theory were discovered by MacLean and Kor [67] in organic salts of Mn^{2+}.

We shall now discuss in detail the measurements of ΔH in diluted salts, in which a portion of the magnetic ions is replaced by diamagnetic ions. Such salts are of greatest interest from the point of view of spectroscopy. Here first of all it is necessary to mention that the narrowing of the lines due to the decrease of the magnetic dipolar interactions between the ions is observed down to rather small relative concentrations of diamagnetic ions ($f \leq 0.01$). The residual line width does not depend on subsequent dilution, and if it is not related to spin-lattice relaxation, it is usually determined by magnetic dipolar interactions with the moments of the neighboring atomic nuclei, in particular, interaction with moments of the water protons in hydrated salts. Hence, in spectroscopic investigations, H_2O is sometimes replaced by heavy water D_2O, which leads to a narrowing of the line on account of the smaller magnetic moment of D. In the initial stages of dilution (with $f > 0.1$) the absorption line is narrowed slightly, and sometimes may even be somewhat broadened, as was mentioned in [63]. This is connected with the fact that exchange interactions decrease with distance more rapidly than do magnetic dipole interactions. Examples of the experimentally determined widths in diluted paramagnetic salts are given in Table 5.2.

Information concerning spin-spin interactions in paramagnetic substances in the absence of steady fields H_0 may be obtained from absolute measurements of the absorption coefficient at $H_0 = 0$. Such measurements were made for a number of salts by Gorter [34], and later by Rivkind [70]. The values of $\tau'(0)$ obtained by Rivkind at a frequency 10 Mc are given in Table 5.3.

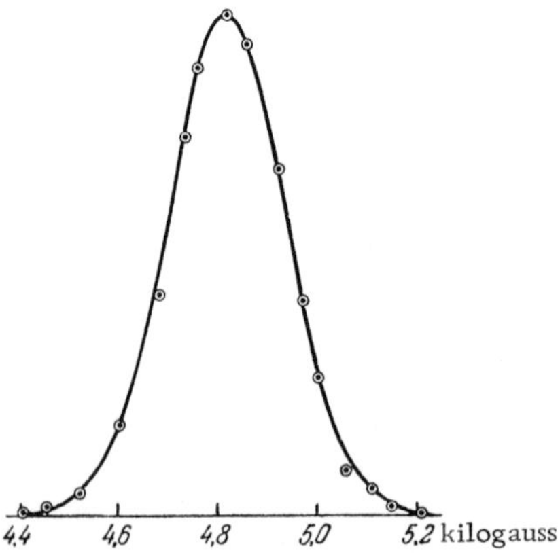

Fig. 5.3. Shape of the paramagnetic resonance line (1/2 ⇄ 3/2) of chrome cesium alums [65].

Table 5.2

Substance	Dilution	Half-width	Exptl. conditions			Ref.
			λ,cm	T, °K	State	
$(Mn^{2+}, Zn^{2+})S$	10^{-3}	7.5±0.5	3.2	300—4.2	Single crystal	[68]
$(Pr^{3+}, La^{3+})Cl_3$	10^{-4}	5.5±0.5	3.2	"	"	[68]
H_0 is parallel to the crystal optical axis	0.11	25	3.2	4.2	"	[69]
H_0 is perpendicular to thecrystal optical axis		180	3.2	4.2	"	[69]

2. Spin-lattice relaxation in solid paramagnetic substances

Investigations of spin-lattice relaxation were initiated by Gorter [34] in the 1930's prior to the discovery of paramagnetic resonance. His method consisted in the measurement of the dependence of the quantities χ' and χ'' on the strength of a static magnetic field $H_{\parallel}$ arranged parallel to an oscillating magnetic field of constant frequency ν_0 The frequency in Gorter's experiments was of the order of 10^6-10^7 cps. The phenomenological theory of spin-lattice relaxation in parallel fields was proposed by Casimir and Dupré [71] for the case in which $\tau \gg \tau'$. Subsequent development of the phenomenological theory of relaxation phenomena in parallel fields was made by Shaposhnikov [4], who took into account the role of spin-spin interactions in the general relaxation effect. A summary of the experimental values of τ obtained up to 1947 by Gorter and his co-workers is contained in his book [34]. The latest measurements of τ by the method of parallel fields may be found in the

Table 5.3

Substance	$2\pi\tau' \cdot 10^9$, sec
$VOCl_2$	10.5
$VOSO_4$	1.85
$CuCl_2 \cdot 2H_2O$	8.65
$CuSO_4 \cdot 5H_2O$	4.05
$Cu(NH_3)_4SO_4 \cdot H_2O$	15.3
$Cu(NO_3)_2 \cdot 6H_2O$	2.70
$CrCl_3$	3.50
CrF_3	0.77
$Cr_2(SO_4)_3$	0.60
$Cr_2(OH)_6 \cdot H_2O$	1.88

works [72 - 74, 41], etc. Here we shall mention only the principal results, without elaborating on the experiments.

Measurements at temperatures from 300 down to 64°K have been conducted in hydrated salts of iron group ions and in salts of Gd^{3+}. The spin-lattice relaxation time was found to be longest in Mn^{2+}, Gd^{3+}, and Cr^{3+} salts; at room temperatures they are of the order 10^{-7} - 10^{-4} sec. For instance, the very short values of τ which are obtained in salts of Co^{2+} or, especially, Ti^{3+} could not be measured by the method of parallel fields in this temperature range, since the condition $\tau > \tau'$ is not fulfilled.

At liquid helium temperatures a small number of salts of Mn^{2+}, Fe^{3+}, Gd^{3+}, Cr^{3+}, Co^{2+} and some other ions were studied. The relaxation times for them are of the order of 10^{-2} - 10^{-4} sec.

We shall first consider the high-temperature region, where Raman processes predominate.

In this region the dependence of τ on $H_{\parallel}$ is well described by the formula proposed by Brons [75] and given a theoretical basis in the paper by Van Vleck [37]:

$$\tau = \tau_0 \frac{\frac{b}{C} + H_0^2}{\frac{b}{C} + pH_0^2}. \tag{5.68}$$

Here $b = C_H T^2$ is the magnetic heat capacity constant; C is the Curie constant; τ_0 is the spin-lattice relaxation time for $H_0 \to 0$; $p = \tau_0/\tau_\infty$, where τ_∞ is the spin-lattice relaxation time for $H_0 \to \infty$. According to Van Vleck, $p < 1$; as the field strength $H_{\parallel}$ increases the magnitude of τ should increase, tending in the limit to τ_∞. The temperature dependence is exhibited mainly by the factor $\tau_0 \sim T^{-2}$ when $T \gg \theta$. Experiment shows, however, that the value of p sometimes changes with temperature. In most cases experimental data obtained for the temperature region from 300 to 64°K qualitatively agree with the predictions of the theory; the value of τ calculated by Van Vleck for chrome alums even agrees with the experimental value in order of magnitude. Nevertheless, it is impossible to speak of strict agreement between theory and experiment. Apparently the main reason for the discrepancy is the fact that measurements of the spin-lattice relaxation time in parallel fields are possible only under the condition $\tau \gg \tau'$, whereas in the Van Vleck theory the spin-spin interactions are only very approximately taken into account.

Another reason why a rough qualitative disagreement with theory may arise in individual cases is the result of phase transitions occurring in the paramagnetic substance when the experimental temperature is changed. In particular, this may explain the decrease in τ with cooling observed by Garif'yanov [76] in iron ammonium alums, for which the measurements give a phase transition point near 200° K.

Chrome potassium alums (phase transition point ~ 90°K) and gadolinium sulfate [34] also behave in this manner.

Tables 5.4 and 5.4a contain some data regarding the magnitude of τ in the high-temperature region (77 - 300°K), obtained by the dynamic polarization method.

In the helium-temperature region, where direct processes should predominate, the Van Vleck theory is in considerably poorer agreement with experiment. In particular, for direct processes, theory

Table 5.4

Spin-Lattice Relaxation Times

Substance	$H_{\parallel}$, gauss	$\frac{b}{C}\cdot 10^{-6}$, gauss^2	$2\pi\tau\cdot 10^6$, sec				Reference
			77° K	90° K	290° K	(Other T, °K)	
$Cr(NO_3)_3\cdot 9H_2O$	0	1.1	2.2	0.7			
	800		3.2	1.1			
	1600		3.9	1.52			[72]
	2400		5	2.13			
	3200		5.3	2.38			
	≥4000		6.3	3.2			
$CrK(SO_4)_2\cdot 12H_2O$	0	0.65	0.9—0.7;	0.33—0.25,			[72]
	≥4000		4.1—2.8;	2.1—2.0			[72]
	0				~0.01;	~0.001 (200)	[76]
$Cr(NH_4)(SO_4)_2\cdot 12H_2O$		2.68					
$[Cr(H_2O)_6]Cl_3$	0	0.96		2.5			
	≥4000			5			[72]
$[Cr(NH_3)_6]Cl_3$	≤3200	13	0.2	0.18			
$[Cr(H_2O)_4Cl_2]Cl\cdot 2H_2O$	0	4.5	1.2	1.05			
	≥4000		1.9	1.5			
	1000				0.04		
	2000	4.1			0.085		[64]
	3000				0.13		
$[CrF_6]K_3$	0	8	0.19	0.15			
	1600		0.22	0.18			
	2400		0.25	0.22			
	3200		0.28	0.24			
$[Cr(-OOC-COO)_3]K_3$	0	27	0.3	0.22			
	1600		0.32	0.24			
	2400		0.36	0.27			
	3200		0.41	0.33			
$Fe(NO_3)_3\cdot 9H_2O$	800	19.5	0.71	0.38		0.8 (64.4)	
	1600		0.78	0.49		1.1 (64.4)	
	2400		0.84	0.56		1.2 (64.4)	
	3200		0.98	0.69		1.35 (64.4)	[72]

Table 5.4 (Cont'd)

Substance	$H_{\parallel}$, gauss	$\frac{b}{C} \cdot 10^{-6}$, gauss^2	$2\pi\tau \cdot 10^6$, sec: 77° K	90° K	290° K	(Other T, °K)	Reference
$Fe(NH_4)(SO_4)_2 \cdot 12H_2O$	0	0.27	0.25	0.04		0.75 (64) <0.02 (195)	[72]
	100		0.26	0.042			
	200		0.27	0.046			
	300		0.28	0.05			
	400		0.33	0.055			
	800		0.62	0.1			
	1600		1.1	0.23			
	3200		1.79	0.53			
	4800		2.06	0.8			
	$\gg$4000		2.1	0.9		3 (64)	
$Fe(ND_4)(SO_4)_2 \cdot 12D_2O$ (93%D)	0				~0.01	~0.001(200)	[74]
	0	0.27	0.32	0.08		0.75 (64)	[72]
	$\gg$4000		2.2	1		3 (64)	
$(Fe, Al)(ND_4)(SO_4)_2 \cdot 12D_2O$	~0	0.27	<0.32	<0.08			
$Gd_2(SO_4)_3 \cdot 8H_2O$	0	3.9	1.6	1.95	0.42		[72]
	800		1.75	2.1	0.5		
	1600		2.1	2.5	0.55		
	2400		2.5	2.85	0.69		
	3200		2.8	3.15	0.79		
	$\gg$4000		4	4.2	1.25		
$Gd(CH_3-COO-)_3 \cdot 4H_2O$	1600		0.67	0.41	0.11	0.27 (195)	
	2400		0.71	0.46	0.125	0.28 (195)	
	3200		0.77	0.51	0.14	0.29 (195)	
$Gd_2(-OOC-COO-)_3 \cdot 10H_2O$	0	1.8	1.5	1.5		0.24 (195)	
	800		1.75	1.8		0.31 (195)	
	1600		2	2		0.45 (195)	
	2400		2.7	2.7		0.69 (195)	
	3200		2.9	2.95		0.85 (195)	
	$\gg$4000		3.6	3.6		1.5 (195)	
$Gd(NO_3)_3 \cdot 6H_2O$	800	2.06			0.55		[74]
	1600				0.72		
	2400				0.86		
	3200				0.96		
	4000				1		
	5000				1.1		
$GdCl_3 \cdot 4H_2O$	800	5.1			0.53		
	1600				0.59		
	2400				0.64		
	3200				0.69		
	4000				0.72		
	5000				0.75		
$MnCl_2 \cdot 4H_2O$	800	19.8			1.41		[98]
	1200				1.56		
	1600				1.6		
	2000				1.79		

Table 5.4 (Cont'd)

Substance	$H_{\parallel}$, gauss	$\frac{b}{C}\cdot 10^{-6}$, gauss^2	$2\pi\tau\cdot 10^6$, sec: 77° K	90° K	290° K	(Other T, °K)	Reference
$MnCl_2\cdot 4H_2O$	2400				1,94		[98]
	2800				2.12		
	3200				2.2		
	3600				2.4		
$Mn(NO_3)_2\cdot 6H_2O$	800	1.2					[73]
	1200				0.3		
	1600				0.35		
	2000				0.37		
	2400				0.38		
	3200				0.39		
$MnSO_4\cdot 4H_2O$	0	6.2	4	3.2	0.32		$T=$290°K [73], at low temperatures [72]
	800	5±2			0.28		
	1600				0.37		
	2400				0.47		
	3200				0.53		
$Mn(NH_4)_2(SO_4)_2\cdot 6H_2O$	0	0.64		5.5	0.40	0.93 (195)	$T=$290°K [98], at low temperatures [72]
	≫4000			11	0.80	1.85 (195)	
	1200				0.66		
	1600				0.74		
	2000				0.77		
	2400				0.8		
	2800				0.82		
	3200				0.83		
	3600				0.835		
$NiSO_4\cdot 7H_2O$		90?	0.1?	0.08?			[72]
$Ni(NH_4)_2(SO_4)_2\cdot 6H_2O$		90?	0.14?	0.11?			
$V(NH_4)_2(SO_4)_2\cdot 6H_2O$		4.8					

Table 5.4 a

Substance	$H_{\parallel}$, gauss	$\frac{b}{C}\cdot 10^{-6}$, gauss^2	$2\pi\tau\cdot 10^6$, sec: 77° K	90° K	290° K: Powder	Axis K_1	Axis K_2	Axis K_3	Reference
$CuSO_4\cdot 5H_2O$	800	0.47 (Powder)			0.01	0.01	0.01	0.008	At low temperatures [72]
	1600	0.4 (Axis K_1)			0.015	0.015	0.014	0.012	

Table 5.4a (Cont'd)

Substance	$H_{\parallel}$, gauss	$\frac{b}{C}\cdot 10^{-6}$, gauss^2	$2\pi\tau \cdot 10^{-6}$, sec: 77° K	90° K	290° K: (Powder)	Axis K_1	Axis K_2	Axis K_3	Reference
$CuK_2(SO_4)_2 \cdot 6H_2O$	2400				0.02	0.025	0.023	0.017	At $T=290°$ K [41]
	3200	0.6 (Axis K_3)			0.025	0.03	0.027	0.02	
	4000				0.028	0.033	0.03	0.022	
	4800				0.03	0.035	0.032	0.023	
	5600				0.031	0.036	0.033	0.024	
	400	0.12 (Powder)	0.66	0.43					At low temperatures
	800		0.8	0.48	0.008	0.008		0.008	
	1600	0.11 (Axis K_1)			0.009	0.009		0.009	[72], at $T=290°$ K [41]
	2400	0.15 (Axis K_3)	0.9	0.54	0.01	0.01		0.009	
	3200				0.01	0.01		0.009	
	4000				0.01	0.01		0.009	
	4800				0.01	0.01		0.009	
	5600				0.01	0.01		0.009	
$Cu(NH_4)_2(SO_4)_2 \cdot 6H_2O$	400	0.18	0.47	0.28					At low temperatures
	800	0.16 (Powder)	0.59	0.33	0.008	0.008		0.008	
	1600	0.16 (Axis K_1)			0.01	0.012		0.01	[72], at $T=290°$ K [41]
	2400	0.16 (Axis K_3)	0.67	0.44	0.012	0.013		0.011	
	3200				0.013	0.014		0.012	
	4000				0.014	0.015		0.013	
	4800				0.014	0.015		0.013	
	5600				0.014	0.015		0.013	

Note: K_1, K_2, K_3 are the principal magnetic axis of the crystal; see Section 4.1.

requires that τ be proportional to H_0^{-2} and T^{-1} in addition, naturally, there should be no observable dependence of τ on the magnetic concentration N_0. However, according to [77], experiments on concentrated salts show a temperature dependence which is stronger than T^{-1} while the dependence on H_0 up to rather strong fields takes the form $\tau \sim (b + CH_0^2)$. Finally, in the majority of cases,[1] upon dilution, τ ($\tau \sim N_0^{-1}$) is observed to lengthen. It might be added that for concentrated salts the Casimir and DuPre formula itself does not agree sufficiently well with experimental results. These results can only be satisfactorily described by employing the whole

[1] The only exceptions are Cu^{2+} Tutton salts.

range of values of τ. But as the magnetic dilution of the samples increases, the departures from the Casimir and DuPre formula decrease. The dependence of τ on concentrations also lessens, and with sufficient dilution, the relaxation time becomes constant.

The function $\tau(H_0)$ in diluted samples is complicated. For small values of H_0 the relaxation time increases with field, but rapidly reaches a maximum (corresponding to several hundred gauss), after which τ approximately becomes proportional to H_0^{-1}. Thus, in diluted paramagnetic substances, the discrepancy with theory becomes somewhat less, but it is not entirely removed.

Tables 5.5 and 5.5a give data obtained by Gorter and his coworkers [72] from measurements of paramagnetic relaxation in the helium temperature region.

Table 5.5

Spin-Lattice Relaxation at Low Temperatures

Substance	T, °K	$H_{\parallel}$, gauss	$2\pi\tau \cdot 10^3$, sec	Method
$KCr(SO_4)_2 \cdot 12H_2O$	20.4	4000	0.21	Absorption in parallel fields
	14.3	4000	0.31	
$Gd_2(SO_4)_3 \cdot 8H_2O$	20.4	800	0.0054	Dispersion of susceptibility in parallel fields
		1600	0.006	
		2400	0.0074	
		3200	0.009	
		4000	0.012	
$MnSO_4 \cdot 4H_2O$	20.5	670	1.37	Absorption and dispersion in parallel fields
		1120	1.52	
		1685	1.82	
		2250	2.13	
		3370	2.64	
		4030	2.78	
	18.4	670	2.56	Absorption and dispersion in parallel fields
		1120	2.82	
		1685	3.30	
		2250	3.90	
		3370	4.90	
		4030	5.12	
	14.4	670	9.3	Absorption and dispersion in parallel fields
		1120	10.5	
		1685	12.5	
		2250	14.5	
		3370	18.2	
		4030	19.0	
$Mn(NH_4)_2(SO_4)_2 \cdot 6H_2O$	20.3	0	1.06	Absorption and dispersion in parallel fields
		$\to \infty$	2.47	
	14.3	0	5.86	
		$\to \infty$	13.6	
	4.21	0	50.3	
		$\to \infty$	117	

Table 5.5a

Average Time of Spin-Lattice Relaxation at Low Temperatures

Substance	$H_{\parallel}$, gauss	$2\pi\bar{\tau}\cdot 10^3$, sec	$\frac{\tau_{1/2}}{\bar{\tau}}$	T, °K
$KCr(SO_4)_2\cdot 12H_2O$				
sample A	790	2.48	—	4.04
	2250	5.1	—	4.04
	3370	6.7	—	4.04
	790	9.8	—	2.58
	2250	19.5	—	2.58
	3370	23.5	—	2.58
	790	20.0	—	1.95
	2250	36.3	—	1.95
	3370	44.1	—	1.95
sample B	710	1.6	1.3	2.68
	2480	3.6	1.29	2.68
	3100	4.2	1.34	2.68
	710	12.5	1.0	1.34
	2480	29	1.28	1.34
	3100	34	1.27	1.34
$K_2Cu(SO_4)_2\cdot 6H_2O$	225	30	1.6	4.015
	340	40	1.5	
	450	45	1.4	
	657	50	1.3	
	226—339			2.16
	226—339			1.0
$Cu(NH_4)_2(SO_4)_2\cdot 6H_2O$	286—428	210		2.18
	286—428	240—250		0.97
$Fe(NH_4)(SO_4)_2\cdot 12H_2O$				
sample A	2250	2.40	1.24	3.61
	3370	4.78	1.27	3.61
	4500	7.58	1.33	3.61
	450	0.98	1.00	3.00
	675	1.50	1.11	3.00
	1120	3.01	1.14	3.00
	1685	5.74	1.21	3.00
	2250	9.90	1.30	3.00
	3370	18.0	1.31	3.00
	4500	26.9	1.40	3.00
	450	2.10	1.21	2.51
	675	3.38	1.11	
	1120	5.78	—	
	1685	11.3	1.27	
	2250	19.1	—	
	3370	42.0	—	
	113	4.26	—	1.89
	225	4.46	—	
	450	6.58	1.16	
	675	8.70	1.15	
	1120	18.7	1.17	
	225	9.09	—	1.61

Table 5.5a (Cont'd)

Substance	$H_{\parallel}$, gauss	$2\pi\bar{\tau}\cdot 10^3$, sec	$\frac{\tau_{1/2}}{\bar{\tau}}$	T, °K
	450	12.2	—	
	675	15.9	—	
	1120	36	—	
sample B	450	1.82	4.02	4.08
	675	2.29	3.53	
	1120	5.72	3.49	
	1685	11.8	2.83	
	2250	15.9	2.50	
	3370	27	2.32	
	4500	36	1.68	
	450	8.5	2.12	2.98
	675	14.9	1.41	
	1120	29	2.24	
	2250	83	1.62	
	3370	133	1.47	
	4500	180	1.33	
sample C	225	2.9		2.96
	450	4.6	2.01	
	675	7.5	1.98	
	1120	15.5	1.74	
	1685	31.7	1.81	
	113	11	1.2	2.32
	225	13.1	1.48	
	450	19.2	1.63	
	675	26.7	1.63	
	1120	58	1.53	
	1685	100	1.27	
$Gd(SO_4)_3\cdot 8H_2O$	1120	25		4.15
	1685	29		
	2250	37		
	3370	45		
	4030	55		
	570—851	44—50		2.16
	570—851	314		0.99

Note: For calculations of these data, obtained by the method of measuring $\chi'(H_0)$ and $\chi''(H_0)$ in parallel fields $H_{\parallel}$, the factors $(1+\tau^2\omega^2)^{-1}$ and $\tau(1+\tau^2\omega^2)^{-1}$ in the Casimir and DuPré formulas are replaced, respectively, by

$$\int \frac{g(\tau)}{1+\tau^2\omega^2}\,d\tau \quad \text{and} \quad \int \frac{\tau g(\tau)}{1+\tau^2\omega^2}\,d\tau,$$

where $\int g(\tau)\,d\tau = 1$. $\bar{\tau}$ denotes the mean value of τ in the continuous distribution $g(\tau)$; $\tau_{1/2}$ denotes the value of τ given by the relation $g(\tau_{1/2}) = 1/2g(\tau)$; the ratio $\tau_{1/2}/\bar{\tau}$ characterizes the width of the distribution of the relaxation time.

Along with the dynamic polarization method, in recent years a number of measurements of the relaxation time have been made by the method of saturation of the paramagnetic resonance line. In this case it is possible in principle to use much greater magnetic dilutions. Moreover, the saturation method makes possible a determination of the relaxation constant for an individual resonance transition, whereas the dynamic polarization method yields only the total magnitude. On the other hand, the saturation method is not devoid of shortcomings: 1) it is very difficult to determine the relation $\tau(H_0)$ by means of it, because it is necessary to conduct measurements over a wide frequency range; 2) for a study of short relaxation time, one must use very large oscillatory field power; and finally 3) the experimental arrangements themselves are considerably more complicated than in the method of parallel fields.

The first relaxation measurements on the basis of the saturation method were made by Slichter and Purcell [78] in 1949 in undiluted salts of Mn^{2+} and Cu^{2+} at room temperature and at dry ice temperature. The sample was placed in a resonant cavity, which terminated one of the arms of a T bridge. In order to generate the strong microwave magnetic fields (with an amplitude of about 30 gauss) necessary for saturation of the broad absorption lines, a pulsed magnetron was used. In view of the transition effects, related to the short pulses, the usual bridge technique was somewhat modified. The relaxation times T_1 for $Mn(NH_4)_2(SO_4)_2 \cdot 6H_2O$, Mn^{2+} sulfate and Cu^{2+} sulfate were found to be on the order of 10^{-8} sec.

Schneider and England [79] have measured T_2 in a sample of ZnS containing a small amount of Mn^{2+} at 90° K. Since the absorption lines are narrow, the saturation experiments were conducted with an ordinary klystron as the source of the microwave field. The measurements were performed at liquid air temperature and led to a value of the spin-lattice relaxation time that is close to those observed by Gorter in undiluted Mn^{2+} salts.

Eschenfelder and Weidner [80] have conducted saturation experiments in single crystals of diluted chrome potassium and iron ammonium alums at 2 - 4° K. The measurements were performed by the reflection method using a T bridge. The source of the microwave field was a klystron, which supplied an output power of one watt. A toroidally shaped sample was placed in the cylindrical resonant cavity coupled to the waveguide. To ensure thermal isolation a portion of the waveguide was made of glass coated with a thin layer of silver.

The spin-lattice relaxation times were determined by means of the formula

$$\frac{Q_M}{Q_L} = B\frac{T}{g(\nu)} + ATT_1p_i(1-\Gamma)^2.$$

Here Q_M and Q_L are the Q factors of the cavity with and without magnetic losses, B is a certain constant,

$$A = \frac{4(2S+1)k}{N(h\nu)^2(1-\Gamma_0)},$$

Γ is the reflection coefficient at the resonance value of the field $H = H_{res}$, Γ_0 is the same value for $H \gg H_{res}$, p_i is the incident power,

$$\frac{Q_M}{Q_L} = \frac{(1-\Gamma)}{(\Gamma-\Gamma_0)}.$$

From the experimental relation $\Gamma(p_i)$, one may determine the spin-lattice relaxation time $T_1 = 1/2W$, where W is the probability of relaxation transitions. This can be most conveniently done by plotting a graph of the magnitude of Q_M/Q_L as a function of $p_i(1-\Gamma)^2$; and from the slope of the resulting straight line it is possible to determine TT_1 independently of $g(\nu)$.

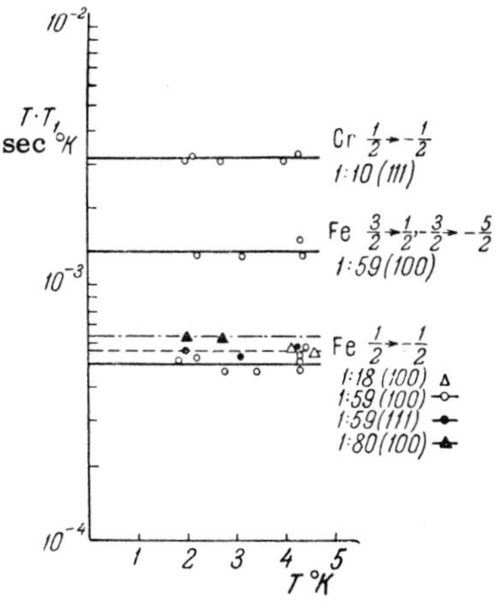

Fig. 5.4. Results of measurement by the saturation method of the temperature dependence of the relaxation time T_1 for $KCr(SO_4)_2 \cdot 12H_2O$ and $Fe(NH_4)(SO_4)_2 \cdot 12H_2O$ [80].

The basic results, obtained for $KCr(SO_4)_2 \cdot 12H_2O$ and $Fe(NH_4)(SO_4)_2 \cdot 12H_2O$ are given in Figure 5.4. The corresponding resonance transitions, magnetic dilutions and crystal orientations are given for both salts on the right side of the figure. It is apparent from the figure that in agreement with theory the time T_1 is inversely proportional to the absolute temperature. Magnetic dilution, which was studied in iron ammonium alums, only very weakly increases the time T_1.

By means of pulse techniques Bloembergen and Wang [48] have extended the experiments of Slichter and Purcell on the study of spin-lattice relaxation time in substances with broad absorption lines. Their apparatus enables them to obtain in a resonant cavity a microwave magnetic field with an amplitude up to 50 gauss per pulse. Under paramagnetic resonance conditions, the following relation, obtained from the Bloch formula (5.1), holds:

$$\frac{M_Z}{M_0} = \frac{\chi''}{\chi_0} = \frac{1}{1 + \frac{1}{4}\gamma^2 H_1^2 T_1 T_2}.$$

Here χ'' and χ_0 are the absorption coefficients for a given amplitude of H_1 and for $H_1 \to 0$, i.e., when saturation does not exist. If the magnitude of γ and the width of the resonance line are known, the time T_1 may be found both by means of the measurement of χ''/χ_0 and by means of the measurement of M_{z_1}/M_0 for different amplitudes of H_1. Measurements performed by both methods with $MnSO_4 \cdot 4H_2O$ have shown close agreement with the data of Gorter, as is apparent from Table 5.6.

Table 5.6

Relaxation Times in $MnSO_4 \cdot 4H_2O$

Method	300°K	77°K
Nonresonant dispersion	$1.0 \cdot 10^{-7}$ sec	$1.3 \cdot 10^{-6}$ sec
Saturation	$0.78 \cdot 10^{-7}$ sec	$1.2 \cdot 10^{-6}$ sec

Extensive application of the saturation method in the immediate future will undoubtedly greatly enlarge the presently insufficient experimental data on spin-lattice relaxation times in crystalline paramagnetic substances.

A great step forward in the study of relaxation at low temperatures was made recently in the work of Giordmaine, Alsop, Nash and Townes [58]. These authors measured the relaxation times in $Gd_2Mg_3(NO_3)_{12} \cdot 24H_2O$, $K_3Cr(CN)_6$ and $Cu(NH_4)_2(SO_4)_2 \cdot 6H_2O$ in the temperature range 1-4°K. Two methods were used: 1) the ordinary method of saturation of a paramagnetic resonance line and 2) saturation of the line by strong pulses of microwave energy with a subsequent measurement of the rate at which equilibrium was restored by observing the absorption of a small microwave signal as a function of time after the saturating energy was removed. This observation was made by synchronously sweeping the frequency of two different klystron oscillators past the paramagnetic resonance. The pulses are ordinarily repeated at a rate that is slow compared with the relaxation time. The time difference between saturation and probing may, of course, easily be varied by changing the frequency difference between the two oscillators or by changing the rate of sweep. The relaxation times found by means of both methods turned out to be close together except for copper salts. The values of T_1 obtained together with line width data are given in Table 5.7.

For the Gd^{3+} salt the observed width is related to the hyperfine interactions, while the time T_1 varies by a factor of approximately two, depending on the transition considered. They also depend somewhat on the chosen samples, on the concentration of the Gd^{3+} ions, and on the temperature.

Table 5.7

Substance (concentration $\leq 1:100$ at. %) and transition	Diamagnetic diluent	ΔH, gauss (width for half max. intensity)	T_1 from time of exponential drop, sec	T_1 from saturation, sec
$Gd_2Mg_3(NO_3)_{12} \cdot 24H_2O$ $M\left(-\frac{1}{2}\right) \to M\left(\frac{1}{2}\right)$	La	2.0	$7 \cdot 10^{-3}$	$15 \cdot 10^{-3}$
$K_3Cr(CN)_6$ $M\left(-\frac{1}{2}\right) \to M\left(\frac{1}{2}\right)$	Co	12	$3 \cdot 10^{-2}$	$4 \cdot 10^{-2}$
$Cu(NH_4)_2(SO_4)_2 \cdot 6H_2O$ $M\left(-\frac{1}{2}\right) \to M\left(\frac{1}{2}\right)$ $m\left(\frac{3}{2}\right) \to m\left(\frac{3}{2}\right)$	Zn	20	20	2

5.6. Solutions of Paramagnetic Salts. Theory

1. Up to the present time calculations of the shape of a paramagnetic resonance line in liquids have always been made by means of correlation theory. Use of the correlation method is quite natural, since it enables one to take into account most simply the influence of Brownian motion of the particles on the width of the absorption line. We shall briefly describe this method and its application to calculations of the broadening of resonance lines.

Let $F(t)$ be a certain random function of time, whose mean value is denoted by $\langle F(t)\rangle$. We assume that $F(t) = 0$. The correlation function, as is well known [81], is

$$K(\tau) = \langle F(t)\, F(t+\tau)\rangle. \tag{5.69}$$

We introduce the Fourier component $I(\nu)$ of the correlation function by means of the following substitution:

$$K(\tau) = \int_{-\infty}^{\infty} I(\nu)\, e^{-2\pi i\nu\tau}\, d\nu, \quad I(\nu) = \frac{1}{2\pi}\int_{-\infty}^{\infty} K(\tau)\, e^{+2\pi i\nu\tau}\, d\tau. \tag{5.70}$$

As τ increases, the correlation function obviously decreases. In the majority of cases that will be considered below, it may be assumed that the correlation function decreases with time according to the Markov law:

$$K(\tau)=\langle |F(t)|^2\rangle e^{-\frac{|\tau|}{\tau_c}}, \tag{5.71}$$

where τ_c is a certain parameter called the correlation time. Substituting (5.71) into (5.70), we obtain

$$I(\nu)=\frac{1}{2\pi}\langle |F(t)|^2\rangle \frac{2\tau_c}{1+4\pi^2\tau_c^2\nu_{lk}^2}. \tag{5.72}$$

Suppose we have a quantum system with energy levels E_l, subjected to the action of a time-varying random perturbation $\mathscr{H}'(t)$. The matrix element of the perturbation $\mathscr{H}_{lk}(t)$ will be a random function of time. Using ordinary time-dependent perturbation theory, it is easily shown that the probability of a transition in the quantum system during 1 sec from state E_l to state E_k under the influence of the perturbation $\hat{\mathscr{H}}'(t)$ equals

$$A_{lk}=\frac{4\pi^2}{h^2} I(\nu_{kl}). \tag{5.73}$$

By means of (5.72) we finally obtain

$$A_{lk}=\frac{2\pi}{h^2}\langle |\mathscr{H}'_{lk}(t)|^2\rangle \frac{2\tau_c}{1+4\pi^2\tau_c^2\nu_{lk}^2}. \tag{5.74}$$

For further calculations it is necessary to clarify the nature of the relaxation mechanism, or in other words, the origin of the perturbation $\hat{\mathscr{H}}'(t)$.

2. The first theory of the shape of a paramagnetic resonance line in liquids was proposed by Bloembergen, Purcell and Pound [82]. It is true that the cited paper specifically considers nuclear resonance, but its results may be directly applied to a liquid electronic paramagnetic. In the theory of Bloembergen et al., just as in Waller's work with crystals, it is assumed that the relaxation is due to magnetic interactions between particles. Hence, the perturbation $\hat{\mathscr{H}}'(t)$ can be expressed by means of (5.9), assuming that r, ϑ and φ vary with time as a result of the Brownian motion. Let us assume that all the Zeeman levels of the magnetic particle are equidistant, so that only one Larmor precession frequency ν_0 occurs. If we calculate the off-diagonal matrix elements of $\hat{\mathscr{H}}'(t)$, perform the necessary averaging, and then substitute the resulting expressions for A_{lk} into (5.40), we obtain for the longitudinal relaxation time,

$$\frac{1}{T_1}=\frac{8\pi^2}{5h^2} g^4\beta^4 S(S+1)\left[\frac{\tau_c}{1+4\pi^2\tau_c^2\nu_0^2}+\frac{4\tau_c}{1+16\pi^2\tau_c^2\nu_0^2}\right]\sum_k \left\langle \frac{1}{r_k^6}\right\rangle. \tag{5.75}$$

If r is the distance between two interacting particles, for the correlation time one should take the average time required for this distance to double as a result of the Brownian motion. Thus, the magnitude of τ_c clearly will be a function of r, namely $\tau_c = r^2/12D$, where D is the diffusion coefficient, which according to the Stokes formula is given by

$$D = \frac{kT}{6\pi a_0 \eta}. \tag{5.76}$$

Here a_0 is the radius of the particle, and η is the coefficient of viscosity. Now we must allow for the fact that $2\pi\nu\tau_c \ll 1$ for all particles close enough to have an appreciable effect on the relaxation process, so that after replacing the summation by an integration over r, formula (5.75) gives the following relaxation rate:

$$\frac{1}{T_1} = \frac{8\pi^4 g^4 \beta^4 N_0 \eta S(S+1)}{h^2 kT}. \tag{5.77}$$

Bloembergen, Purcell and Pound have also allowed for the effect of Brownian motion on the magnitude of the transverse relaxation time. This subject was then investigated in detail in papers [30-32]. An estimate of the transverse relaxation time, determined by magnetic interactions of the particle, may be made using the following formula:

$$\frac{1}{T_2} = \sqrt{\frac{3}{\pi} K_1 \operatorname{arctg}\frac{2\tau_c}{T_2}}, \quad K_1 = \frac{2}{5}\frac{g^2\beta^2}{h^2} S(S+1)\sum_k \left\langle \frac{1}{r_k^6} \right\rangle. \tag{5.78}$$

If $\tau_c \ll T_2$, then after completing the transformations in the passage from (5.75) to (5.77) from (5.78), we obtain

$$\frac{1}{T_2} = \frac{48\pi^3}{5}\frac{g^4\beta^4 N_0 \eta}{h^2 kT} S(S+1). \tag{5.79}$$

For example, let us note that for an aqueous solution of a divalent manganese salt when $N_0 \approx 6 \cdot 10^{20}$ cm^{-3} we obtain $1/T_1 \approx 4 \cdot 10^9$ sec^{-1} from (5.77).

For large concentrations of paramagnetic ions it should be borne in mind that exchange interactions may also have an appreciable effect on the line shape. Paramagnetic resonance experiments in ionic crystals, however, are carried out for the most part at those low concentrations of magnetic particles at which the relaxation mechanism is determined no longer by magnetic or by exchange interactions.

3. From the analysis of experimental data on paramagnetic absorption in solutions, Kozyrev [83] reached the conclusion that a solvate complex, formed from a paramagnetic ion and a neighboring

dipole molecule of the diluent, has such a great stability that it may be considered in paramagnetic resonance experiments as having the nature of a "microcrystallite." Hence, in many respects, "spin-lattice" interactions in solution were found to be analogous to those in solids. The "spin-spin" part of the absorption line width is connected with the fact that in a solution the "microcrystallites" are randomly oriented; this should lead to a broadening of the line as a consequence of a possible anisotropy of the g factor, and also as a consequence of the fact that the splitting of the spin level by the "crystallite" electric field depends on the orientation of the "microcrystallites" in the external magnetic field H_0.

McConnell [84] has considered the following relaxation mechanism, which is connected with the existence of stable solvate shells. On rotation of the "microcrystallite" under the influence of Brownian forces, the intervals between the spin levels of the paramagnetic ions will change. Hence, as the "microcrystallite" rotates, an exchange of energy will occur between the paramagnetic ions and the Brownian motion.

McConnell made calculations for Cu^{2+}, for which he adopted the following spin Hamiltonian:

$$\hat{\mathscr{H}}_{sp}=\beta[g_{\|}H_rS_r+g_{\perp}(H_pS_p+H_qS_q)]+AI_rS_r+B(I_pS_p+I_qS_q). \quad (5.80)$$

Here r, q, p are unit vectors of the axes of the rectangular system of coordinates, rigidly connected to the octahedron of the water molecules; XYZ denote the stationary coordinate system. Let the direction of the external magnetic field H_0 coincide with the Z axis. The spin Hamiltonian may be represented in the form

$$\hat{\mathscr{H}}_{sp}=\hat{\mathscr{H}}_0+\hat{\mathscr{H}}'_z,\ \hat{\mathscr{H}}_0=\frac{1}{3}(g_{\|}+2g_{\perp})\beta HS_z+\frac{1}{3}(A+2B)SI. \quad (5.81)$$

The main part of the Hamiltonian $\hat{\mathscr{H}}_0$ is a constant of motion. Having calculated the matrix elements of the time-dependent perturbation $\hat{\mathscr{H}}'_z(t)$ and substituted them into (5.74) and (5.40), we obtain:

$$\frac{1}{T_1}=\frac{8\pi^2}{15}\frac{(\Delta g\beta H_0+bI_z)^2h^{-2}\tau_c}{1+4\pi^2\nu_0^2\tau_c^2},$$
$$\Delta g=g_{\|}-g_{\perp},\qquad b=A-B. \quad (5.82)$$

For the correlation time we may adopt an expression resulting from the well-known Debye theory [82]:

$$\tau_c=\frac{4\pi\eta a_0^3}{3kT}. \quad (5.83)$$

McConnell has also considered the contribution to the magnitude of the transverse relaxation time T_2, which is related to the Brownian rotation of the microcrystalites, in which the resonance levels change. The broadening of the paramagnetic resonance line of the particle, whose state is described by the spin Hamiltonian (5.80), may be evaluated by means of the following formula for the time T_2:

$$\frac{1}{T_2^2}=\frac{32\pi}{45}(\Delta g\beta H_0+bI_z)^2 h^{-2}\,\mathrm{arctg}\,\frac{2\tau_c}{T_2}. \quad (5.84)$$

Two interesting facts result from formulas (5.82) and (5.84): 1) the width of the absorption line must depend strong on the intensity of field H_0 ; 2) different hyperfine components of the paramagnetic resonance line must have different widths.

McGarvey [85] has extended the McConnell theory to an ion with $S > 1/2$. For Cr^{3+} he adopted the spin Hamiltonian

$$\mathscr{H}_{\mathrm{sp}}=\beta g H_0 S+D\left[S_z^2-\frac{1}{3}S(S+1)\right] \quad (5.85)$$

and obtained

$$\frac{1}{T_1}=\frac{32\pi^2}{5}\frac{D^2}{h^2}\left[\frac{\tau_c}{1+4\pi^2\tau_c^2\nu_0^2}+\frac{\tau_c}{1+16\pi^2\tau_c^2\nu_0^2}\right], \quad (5.86)$$

$$\frac{1}{T_2}=\frac{64\pi}{15}\frac{D^2}{h^2}\,\mathrm{arctg}\,\frac{2\tau_c}{T_2}. \quad (5.87)$$

For the Mn^{2+} and Fe^{3+} ions an additional term was added to the spin Hamiltonian (5.75)

$$\frac{1}{6}a\left[(S_x^4+S_y^4+S_z^4)-\frac{1}{5}S(S+1)(3S^2+3S-1)\right]. \quad (5.88)$$

Calculations have shown that

$$\frac{1}{T_1}=\frac{16\pi^2}{25}\frac{D^2}{h^2}\left[\frac{67\tau_c}{1+4\pi^2\tau_c^2\nu_0^2}+\frac{52\tau_c}{1+16\pi^2\tau_c^2\nu_0^2}\right], \quad (5.89)$$

$$\frac{1}{T_2}=\frac{64\pi}{5}\frac{D^2}{h^2}\,\mathrm{arctg}\,\frac{2\tau_c}{T_2}+\frac{656\pi}{105}\frac{a^2}{h^2}\,\mathrm{arctg}\,\frac{0{,}6\tau_c}{T_2}. \quad (5.90)$$

In the calculation of T_1 we set $a = 0$. All the calculations were carried out under the assumption that the fine-structure components of lines of Cr^{3+}, Mn^{2+} and Fe^{3+} coalesce into a single line.

4. It will be shown below that in many cases the experimental data concerning the dependence of the width of the resonant lines on temperature and on static magnetic field intensity cannot be explained by the McConnell theory. Al'tshuler and Valiyev [86] have assumed that the main mechanism of the longitudinal (spin-lattice) relaxation consists of the following.

In solid paramagnetic ionic crystals the paramagnetic particle M together with the nearest diamagnetic particles X form an ordinary paramagnetic complex, for example, MX_6 (M is a metal ion and X is a water molecule or other diamagnetic particle), the interaction inside of which must be taken into account first when explaining the magnetic properties of a substance. In liquids the existence of a solvate shell enables us to make similar assumptions. It may be assumed that in the course of time greater than the correlation time of the spin-lattice interaction the paramagnetic ion together with the neighboring molecules of the solvent form a stable complex, whose vibrations may be characterized by a set of normal coordinates Q_i; the Brownian motion of the liquid molecules perturbs the oscillations of the paramagnetic complex and in this way alters the electric field in which the paramagnetic particle is located. These changes affect the spin-orbit interactions of the electrons of the paramagnetic ion and hence may lead to a reorientation of its magnetic moment.

If we expand the matrix element of the spin-lattice perturbation in terms of the normal cordinates

$$\mathscr{H}'_{lk}(t) = \sum_i V_{lk}^{(i)} Q_i(t) \tag{5.91}$$

and denote the mean frequency of oscillation of the paramagnetic complex by ν_0, then by means of (5.74) we obtain:

$$A_{lk} = \frac{4\pi^2 \overline{Q_i^2}}{h^2} \sum_i |V_{lk}^{(i)}|^2 \frac{2\tau_c}{1 + 4\pi^2 \nu_{lk}^2 \tau_c^2}. \tag{5.92}$$

Here $\overline{Q^2}$ is the mean value of the square amplitude of the oscillator, which may be calculated from the formula [81]:

$$\overline{Q^2} = \frac{h}{8\pi m \nu_0} \operatorname{cth}\left(\frac{h\nu_0}{2kT}\right), \tag{5.93}$$

if m denotes the mass of the complex. The vibrations of the paramagnetic complex will be perturbed on account of the effect of the surrounding particles, which perform a Brownian motion. Consequently, the correlation time will naturally be defined as the reciprocal of the magnitude of the damping coefficient γ, which may be evaluated from the width of the satellite lines in the Raman spectra of paramagnetic ions: $\gamma \approx 10\,\text{cm}^{-1}$ and $\tau_c \sim 1/\gamma \approx 10^{-12}$ sec. From the experimental data [87] on the temperature dependence of the line width of the vibrational structure of the optical spectra of ions in crystals it follows that the width increases with heating in proportion to $\sqrt{T}$[1]. In such a case the temperature dependence

[1] A detailed analysis of the interaction of the oscillators Q_i with the Brownian motion, given by K. A. Valiyev (an unpublished paper), has shown the possibility of another interpretation of the constant τ_c; in this case the character of the temperature dependence of A_{lk} is preserved.

of the probability of a relaxation transition will be determined from the formula

$$A_{lk} \sim \frac{1}{\sqrt{T}} \operatorname{cth}\left(\frac{h\nu_0}{2kT}\right) \qquad (5.94)$$

for $4\pi^2\nu_{lk}^2\,\tau_c^2 \ll 1$ and

$$A_{lk} \sim \sqrt{T} \operatorname{cth}\left(\frac{h\nu_0}{2kT}\right) \qquad (5.95)$$

for $4\pi^2\nu_{lk}^2\,\tau_c^2 \gg 1$.

Let us consider several typical paramagnetic ions.

Cu^{2+}. The system of energy levels arising in a strong cubic field plus a weak field of lower symmetry and an external magnetic field H_0 is given in Figure 5.5. It is characteristic of this case that two relatively close orbital levels exist, the interval between which is of the order of 1000 cm^{-1} in solid salts. The width of the resonance line in liquids is apparently determined by the relaxation transition between these energy levels without a change in the spin direction. The width of the resonance line is given by the following expression:

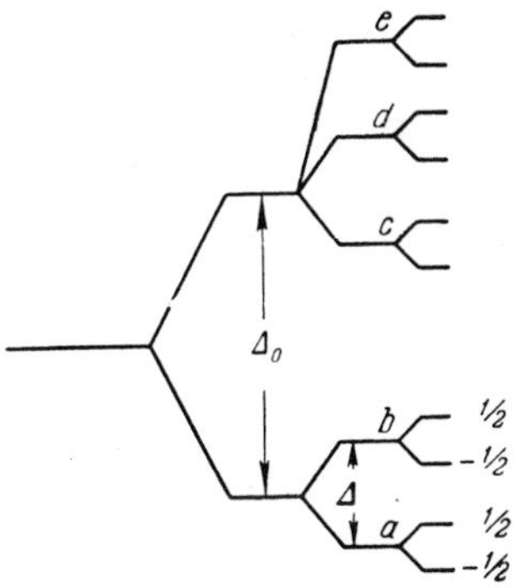

Fig. 5.5. Successive splitting of the ground energy state of Cu^{2+} under the action of a strong cubic, weak tetragonal field and of an external magnetic field.

$$\Delta\nu = 2A_{ab} = \qquad (5.96)$$
$$= 12\left(\frac{16}{7}\frac{e\mu}{R^2\Delta_0}\frac{\overline{r^2}}{R^2}\right)^2 \frac{\overline{Q^2}}{R^2}\,\frac{e^{-\frac{\Delta}{2kT}}}{\tau_c}.$$

Here R is the equilibrium distance from the Cu^{2+} ion to the water molecule, whose dipole moment equals μ. In contrast to the McConnell theory, it follows from this formula that the width should be independent of the field H_0. If we assume that $\nu_0 \approx 500$ cm^{-1} [88], the temperature dependence will be given by the formula

$$\Delta\nu = \sqrt{T} \exp\left(-\frac{\Delta}{2kT}\right). \qquad (5.97)$$

The relation between the relaxation time and the half-width is somewhat unusual in this case and has the form

$$\frac{1}{T_1} \approx \frac{\Delta\nu}{2}\,\frac{\exp\frac{\Delta}{kT}}{1-\exp\left(-\frac{\Delta}{kT}\right)}. \qquad (5.98)$$

It is interesting to note that, in contrast to $\Delta\nu$, the magnitude of $1/T_1$ decreases as the temperature increases. Thus, at first glance, the strange temperature dependence of the relaxation time is explained by the fact that in our case the specific heat of the spin system upon heating increases more rapidly than the probability of the relaxation transition. It should be kept in mind that the non-equilibrium distribution of particles between the levels $a, -1/2$ and $a, 1/2$ (or the levels $b, -1/2$ and $b, 1/2$) may not be destroyed by means of the relaxation transitions $a, -1/2 \to b, -1/2$ and $a, 1/2 \to b, 1/2$. Therefore, besides the time T_1, still another relaxation time T_1', will exist, whose magnitude may be evaluated by the formula

$$\frac{1}{T_1'} = 6\frac{\overline{Q^2}}{\hbar^2 R^2}\left(\frac{\lambda g\beta H_0}{\Delta_0^2}\right)^2\left(\frac{16}{7}\frac{e\mu}{R^2}\frac{\overline{r^2}}{R^2}\right)^2 2\tau_c. \tag{5.99}$$

Cr^{3+}. Calculations were carried out for two extreme cases of strong and weak magnetic fields. If the field H_0 is strong and the spin levels are equidistant,

$$\frac{1}{T_1} = \frac{96}{20}\frac{\overline{Q^2}}{\hbar^2}(13\varepsilon_1^2 + 4\varepsilon_2^2)\,\tau_c',$$

where

$$\begin{aligned} \varepsilon_1 &= 54\sqrt{3}\,\frac{\lambda^2}{\Delta_0^2}\frac{e\mu}{R^3}\frac{\overline{r^4}}{R^4}, \\ \varepsilon_2 &= \frac{12\cdot 324}{175}\frac{\lambda^2}{\Delta_0^2}\frac{e\mu}{R^3}\left(\frac{\overline{r^2}}{R^2} - \frac{55}{36}\frac{\overline{r^4}}{R^4}\right). \end{aligned} \tag{5.100}$$

If, however, $H_0 = 0$,

$$\frac{1}{T_1} = 36\frac{\overline{Q^2}}{\hbar^2}(\varepsilon_1^2 + \varepsilon_2^2)\,\tau_c. \tag{5.101}$$

If we allow for the fact that for chromium complexes $\nu_0 \approx 800$ cm^{-1} [89], we obtain $T_1 \approx T_2$.

Mn^{2+}. If D denotes the spin Hamiltonian constant that determines the splitting of the spin levels in a zero magnetic field, it is found that

$$\frac{1}{T_1} = C\frac{D^2}{\hbar^2}\frac{\overline{Q^2}}{R^2}\tau_c, \tag{5.102}$$

where in the case of a strong magnetic field $C = (274\cdot 64\cdot 12)/35$; if, however, $H_0 = 0$, then $C = (36\cdot 16\cdot 157)/7$. At temperatures from 300 to 400°K for Mn^{2+} [56], $h\nu_0 \approx kT$, and therefore the magnitude of $1/T_1$ at first decreases with heating and then begins to increase.

5.7. Solutions of Paramagnetic Salts. Experimental Results

As was pointed out in Chapter IV, paramagnetic absorption in liquid solutions of Mn^{2+} salts was first detected by Zavoyskiy. He investigated this absorption at frequencies of 1-10 Mc in the presence of static magnetic fields, arranged both perpendicular and parallel [89] to the oscillating magnetic field. Later a number of measurements of the width of the paramagnetic resonance line were undertaken not only in Mn^{2+} solutions [90-94], but also in solutions of other ions of the iron group and of the Gd^{3+} ion [64, 94, 84, 85]. In addition to simple ions several complex ions were investigated [95, 85]. Measurements show that ΔH in solutions depends strongly on the nature of the ion, on the solvent and on the temperature. Furthermore, the ultimate width attainable at sufficiently low concentrations is independent of further dilution and varies with the nature of the ion. In particular, solutions of salts of hydrated Ti^{3+}, Fe^{3+}, Co^{2+} ions produced such broad lines at all dilutions that the resonance effect could not be detected. The reason for this failure appears to be the extremely short spin-lattice relaxation time.[1]

In the course of investigations over the frequency range 10-10^4 Mc [64], resonance was not observed in salts of ions with an even number of electrons (Cr^{2+}, Ni^{2+}, V^{3+}); this may be attributed, as in solid salts, to the smallness of the radio-frequency field quantum in comparison with the zero-field splitting of the spin sublevels.

Some data concerning the values of ΔH in iron group ions at room temperature are given in Table 5.8.

For certain ions (Mn^{2+}, Cr^{3+}, Cu^{2+}) the temperature dependence of ΔH has been investigated [94]. It is illustrated in Figures 5.6-5.8.

The following conclusions can be drawn concerning the nature of the line width in solutions.

1) In highly concentrated solutions we sometimes observe relatively narrow lines having no hyperfine structure. Dilution causes a broadening of the lines and gives rise to hyperfine structure. An example is a solution of $VOCl_2$, investigated by Garif'yanov and Kozyrev [96]. It must be assumed that substantial exchange interactions occur in concentrated solutions of this ion. A similar result has also been noted in liquid melts of hydrated Mn^{2+} salts [93].

2) In moderately concentrated solutions of Cr^{3+} salts, dilution cause a narrowing of the line [64, 85]. This narrowing should be attributed to a diminution of magnetic dipole interactions, and may

[1]This is confirmed by the detection of resonance in VO^{2+} [96] and also by the reported observation of a resonance effect in a complex Ti^{3+} salt [84]. In these cases the strong low-symmetry components of the crystalline field are able to provide a time τ of sufficient length.

be partially due to a raising of the symmetry of the local electric field which acts on the ion, and consequently on the decrease of the spread of the unresolved fine-structure peaks. The ultimate line width, which no longer depends on further dilution, may be due both to spin-lattice interactions and to the spread of the fine-structure peaks.

Table 5.8

Width of the Absorption Line in Aqueous Solutions of Iron Group Salts at Room Temperature

Substance	Concentration, moles/liter	ΔH, gauss	ν, Mc
$MnCl_2$	4.0	300	10
"	3.0	255	10
"	2.0	200	10
"	1.0	131	10
"	0.5	90	10
"	0.1	48	10
"	0.05	41	10
"	0.03	38	10
"	0.01	35	10
$Cr(NO_3)_3$	3.0	440 ± 20	9452
"	2.0	310 ± 20	9452
"	1.5	270 ± 20	9452
"	1.0	240 ± 20	9452
"	0.6	220 ± 20	9452
"	0.4	200 ± 20	9452
"	0.2	190 ± 20	9452
$Cu(NO_3)_2$	4	140	207
"	2	140	207
"	1	140	207
"	0.5	140	207
$CuCl_2$	4	225	207
"	3	185	207
"	2	160	207
"	1	140	207

3) In aqueous solutions of Cu^{2+} salts [64] the line width is independent of concentration and viscosity (since viscosity decreases approximately fivefold with change in concentration from 4 to 0.5 M). Consequently, the width in this case cannot be due to spin-spin interactions, but must be attributed to spin-lattice interactions.

Comparison of the experimental results with the proposed theories is easily carried out for individual ions.

Cr^{3+}. The independence of ΔH and the field strength H_0 may be equally well explained by the calculations of Al'tshuler and Valiyev or by those of McGarvey. This also applies to the qualitative explanation of the relation $\Delta H(T)$.. However, beginning at about 250°C there exists an experimental indication of line broadening with an increase of temperature, and this broadening may be understood only by means of the Al'tshuler and Valiyev theory.

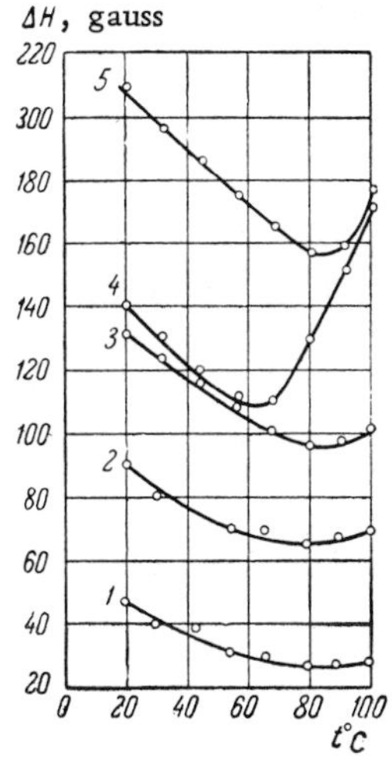

Fig. 5.6. Temperature dependence of the line width ΔH in aqueous solutions of $MnCl_2$ of various concentrations.
1) 0.005 M; 2) 0.5 M; 3) 1 M; 4) 1 M $MnCl_2$ + 3 M LiCl; 5) 2M $MnCl_2$; $\nu = 12.6$ Mc.

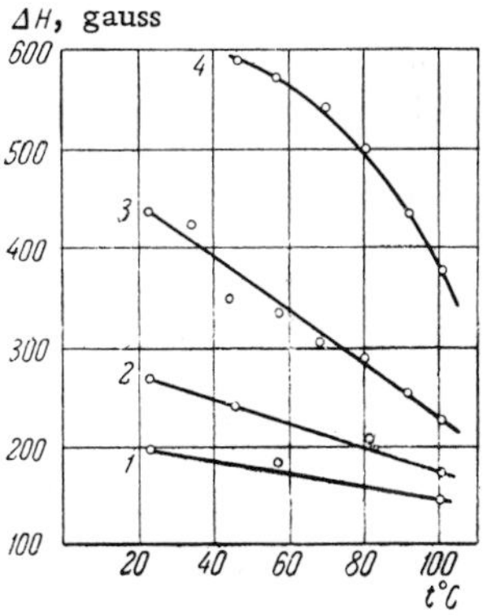

Fig. 5.7. Temperature dependence of the line width ΔH in aqueous solutions of trivalent chromium of various concentrations.
1) 0.4 M; 2) 1.5 M; 3) 3 M $Cr(H_2O)_6(NO_3)_3$; 4) 1 M $[Cr(H_2O)_4Cl_2]Cl$.

Mn^{2+}, Fe^{3+}. The calculations of McCarvey cannot explain the pronounced differences in the line widths measured in solutions of Mn^{2+} and Fe^{3+} ions, nor the line broadening of Mn^{2+} upon heating above 70°C. The theory of Al'tshuler and Valiyev enables us to understand the observed relation $\Delta H(T)$; the differences in the line widths of Mn^{2+} and Fe^{3+} do not in this instance contradict this theory.

Cu^{2+}_{aq}. For the Cu^{2+}_{aq} ion the theory of Al'tshuler and Valiyev explains why ΔH is independent of H_0 and of concentration, and also why the line broadening is unaffected by heating. However, in solutions of complex copper salts which give hyperfine structure peaks [97], we observe the effect of I_z on the width of an individual peak. This dependence of ΔH on I_z for complex copper ions is qualitatively explained by the McConnell theory. This apparently applies to solutions of vanadium salts, in which the width of each hyperfine structure peak also depends on I_z.

Recently Tishkov [98] carried out measurements of paramagnetic relaxation in parallel fields in solutions of Mn^{2+} salts in water, glycerol and water-glycerol mixtures. His basic results lead to the following.

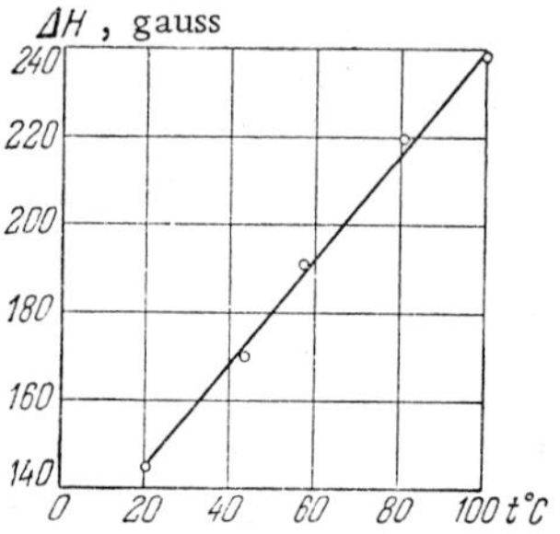

Fig. 5.8. Temperature dependence of ΔH in an aqueous solution of 1 M $Cu(NO_3)_2$. The curve is plotted from the equation $\Delta H = aT^2$.

1) The experimental curves $\chi''(H_{\|})$ are well described by the Casimir and Du Pré theory with inclusion of the spin-spin relaxation following Shaposhnikov.

2) The magnitude of τ rises with an increase of field $H_{\|}$. The relation $\tau(H_{\|})$ is in good agreement with the Brons-Van Vleck formula.

3) On reducing the Mn^{2+} concentration from 3 M to 1 M in an aqueous solution of $Mn(NO_3)_2$ the magnitude of τ increases somewhat; further dilution does not affect τ.

4) A change in the microscopic viscosity of the solution does not affect τ.

5) A change in the immediate environment of the Mn^{2+} ion brings about a change in τ.

6) The magnitude of τ as a function of temperature passes through a maximum, corresponding to about 20°C for 1 mole of an aqueous solution of $Mn(NO_3)_2$.

None of these results contradict the theory of Al'tshuler and Valiyev; indeed, the temperature dependence of τ directly corroborates it.

In summary, one may assert that in the case of ions with a small g-factor anisotropy the perturbation by Brownian motion of the solvate complex is a spin-lattice relaxation mechanism. Examples of such ions are Mn^{2+}, Cr^{3+}, and hydrated Cu^{2+} However, in the case of ions with a strong g-factor anisotropy (complex Cu^{2+}. ions and possibly VO^{2+}) a stronger relaxation mechanism is that related to the rotation of the solvate complex.

5.8. Line Shape under Saturation Conditions

We speak of saturation of paramagnetic resonance when the magnitude of the resonance effect and the shape of the resonance line depend markedly on the microwave power. The saturation behavior is twofold, corresponding to two possible types of absorption line broadening [99]. The broadening will be called homogeneous if the energy absorbed from the radiation field is distributed to all the spins, so that thermal equilibrium of the spin system is maintained throughout the paramagnetic resonance. Sources of homogeneous broadening include:

1) dipolar interaction between like spins;
2) spin-lattice relaxation;
3) interaction of spins with the radiation field;
4) exchange interactions;
5) motion of the unpaired spins in the microwave field;
6) diffusion of spin system excitation through the paramagnetic sample.

We are already acquainted with some of these line-broadening mechanisms, and the others will be encountered in the study of the resonance effect in metals, semiconductors and other paramagnetic substances.

If the broadening comes from variations in the local magnetic field, the microwave energy will be transferred only to those spins whose local magnetic fields satisfy the resonance conditions. Furthermore, if the processes for spin-spin interaction are slow compared with the direct interaction between the spins and the lattice, the spin system will not succeed in reaching a state of thermodynamic equilibrium. We shall call this type of broadening inhomogeneous. It is useful for this case to visualize the paramagnetic substance as an assemblage of spin packets having no interaction with each other. Each packet is characterized by a certain absorption line, whose width is determined by the dipole-dipole interactions. The over-all response of the paramagnet to external interactions will be the superposition of the independent responses of the individual spin packets. Clearly, such a system will react differently than a paramagnetic substance with a homogeneous broadening mechanism. This broadening is called inhomogeneous.

Examples of sources of inhomogeneous broadening include:

1) hyperfine interaction of the spins of paramagnetic centers with the nuclear moments of neighboring diamagnetic particles;
2) anisotropy of the splitting of spin levels;
3) dipolar interaction between spins with different Larmor frequencies;
4) inhomogeneities in the applied DC magnetic field.

If the broadening is homogeneous, it is easily shown that the imaginary part of the RF susceptibility (paramagnetic absorption) is determined by the following formula:

$$\chi''(\nu) = \frac{\pi}{2}\chi_0\nu_0 \frac{g(\nu-\nu_0)}{1+\frac{1}{8}\gamma^2 H_1^2 T_1 g(\nu-\nu_0)}. \tag{5.103}$$

The shape factor $g(\nu)$ (see Sec. 1.3) will be represented here as $g(\nu - \nu_0)$, as we shall also be interested in its dependence on the resonance frequency ν_0.

In order to obtain the Bloch formula under resonance conditions, we set

$$g(0) = 2T_2; \tag{5.104}$$

then

$$\chi''(\nu_0) = \frac{\pi\chi_0\nu_0 T_2}{1 + \frac{1}{4}\gamma^2 H_1^2 T_1 T_2}, \tag{5.105}$$

which agrees with formula (5.2) for $\nu = \nu_0$.

The dispersion (real part of the RF susceptibility) is characterized by the following expression:

$$\chi'(\nu) = \frac{\pi}{2}\chi_0\nu_0 \frac{1}{1 + \frac{1}{8}\gamma^2 H_1^2 T_1 g(\nu - \nu_0)} \int_0^\infty \frac{2}{\pi}\frac{\nu' g(\nu' - \nu_0)}{\nu'^2 - \nu^2} d\nu'. \tag{5.106}$$

We shall now assume that the broadening is inhomogeneous. Let the distribution in local fields be given by the function $h(\nu - \nu_0)$, which is normalized so that

$$\int_0^\infty h(\nu - \nu_0)\, d\nu = 1.$$

In analogy with (5.104) it is useful to introduce the time

$$T_2^* = \frac{1}{2} h(0). \tag{5.107}$$

For absorption in the inhomogeneous case we obtain

$$\chi''(\nu) = \frac{\pi}{2}\chi_0 \int_0^\infty \frac{\nu g(\nu - \nu')}{1 + \frac{1}{8}\gamma^2 H_1^2 T_1 g(\nu - \nu')} h(\nu - \nu')\, d\nu'. \tag{5.108}$$

Since the over-all broadening is large compared to the line width of an individual spin packet, this expression can be simplified:

$$\chi''(\nu) = \frac{\pi}{2}\chi_0 \nu h(\nu - \nu_0) \int_0^\infty \frac{g(\nu' - \nu_0)}{1 + \frac{1}{8}\gamma^2 H_1^2 T_1 g(\nu' - \nu_0)} d\nu'. \tag{5.109}$$

The corresponding formula for the dispersion is

$$\chi'(\nu) = \chi_0 \int_0^\infty \frac{\nu'^2 h(\nu' - \nu_0)}{\nu'^2 - \nu^2} d\nu'. \tag{5.110}$$

We note that the absorption line in the case of inhomogeneous broadening does not change shape with saturation, since the integral in Eq. (5.109) is not a function of ν. The details of how the maximum absorption changes with the periodic magnetic field power depends on the shape function $g(\nu - \nu_0)$. Consequently, an experimental study of the saturation of a homogeneously broadened line allows the determination of the shape function $g(\nu - \nu_0)$, even though in this case it is masked by the over-all broadening.

In conclusion it should be noted that under saturation conditions the Kramers-Kronig relations (1.18) cease to be valid. The Kramers-Kronig relations are a direct consequence of the stipulation that the complex susceptibility be an analytic function of frequency over the lower half of the complex frequency plane. Van Vleck has established this condition on the basis of the linearity of the system. Since the system is nonlinear under saturation conditions, clearly the Kramers-Kronig relations must be reexamined.

A general theory of paramagnetic resonance under saturation conditions has been proposed recently by Tomita [100]. He has explained a number of the interesting phenomena that are encountered in the observation of both electron and nuclear magnetic resonances.

In many cases of inhomogeneous broadening, saturation will nevertheless be homogeneous because of cross relaxation.

5.9. Cross Relaxation

The two characteristic time parameters T_1 and T_2 (or τ and τ') are not always sufficient for a description of paramagnetic relaxation processes. Thus, at very low temperatures one must take into account the time for establishment of thermal equilibrium between the lattice and the helium bath. In the case of strong exchange interactions, it is necessary to divide the exchange system and introduce new time parameters characterizing the rapid establishment of equilibrium of this system with the lattice, the Zeeman system, etc. By extending the investigations of Kronig and Bouwkamp [101], Gorter [102], and Abragam and Proctor [103], Bloembergen [104] has shown that a wide range of numerous phenomena can be explained from a single point of view by introducing the concept of cross relaxation.

In the following we shall always assume that $T_2 \ll T_1$. The spin-spin relaxation time T_2 has double significance: first, the magnitude of $1/T_2$ is of the order of the width of the paramagnetic resonance absorption, and second, the magnitude of T_2 is the time for establishment of thermal equilibrium inside the spin system.

If the Zeeman and the internal crystalline Stark splittings of the spin levels are much greater than the mean energy of interaction of the spins of two neighboring magnetic particles, the second interpretation of the time T_2 loses meaning. In this case the conversion of Zeeman and Stark energy to dipolar interaction energy becomes more difficult, and consequently it is impossible to speak of a single spin system. The rate of establishment of thermal equilibrium between the system of individual spin levels of the paramagnetic particles, on the one hand, and the system of dipolar interactions, on the other hand, will be characterized by means of the cross-relaxation time T_{21}. We shall consider the case $T_{21} < T_1$, which is of greatest interest.

Let us assume at the beginning that the paramagnetic substance contains one species of magnetic particle with effective spin $S' = 1/2$. Let the Zeeman splitting of an individual ion $h\nu_{12} = g\beta H_0$ be so large that the energy of interaction between the spins of different particles may be treated as a perturbation. It is necessary to calculate the probability that a quantum of energy $h\nu_{12}$ is converted into dipole-dipole interaction energy as a result of a redistribution over the system of magnetic dipoles. Direct application of perturbation theory is impossible because of the enormous number of degrees of freedom of the spin system. The goal may be achieved most simply by means of a hybrid method which combines the perturbation theory and the method of moments.

Successive application of perturbation theory requires a knowledge of the eigenvalues of that part of the dipolar interaction operator which commutes with the Zeeman energy operator. In order to avoid considering the enormous number of energy levels belonging to the eigenvalues of matrices A and B (5.9), which commute with the Zeeman energy matrix, we shall introduce the shape function $g(\nu)$, which has a symmetrical maximum at the frequency ν_{12}. Transitions between the energy levels of the dipolar system are caused by the part of the dipolar interactions which is represented by the matrices C and D, and do not commute with the Zeeman energy matrix. We shall see below that in our case the terms E and F. are negligible. In first order time-dependent perturbation theory, the transition probability for the Zeeman energy $h\nu_{12}$ of a spin to be converted into dipolar energy is

$$w \equiv (2T_{21})^{-1} = \hbar^{-2} |c_{12}|^2 N_0^{-1} g(0). \tag{5.111}$$

Here c_{12} denotes the off-diagonal element of the matrix C, which connects the states 1 and 2. The shape function $g(\nu)$ can be determined by means of its moments. The second moment of this function with respect to frequency ν_{21} can be calculated from the following formula:

$$M_2 = \frac{\operatorname{Sp}\left\{\left[(\hat{A}+\hat{B})\sum_{j>i}\hat{S}_{zi}\hat{S}_{+j} - \sum_{j>i}\hat{S}_{zi}S_{+j}(\hat{A}+\hat{B})\right]^2\right\}}{\operatorname{Sp}\left\{\left[\sum_{j>i}\hat{S}_{zi}\hat{S}_{+j}\right]^2\right\}}. \tag{5.112}$$

This differs from formula (5.12) since the operator $\sum\hat{S}_x$, related to the action of an oscillatory magnetic field externally applied along the x axis, is replaced by the matrix operator $\hat{C}\sim\sum\hat{S}_{zi}\hat{S}_{+j}$, whose elements determine the intensity of the transition under consideration. The moment (5.112) is evidently of the same order, but not equal to the moment (5.12), which refers to a radio-frequency field absorption line.

If $g(\nu)$ is assumed to have a Gaussian shape, the cross-relaxation probability becomes

$$w=\frac{\frac{3}{4}g^2\beta^2S(S+1)}{\hbar^2\sqrt{2\pi M_2}}\sum_j r_{ij}^{-6}\sin^2\vartheta_{ij}\cos^2\vartheta_{ij}e^{-\frac{g^2\beta^2H_0^2}{2h^2M_2}}. \qquad (5.113)$$

For large fields H_0 the cross-relaxation time T_{21} increases very rapidly as the spacing between the Zeeman levels of the ion becomes large. For this reason processes with $\Delta M=\pm 2$ caused by the terms E and F may be neglected.

If $H_0\to 0$, then $T_{21}\to T_2$ and according to Kronig and Bouwkamp [101]

$$w=2\pi\sqrt{M_2'}e^{-\frac{g^2\beta^2H_0^2}{2M_2'}}. \qquad (5.114)$$

Here M_2' is the second moment, which is computed by taking the terms E and F into account.

Warning is given that the assumption of a Gaussian shape of the curve $g(\nu)$ may lead to serious errors, in particular in the case of strong exchange interactions and in the case of random paramagnetic dilutions.

We shall now consider substances containing either two species of unpaired spins or one species of magnetic particles with spin $S>1/2$. The establishment of equilibrium between the Zeeman and dipolar systems may be greatly accelerated, of two pairs of levels with nearly equal spacings exist: $h\nu_\alpha\approx h\nu_\beta$. Then under the influence of dipolar interactions the following processes will occur: ion i absorbs energy $h\nu_\alpha$; ion j loses energy $h\nu_\beta$; the energy $h(\nu_\alpha-\nu_\beta)$ passes to the dipolar system. The probability of such a process is

$$w_{ij}=\hbar^{-2}|\langle E_i, E_j|\hat{\mathscr{H}}_{ij}|E_i+h\nu_\alpha, E_j-h\nu_\beta\rangle|^2 g_{\alpha\beta}(0), \qquad (5.115)$$

where $\hat{\mathscr{H}}_{ij}$ is the operator of the interaction between ions i and j; $g_{\alpha\beta}(\nu_\alpha-\nu_\beta)$ is the shape function, having a maximum at the point $\nu_\alpha-\nu_\beta=0$. The second moment of this function may be determined from a formula similar to (5.112).

We shall indicate some important cases, in which two pairs of energy levels with nearly identical spacing are encountered: 1) the

Ni^{2+} ion ($S = 1$) in an axially symmetric crystalline field and a weak magnetic field (Figure 5.9a); 2) the Ni^{2+} ion in intermediate crystalline and magnetic fields (Figure 5.9b); 3) the Cr^{3+} ion ($S = 3/2$) in a weak magnetic field parallel to the crystalline axis (Figure 5.9c); 4) two nonequivalent Cu^{2+} ions ($S = 1/2$) (Figure 5.9d).

If the shape functions g_α and g_β are known for the paramagnetic resonance absorption lines ν_α and ν_β, $g_{\alpha\beta}$ can be calculated approximately from the formula

$$g_{\alpha\beta} = \iint g_\alpha(\nu') g_\beta(\nu'') \delta(\nu' - \nu'') d\nu' d\nu''; \tag{5.116}$$

and if g_α and g_β have a Gaussian shape, then

$$w_{ij} = \frac{|\mathcal{H}_{ij}|^2}{\sqrt{2\pi}\,\hbar^2 \sqrt{(\Delta\nu_\alpha)^2 + (\Delta\nu_\beta)^2}} e^{-\frac{(\nu_\alpha - \nu_\beta)^2}{2[(\nu_\alpha)^2 + (\nu_\beta)^2]}}. \tag{5.117}$$

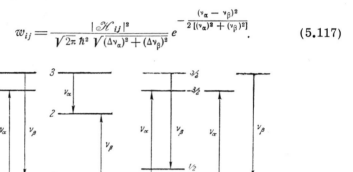

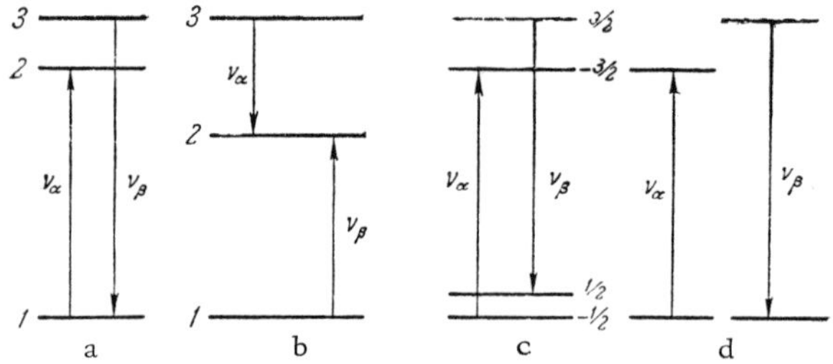

Fig. 5.9. Typical examples of cross-relaxation transitions.

Kopvillem [115] has made detailed calculations of the shape function $g_{\alpha\beta}(\nu)$ by the method of moments. He obtained a somewhat unexpected result, which contradicts the assertions of Bloembergen. It was found that the shape function $g_{\alpha\beta}(\nu)$ remains virtually constant upon magnetic dilution if the energy $h(\nu_\alpha - \nu_\beta)$ is less than the mean energy of magnetic dipolar interactions E_{dip} experienced by one paramagnetic ion in a magnetically concentrated crystal. If, however, $h(\nu_\alpha - \nu_\beta) > E_{dip}$, the increase of energy $h(\nu_\alpha - \nu_\beta)$ leads to a rapid decrease of $g_{\alpha\beta}(0)$.

In the preceding sections we have assumed that a change in the populations of the spin levels may occur under the action of an externally applied oscillatory magnetic field and on account of spin-lattice interactions. The probability of the corresponding transitions will be denoted by p_{ij} and A_{ij}. We shall now see that a change in the populations of the spin levels is also possible by cross relaxation. Thus, for the case depicted in Figure 5.9a, we have

$$\left(\frac{\partial N_2}{\partial t}\right)_{\text{cross}} = -\left(\frac{\partial N_3}{\partial t}\right)_{\text{cross}} = w[N_3 - N_2 - (N_3 - N_2)_{ad}] + \\ + N_0^{-1} \sum w_{ij} [(N_3 N_1 - N_2 N_1) - (N_3 N_1 - N_2 N_1)_{ad}]. \tag{5.118}$$

Here $(N_k)_{ad}$ is the population of level k after the spin system has come into internal equilibrium on the assumption that it is isolated from the lattice. If T is the lattice temperature, and T_{ad} is the temperature of the spin system under adiabatic conditions, we have the following system of differential equations which determine the populations of the levels of particles with spin $S = 1$:

$$\left.\begin{aligned}
\frac{dN_3}{dt} &= p_{32}(N_2 - N_3) + A_{13}\left(N_1 - N_3 - \frac{1}{3}N_0\frac{h\nu_{31}}{kT}\right) + \\
&\quad + A_{23}\left(N_2 - N_3 - \frac{1}{3}N_0\frac{h\nu_{32}}{kT}\right) + \\
&\quad + \left(w + \frac{1}{3}\sum w_{ij}\left[N_2 - N_3 - \frac{1}{3}N_0\frac{h\nu_{32}}{kT_{ad}}\right]\right), \\
N_1 + N_2 + N_3 &= N_0, \\
\frac{dN_2}{dt} &= p_{32}(N_3 - N_2) + A_{23}\left(N_3 - N_2 + \frac{1}{3}N_0\frac{h\nu_{32}}{kT}\right) + \\
&\quad + A_{12}\left(N_1 - N_2 - \frac{1}{3}N_0\frac{h\nu_{21}}{kT}\right) - \\
&\quad - \left(w + \frac{1}{3}\sum_j w_{ij}\left[N_2 - N_3 - \frac{1}{3}N_0\frac{h\nu_{32}}{kT_{ad}}\right]\right).
\end{aligned}\right\} \qquad (5.119)$$

We have assumed here that the RF signal is supplied at the frequency ν_{32}.

Solution of equations of the type (5.119) makes it possible to judge the behavior of a paramagnetic substance under prescribed external conditions and the role of cross relaxation. Space does not permit detailed consideration of the phenomena that find an explanation in cross relaxation, but we shall briefly discuss some of them.

a) Intermediate relaxation in the case of measurement in parallel fields

Measurements of paramagnetic absorption in parallel fields in diluted paramagnetic salts show that besides the usual relaxation maxima, whose positions are determined by the magnitudes of τ and τ', a number of cases of temperature-independent intermediate absorption peaks are observed. A quantitative comparison shows that the experimentally established region of dispersion and absorption corresponds to the frequency $\nu \approx T_{21}/2\pi$.

b) Thermal contact of two different spin systems

If the paramagnetic salt contains two species of paramagnetic particles, the theory of cross relaxation makes possible an evaluation of the amount of energy transported from one spin system to another, if thermal equilibrium between these systems is disturbed.

c) Cross saturation

In the previously mentioned experiments of Giordmaine et al. [58], performed at liquid helium temperatures, it was shown that saturation of one of the hyperfine components of the copper ion leads to a rapid saturation of all other components which are not subjected to the RF field. These experimenters attempted to explain the energy-level broadening of the effective lattice oscillators as a consequence of their weak coupling with oscillators of other frequencies and with the helium bath (see Sec. 5.4). However, the actual cause of cross saturation is evidently cross relaxation. Thus, processes with the simultaneous participation of four ions played a leading role. Let the frequencies of the three resonance lines ν_α, ν_β, ν_γ be such that $(\nu_\beta - \nu_\alpha) \approx (\nu_\gamma - \nu_\beta)$; thus, $h\nu_{\alpha\beta\gamma} = E^{(2)}_{\alpha\beta\gamma} - E^{(1)}_{\alpha\beta\gamma}$. Let us take four ions, two of which are located on the energy level $E^{(2)}_\beta$ and one each on the levels $E^{(1)}_\alpha$ and $E^{(1)}_\gamma$. A simultaneous reorientation of the spins is possible as a result of the dipolar interaction between these ions. In this manner the RF energy supplied at the frequency ν_β will be transported and the paramagnetic resonance will be saturated at the frequencies ν_α and ν_γ. A numerical estimate of the magnitude of T_{21} is found to be in good agreement with experimental data. Bloemenbergen et al. [104] have set up special experiments which resulted in the important conclusion that in dilute paramagnetic salts at temperatures greater than 1°K processes associated with heating of the system of effective oscillators play no role in relaxation.

d) Inhomogeneous broadening and homogeneous saturation

In sufficiently diluted paramagnetic salts the line width is primarily determined by the initial magnetic fields of nuclear spins of diamagnetic atoms and by the distribution of crystalline field parameters. This type of inhomogeneous broadening will be called microscopic to distinguish it from macroscopic broadening, produced by the inhomogeneity of the external magnetic field and by polycrystalline samples.

Let the over-all line width be determined by the magnitude of $1/T_2{}^*$, and the homogeneous part of the broadening by $1/T_2$. On account of cross relaxation, the RF energy absorbed by the fields, whose resonance frequencies are distributed within the range $\nu \pm 1/T_2$, will be transferred to fields with resonance frequencies outside of this range. Furthermore, if the corresponding cross-relaxation time $T_{21} > T_1$, then saturation of the entire resonance line will occur just as if the broadening were homogeneous, and in the expression for the saturation factor $T_2{}^*$ will appear instead of T_2. Cross relaxation within the resonance line may be determined either by Kronig-Bouwkamp type processes or by a multiplicity of processes similar to those considered under Subsec. (c). In the case of Kronig-Bouwkamp processes it is easy to obtain

$$T_{21} = \frac{T_2^4}{(T_2^*)^3}. \tag{5.120}$$

Thus the majority of conditions realizable in practice, including inhomogeneous broadening, produce homogeneous saturation. One experiment directly supporting the arguments given here is the paramagnetic resonance saturation experiment in nickel fluosilicate, performed with the aid of radio-frequency pulses [106].

5.10. Acoustic Paramagnetic Resonance

In analogy with ordinary paramagnetic resonance, consisting of selective absorption of energy from the periodic magnetic field by a paramagnetic substance, the paramagnetic resonant absorption of ultrasonic energy is also possible. The theory of this phenomena has been proposed by Al'tshuler [107]. It was first detected experimentally in nuclear paramagnetic substances [108, 109] and recently also in Mn^{2+} ions substituted into a quartz crystal [111].

Acoustic paramagnetic resonance consists in the transfer of ultrasonic energy to a system of unpaired spins. This transfer occurs when the quantum of elastic vibrational energy equals the energy difference between the magnetic levels. Thus, just as in the case of ordinary paramagnetic resonance, acoustic paramagnetic absorption will occur if condition (1.2) is fulfilled in which ν now means the ultrasonic frequency.

The mechanism effecting the transfer of acoustic vibrational energy to the paramagnetic particle is of the same nature as the mechanism of paramagnetic lattice relaxation, which was accomplished by means of one-phonon processes. Ultrasonic resonance absorption may therefore be considered as an inverted paramagnetic relaxation phenomenon. Acoustic vibrations will cause a periodic change in the forces which act on the spins so that transitions will arise from one magnetic energy sublevel to another. Total population of the lower sublevels leads to the fact that the number of transitions associated with energy absorption will exceed the number of inverse transitions. Equilibrium will be restored via transfer of excess energy of the unpaired spins to the thermal vibrations of the lattice.

A calculation of ultrasonic absorption by paramagnetic substances is similar to the calculation of the paramagnetic lattice relaxation time due to first-order processes. This makes possible an evaluation of ultrasonic absorption in solids and leads to the following formula:

$$\sigma = \frac{h^2}{8\pi\tau} \frac{N_0 v^2}{kT \cdot kT_0 \Delta\nu}. \tag{5.121}$$

Here σ is the coefficient of sound absorption, i.e., the ratio of the energy absorbed per cm^3 to the incident energy per cm^2 per sec; T is the temperature of the solid; T_0 is the temperature at which the relaxation time τ is determined. The experimental data lead to coefficients of the order of 0.1 cm^{-1}. Thus, the acoustic resonance effect turns out to be easily observable. Consequently, in the following, we undertake calculations of σ for many types of paramagnetic substances, under the assumption of different spin-lattice coupling mechanisms.

At the beginning we studied acoustic resonance absorption by paramagnetic salts in which the spin-lattice coupling is realized via modulation of the internal electric field of the crystal by elastic lattice vibrations. The coefficient σ was calculated for some typical salts of iron group elements (titanium and chrome alums), salts of rare earth elements (cerium nitrate, praseodymium ethylsulfate) and, finally, salts whose magnetic ions are in the S state (iron alums). The absorption coefficient in titanium alums is found to be

$$\sigma \approx h^2 P \left(\frac{\lambda}{\Delta_0^2}\right)^2 \left(\frac{e\mu}{R^2}\right)^2 \nu^4, \tag{5.122}$$

where $P = \pi^2 N_0 / \rho kTv^3 \Delta\nu$. At $T = 20^\circ$ K a numerical estimate gives $\sigma \approx 2 \cdot 10^{-88} \nu^4 cm^{-1}$. For chrome alums we have

$$\sigma \approx \left(\frac{e\mu}{R^2}\right)^2 \left(\frac{\lambda}{\Delta_0}\right)^4 P\nu^2. \tag{5.123}$$

A numerical estimate gives $\sigma \approx 10^{-21} \nu^2 cm^{-1}$ at room temperature.

Equation (5.123) refers to transitions between spin levels belonging to different Kramers doublets. Consequently, in contrast to titanium salts here $\sigma \sim \nu^2$. In the perturbation theory approximation, which gave Eq. (5.123), the coefficient $\sigma = 0$ for transitions within the Kramers doublets. At the higher-order approximations, we obtain, just as for the Ti^{3+} ion, $\sigma \sim \nu^4$. Physically this result is understandable and has great significance. A lowering of the symmetry of the crystalline field, produced by elastic lattice vibrations, may alter the splitting of spin levels belonging to different Kramers doublets, but has almost no effect on the splittings of the Kramers doublets themselves.

For salts of rare earth elements a calculation has shown that the ultrasonic resonance-absorption effect is small in those cases in which the crystalline field leaves only the Kramers degeneracy of the energy levels in the magnetic ions, and this cannot be removed by variations of the electric field produced by lattice vibrations.

In rare earth ethylsulfates, the crystalline field possesses hexagonal symmetry. If the rare earth ions contain an even number of electrons, the energy levels retain a non-Kramers degeneracy and the acoustic absorption effect must therefore be large. Thus, for praseodymium we obtain

$$\sigma \approx P\left(\frac{e\mu_e}{R^2}\right)^2\left(\frac{\overline{r^2}}{R^2}\right)^2 \nu^2. \tag{5.124}$$

Hence at $T = 20°$ K we have $\sigma \approx -10^{-15}\nu^2$ cm^{-1}. The effect is so large that this praseodymium salt evidently is most suitable for the experimental detection of acoustic absorption. In [110] the acoustic effect in rare earth salts is examined in detail.

For iron alums in which the Fe^{3+} ion is in the state, the absorption coefficient turns out to be comparatively small, of the order of $10^{-24}\nu^2$ cm^{-1} at room temperature.

In gadolinium salts, in which the splitting of the ground state of the paramagnetic ion by the electric field of the crystal is known to be far greater than in the iron ion, the acoustic effect is expected to be approximately 10^4 times stronger.

Ultrasonic resonance absorption has also been examined under the assumption that the spin-lattice coupling arises from a variation of the magnetic interaction of particles by elastic lattice vibrations (Waller mechanism). In this case the absorption coefficient is found to be

$$\sigma = \frac{253}{21} P_Z \left(\frac{g^2\beta^2}{a^3}\right)^2 S(S+1)^2(2S+1)\nu^2. \tag{5.125}$$

In substances with a large density of type MnF_2 magnetic ions, this mechanism can make the coefficient σ at room temperature equal to $\sim 10^{-19}\nu^2$ cm^{-1}.

Ultrasonic resonance absorption evidently will occur not only in electronic paramagnetics, but also in substances possessing nuclear paramagnetism. Favorable circumstances for the nuclear effect include a small width of the paramagnetic absorption line and a large density of unpaired spins. The small values of magnetic and quadrupole moments of the nuclei serve as the cause of the relatively weak spin-lattice coupling, which of course will diminish the ultrasonic resonance-absorption effect.

In solid dielectrics, in which the spin-lattice coupling is determined by magnetic interactions of the nuclei, the coefficient of ultrasonic resonance absorption may be calculated from Eq. (5.125), where β now means the nuclear magneton. For a NaBr crystal, for example, at $T = 300°$K the coefficient $\sigma \approx 10^{-25}\nu^2$ cm^{-1}. For substances in which the spin-lattice coupling is due to quadrupole interactions of nuclei, the coefficient σ may become far greater of the order $10^{-20}\nu^2$cm^{-1}. An even greater effect may be expected in metals, in which the coupling between nuclear spins and lattice vibrations is intensified by the interaction between the nuclei and the conduction electrons. An appreciable effect may also be obtained by single electron levels of paramagnetic particles whose nuclei possess nonzero magnetic moments [110].

It is of interest to compare the phenomenon of ultrasonic resonance absorption with the paramagnetic resonance by periodic magnetic fields.

a) A comparison of the magnitudes of both effects is readily made if we keep in mind that the coefficient of absorption of electromagnetic field energy equals

$$\sigma_e = \frac{8\pi}{c}\nu\chi'' \approx \frac{8\pi^2}{c\Delta\nu}\chi_0\nu^2. \tag{5.126}$$

In many electronic paramagnetic substances $\Delta\nu \approx 10^9$ cps, $\chi_0 \approx 10^{-6}$ and consequently, $\sigma \approx 10^{-22}\nu^2 \mathrm{cm}^{-1}$. In many cases we also obtain for the ultrasonic absorption coefficient an expression proportional to ν^2, the proportionality factor being strongly dependent on the magnitude of the matrix element of the spin-lattice interaction operator. If this matrix element differs from zero in the first approximation, we obtain for the coefficient σ a value which greatly exceeds σ_e. If, however, higher approximations are required usually σ_e and σ are of the same order of magnitude.

It should be remarked that the absorption coefficient for longitudinal and transverse waves will in general be different. For solids we have at all times cited mean values of the coefficient σ.

b) Ordinary paramagnetic resonance depends strongly on the angle between the static and periodic magnetic fields. The acoustic effect is not very sensitive to a variation in direction of propagation of the acoustic wave relative to the field H_0.

c) Ultrasonic absorption is frequently possible as a result of transitions between those sublevels between which magnetic dipole transitions are forbidden.

d) The shape of an absorption line in the case of the acoustic and the ordinary effects may be quite different. This is explained by the fact that in both phenomena we deal with the same energy level bands, produced by magnetic and other interactions; however, the laws which determine the probability of transitions between these levels under the influence of ultrasound, and under the action of an external periodic magnetic field, are quite different in nature.

In spite of the fact that in many cases the coefficient of ultrasonic absorption is much larger than the coefficient of absorption of the RF field energy, the low sensitivity of the ultrasonic methods of investigation makes it desirable to use indirect methods for the detection of acoustic paramagnetic resonance. It may be observed by "saturation" of magnetic sublevels of the nuclei, which sets in at large acoustic intensities [108]. Another method may be based on a variation of magnetization of the body under the influence of ultrasound.

The generation and, in particular, the transmission of ultrahigh frequency acoustic vibrations from the generator to the specimen is a very complex experimental problem. It is of great interest therefore to clarify the conditions under which an appreciable effect may be expected in electron paramagnetic substances at relatively low frequencies, of the order of 100 Mc. This subject was considered in [113]. As the largest effect is associated with transitions between different Kramers doublets, evidently it is highly advantageous to observe transitions between spin levels near their point of intersection, which occurs for instance in the case depicted in Figure. 1.3.

Finally we note that if magnetically dilute crystals are used, the scattering of acoustic waves by crystalline defects may turn out to be very significant. For the reasons indicated in Chapter VII, Sec. 5.3, resonance absorption of these waves will be very strong. Great advantages must therefore lie in the indirect methods of measurement, which permit direct determination of the population differences of the spin levels.

The experimental study of resonant paramagnetic ultrasonic absorption should appreciably supplement the data obtained by investigations of ordinary resonance and of paramagnetic relaxation because it make possible a more profound explanation of the nature of the spin-lattice interaction and a determination of the constants characterizing it. In addition it reveals new absorption lines whose appearance under the influence of a radio-frequency field is impossible because they are forbidden as magnetic dipole transitions.

Literature for Chapter V

1. Bloch, F. Phys. Rev. 70, 460, 1946.
2. Garstens, M. A. Phys. Rev. 93, 1228, 1954.
3. Van Vleck, J. H., V. F. Weisskopf. Rev. Mod. Phys. 17, 227, 1945.
4. Shaposhnikov, I. G. Zh. Eksp. Teoret. Fiz. 18, 533, 1948.
5. Shaposhnikov, I. G. Zh. Eksp. Teoret. Fiz. 19, 2 5, 1949.
6. Skrotskiy, G. V., L. V. Kurbatov, Izvest. Akad. Nauk SSSR, Ser. Fiz. 21, 833, 1957.
7. Wangsness, R. K., F. Bloch. Phys. Rev. 89, 728, 1953.
8. Waller, J. Z. Physik 79, 370, 1932.
9. Broer, L. J. F. Physica 10, 801, 1943.
10. Van Vleck, J. H. Phys. Rev. 73, 1249, 1948.
11. Al'tshuler, S. A., M. G. Odintsov. Izvest. Karelo-Finn. AN SSSR, Ser. Fiz.-Tekh. 3, 39, 1953.
12. Glebashev, G. Ya. Zh. Eksp. Teoret. Fiz. 32, 82, 1957.
13. Al'tshuler, S. A., Ye. K. Zavoyskiy, B. M. Kozyrev. Zh. Eksp. Teoret. Fiz. 17, 1122, 1947.
14. Gorter, C. J., J. H. Van Vleck. Phys. Rev. 72, 1128, 1947.
15. Kittel, C., E. Abrahams. Phys. Rev. 90, 238, 1953.
16. Glebashev, G. Ya. Zh. Eksp. Teoret. Fiz. 30, 612, 1956.

17. Pryce, M. H. L., K. W. H. Stevens. Proc. Phys. Soc. A63, 36, 1950.
18. Glebashev, G. Ya. Uch. Zap. Kharkov. Gos. Univ. 116, 121, 1956.
19. Ishiguro, E., K. Kambe, T. Usui. Physica 17, 310, 1951.
20. Holden, A. N., C. Kittel, W. A. Yager. Phys. Rev. 75, 1443, 1949.
21. Griffiths, J. H. E., J. Owen. Proc. Roy. Soc. A213, 459, 1952.
22. Stevens, K. W. H. Proc. Roy. Soc. A214, 237, 1952.
23. Kambe, K., F. Ollom. J. Phys. Soc. Japan 11, 50, 1956.
24. Abragam, A., K. Kambe. Phys. Rev. 91, 894, 1953.
25. Bersohn, R. J. Chem. Phys. 20, 1505, 1952.
26. Kopvillem, U. Kh. Zh. Eksp. Teoret. Fiz. 34, 1040, 1958.
27. Bagguley, D. M. S., J. H. E. Griffiths. Nature 162, 538, 1948.
28. Pryce, M. H. L. Nature 162, 539, 1948.
29. Van Wieringen, J. S. Disc. Faraday Soc. 19, 118, 1955.
30. Anderson, P. W., P. R. Weiss. Rev. Mod. Phys. 25, 269, 1953.
31. Anderson, P. W. J. Phys. Soc. Japan 9, 316, 1954.
32. Kubo, R., K. J. Tomita. J. Phys. Soc. Japan 9, 888, 1954; R. Kubo. J. Phys. Soc. Japan 9, 935, 1954; M. Yokota, S. Koide. J. Phys. Soc. Japan 9, 953, 1954.
33. Archer, D. H. Thesis, Harvard, 1953; H. S. Gutowsky, D. M. McCall, C. P. Slichter. J. Chem. Phys. 21, 279, 1953.
34. Gorter, C. Paramagnetic Relaxation, Elsevier, Amsterdam, 1947.
35. Lloyd, J. P., G. E. Pake. Phys. Rev. 94, 579, 1954.
36. Heitler, W. Quantum Theory of Radiation, IL, Moscow, 1956.
37. Van Vleck, J. H. Phys. Rev. 57, 426, 1052, 1940.
38. Kronig, R. L. Physica 6, 33, 1939.
39. Al'tshuler, S. A., Izvest. Akad. Nauk SSSR, Ser. Fiz. 20, 1207, 1956.
40. Bashkirov, Sh. Sh. Zh. Eksp. Teoret. Fiz. 34, 1465, 1958.
41. Volokhova, T. I. Zh. Eksp. Teoret. Fiz. 33, 856, 1957.
42. Abe, H., K. Ono. J. Phys. Soc. Japan 11, 947, 1956.
43. Avvakumov, V. I. Fiz. Metallov i Metalloved. 4, 199, 1957.
44. Bashkirov, Sh. Sh. Fiz. Metallov i Metalloved. 6, 577, 1958.
45. Al'tshuler, S. A. Zh. Eksp. Teoret. Fiz. 24, 681, 1953.
46. Shekun, L. Ya. Dissertation, Kharkov State Univ. 1956.
47. Akhiyezer, A. I., I. Ya. Pomeranchuk, Zh. Eksp. Teoret. Fiz. 14, 342, 1944; Doklady Akad. Nauk SSSR 87, 917, 1952.
48. Bloembergen, N., S. Wang. Phys. Rev. 93, 72, 1954.
49. Kramers, H. A., D. Bijl, C. J. Gorter. Physica 16, 65, 1950.
50. Vrijer, F. W., C. J. Gorter. Physica 18, 549, 1952.
51. Benzie, R. J., A. H. Cooke. Proc. Phys. Soc. A63, 201, 1950.
52. Gorter, C. J., L. C. Van der Merel, B. Bolger. Physica 21, 103, 1955.
53. Van der Marel, L. C., J. Van den Broek, C. J. Gorter. Physica 23, 361, 1957.
54. Frölich, H., W. Heitler. Proc. Roy. Soc. A155, 640, 1936.

55. Van Vleck, J. H. Phys. Rev. 59, 730, 1941.
56. Bridgman, P. W. Proc. Ams. Acad. 64, 63, 1929.
57. Van Vleck, J. H. Phys. Rev. 59, 724, 1941.
58. Giordmaine, J. A., L. E. Alsop, F. R. Nash, C. H. Townes. Phys. Rev. 109, 302, 1958.
59. Strandberg, M. W. P. Phys. Rev. 110, 56, 1958.
60. Bloembergen, N. Phys. Rev. 109, 2209, 1958.
61. Andrews, E. Nuclear Magnetic Resonance, IL, Moscow, 1957.
62. Van Vleck, J. H. Nuovo Cimento 6, suppl. No. 3, 1081, 1957.
63. Kashayev, S. Kh. G. Doklady Akad. Nauk SSSR 110, 362, 1956.
64. Kozyrev, B. M. Doctoral Dissertation, Phys. Inst. Acad. Sci., Moscow, 1957.
65. Bleaney, B. Proc. Roy. Soc. A204, 203, 1950.
66. Kumagai, H., K. Ono, I. Hayashi, H. Abe, H. Shono, H. Ibamoto, J. Shimoda. Phys. Rev. 83, 1077, 1951.
67. MacLean, C., G. J. Kor. Appl. Sci. Rev. B4, 425, 1955.
68. Müller, K. A. Helv. Phys. Acta 28, 450, 1955.
69. Anderson, J. H., C. A. Hutchison. Phys. Rev. 97, 76, 1955.
70. Rivkind, A. I. Izvest. Akad. Nauk SSSR, Ser. Fiz. 16, 541, 1952.
71. Casimir, H. B. G., F. K. du Pré. Physica 5, 507, 1938.
72. Gorter, C. J., L. J. Smits. Tables de constantes et données numeriques. 7. Relaxation paramagnétique. Masson et Cie, 1957.
73. Kozyrev, B. M. Izvest. Kaz. Ped. Inst. 1, 83, 1947.
74. Garif'yanov, N. S., Dissertation, Kharkov State Univ., 1953.
75. Brons, F. Thesis, Groningen, 1938.
76. Garif'yanov, Zh. Eksp. Teoret. Fiz. 35, 612, 1958.
77. Kramers, H. A., D. Bijl, C. J. Gorter. Physica 16, 65, 1950; F. W. de Vrijer, C. J. Gorter. Physica 18, 549, 1952; R. J. Benzie, A. H. Cooke. Proc. Phys. Soc. A63, 201, 1950.
78. Purcell, E. M., C. P. Slichter. Phys. Rev. 76, 466, 1949; R. W. Damon. Rev. Mod. Phys. 25, 239, 1953.
79. Schneider, E. E., T. S. England. Physica 17, 221, 1951.
80. Eschenfelder, A. H., R. T. Weidner. Phys. Rev. 92, 869, 1953.
81. Landau, L. D., Ye. M. Lifshits. Statistical Physics, Gostekhizdat, Moscow, 1951.
82. Bloembergen, N., E. M. Purcell, R. V. Pound. Phys. Rev. 73, 678, 1948.
83. Kozyrev, B. M. Disc. Faraday Soc. 19, 135, 1955.
84. McConnel, H. M. J. Chem. Phys. 25, 709, 1956.
85. McGarvey, B. R. J. Phys. Chem. 61, 1232, 1957.
86. Al'tshuler, S. A., K. A. Valiyev. Zh. Eksp. Teoret. Fiz. 947, 1958.
87. Yel'yashevich, M. A. Spectra of Rare Earths, Gostekhizdat, 1953.
88. Schultz, M. L. J. Chem. Phys. 10, 194, 1942; S. Freed, S. I. Weissman, J. Chem. Phys. 8, 840, 1940; M. Kobajshi, I. Fujita. J. Chem. Phys. 23, 1354, 1955.

89. Zavoyskiy, Ye. Doctoral Dissertation, Phys. Inst. Acad. Sci., Moscow, 1944.
90. Kozyrev, B. M. Izvest. Akad. Nauk SSSR, Ser. Fiz. 16, 533, 1952.
91. Rivkind, A. I. Dissertation, Urals State Univ., Sverdlovsk, 1951.
92. Tinkham, M., R. Weinstein, F. Kip. Phys. Rev. 84, 848, 1951.
93. Garstens, M., S. Liebson. J. Chem. Phys. 20, 1677, 1952.
94. Kozyrev, B. M. Izvest. Akad. Nauk SSSR, Ser. Fiz. 21, 828, 1957.
95. Cohn, M., J. Townsend. Nature 173, 1090, 1954.
96. Garif'yanov, N. S., B. M. Kozyrev. Doklady Akad. Nauk SSSR 98, 929, 1954.
97. McGarvey, B. R. J. Phys. Chem. 60, 71, 1956.
98. Tishkov, P. G. Zh. Eksp. Teoret. Fiz. 36, 1337, 1959.
99. Portis, A. M. Phys. Rev. 91, 1071, 1953.
100. Tomita, K. Progr. Theor. Phys. 19, 541, 1958.
101. Kronig, R., C. J. Bouwkamp. Physica 5, 521, 1938; 6, 290, 1939.
102. Verstelle, J. C., G. W. J. Drewes, C. J. Gorter. Physica 24, 632, 1958.
103. Abragam, A., W. G. Proctor. Phys. Rev. 109, 1441, 1958.
104. Bloembergen, N., S. Shapiro, P. S. Pershan, J. O. Artman. Phys. Rev. 114, 445, 1959.
105. Smits, L. J., H. E. Derksen, J. C. Verstelle, C. J. Gorter. Physica 22, 773, 1956.
106. Bowers, K. D., W. B. Mims. Bull. Amer. Phys. Soc. ser. II, 3, 325, 1958.
107. Al'tshuler. Doklady Akad. Nauk SSSR 85, 1235, 1952; Zh. Eksp. Teoret. Fiz. 28, 38, 49, 1955.
108. Proctor, W. G., W. H. Tantila. Phys. Rev. 98, 1854, 1955; 101 1757, 1956; W. G. Proctor, W. A. Robinson. Phys. Rev. 102, 1183, 1956; O. Kraus, W. H. Tantilla. Phys. Rev. 109, 1052, 1958; D. A. Jennings, W. H. Tantilla. Phys. Rev. 109, 1059, 1958.
109. Menes, M., D. I. Bolef. Phys. Rev. 109, 218, 1958.
110. Al'tshuler, S. A., M. M. Zaripov, L. Ya. Shekun. Izvest. Akad. Nauk SSSR, Ser. Fiz. 21, 844, 1952.
111. Jacobsen, E. H. N. S. Shiren, E. B. Tucker. Phys. Rev. Letters 3, 81, 1959.
112. Kochelayev, B. I. Doklady Akad. Nauk SSSR 131, 1053, 1960.
113. Al'tshuler, S. A., Sh. Sh. Bashkirov, Conference on Paramagnetic Resonance, Kazan, 1960, p. 78.
114. Kopvillem, U. Kh. Fizika Metall. i Metalloved. 8, 8, 1959; Izvest. MVO, Fizika 3, 13, 1958; Zh. Eksp. Teoret. Fiz. 35, 506, 1958; N. G. Koloskova, U. Kh. Kopvillem. Fiz. Tverd. Tela 2, 1368, 1960; Izvest. MVO, Fizika 3, 223, 1960; I. D. Morozova, R. Mineyeva, U. Kh. Kopvillem. Conference on Paramagnetic Resonance, Kazan, 1960, p. 92.
115. U. Kh. Kopvillem, Zh. Eksp. Teoret. Fiz. 38, 151, 1960.

CHAPTER VI

Metals and Semiconductors. Defects in Crystals

6.1. Effect on Conduction Electrons

Conduction electrons are the carriers of paramagnetism in metals. In transition metals paramagnetism may also be associated with the ions forming the framework of the crystal lattice. One might also expect the appearance in metals of paramagnetic resonance absorption lines whose positions would determine the g factor of conduction electrons, as well as that of the atomic d or f shells. Observations of paramagnetic resonance in metals, however, entails a number of difficulties: 1) the skin effect reduces the absorption of radio-frequency energy and complicates the shape of the resonance line; 2) small ferromagnetic inclusions may be the cause of quite erroneous results; 3) in many metals strong spin-lattice interactions smear out the paramagnetic resonance curve.

To reduce the skin effect one usually uses finely divided particles of the metal immersed in paraffin and crushed with the aid of ultrasound. To get rid of ferromagnetic impurities the metallic samples must be subjected to repeated purification. A definite effect by conduction electrons has been obtained in the following metals: Li, Na, K, Be, Cs [1-11]. Investigations of many other substances, such as Al, Mg, Pd, W, do not give a positive result, apparently as a result of the extreme width of the resonance line.

The g factor for conduction electrons was first computed by Yafet [12], using Na as an example. Only the spin-orbit interaction was considered, as the correlation and exchange effects are insignificant, while the influence of the interaction between electronic and nuclear spins becomes marked only at a temperature $T < 1°$K. The proximity of the experimental values of the g factors to the pure spin magnitude of $g_{spin} = 2.0023$ shows that the spin-orbit interaction may be considered as a perturbation. Calculations were performed using the Bardeen method [13], which makes unnecessary a calculation of the matrix elements. In this manner, we obtained $\Delta g = g - g_{spin} = -3.7 \cdot 10^{-4}$, whereas experimental investigation [8, 9] resulted in $\Delta g = -(8 \pm 2) \cdot 10^{-4}$. Brooks [14] has performed a calculation on the basis of the atomic value of the spin-orbit coupling constant. The value obtained in this manner, $\Delta g = -6.6 \cdot 10^{-4}$, agrees with the experimental data within the limits of error. For Li the theoretically obtained value [15] of $\Delta g = -6 \cdot 10^{-5}$ is very small, which agrees with the results of measurements [8, 9]: $|\Delta g| \leq 10^{-4}$. For Be, experiment [8] gives $\Delta g = +(9 \pm 1) \cdot 10^{-4}$ and no theoretical calculations exist. For K the g factor could not at first be determined, because the effect was small and became observable only at a temperature below 4°K.

The original method of obtaining pure and well pulverized samples of metals had been proposed by Levy [9] who congealed solutions of alkaline metals in ammonia at liquid nitrogen temperature. In this manner he succeeded in measuring the paramagnetic resonance absorption in K at the temperature of 180°K and in Cs at 25°K. The measured values of the g factor equal 1.99 and 1.93, respectively, which is in good agreement with the theoretical values [14] of 1.99 and 1.94.

In metals, in which the paramagnetism is associated with conduction electrons, the shape of the resonance line is determined by the spin-lattice interaction. Spin-spin relaxation is unimportant, because of the large velocity of electrons and the relatively small magnitude of the spin-spin interaction. A theoretical treatment of paramagnetic relaxation in metals was first given by Overhauser [16], who used the one-electron model of a degenerate gas to calculate the interaction between the spins of the conduction electrons and the other particles of the metal. The self-interaction among them was studied as a small perturbation.

One might think that, just as in ionic paramagnetic crystals at high temperatures, second-order processes (Raman phonon scattering) play a fundamental role in the exchange of energy between electronic spins and lattice vibrations. This assumption, however, must be discarded because two-phonon processes are neglected in calculations of the electrical resistance of metals.

Overhauser has considered the following relaxation mechanisms.

1) Interaction with transverse phonons. We shall assume that relaxation is caused by the interaction of the magnetic moments of electrons with the magnetic field produced by the charged particles (ions), which participate in the lattice vibrations. Thus evidently only transverse vibrations exist. We shall denote the Fermi energy in the absence of an external magnetic field by $\epsilon_0 = \hbar^2 k_0^2 / 2m_0$, the diameter of the particle of the metal by d, the side of the cube of atomic dimensions by a, the number of electrons in 1 cm^3 by N_e, and finally the density of the metal by ρ. If the correlation between the translational motion of the conduction electrons and the lattice is neglected, the relaxation times are calculated from the following expressions:

$$\tau = \frac{3\rho m_0 \hbar k_0 c^4}{16\pi e^4 N_e^2 kT \ln \frac{d}{a}}. \tag{6.1}$$

Hence, for Li, as an example, at room temperature we obtain $\tau \approx 6 \cdot 10^{-2}$ sec.

2) Interaction with longitudinal phonons. Relaxation may be caused by the interaction of the electronic spins with the electric field produced by the vibrations of positive ions of the lattice. This type of interaction in atoms is the cause of spin-orbit coupling. Transverse vibrations produce a relatively weak electrical field and we may therefore restrict ourselves to the treatment of longitudinal vibrations. Calculation shows that the relaxation time is

$$\tau = \frac{96\rho k_0 m_0^5 c^4 v^2}{\pi^3 N_e^2 \hbar^5 \left(\frac{k\theta}{\hbar v}\right)^4 kT}. \tag{6.2}$$

Here v is the mean velocity of sound, and θ is the Debye temperature.

For Li it follows from (6.2) that $\tau \approx 3 \cdot 10^{-4}$ sec at room temperature.

3) Magnetic dipolar interactions of the electron spins. In this case the relaxation process may be the result of both a simultaneous reorientation of the spins of both interacting electrons, and the spin of only one electron (see Secs. 5.2, 5.3). If we take into account only the first processes, which play a dominant role, we obtain for the relaxation time

$$\tau = \frac{15 m_0 \hbar^3 c^4}{8\pi e^4 k^2 T^2}. \tag{6.3}$$

Hence, at room temperature we have $\tau \approx 6 \cdot 10^{-3}$ sec.

4) Interaction with nuclear spins. A cause of the relaxation may also be the interaction between electrons and the nuclear spins. Thus, just as in atoms, a dominant role is played by hyperfine interaction with electrons in S states [17]. Calculations show that

$$\frac{\tau_N}{\tau} = \frac{8I(I+1)\varepsilon_0}{9kT}, \tag{6.4}$$

if τ_N denotes the relaxation time of nuclear spins, which according to the calculations of Korringa [17] equals

$$\tau_N = \frac{9\pi \hbar^5 I^2}{64 m_0^2 k_0^2 \beta^2 \beta_N^2 kT |\psi(0)|^4}. \tag{6.5}$$

Here $\psi(0)$ is the wave function of an electron at the Fermi surface; the argument is equated to zero because one must take the value of this function at the site of the nucleus. It is noteworthy that the relaxation time τ is temperature independent. Therefore one may expect that the relaxation mechanism (4) should be of decisive significance at sufficiently low temperatures.

5) Interaction of electron spins with the magnetic field of currents arising from translational motion of conduction electrons. This relaxation mechanism leads to the following expression:

$$\tau = \frac{9m_0^2c^4\hbar}{20e^4k_0^2kT\ln\frac{kT}{\beta H_0}}. \qquad (6.6)$$

The weak dependence on the applied magnetic field H_0 which is exhibited in this formula may be used to clarify the question of whether the mechanism under consideration plays an important role in the paramagnetic relaxation processes. A numerical calculation shows that for $H_0 = 5$ gauss and $T = 293°$K we obtain $\tau \approx 8 \cdot 10^{-7}$ sec.

Experimental determinations of the relaxation time [8, 9] have shown that even the shortest values of τ, given by the mechanism (5) proposed by Overhauser, are approximately two orders of magnitude greater than the experimental results. Moreover, in contradiction to (6.6), the relaxation time was found to be constant during a variation of the field H_0 from 300 to 3000 gauss.

The shortcoming of the Overhauser theory evidently does not lie in the neglect of some important relaxation mechanism. The description of the motion of conduction electrons in terms of plane waves must lead to results that are too crude. Elliott [18] has obtained good agreement with experimental data by calculating the relaxation time, using the ordinary energy band theory of a metal, assuming that the exchange of energy between the electron spins and the lattice vibrations occurs on account of the spin-orbit interaction. The coupling between the lattice vibrations and the motion of the electrons is so much stronger than the direct interaction between the electron spins and the lattice that even weak spin-orbit coupling is sufficient to produce a highly effective relaxation mechanism. Elliott obtained the following formula for the relaxation time:

$$\tau = \frac{\alpha\tau_R}{(\Delta g)^2}. \qquad (6.7)$$

Here τ_R is the collision time of conduction electrons, which as we know is easily determined if the electrical resistance of the metal is known, for Li, Na and K the collision times are $\tau_R = 1 \cdot 10^{-14}$,

$3 \cdot 10^{-14}$ and $2 \cdot 10^{-14}$ sec, respectively. The collision time may to a good approximation be considered as proportional to the electrical conductivity of the metal, and therefore for temperatures $T > \theta$ it will be $\sim 1/T$, while at low temperatures $\tau_R \sim 1/T^5$. For temperatures $T > \theta$ the numberical factor is $\alpha = 1/[2^5 \cdot 3 \ln(d/a)]$ [see (6.1)]; for $T < \theta$ the factor α depends on temperature, and thus at high temperatures $\tau \sim 1/T$.

An attractive feature of the Elliott theory is the simple relation between the relaxation time τ and the deviation of the g factor from the purely spin value, which as we have seen is determined by the spin-orbit interaction. Equation (6.7) easily explains why we fail to observe paramagnetic resonance in heavy metals. In fact, as the atomic number of the element increases, the spin-orbit coupling, and along with it, the deviation Δg, rapidly increases.

Andreyev and Gerasimenko [19] have considered the subject of paramagnetic relaxation in metals by solving the kinetic equation for conduction electrons. They demonstrated that for temperatures $T \gg \beta H_0/k$ under paramagnetic resonance conditions the magnetization vector is subject to the Bloch equation (5.1), in which the longitudinal and transverse relaxation times are equal to one another. In addition they improved and corrected the Elliott formula for the paramagnetic relaxation time, obtaining the following expression:

$$\tau = \frac{u}{T}\left(\ln\frac{\operatorname{th}\frac{\theta}{T}}{\operatorname{th}\frac{T_k}{T}}\right)^{-1}, \quad u = \frac{3\beta^2\hbar\rho v^2}{16\pi\chi_0 k\overline{\varepsilon^2}(\Delta g)^2}, \tag{6.8}$$

where $\bar{\epsilon}$ is the mean energy of the electron in the lattice, and $T_k = (v/kv_F)\, 2\beta H_0$ if the dimensions of the metal sample are such that $d > \hbar v_F/2\beta H_0$; if, however, the dimensions of the sample do not satisfy this inequality, then $T_k = \hbar v\, kd$; v_F here denotes the electron velocity at the Fermi level. For temperatures $T \gg \theta$, Eq. (6.8) takes the form

$$\tau = \frac{u}{T}\ln\frac{\theta}{T_k}. \tag{6.9}$$

If, however, $T \ll \theta$, then

$$\tau = \frac{u}{T}\ln\frac{T}{T_k}. \tag{6.10}$$

Experimental investigations of the relaxation time have shown that in the case of Na as the temperature changes from 4 to 293°K, $\tau \sim 1/T$ just as theory demands.

Measurements at room temperature give the value $\tau = 9 \cdot 10^{-8}$ sec, which is in good agreement with the theoretical value $\tau \approx 10^{-6}\, T^{-1}$ sec.

In Li and Be, experiments revealed a constant relaxation time when the temperature is changed over wide limits.[1] At the same time it was established that when the sample is purified and the amount of Li is increased from 99.0 to 99.9% the relaxation time is lengthened from $3 \cdot 10^{-9}$ to $2.5 \cdot 10^{-8}$ sec. All these facts find a simple explanation. Since the magnitude of Δg in light metals is small, paramagnetic relaxation is determined by the spin-orbit coupling of conduction electrons with impurities. The "real" relaxation time could be measured in samples subjected to exceptionally careful purification.

Potassium has a resonance line width approximately 50 times greater than does Na [9]. At liquid helium temperature, cesium has a line width of about $2 \cdot 10^{8}$ cps.

Garif'yanov and Starikov [11] found that slight impurities of heavy metals (Hg, Pb) in Na and Li samples are capable of broadening the resonance line by a factor of 10^4. This broadening apparently occurs because of the shortening of the relaxation time on account of the strong spin-orbit coupling in atoms of heavy metals.

In conclusion we note that the area under the paramagnetic resonance absorption curve is proportional to the purely paramagnetic part of the static susceptibility. Hence, measurements of the paramagnetic resonance may make possible a separation of the diamagnetic part of the susceptibility from the paramagnetic part [20]. The main difficulty which arises in an attempt to accomplish this separation is the great difficulty of making absolute measurements of paramagnetic absorption. This difficulty was ingeniously circumvented by Schumacher, Carver and Slichter [5], who simultaneously observed electron and nuclear resonances in metallic lithium at the same frequency, $1.7 \cdot 10^{7}$ cps. The absolute value of the intensity of the nuclear lines may be easily explained. It was found by a comparison of both resonance curves that the static susceptibility equals $(2.0 \pm 0.3)\ 10^{-6}$ cgs units; and a theoretical calculation [21] gave $1.87 \cdot 10^{-6}$ cgs units.

6.2. Influence of the Skin Effect and Diffusion of Electrons on the Shape of the Resonance Line

It has been proven experimentally and theoretically that the skin effect and diffusion of electrons inside the skin layer

---

[1]Levy [9] studied the temperature dependence of the Li resonance line width and at ~80°K established the presence of a discontinuity which is probably due to the existence of a phase transition.

substantially alter the shape of a paramagnetic resonance line. The distortion of the shape of the resonance line must occur because, in contrast to paramagnetic dielectrics, where the variable part of the magnetization is determined by the magnitude of the applied oscillatory field, in a metal as a result of the skin effect there also is an inverse dependence of the values of this local field on the magnetization. By virtue of this, if the energy absorbed in dielectrics is proportional to the coefficient χ'', then in a metal it will also depend on the real part of the dynamic susceptibility χ'. In addition, the line shape will be distorted because diffusion transports the same electron inside the skin layer, where it is subjected to an oscillatory magnetic field, whose amplitude and phase change continuously. Thus, interesting information concerning the nature of the metallic state, given by the paramagnetic resonance method, may be extracted from this distortion only if we take the influence of the skin effect and electron diffusion into account. The theoretical treatment of this subject is due to Dyson [22], who used a very simple model of a metal to obtain formulas suitable for practical application. He assumed that the conduction electrons diffuse like free particles, and treated the spin of each electron as an independent quantum variable. The spin is very weakly coupled to the orbital motion and consequently is unaffected by the collisions which the electrons experience. Judging from the magnitude of the spin-lattice relaxation time in the case of sodium, for instance, only one in 10^5 collisions causes a change in orientation of the spin. It may be assumed therefore that the spin reacts first and foremost to a change in the local magnetic field.

Let us denote the skin depth by δ and the mean free path of the electron by λ. An average electron will traverse the skin depth in a time

$$t_D = \frac{3}{2}\frac{\delta^2}{\lambda^2}\tau_R. \tag{6.11}$$

In the time t_D the amplitude and phase of the oscillatory magnetic field will change by factors of the order of e. Therefore, the electron inside the skin layer will not experience a magnetic field with a fixed frequency, but rather one with a band of frequencies of width $1/t_D$ Since ordinarily $t_D \ll \tau_R$, at first glance the width of the resonance line would be expected to increase from $1/\tau$ to $1/t_D$. Actually, however, the width remains almost unchanged, although the shape of the line is changed.

This unexpected result is explained as follows. The periodic magnetic field can be represented in the form

$$F(t) = f(t)e^{-2\pi i\nu t} + f^*(t)e^{2\pi i\nu t}, \tag{6.12}$$

where $f(t)$ is a modulation factor, which cannot, however, be regarded as an entirely random function of time. In the time τ each electron experiences a large number of individual pulses, separated by irregular intervals. The pulses arise close to the surface of the metal, where the amplitude of $f(t)$ is large. The intervals occur when the electron is for the most part far from the surface, where $f(t)$ is almost zero. The following two facts are of decisive importance: 1) there is a high probability that during the time τ the electrons repeatedly encounter the surface of the metal; 2) the phase of $f(t)$ takes the same value each time the electron approaches the surface, as a consequence of which the integral of $f(t)$ over the time interval between two pulses has a value which is not zero.

We shall now consider the form of the spectrum of $F(t)$. Each pulse gives a spectrum distributed with approximately the same intensity over a band of width $1/t_D$. As a consequence of factors (1) and (2) the interference pattern produced by the large number of pulses leads to a separation in the middle of the bandwidth $1/\tau_D$ with a central maximum corresponding to the frequency ν. The interval between two successive pulses is a random variable, taking on values from 0 to τ. Therefore the spectrum of each electron will average out over all electrons to a curve with a flat maximum of width $1/\tau_D$, in which we have separated out a sharp peak with width of the order of $1/\tau$.

We shall quote the results of Dyson's calculations. In addition to the previously encountered time parameters, τ and t_D, one more is necessary—the time t_T required for the electron to traverse the entire metal sample. If the metallic particles are so finely divided that $t_T \ll t_D$, the skin effect is insignificant and the power absorbed by the paramagnetic substance in a volume V, according to (1.9), (1.19) and (5.2), may be represented in the following form:

$$P_V = \pi^2 \nu H_r^2 V \nu_0 \chi_0 \tau \frac{1}{1 + 4\pi^2 (\nu - \nu_0)^2 \tau^2}. \tag{6.13}$$

Throughout we assumed that no saturation exists; thus, we have considered that in a metal $T_2 = \tau$. Moreover, here and in the following, we shall neglect nonresonance absorption proportional to g_2 (see Secs. 1.4 and 5.1).

Conversely, when $t_T \gg t_D$, in solving the problem of resonance line shape in metals it is necessary to distinguish between the regions of normal and of anomalous skin effect. In the first case the penetration depth of a periodic field in a metal is determined by the classical quantity $\delta = c/(2\pi\sqrt{\sigma})$, where σ is the electrical conductivity of the metal, and in the second case the depth of penetration is characterized by the path length λ. First we shall consider the case of the classical skin effect. The general formula for the absorbed power is

$$P_v = -\pi^2 \nu H_r^2 (\delta A_0) \nu_0 \chi_0 \tau \frac{t_D}{2\tau} \left\{ \frac{R^4(\varkappa^2 - 1) + 1 - 2R^2\varkappa}{[(R^2\varkappa - 1)^2 + R^4]^4} \times \right.$$
$$\times \left[\frac{2\xi}{R(1+\varkappa^2)^{\frac{1}{2}}} + R^2(\varkappa + 1) - 3 \right] + \frac{2R^2 - 2\varkappa R^4}{[(R^2\varkappa - 1)^2 + R^4]^2} \times \tag{6.14}$$
$$\left. \times \left[\frac{2\eta}{R(1+\varkappa^2)^{\frac{1}{2}}} + R^2(\varkappa - 1) - 3 \right] \right\},$$

where

$$\varkappa = 2\pi(\nu - \nu_0)\tau, \quad \xi = \frac{\varkappa}{|\varkappa|}[(1+\varkappa^2)^{\frac{1}{2}} - 1]^{\frac{1}{2}},$$

$$\eta = [(1+\varkappa^2)^{\frac{1}{2}} + 1]^{\frac{1}{2}}, \quad R = \left(\frac{t_D}{\tau}\right)^{\frac{1}{2}}$$

and A_0 is the surface area of the metal. This equation can be simplified for certain cases of practical importance.

Let us assume that $t_D/\tau \ll 1$. If this condition referring to a metal with a high conductivity (low temperatures and narrow lines) is fulfilled, then, accurate to magnitudes proportional to R, we have

$$P_v = -[\pi^2 \nu H_r^2 (\delta A_0) \nu_0 \chi_0 \tau] \left(\frac{t_D}{\tau}\right)^{\frac{1}{2}} \frac{\varkappa}{|\varkappa|} \frac{[(1+\varkappa^2)^{\frac{1}{2}} - 1]^{\frac{1}{2}}}{(1+\varkappa^2)^{\frac{1}{2}}}. \tag{6.15}$$

If $t_D/\tau \gg 1$, which is valid when the diffusion of magnetic dipoles occurs very slowly, (6.14) takes the form

$$P_v = [\pi^2 \nu H_r^2 (\delta A_0) \nu_0 \chi_0 \tau] \cdot \frac{1}{2} \frac{1 - 2\pi\tau(\nu - \nu_0)}{1 + 4\pi^2\tau^2(\nu - \nu_0)^2}. \tag{6.16}$$

This formula had been previously obtained by Bloembergen [23], who studied the subject of the influence of the skin effect on the shape of a resonance line in the case when the diffusion phenomenon plays no role. This case is encountered when we speak of paramagnetic resonance in metals, due to paramagnetic impurities, nuclear spins or the structure of the crystal lattice (transition metals).

At low temperatures, the skin effect acquires an anomalous character. If we assume that $t_D/\tau \ll 1$, the formula for the absorbed power takes the form

$$P_v = [\pi^2 \nu H_r^2 (\delta A)_0 \nu_0 \chi_0 \tau] \cdot 6 \frac{\tau_R}{\tau} \left\{ \frac{(Z_2 - Z_1)[(1+\varkappa^2)^{\frac{1}{2}} + 1]^{\frac{1}{2}}}{(1+\varkappa^2)^{\frac{1}{2}}} + \right.$$
$$\left. + 2Z_1 Z_2 \frac{[(1+\varkappa^2)^{\frac{1}{2}} - 1]^{\frac{1}{2}} \varkappa}{(1+\varkappa^2)^{\frac{1}{2}} |\varkappa|} \right\}, \tag{6.17}$$

where Z_1 and Z_2 determine the complex impedance $Z = Z_1 + iZ_2$.

A number of authors have supplied the theory of paramagnetic resonance with a rigorous foundation and a subsequent development both under conditions of classical and anomalous skin effect. An exquisite method using the kinetic equation for the statistical density operator of conduction electrons enabled Silin [24] to obtain a differential equation for the magnetization vector, which lies at the basis of Dyson's work. Lifshits, Azbel' and Gerasimenko [25] obtained a similar kinetic equation and independently of Silin developed a general treatment of the behavior of conduction electrons in a steady magnetic and an arbitrary periodic electromagnetic field.

In the manifold results obtained by these authors we note that the shape of the paramagnetic resonance line has been calculated under saturation conditions. It is interesting that the saturation of the resonance in bulk samples requires far greater power than in the case when the skin effect is insignificant. In [26] the subject of paramagnetic resonance in superconductors was considered, and in particular, it was shown that in bulk conductors the effect is immaterial.

We shall compare the theoretical results with the experimental data cited mainly in [8]. Figure 6.1 gives the characteristic curve of paramagnetic resonance absorption in a thick layer of a metal. We note that it represents the result of a certain superposition of the ordinary curves for χ' and χ''. Figure 6.2 gives a similar curve for the derivative of the absorption with respect to the field

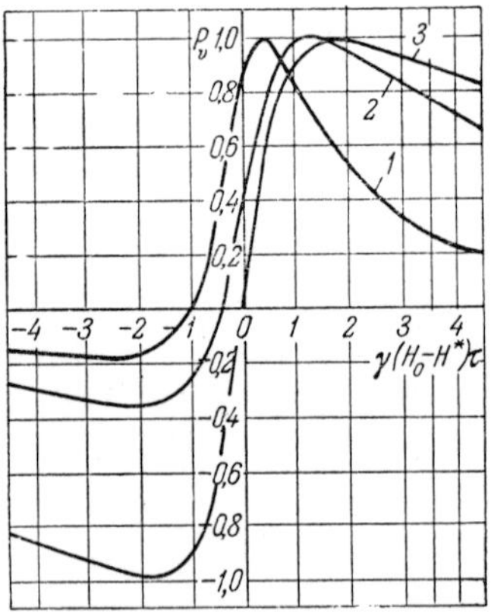

Fig. 6.1. Paramagnetic resonance absorption in a thick metallic layer. Curves of the dependence of the absorbed power P_v on the value of $\gamma(H_0 - H^*)\tau$ for different values of R.

1–$R = \infty$; 2–$R = \sqrt{0.1}$; 3–$R = 0$.

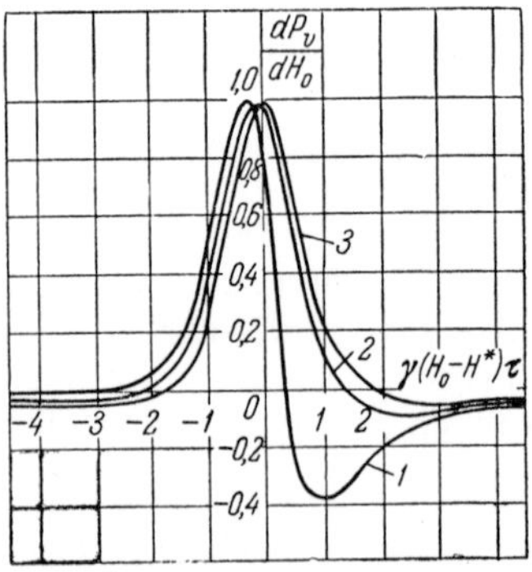

Fig. 6.2. Paramagnetic resonance absorption in a thick metallic layer. Curves of the derivative dP_v/dH_0 of the power absorbed from the field vs. the value of $\gamma(H_0 - H^*)\tau$ for different values of R.

1–$R = \infty$; 2–$R = \sqrt{0.1}$; 3–$R = 0$.

dP_v/dH, which is often measured experimentally. For a comparison with experiment, it is convenient to plot the values of the ratio A/B or A'/B'. Figure 6.3a shows how these ratios change as a function of the value $R = (t_D/\tau)^{1/2}$. The variation of R over wide limits is easily realizable by means of a transition from room temperature to liquid helium temperature. For Na and Be, in which the surface of the samples was very smooth, the experimental curves lie close to the theoretical curve. For other metals, divergences were detected, which are evidently related to the appreciable change in the diffusion time t_D because of the unevenness of the metallic surface.

From the experimental values of A/B we may obviously determine the diffusion time t_D. The diffusion time for Be measured in this manner was found to be in good agreement with the value obtained by means of (6.11).

Knowledge of the ratio A/B or A'/B' is also very important because it permits separation of the effect due to the conduction electrons from the effect due to paramagnetic impurities. It is apparent from Figure 6.3b that for conduction electrons the ratio A'/B' is always greater than 2.7; for impurities it may be shown that $A'/B' < 2.7$.

For alkali metals the depth of penetration of the field of frequency $3 \cdot 10^8$ cps at the temperature 40°K becomes equal to the path length. It is apparent therefore that the experimental curve of absorption obtained for Na at 4°K corresponds to Eq. (6.17), which is valid under the conditions of the anomalous skin effect.

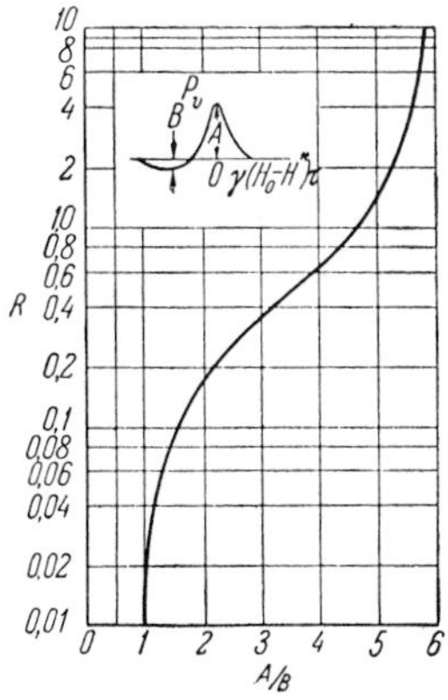

Fig. 6.3a. Dependence of the ratio A/B on $R = (t_D/\tau)^{1/2}$.

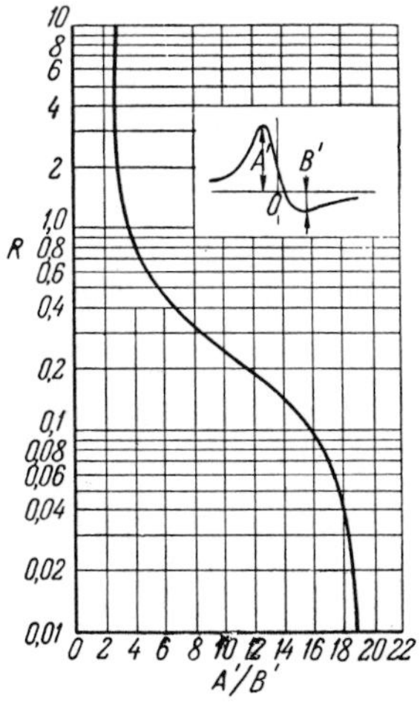

Fig. 6.3b. Dependence of the ratio A'/B' on $R = (t_D/\tau)^{1/2}$.

6.3. Transition Metals

In transition metals one expects that paramagnetic resonance can be detected from the atoms forming the framework of the crystal lattice. The first positive result in iron group elements was obtained in Cu-Mn alloys containing from 11 to 0.07% manganese [27, 28]. The choice of substance is determined by the following considerations: a) the conduction band of copper has a simple structure because it contains a $4s$ electron with an isotropic effective mass close to the free electron mass; b) from the static susceptibility data one may conclude that the two $4s$ electrons of manganese atoms occur in the particles which fill the conduction band, and the manganese ions are therefore in the $^6S_{5/2}$ state; c) since the manganese ions are in the S state, one may expect the spin-lattice relaxation mechanism, whose action depends on the magnitude of the spin-orbit coupling, to have little effect; d) one may expect that the ferromagnetic coupling between the Mn atoms is caused by indirect sd-exchange forces.

The sd-exchange interaction operator has the simple form

$$\hat{\mathcal{H}}' = I\hat{S}\hat{s}, \tag{6.18}$$

where $\hat{S}$ refers to the spin of the Mn ion, and $\hat{s}$ to the spin of the conduction electron. On the basis of optical data concerning the magnitude of the exchange interaction in a free Mn atom one may evaluate the sd-coupling constant: $I = 7 \cdot 10^{-13}$ erg. Operator (6.18) has the same form as the $A\hat{I}\hat{s}$ hyperfine interaction operator between the conduction electrons and the nuclear spins of the metal. This interaction, as is well known, determines the shape of the paramagnetic nuclear resonance line in metals [17]. It primarily causes the so-called Knight shift [29] of the position of the resonance peak; as a consequence of the magnetization of the conduction electrons by the external magnetic field H_0, the nuclear spin will experience, apart from this field, also an internal field $H_A = \lambda M_e$, where

$$\lambda = -\frac{A}{4\beta^2 N_e}, \tag{6.19}$$

and M_e is the vector magnetization of conduction electrons. Second, the interaction $A\hat{I}\hat{s}$ is the origin of the main mechanism of spin-lattice relaxation.

Applying the derivation of nuclear theory to our case for an alloy containing, for example, 5% manganese, we obtained the following formula determining the relative g shift:

$$\frac{\Delta g}{g} = \frac{12}{T}. \tag{6.20}$$

The formula for the spin-lattice relaxation time (6.5) may be rewritten in the following form:

$$\tau = \frac{8h\varepsilon_0^2}{9\pi^2 kTI^2}. \tag{6.21}$$

Experimental investigations were performed at the wavelengths of 3.3 and 1.2 cm over the temperature range from 2 to 300°K. After taking into account the distortions of line shape introduced by the skin effect, the method indicated in the previous section gave measured values of the *g* factor very close to 2. The measured width of the resonance line, however, was approximately one fifth of the value given by Eq. (6.21). Thus, if the exchange *sd* interaction also determines the magnetic properties of the alloys under consideration, the quantity must be approximately one order smaller than that for free atoms.

The splitting of the spin levels by the electric field of the crystal was not found experimentally, and this is explained by the fact that these splittings are very small owing to the screening action of the conduction electrons. Nor was a hyperfine structure of the absorption line detected, which is an apparent indication of the extremely weak s-configuration interaction.

In addition to Cu-Mn, Ag-Mn and Mg-Mn alloys were also studied. At low temperatures all these alloys acquired the properties of antiferromagnetic substances.

We shall now consider the rare earth metals. Experimental data on paramagnetic resonance for this group of transition elements is extremely scanty [30, 31] and does not enable us to make a correct theoretical generalization. Several theoretical conclusions are found in [32].

Metals of rare earth elements occupy a special place regarding their metal properties, since the paramagnetism of these metals is caused almost entirely by the lowest lying $4f$ electrons inside the atoms and the conduction electrons have an insignificant effect on magnetic susceptibility. Consequently, one may assume that the general methods of calculation of paramagnetic properties developed and applied with success to salts of rare earth elements, to a first approximation are also applicable to metals. Interpretation of the paramagnetic resonance spectra in rare earth elements is simplified owing to the fact that, in contrast to salts, the symmetry of the internal electric field of a metal always coincides with the symmetry of the crystalline lattice.

Special interest is created by paramagnetic absorption lines whose positions are independent of the direction of the static magnetic field with respect to the crystal axes, since existing experimental data refer only to polycrystalline samples. Such lines may appear in crystals having a cubic lattice, since it is not difficult to show that if a twofold or threefold degenerate level appears under the influence of an electric field of cubic symmetry, then further splitting of these levels by a weak magnetic field will not be independent of the direction of this field with respect to the axes of the cube. Of the rare earth elements, β cerium, β praseodymium, europium and ytterbium possess cubic symmetry. Theoretical conclusions coneerning the spectrum of β cerium are found to be in good agreement with experimental results. In the calculations it is assumed that the metal atom lacks three electrons. This assumption follows from static susceptibility data and finds here direct verification.

Of the metals having a hexagonal lattice, we shall first of all discuss α Ce, Nd and Dy, whose ions have an odd number of electrons.[1] These ions have doubly degenerate energy levels, arising in the electric field of the crystal. If we make certain natural assumptions, it turns out that there should exist only one absorption line, whose position is determined by the spectroscopic splitting factor

$$g = g_0 \sqrt{1 + q \sin^2 \vartheta}, \quad q = J^2 + J - \frac{3}{4}, \tag{6.22}$$

where g_0 is the Landé factor for the free ions and θ is the angle between the direction of the static magnetic field and the hexagonal axis of the crystal. Calculations show that for polycrystalline samples, the intensity of the absorption line is proportional to

$$P \sim \left(J + \frac{1}{2}\right)^2 g_0^2 \sin \vartheta \frac{2q \sin^2 \frac{\vartheta}{2}}{1 + q \sin^2 \vartheta}. \tag{6.23}$$

Elimination of θ from Eqs. (6.22) and (6.23) makes it possible to establish by means of (1.2) a dependence of the magnitude of the paramagnetic absorption on the static field strength. The theoretical curves obtained by this method are in satisfactory agreement with the experimental absorption curves for Ce and Nd.

Samarium is the only rare earth metal having a tetragonal lattice, and under the simplest assumptions concerning the coefficients which determine the crystalline field potential, it should have the same spectrum as α cerium. Metals whose ions contain an even number of electrons (α Pr, Tb, Ho and Tm) have a hexagonal lattice. In this case it is easily shown that to a first approximation the probabilities of magnetic dipole transitions between the nearest-neighbor Zeeman sublevels equal zero.

---

[1]Gadolinium, whose ions also have an odd number of electrons, will be given particular consideration.

If we assume that the previously developed theory of spin-lattice relaxation for salts of rare earth elements (see Sec. 5.3) is also applicable to metals, then the values of the spin-lattice relaxation time τ are several orders of magnitude greater, as a consequence of the fact that the density and velocity of sound in metals have enormously larger values. In addition, we must remember that the internal crystalline electric field in metals is much weaker because of the screening action of the conduction electrons. Hence, the possibility of observing paramagnetic resonance in rare earth metals at room temperature should also arise.

A triply charged Gd ion which is in the S state occupies a special place. Gadolinium is paramagnetic at temperatures above 16°C. Measurements of resonance absorption [30], performed at the frequency $2.43 \cdot 10^{10}$ cps at the temperature 105.5°C, have shown that $g = 1.95$, and that the line width is temperature independent and equals ~ 4000 gauss.

The subject of resonance absorption of ultrasound by rare earth metals has also been treated theoretically [33]. In certain cases this effect should be very substantial.

6.4. Impurity Semiconductors

In the first paper [34] devoted to paramagnetic resonance in impurity semiconductors, a resonance effect was found at the frequency $\nu = 9 \cdot 10^9$ cps in powdered samples of n-type silicon containing from $1 \cdot 10^{18}$ to $2 \cdot 10^{18}$ phosphorus atoms/cm^3. To avoid the influence of the skin effect, finely divided pellets of silicon having a radius one order of magnitude smaller than the skin depth were immersed in paraffin. The measurements were conducted at temperatures ranging from 4 to 300°K, and a single Lorentzian-shaped absorption line was observed. The absorption peak was independent of temperature and was located at the g factor = 2.001 ± 0.001. The width of the resonance line rapidly increased with temperature from about 2 gauss at 4°K to 30 gauss at 300°K. A klystron oscillator was used, and saturation of the paramagnetic resonance was not observed even at liquid helium temperatures. From this one may conclude that at the temperature 4°K the longitudinal time $T_1 < 10^{-3}$ sec. Willenbrock and Bloemenbergen [35] observed a paramagnetic resonance at the same microwave frequency in both n-type and p-type silicon. The measurements were conducted at the temperature 78°K and the impurity concentration varied from $5 \cdot 10^{17}$ to $5 \cdot 10^{18}$ atoms/cm^3. For both electrons and holes the position of the absorption peak was the same and corresponded to $g = 2.00$. The absorption line intensity was proportional to the impurity concentration.

Fletcher et al. studied paramagnetic resonance at liquid helium temperatures in single crystals of silicon doped with phosphorous, arsenic [36], and antimony [37]. At concentrations of about 10^{18} atoms/cm^3 one absorption peak was observed, whose position changed slightly as a function of the inclination of the static magnetic field with respect to the crystal axes. With the field parallel to the [100] axis for the case of As we have $g = 2.0004 \pm 0.0005$. The line width was always less than 3 gauss.

From the foregoing it may be concluded that paramagnetic resonance absorption is due to the spin of the conduction band electrons. This conclusion results first and foremost from the possibility of observing the resonance effect at temperatures corresponding to the mean energy of thermal motion, which greatly exceeds the ionization energy of the impurity atom ($\sim$0.05 ev). The relatively high impurity concentration of the samples under investigation and the absence of hyperfine splittings of the resonance line also indicate the validity of this conclusion.

The broadening of the paramagnetic absorption line apparently is of a spin-lattice nature. Actually the width due to the magnetic dipolar interactions of the electron spins is easily estimated to the order of 0.1 gauss. Hyperfine interactions of the electron spins with the nuclei of phosphorus and the odd isotope of silicon[1] cannot make an appreciable contribution to the line width because of the rapid motion of the electrons. Also surface recombination of electrons and holes can scarcely play any role, since this process is fairly slow.

Elliott [18] has considered the subject of the effect of spin-orbit interaction of the conduction electrons on the magnitude of the g factor and the spin-lattice relaxation time of semiconductors. He found that the g factor shift equals

$$\Delta g \approx \frac{\lambda}{\Delta E}, \tag{6.24}$$

where ΔE is the gap between the lowest conduction band and the nearest band possessing the same transformation properties. If we allow for the fact that the spin-orbit coupling constant for a silicon atom is $\lambda \approx 100$ cm^{-1} and that experiments yield $\Delta g \approx 3 \cdot 10^{-3}$, by means of (6.24) we obtain for the interval ΔE the reasonable value of about 4 ev.

The spin-lattice relaxation time may be calculated from the formula [see (6.7)]

$$\tau \sim \frac{\tau_R}{(\Delta g)^2}, \tag{6.25}$$

if Δg is small. For n-type silicon the collision time at high temperatures is independent of the impurity concentration and equals [38]

---

[1] In a natural sample of silicon containing 4.68% of the Si^{29} isotope.

$$\tau_R \approx 10^{-9} T^{-\frac{3}{2}} \text{ sec.} \tag{6.26}$$

Hence, $\tau \approx 10^{-9}$ sec at $T = 300°K$, i.e., the line width equals ~50 gauss, which is in good agreement with the measured value of ~30 gauss. For germanium the constants τ_R and λ exceed those of silicon by factors of 5 and 20, respectively. Consequently, the line width of germanium must be approximately 100 times greater than in silicon, which evidently also explains the negative result of the first experiments with germanium.[1]

At low temperatures and small impurity concentrations, paramagnetic resonance absorption is due to the electron spins associated with donors. This fact is most clearly evident when hyperfine structure of resonance lines exists, which definitely indicates a coupling between the electron spin and the nuclear moment of the impurity atom. Measurements [36] performed at the frequency $\nu = 2.4 \cdot 10^{10}$ cps and the temperature 4.2°K in samples containing from $5 \cdot 10^{16}$ to 10^{18} atoms/cm³ of arsenic revealed four lines which are equally spaced in accordance with the nuclear spin of As^{75}, which equals 3/2. The interval between the neighboring hyperfine components is ~ 73 gauss and the width of each component is ~10 gauss. When silicon is doped with acceptors (boron), the magnitude of this effect decreases. In addition, it has been established that preliminary elastic deformation of the semiconductors at the temperature 1000°C leads to a substantial increase of the intensity of the absorption lines, but the nature of this phenomenon is not completely clear.

In phosphorus-doped samples there were observed two components separated by 42 gauss in accordance with the nuclear spin of P^{31}, which equals 1/2.

In samples containing $4 \cdot 10^{17}$ atoms/cm³ of antimony, the presence of two odd isotopes, Sb^{121} and Sb^{123} with nuclear spins equal to 5/2 and 7/2 respectively, gives a paramagnetic resonance spectrum consisting of 6 + 8 hyperfine components [37]. The ratio of intensities of these two groups of lines strictly corresponds to the percentage content of these isotopes, and the over-all splittings of these groups of lines (69 and 38 gauss) correspond precisely to the magnetic moments of the nuclei Sb^{121} ($\mu = 3.360\ \beta_N$) and Sb^{123} ($\mu = 2.547\ \beta_N$).

An attempt to detect paramagnetic resonance in semiconductors containing 10^{17} atoms/cm³ of boron and $3 \cdot 10^{17}$ atoms/cm³ of aluminum gave a negative result.

Honig and Kip [39] have observed a paramagnetic resonance in a silicon sample containing $7 \cdot 10^{16}$ atoms/cm³ of lithium at the

---

[1] Recently, investigations of paramagnetic resonance in germanium have given a positive result [110].

frequency $\nu = 8.8 \cdot 10^9$ cps in the temperature range 4 - 20°K. No hyperfine structure was found. The position of the single absorption peak corresponded to $g = 1.999$, the line width was 1.5 gauss, and the shape of the line was Gaussian.

Kohn and Luttinger [40] undertook the task of explaining to what extent the experimentally obtained hyperfine splitting constants of a paramagnetic resonance line are consistent with the assumptions that the hyperfine structure is caused by the interaction between the donor nucleus and the electrons which are localized near the donors and which exist in the well-known donor states with ionization energy 0.04 - 0.05 ev. The over-all hyperfine splitting $(\Delta H)_{\text{hfs}}$ of the energy level, expressed in gauss, may be given in the form

$$(\Delta H)_{\text{hfs}} = \frac{16\pi}{3} |\psi(0)|^2 \mu_D, \qquad (6.27)$$

where μ_D is the nuclear magnetic moment, $\psi(\mathbf{r})$ is the wave function of the electron coupled to a donor, and r is the radius vector extending from the nucleus to the electron. In Table 6.1 are given the experimental values of $|\psi(0)|^2$.

Table 6.1

Experimental Values of $|\psi(0)|^2$

	I	g_N	$\|\psi(0)\|^2 \times 10^{-14}$, cm^{-3}	$A \cdot 10^{19}$, ergs	T_x, min	T_{Si}/T_x
Li^7	$\frac{3}{2}$	2.17	0.055	0.056	$3.64 \cdot 10^6$	0.1
P^{31}	$\frac{1}{2}$	2.26	0.44	7.8	560	150
As^{75}	$\frac{3}{2}$	0.957	1.80	14.0	56	1000
Sb^{121}	$\frac{5}{2}$	1.37	1.20	13.0	41	2000
Sb^{123}	$\frac{7}{2}$	0.724	1.20	7.0	97	820

The function $\psi(r)$ obeys the Schrödinger equation:

$$\left[-\frac{\hbar^2}{2m}\nabla^2 + V(r) + U(r) - E\right]\psi(r) = 0, \tag{6.28}$$

where $V(r)$ is the potential energy of the electron in the periodic field of the silicon crystalline lattice, and $U(r)$ is the additional energy arising when one of the silicon atoms is replaced by an impurity atom. At distances large in comparison with the interatomic distances, $U(r)$ equals $-e^2/\epsilon r$, where ϵ is the dielectric constant of the medium. For silicon $\epsilon = 13$. Great difficulties are associated with the solution of Eq. (6.28) since in the first place the band wave function is unknown for silicon and second the introduction of the concept of the effective mass of an electron is inadmissible near the donor. As a result of detailed calculations undertaken for phosphorus, it was found that $|\psi(0)|^2 = 0.4 \cdot 10^{24}$ cm^{-3}, which is in much better agreement with the experimental data than might be expected on the basis of the assumptions made. A rough estimate gives for the ratio $|\psi(0)|^2_{Li}/|\psi(0)|^2_P = 0.004$. Such a small value of $|\psi(0)|^2_{Li}$ completely explains the negative results of the attempts to detect hyperfine structure of the absorption line in silicon doped with lithium.

In observations of the hyperfine structure of the paramagnetic resonance spectrum in silicon containing impurities of group V elements, in addition to the $2I + 1$ lines, weak satellites were detected, located in the middle between each pair of hyperfine components [36, 37]. Slichter [41] has shown that such satellites must emerge if we assume exchange interaction of the type $I\hat{S}_1\hat{S}_2$ between the pair of electrons belonging to two donors which are accidentally found to be in the vicinity of one another. It follows from this interpretation of the nature of the satellites that: a) the intensity of the central satellite is twice as great as the end one; b) the intensity of the satellite should depend on the impurity concentration: at small concentrations it must be proportional to it, and at large concentrations additional satellites should appear, associated with families of 3 and 4 electrons; c) if $I \sim kT$, the intensity of the satellites must greatly depend on the temperature of the semiconductor, approximately as $\exp(-I/kT)$; d) dependence on mechanical treatment is also possible, if it affects the character of the donor distribution.

In the experiments undertaken to check the theory of Slichter [42] measurements were conducted at the temperature 1.2°K and at the frequency of the periodic field $\nu = 9 \cdot 10^9$ cps, using two silicon samples containing 10^{17} and $4 \cdot 10^{17}$ phosphorus atoms/cm^3. Under the circumstances predicted by the theory, additional absorption maxima were observed, which correspond to the exchange of pairs, triplets and quadruplets of electrons.

We now consider the spin-lattice relaxation of electrons localized near the donors. As a result of experiments on silicon samples, containing up to 10^{17} impurity atoms/cm^3, the spin-lattice relaxation time at liquid helium temperatures is measured in minutes [43, 44]. Such large values of relaxation time are usually characteristic of nuclear spins. As the impurity concentration rises, the time τ begins to rapidly diminish, evidently because of the strengthening of the interaction of the bound electrons with the conduction band electrons. The correctness of this explanation is directly confirmed by the decrease of the time τ to milliseconds when the semiconductor is exposed to light [45].

The theory of this subject has been given by Pines, Bardeen, and Slichter [46] and subsequently developed by Abrahams [47]. The calculations were performed with the purpose of evaluating the order of magnitude, and a number of simplifications were therefore made: a) the complicated wave function of a bound electron was replaced by the wave function of an electron with effective mass $m^* = 0.3\ m_e$, located in a state with minimal energy; b) all angular dependences were omitted; c) only the effect of longitudinal phonons was taken into account. Of the various relaxation mechanisms, only the following were considered.

1. Modulation of the electron-nuclear hyperfine interaction. The change of the potential energy $V(r)$, occurring in Eq. (6.28), due to lattice vibrations affects the wave function, and consequently also the magnitude of the interaction of electron and nuclear spins. The relaxation time equals

$$T_x = \frac{h^2 v^5 \rho}{8\pi^2 \nu_0^2 k T \alpha^2 I A^2}\,, \tag{6.29}$$

where ν_0 is the resonance frequency, A is the hyperfine structure constant, and α is a numerical factor of the order 10–100.

Table 6.1 gives values of T_x for different impurities in silicon, calculated under the assumption that $\alpha = 50$, $\nu_0 = 9 \cdot 10^9$cps, and $T = 1.2$°K.

2. Modulation of the hyperfine interaction of bound electrons with the Si^{29} nuclei. Let T_{Si} denote the relaxation time due to this mechanism. Calculation shows (see Table 6.1) that $T_{Si} / T_x \gg 1$ in all cases except lithium. Consequently, the mechanism under consideration may be important only for lithium-doped silicon.

3. Modulation of the spin-orbit interaction of the electrons. This mechanism, which is very important for conduction electrons, has little effect in our case, if one-phonon processes are taken into account. Raman phonon scattering processes give for the relaxation time

$$\mathrm{T}_{LS} \sim 10^{15} T^{-13}. \tag{6.30}$$

This shows that the above mechanism must play a leading role above liquid hydrogen temperature.

4. Modulation of exchange interactions between neighboring atoms of the impurity. At the donor concentrations employed, this mechanism is completely ineffective.

To explain the dependence of the relaxation processes on impurity concentration, the following mechanisms, based on the following interactions of bound electrons with conduction band electrons, were considered:

1) Coulomb interactions; reorientation of the spin is possible, if the spin-orbit coupling of the electron in the donor state is taken into account;

2) interaction of the spins of bound electrons with the magnetic field of currents produced by conduction electrons;

3) magnetic dipole-dipole interactions;

4) exchange interactions.

According to the calculations, the exchange interaction is the most effective mechanism, since, after exchange, the spins of the bound electrons arrive in the conduction band and are subjected to the strong action of lattice vibrations. Even this mechanism, however, does not successfully explain the experimental data. It may be that none of the mechanisms considered here is stronger than the spin-lattice interaction.

6.5. Color Centers in Ionic Crystals

It is well known that crystals of alkali metal halides become strongly colored if their stoichiometric composition is disrupted by any means and this leads to an excess of metallic atoms. It has been established that the cause of the discoloration is the creation of color centers. Various methods of producing colored crystals exist such as irradiation by x rays and γ rays; bomdardment by α and β particles, neutrons or protons; passage of current through a crystal placed between metallic electrodes; heating of the crystal in alkali metal vapors, etc. We note that the color centers arise not only in alkali halide salts, but also in other dielectric and semiconducting crystals. A large number of papers have been devoted to the experimental and theoretical study of different types of color centers (see, for instance, the review [48]).

In most cases color centers are also unpaired electrons, which situation enables us to study their properties by magnetic methods, in particular, by means of paramagnetic resonance.

The most extensively studied of the various types of color centers are F centers having a characteristic light absorption band. It may be regarded as proven that any F center in an alkali halide crystal is an electron trapped near a vacancy formed when a negative ion is displaced from a crystal lattice site (Figure 6.4). Thus there is a qualitative similarity between a hydrogen atom and an F center, since the anion vacancy may be identified with a positive charge.

Paramagnetic resonance from F centers was first observed by Hutchison [49], who used for this purpose LiF crystals irradiated for 24 hours in a flux of 10^{12} neutrons/sec·cm^2. The measurements were conducted at the frequency 9350 Mc, and one absorption peak was detected with a position corresponding to $g = 2.00$ and a width of approximately 160 gauss. When the colored crystals were bleached by heating at 500° C, the paramagnetic resonance absorption disappeared. Later the range of the substances investigated was appreciably broadened. A review of the principal experimental results is given in Table 6.2.

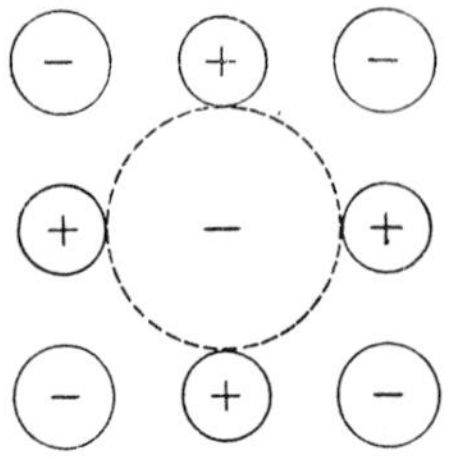

Fig. 6.4. The F center here is an electron trapped in an alkali halide crystal near a vacancy formed on removal of a negative ion from the crystal lattice site.

It is apparent from the table that the values of the spectroscopic splitting factor are very close to the g factor of a free electron, which indicates the unimportant role of orbital magnetism. Experiments show that the resonance line has a Gaussian shape and that its width in alkali halide crystals is independent of the F center concentration. From this it may be concluded that the dipole-dipole interactions of electron spins of F centers do not play a prominent role in the broadening of the absorption line. We reach this conclusion on the basis of a simple calculation, which shows that for the experimentally studied concentrations of F centers the width should not exceed 0.1 gauss. It is apparent from Table 6.2 that the experimental values for the line width of alkali halide crystals are 2-3 orders of magnitude larger.

Kip, Kittel et al. [53], hypothesized that the broadening of F-center resonance lines takes place because of the hyperfine interactions between the electrons localized near the vacant lattice site and the nuclei of adjacent atoms. This hypothesis was proved conclusively. Measurements of paramagnetic resonance in KCl crystals [53] containing both a natural mixture of potassium isotopes and a mixture greatly enriched with the isotope K^{41} showed that the widths of the resonance lines in both cases are entirely different, the ratio of these widths corresponding exactly to the magnitude of the magnetic moments of the K^{39} and K^{41} nuclei.

Portis [58] used the saturation method to measure the longitudinal relaxation time for F centers in a KCl crystal at room temperature and obtained $T_1 = 2.5 \cdot 10^{-5}$ sec. These experiments showed that the broadening is of an inhomogeneous character, as would be the expected result of hyperfine interactions (see Sec. 5.8). As yet, neither theoretical nor experimental studies have been made on the subjects of the nature of spin-lattice relaxation of colored crystals, on the dependence of T_1 on temperature, on the strength of the static magnetic field, etc.

Table 6.2

Substance	No. of F centers per cm^3	Method of coloration	g factor	Line width in gauss	Reference
LiF	10^{16}—10^{17}	Flux of neutrons, protons, X rays	2.008±0.001	77—160	[49, 54, 55, 60, 79, 108]
NaCl	$5 \cdot 10^{16}$ — 10^{18}		1.987	162	[53]
NaF			2.0021±0.0001		[55]
KBr	10^{19}—10^{20}	γ rays, electrolytic	1.980	146	[50, 51, 52, 53]
KCl	$5 \cdot 10^{16}$—$5 \cdot 10^{18}$	X rays	1.995±1	54	[51, 52, 53, 59]
$K^{41}Cl$	$5 \cdot 10^{16}$	"	1.995±1	36	[53]
KI	—	—	1.971±0.001	200	[109]
MgO	10^{18}—10^{19}	Flux of neutrons heated in vapors	2.0028±0.0001	0.7—0.9	[56]
$NaNO_3$			2.000±0.003		[57]

Lord [55] succeeded in determining the hyperfine structure of resonance lines from F centers in LiF and NaF crystals. A large number of components was observed. They are due to the interaction between the spin of the F electron and the nuclei of the six adjacent atoms of alkali metal; the interactions with the next layer of fluorine atomic nuclei give an unresolved spectrum and determine the width of the resonance line. The experiments determine the hyperfine interaction constant A and the values of $|\psi|^2$ at the nuclei of alkali metal and fluorine atoms [see Eq. (6.27)]. The corresponding data are given in Table 6.3 (the constants A_1 and A_2 are expressed in gauss).

Table 6.3

Substance	A_1 (alkali metal)	$\left\|\psi\begin{pmatrix}\text{alkali}\\ \text{metal}\end{pmatrix}\right\|^2$, cm^{-3}	$A_2(F)$	$\|\psi(F)\|^2$, cm^{-3}
LiF	14.1 ± 0.1	$1.53 \cdot 10^{23}$	4.6 ± 0.5	$0.21 \cdot 10^{23}$
NaF	37.8 ± 0.3	$6.05 \cdot 10^{23}$	8.6 ± 0.1	$0.39 \cdot 10^{23}$

Feher [59] used the double resonance technique (see Sec. 8.2) to exhibit the hyperfine structure of the paramagnetic resonance line in a colored crystal of KCl. The measurements were conducted in samples containing $2 \cdot 10^{17}$ centers per cm^3 at the temperature of 1.2°K; an electron resonance absorption line was observed at the frequency $\nu \approx 9000$ Mc and had a width of about 150 Mc; the nuclear resonance frequency changed from 10 to 100 Mc; the width of the nuclear resonance was about 20,000 cps. Since a nuclear resonance line is about 7500 times narrower than an electronic line, it is natural that a nuclear resonance, in spite of the relatively small intensity of its absorption line, should noticeably affect the shape of the electron resonance line. The results obtained in this manner may be explained with the aid of the spin Hamiltonian

$$\hat{\mathscr{H}} = a(\hat{I}\hat{S}) + b(3\hat{I}_z\hat{S}_z - \hat{I}\hat{S}) + Q'[\hat{I}_z^2 - \frac{1}{3}I(I+1)], \qquad (6.31)$$

from which it follows that the resonance frequencies due to nuclear transitions are equal to:

$$h\nu = \pm q_N\beta_N H_0 + \frac{1}{2}[a + b(3\cos^2\vartheta - 1)] + + Q'\left(3\cos^2\vartheta - 1\right)\left(m - \frac{1}{2}\right), \qquad (6.32)$$

where θ is the angle between the field H_0 and the axis of symmetry. From the experimental data on the nuclear resonance frequencies, and with the use of this formula, for K^{39} we obtain $(a/h) = 2.16$ Mc,

$(b/h) = 0.95$ Mc, and $(Q'/h) = 0.20$ Mc; while for Cl^{35} we have $(a/h) = 7.0$ Mc and $(b/c) = 0.5$ Mc. The magnitude of a for K^{39} is in good agreement with the value obtained previously from the width of the resonance line with unresolved hyperfine structure. Lord [60] applied the double resonance technique of Feher to study F centers in LiF crystals. He succeeded in improving the previous results, referring to the hyperfine interaction between an F electron and a nucleus of the second coordination sphere.

From the foregoing it is clear that there is definite interest in paramagnetic resonance measurements in crystals containing only atoms whose nuclear spins equal zero. Wertz and his collaborators [56] approach the solution of this problem by performing paramagnetic resonance experiments on F centers in MgO crystals. It is true that these crystals cannot be classified as ionic, but we shall so consider them in this paragraph, because the properties of interest to us do not depend on the character of the chemical bonding.

Two methods have been employed to color MgO single crystals: irradiation by a flux intensity of $(1\text{-}3) \cdot 10^{19}$ neutrons/cm^2 (5-7 neutrons form one center), heating in Mg vapors at 1500°C, then rapid cooling and irradiation by x rays.

In magnesium oxide only the odd isotope Mg^{25}, which comprises 10.11% of natural magnesium, has a nonzero nuclear spin. Hence, 53% of the octahedra of magnesium isotopes surrounding the vacancy contain only the isotopes Mg^{24} and Mg^{26}, 36% of the octahedra are composed of only one atom Mg^{25}, and 10% contain two Mg^{25} atoms each. One expects that the magnetic resonance spectrum will consist of a narrow intense central line plus a broad, weak line, containing six hyperfine components $[I(Mg^{25}) = 5/2]$ and in addition a family of still weaker lines. The central line actually turns out to be very narrow, of width approximately 0.7 gauss; its position corresponds to a g factor which agrees to within 0.0001 with the value for a free electron. The hyperfine structure is of a rather complex character, which is related to the anisotropy of the electron-nuclear coupling constant.

From the magnitude of the isotropic part of the hyperfine structure one may deduce by means of (6.27) that $|\psi(\text{Mg})|^2 = 0.276 \cdot 10^{24}$ cm^{-3}, whereas a doubly charged free magnesium ion has $|\psi(Mg^{2+})|^2 = 17.1 \cdot 10^{24}$ cm^{-3}. It is of interest to compare these values with the corresponding values for potassium in a KCl crystal; for an F center $|\psi(\text{K})|^2 = 0.70 \cdot 10^{24}$, while for a free potassium ion $|\psi(K^+)|^2 = 7.5 \cdot 10^{24}$ cm^{-3}. It is apparent from these data that in a MgO crystal the electron is localized inside the vacancy to a substantially greater extent than in KCl, which evidently is explained by the relatively large Madelung energy in divalent crystals.

Paramagnetic resonance from F centers may be used for several practical purposes. Measurements of the relative intensity of a paramagnetic absorption line reveal the possibility of determining the number of F centers to an accuracy which exceeds the accuracy of all other methods by 1-2 orders of magnitude. Gordy [61] points out that paramagnetic resonance absorption from F centers may be used to construct an instrument for measuring the flux intensity of neutrons and x rays.

We now consider the theory of paramagnetic resonance of F centers. In the general theory of F centers two models are adopted, the continuum [62] and the molecular orbital [63]. In [59, 64] it is shown that even elementary calculations on the basis of the molecular orbital model make it possible to obtain the correct order of magnitude of the g shift and the width of a resonance line. According to the molecular orbital model an F-center electron is a valence electron, shared with each of six atoms of the immediate surrounding of the vacancy. In other words the F-electron wave function is to a first approximation a linear combination of s functions, which refer to the metallic atoms situated around the vacancy:

$$\Psi = \frac{1}{\sqrt{6}} \sum_{i=1}^{6} \psi_i. \tag{6.33}$$

It is assumed here that the ψ functions of different atoms do not overlap. Since a negative vacancy is equivalent to a positive charge, it is not necessary to take into account the polarization of the atoms of a metal due to this charge. A perturbation theory calculation shows that p functions should be added to the valence electron s function, so that for one of the atoms we will have

$$\psi_1 = C\left[\psi_s - \frac{\varepsilon}{\sqrt{2}}(\psi_p^1 - \psi_p^{-1})\right], \tag{6.34}$$

where ϵ is a factor equal to 1, and C is a normalization constant. The wave functions of other atoms are constructed in an analogous manner. Calculations with the aid of hydrogenic functions give $\epsilon = 0.9$. In the next approximation it is necessary to take into account the spin-orbit coupling $\lambda \hat{L}S$, which gives the following ψ function:

$$\psi_1 = C\left[\psi_s - \frac{\varepsilon}{\sqrt{2}}\left(1 + \frac{\lambda}{2\Delta}\right)\psi_p^1 + \frac{\varepsilon}{\sqrt{2}}\left(1 - \frac{\lambda}{2\Delta}\right)\psi_p^{-1}\right]. \tag{6.35}$$

Here Δ is the energy spacing between the s and p levels. A calculation by means of this function gives the following expression for the g shift [64]:

$$\Delta g = -\frac{4}{3}\frac{\lambda}{\Delta}\frac{\varepsilon^2}{1+\varepsilon^2}. \tag{6.36}$$

If we use the well-known values for potassium $\Delta = 13200\ \text{cm}^{-1}$, $\lambda = 38\ \text{cm}^{-1}$, we obtain $\Delta g = -1.7 \cdot 10^{-3}$, which agrees in order of magnitude with the experimental value $\Delta g = -0.007 \pm 0.001$.

To calculate the broadening of the resonance line caused by hyperfine interactions between the F electron and the nuclei of the atoms surrounding the vacancy [53], we use the Hamiltonian

$$\mathscr{H}' = \sum_i A_i \hat{S}\hat{I}_i, \tag{6.37}$$

where

$$A_i = -\frac{16\pi}{3} \frac{\beta\mu_i}{I_i} |\psi(i)|^2. \tag{6.38}$$

Here μ_i is the magnetic moment of the nucleus of the i-th atom, I_i is the spin of this nucleus, and $\psi(i)$ is the value of the normalized electron wave function at the site of the i-th nucleus. By means of Hamiltonian (6.37) one may easily calculate the second moment of the paramagnetic resonance absorption line; it equals

$$M_2 = \frac{1}{3} \sum_i A_i^2 I_i (I_i + 1). \tag{6.39}$$

It can be shown that the absorption line is nearly Gaussian in shape, and hence the line width equals $\Delta\nu = 2.36\sqrt{M_2}$. The hyperfine splitting due to the presence of the ψ_p function in the expression (6.35) will be anisotropic. If we take into account only the main isotropic part of the hyperfine structure, it is easy to obtain from (6.35), (6.38) and (6.39) that

$$\Delta\nu = \frac{2.36}{\sqrt{18}} \frac{\sqrt{I(I+1)}}{1+\varepsilon^2} A. \tag{6.40}$$

Here A is the constant of the hyperfine interaction between the electron and the nucleus of the metal closest to the vacancy, and I is the spin of this nucleus. For potassium $I = 3/2$, $A = 0.0077\ \text{cm}^{-1}$ and the line width therefore equals 50 gauss, which is in excellent agreement with the experimental value 54 ± 2 gauss.

The authors of [53] also made a calculation of the line width, using the continuum model. According to this model an F center is an electron moving in a spherically symmetric potential field, whose center coincides with the vacancy, the electron wave function embracing a large number of atoms. The calculated width of the resonance line was found to be several orders of magnitude smaller than the experimental value. The continuum model was therefore judged to be unsatisfactory. The correctness of this conclusion was disputed by a number of authors [65, 66, 67]. Deygen [67] called attention to the following facts. The calculations of Kip, Kittel et al. use Eq. (6.38), in which $\psi(i)$ is the value of the wave function given by the continuum model at the point where the nucleus i is located. Meanwhile formula (6.38), derived by Fermi, is correct only when the center of symmetry of the wave function coincides with the nucleus, which is certainly not the case for an F center, because the nuclei of the ions are displaced relative to the center of symmetry of the wave function by a value equal to the lattice constant. The subject of hyperfine interaction between an electron and a nucleus, displaced relative to the center of symmetry of the wave function, requires special treatment. Deygen gives a solution to this problem, using the following expression for the F center wave function [69]:

$$\varphi(r) = \alpha^{\frac{3}{2}} (1 + \alpha r) e^{-\frac{\alpha r}{\sqrt{7\pi}}}. \tag{6.41}$$

Assuming that the length $(1/\alpha)$ does not greatly exceed the lattice constant, and therefore limiting himself to a consideration of a hyperfine interaction with nuclei of the first coordination sphere, Deygen obtained a value of the order 1-2 gauss for the width of the resonance line in KCl. In order to improve this result, Deygen replaced the smoothed-out wave function (6.41) by the so-called detailed wave function, which has the form

$$\psi(r) = \Omega^{\frac{1}{2}} \varphi u. \tag{6.42}$$

Here Ω is the volume of the unit cell of the crystal, and u is the normalized Bloch electron wave function at the bottom of the conduction band, which, as we know, is a linear combination of atomic wave functions in the tight binding approximation. The line width, calculated by means of the detailed function, was found to equal 15 gauss, which rather closely approximates the experimental value.

To determine whether relativistic corrections influence the line width when calculating hyperfine structure, the conventional Pauli equation of electron motion was replaced by Darwin's relativistic approximation [70], and the corrections were found to be insignificant. Zevin [71], by developing the theory proposed by Deygen, obtained a general expression for the spin Hamiltonian that describes the interaction between the F center electron and the nuclei of the atom adjacent to the vacancy. Using this spin Hamiltonian, Shul'man [72] calculated the broadening caused by the second coordination sphere consisting of halide atoms. In a KCl crystal 19% of the line width is contributed by the chlorine atoms.

Gourary and Adrian [73] employed a wave function obtained by a simplified Hartree method for the calculation of the hyperfine structure in the paramagnetic resonance from F centers. The lattice ions were considered to be point charges. Lattice distortion near the vacancy was taken into account. The theoretical hyperfine splitting was in good agreement with the experimental results for LiF.

The method of Gourary and Adrian was used in calculations of the isotropic and anisotropic structure of the KCl spectrum [74], and the theoretical results are in good agreement with the experimental data of Feher [59]. Adrian [75] has indicated the possibility of finding a simple relation between the g shift and the anisotropic hyperfine structure, as both of these quantities are determined by the mean value of $1/r^3$. Thus, for KCl, on the basis of the experimental value of the hyperfine structure, the anisotropic theory gives $\Delta g = -0.0053$ while experiment gives $\Delta g = -0.007$. Good agreement with the experimental results of Feher was also obtained by Blumberg and Das [76], who in their calculations of hyperfine structure use the g-factor shift and the wave function, obtained under the assumptions that the vacancy is replaced by a potential well and the lattice by a system of appropriate point charges.

In the exposition of the theory of paramagnetic resonance of F centers we use the DeBoer model [62], according to which the F center is an electron localized near a vacant lattice site. It is generally acknowledged that this type of center is formed in alkali halide crystals. In silver halide crystals one may suppose that F centers are of the Gil'sh and Poloya types [62], i.e., are metallic atoms introduced at interstitial sites of the lattice. Glinchuk and Deigen [77] have performed calculations of the hyperfine structure of the energy levels of such a type of F center with an NaCl crystal as an example. Using wave functions of both the continuum and the molecular orbital model, they obtained a spin Hamiltonian, by means of which calculations were made of the paramagnetic resonance structure, spectrum, line shape and the line width. The results were found to be qualitatively different from those obtained previously for the DeBoer model. Thus, the study of paramagnetic resonance has opened up the possibility of making a choice between the two existing models of F centers, and this is particularly valuable since no other effective methods for solving this problem have been proposed up to the present time.

Lord et al. [78] found direct proof of the existence of paramagnetic resonance absorption in M centers (combination of an F center with a pair of vacant sites). It was established that the second moment of the resonance line increases noticeably when the LiF crystal is irradiated by X rays, and we discover by optical methods a rise in the number of M centers in comparison with the number of F centers.

The paramagnetic resonance from V centers has been investigated in greater detail [79, 84]. In the alkali halide crystals that were studied, these centers were created by X-ray irradiation at liquid nitrogen temperatures. Castner, Kanzig and Woodruff [82, 83], who carried out the most complete studies of this subject, interpret their experimental results by means of the following model of a V center: 1) under the influence of X rays an electron is removed from the halogen ion, and the positive electronic hole formed in this manner is shared with the two neighboring ions, oriented along the [110] axis of the crystal; 2) the molecular ion X_2^- (X denotes halogen) arising in this manner is related neither to the holes nor to the distortions of the crystal lattice.

Paramagnetic resonance has been studied in LiF, KCl, KBr, and NaCl crystals. The resonance lines have hyperfine structure due to the interaction between the electron hole and the nuclei of both atoms forming the molecular ion X_2^-. The number and intensity of the hyperfine components in LiF crystals are in conformity with the value of the nuclear spin of fluorine $I = 1/2$, if we take into account the selection rule for singlet and triplet spin states; the spectra of the remaining crystals that were studied consist of exactly six approximately equispaced components with the intensity ratios 1:2:3:4:3:2:1, which corresponds to the nuclear spin of the Cl or Br atom, which is equal to $I = 3/2$. To interpret the paramagnetic resonance spectrum on the basis of the model of the molecular ion X_2^-, a spin Hamiltonian of the type (6.31) may be used, if we take the [110] axis of the crystal as the Z axis. The principal values of the components of the g tensor are given in Table 6.4, in which the width of the absorption line is also given.

Table 6.4

Substance	g_x	g_y	g_z	Maximum error	Width, gauss
LiF	2.0227	2.0234	2.0031	±0.0010	12.3±0.3
KCl	2.0428	2.0447	2.0010	±0.0001	1.34±0.03
NaCl	2.0489	2.0425	2.0010	±0.0001	4.5±0.1
KBr	2.179	2.175	1.980	±0.0001	2.8±0.1

The basic cause of broadening of the resonance line is hyperfine interaction between the electronic hole and the nuclei surrounding the V center. The line shape is close to Gaussian.

Calculations have been made of the g factor for Cl_2^- by the molecular orbital method [85], which gave a value close to the experimental value.

In a KCl crystal Kanzig and Woodruff [86] observed paramagnetic resonance of H centers, having a structure similar to the V centers, but exhibiting greater complexity. The latter is explained by the fact that in the case of H centers the electronic holes are shared among four chlorine ions located along a single straight line.

Kawamura and Ishiwatari [87] observed paramagnetic resonance in Z_1 centers in KCl crystals. The Z_1 centers are formed in alkali halide crystals in which divalent metals are introduced. A singly ionized atom of a divalent metal which occupies the site of the alkali metal ion may serve as the model of the Z_1 center. The experiments were conducted with crystals doped with Ca and Sr atoms to a concentration of approximately 10^{17} cm^{-3}. Since the nuclear spin of both potassium and strontium equals zero, a profound analogy exists between paramagnetic resonance in a Z_1 and an F center. The essential difference lies in the broadening of the Z_1-center resonance line, which occurs primarily due to the hyperfine interaction with nuclei of the anions, whereas in F centers the nuclear spins of the cations play a leading role. Measurements showed that the absorption line has a Gaussian shape of width $\Delta H = 79$ gauss, $g = 1.999$.

6.6. Irradiated Crystals with Covalent Bonding

Paramagnetic resonance may serve as an effective method of investigating defects in crystals. Such a possibility is connected first with the fact that the formation of many types of defects in diamagnetic crystals is accompanied by the formation of paramagnetic centers. Second, in paramagnetic crystals dislocation type effects alter the internal crystalline fields and thereby cause a displacement of the paramagnetic resonance line and a change in the spin-lattice interaction. In the last two sections we have considered paramagnetic resonance due to occlusion type lattice defects, electrons and holes. In this section we shall discuss initially the effect in diamonds irradiated by neutrons and then we shall consider other examples.

Griffiths, Owen and Ward [88] made measurements of irradiated diamond and quartz at the frequencies $\nu = 9000$ and 25,000 Mc over the temperature range 20–280°K. The existence of two types of resonance lines in diamond has been established:

a) An isotropic line with a spectroscopic splitting factor $g = 2.0028 \pm 0.0006$. As the duration of the irradiation increases, the intensity and line width increase. With heating at 1000°C the effect disappears. Changes in the color of the crystal occur in a similar manner. After prolonged neutron irradiation the line width reaches 100 gauss at the temperature 290°K; as the temperature is reduced to 90°K the width decreases by a factor of two.

b) A set of 12 weak anisotropic lines, symmetrically located relative to the central peak. The width of each of these lines is temperature independent and equals approximately 5 gauss. In this case the effect does not decrease with heating up to 1000°C. The paramagnetic absorption spectra may be described by means of the spin Hamiltonian $\hat{\mathscr{H}} = \beta g \boldsymbol{H}_0 \hat{\boldsymbol{S}} + D\hat{S}_z^2$, if we assume the existence of the paramagnetic centers with spin $S = 1$. It must be assumed that the axis of the crystalline field is parallel to one of the edges of the tetrahedron formed by the carbon atoms. Thus, there exist six different orientations of paramagnetic centers, each of which has two absorption lines corresponding to the transitions $-1 \rightarrow 0$ and $0 \rightarrow 1$. The spin Hamiltonian constants have the following values: $D = 0.010$ cm^{-1}, the average value of the g factor is $\bar{g} = 2.0027 \pm 0.0005$, $g_\perp / g_\parallel = 1.00035 \pm 0.00005$.

The central isotropic line evidently has the following nature [89]. Let us consider an isolated vacancy, formed in the crystalline lattice after removal of one of the carbon atoms. Since diamond is not an ionic crystal, there is no basis for expecting the vacancy to attract an electron or to be capable of removing one; rather it must be regarded as an electrically neutral, stable formation. The vacancy is surrounded by four carbon atoms, each of which has one unsaturated covalent bond and therefore one unpaired electron. It may be shown that Hund's rule is applicable to this four-electron system, and accordingly in the ground state all of the electron spins are parallel to one another and therefore the spin of the entire system is $S = 2$. In this state the orbital wave function is nondegenerate, and consequently, to a first approximation, the paramagnetism is purely spin in nature.

In a free carbon atom the spin-orbit coupling is very weak. As a result of the high symmetry of the crystalline field, the splitting of the spin levels resulting from spin-orbit interaction will differ from zero only in fourth-order perturbation theory. Hence, it may be concluded that this splitting should be negligibly small. An estimate shows that it is of the order 10^{-5} cm^{-1}. For this reason there must also be a very small discrepancy between the g factor and its value for a free electron.

It is difficult to give a theoretical interpretation of all the features of anisotropic paramagnetic resonance spectrum. Evidently it is associated with carbon atoms which are found at the interstitial sites of the crystalline lattice.

We shall proceed to a consideration of paramagnetic resonance in the color centers that appear in quartz on X-ray irradiation and disappear upon heating to 350°C. Griffiths, Owen and Ward [88] first observed this effect in quartz and established that the paramagnetic absorption is proportional to the optical absorption. The measurements of the paramagnetic resonance spectrum were performed at 90 and 20°K; at higher temperatures the lines broaden greatly. The existence of six types of paramagnetic centers was established; these were distinguished by the orientation of the magnetic axes. Complex hyperfine structure of the line was also observed at 20°K. The spectrum may be described by means of a spin Hamiltonian with the following values of the constants: $S = 1/2$, $I = 5/2$, $g_\parallel = 2.06$ ± 0.005, $g_\perp = 2.00 \pm 0.005$, $A = 4.8 \cdot 10^{-4}$ cm^{-1}, $B = 5.6 \cdot 10^{-4}$ cm^{-1}, $P = -0.4 \cdot 10^{-4}$ cm^{-1}. The axes of symmetry of the g tensors of different types of paramagnetic centers are approximately parallel to the lines which join pairs of silicon atoms inside the unit cell. The principal axes of the g tensor and the hyperfine structure tensor do not coincide. The axes of symmetry of the hyperfine structure tensor are parallel to the Si-O bond.

All of these experimental facts may be explained as follows [82]. Among the various impurities in quartz is aluminum, whose atoms displace a small fraction of the silicon atoms. Before irradiation of the quartz, the aluminum atoms are Al^- ions, which have the same number of electrons as the silicon atoms, so that there is no coloration in the crystal and no paramagnetic centers exist. The negative charged Al^- ions are compensated by the positive ions H^+, Li^+ and Na^+, located at the interstitial positions of the crystal lattice. As a result of x-ray irradiation, ionization of the atom occurs and uncompensated electron spins appear. Calculations carried out by the electron orbital method show [90] that the electronic structure of the paramagnetism carriers mainly has the form illustrated in Figure 6.5a. The nonzero spin belongs to a positive oxygen ion. This structure is partially mixed with another (Figure 6.5b), which contains neutral oxygen and aluminum atoms, the latter producing a hyperfine structure of the paramagnetic resonance line.

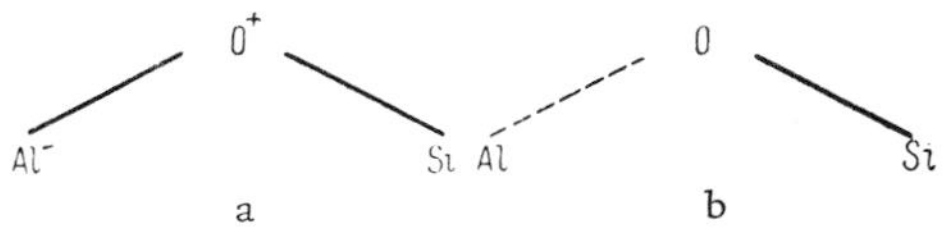

Fig. 6.5. Electronic structure of the paramagnetic species in irradiated quartz.

Paramagnetic resonance in quartz single crystals was also detected after irradiation by fast neutrons [91, 92, 85a]. The observations were made at room temperature. Apparently this effect is not associated with impurities and has an entirely different nature, which is evident from the absence of hyperfine structure of the absorption lines. Perhaps the resonance absorption, just as in diamond, is due to broken bonds which appear as a result of the formation of vacancies in the basic SiO_4 tetrahedron. A similar effect has been detected in silicon irradiated by neutrons at 4.2°K [93]. An explanation of this effect in irradiated quartz crystals must consider the fact that silicate glasses give a similar paramagnetic resonance spectrum [92, 94].

After γ irradiation of ice, a paramagnetic resonance was observed [95, 96] at temperatures 4-225°K. The hyperfine structure of the line is attributed to protons in ordinary ice and deuterons in D_2O. The nature of the paramagnetic species is still unexplained.

6.7. Metal-Ammonia Solutions. Paramagnetic Resonance from Polarons and Excitons

Alkali and alkaline earth metals are readily dissolved in ammonia. The solubilities of Na and K at the boiling point of ammonia

(-33.35°C) are about 5.4 and 4.9 moles/liter, respectively; they change slightly with temperature. The distinguishing property of these solutions is the high electrical conductivity, which, in order of magnitude, approaches the conductivity of metals. Measurements of the dependence of the static magnetic susceptibility on the concentration of the solutions have shown that at high concentrations the addition of the metal is not accompanied by an increase in susceptibility.

The first measurements of paramagnetic resonance in metal-ammonia solutions were conducted in the microwave region [97, 98, 99]. One exceptionally narrow absorption line was found whose width was no greater than 0.2 gauss. Later experiments were usually carried out at lower frequencies [100, 101, 9], which required the application of a static magnetic field of only a few gauss; thus, it was necessary to correct for the earth's magnetic field. The measurements were performed at temperatures from -80 to 20°C. For potassium solutions, the spectroscopic splitting factor equaled $g = 2.0012 \pm 0.0002$. For other metals it differed from this by less than 0.005. As we shall see, the g factor is close to (but substantially less than) the g factor of a free electron. Table 6.5 gives data for the widths of the resonance lines, from which it is apparent that the width decreases as the temperature increases and increases as the concentration rises. In addition to metal-ammonia solutions, studies have also been made of solutions of lithium in methylamine [99, 9] and in ethylenediamine [99]. Galkin et al. [102] observed paramagnetic resonance in solutions of NaCl in ammonia after passing a current through the solution. Apparently the current decomposes the NaCl, and thus an ordinary solution of Na is obtained.

Table 6.5

Substance	Width, gauss	Temperature, °C	Concentration, M	Reference
Li—NH_3	0.1	—72	0.2	[9]
Na—NH_3	0.13	—75	0.1	[9]
K—NH_3	0.1	—70	0.08	[9]
K—NH_3	0.05	—33.45	0.08	[100]
K—NH_3	0.027	20	0.08	[100]
K—NH_3	0.08	20	0.43	[100]
Rb—NH_3	0.16	—70	0.1	[9]
Cs—NH_3	0.4	—70	0.5	[9]
Ca—NH_3	0.14	—70	0.05	[9]
Li—CH_3NH_2	0.6	—70	0.1	[9]
Li—$NH_2CH_2NH_3$	0.6	20	0.1	[99]

Blume [103] measured the longitudinal (T_1) and transverse (T_2) relaxation times at the frequency 17.4 Mc by means of pulse techniques. The time T_2 was determined by a measurement of the duration of the drop in the free induction signal following a 90° pulse (see Sec. 8.4). It varied from 3.2 to 0.7 μsec, when the concentration of Na in NH_3 increases from 0.03 to 0.75 mole/liter. The time T_1 was measured in solutions with concentrations from 0.24 to 0.5 mole per liter. Within an accuracy of 10% it was found that $T_1 = T_2$.

Kaplan and Kittel [104] explained the experimental facts using the Ogg model [105], which is based on the following assumptions: 1) in solutions the atoms of alkali metals dissociate; 2) electrons which have been removed from the metallic atoms are localized in cavities formed in the liquid and have a size from 2 to 4 NH_3 molecules; 3) the wave function of the electrons associated with the cavity is a linear combination of hydrogenic wave functions referring to the protons of the NH_3 molecules that are located around the cavity; 4) the conduction bands lies 1 ev above the energy level of the bound state of the electron; 5) there exist cavities containing one electron each (e centers) and two electrons each (e_2 centers); the electron distribution over the e- and e_2 centers is determined by the conditions of equilibrium in regard to the reaction: $e + e \rightleftarrows e_2 + 0.2$ ev.

There is a great similarity between e centers and the F centers considered in Sec. 6.5. Kaplan and Kittel assume therefore that the broadening of the absorption lines in both cases is of the same nature; hyperfine interaction between the localized electron and the spins of the surrounding nuclei. An estimate of the width performed as in Sec. 6.5 by the molecular orbital method gives $\Delta\nu \approx 7g\beta/h$. There is an essential difference, however, between e and F centers, which we have neglected. The great mobility of the fluid may substantially reduce the width of the absorption line. The correlation time (see Sec. 5.6) may be estimated by means of the Debye expression for the rotational dipole relaxation:

$$\tau_c \approx \frac{3\eta V}{kT}, \tag{6.43}$$

where V is the volume of the molecule. Hence $\tau_c \approx 10^{-11}$ sec. We shall see that the correlation time is far less than the transverse relaxation time $\sim 1/\Delta\nu_0$ so that the motion of the molecules must greatly narrow the resonance line. The resulting width may be estimated from the formula $\Delta\nu \sim (\Delta\nu)^2 \tau_c$, which in our case gives $\Delta H \approx 0.01$ gauss. Such good agreement with the experimental data is accidental, if we recall how crude the theoretical estimate is.

At large concentrations of the solution the dipole-dipole interactions between the various trapped electrons may be expected to begin to play a role. The effect of dipole-dipole interactions on the resonance width may be estimated from Eq. (5.14). A numerical calculation shows that this broadening mechanism may become significant at concentrations greater than 0.1 mole/liter.

As we know, if $\tau_c \ll 1/\Delta\nu_0$, then $T_2 = T_1$, which as we have seen is confirmed by direct measurements. We note that both broadening mechanisms considered by us lead to a proportionality between the line width and the coefficient of viscosity. Experiment also supports this theoretical conclusion.

The Ogg model of e centers, which lies at the foundation of this theory of broadening of a paramagnetic resonance line, was subjected to seriou criticism by Deygen [106], who developed a theory of optical, magnetic and other properties of metal-ammonia solutions, by assuming that in the case of dislocations of metallic atoms in ammonia the electrons jump to polar states. According to Deygen, polarons and nonlocalized electron centers are the cause of the remarkable and peculiar features of solutions of metals in ammonia. Deygen and Pekar [107] show that, to a first approximation, hyperfine interaction does not change the polaron energy and, consequently, it may cause broadening of the paramagnetic absorption line. The exceptional narrowness of resonance lines in metal-ammonia solutions is considered as direct proof of the existence of polarons in these substances.

Deygen and Pekar also consider the subject of the possibility of creating such high concentrations of excitons that the paramagnetic resonance absorption of radio-frequency field energy by excitons could be observed. The steady-state concentration of excitons N obviously may be determined from the following formula:

$$N = \frac{\tau F \varkappa}{h\nu}, \tag{6.44}$$

where τ is the lifetime of an exciton, F is the flux of light energy across 1 cm² during 1 sec, $\varkappa$ is the exciton light-absorption coefficient in the crystal, and ν is the frequency of the absorbed light. If we take $\tau = 10^{-8}$ sec, $h\nu \approx 1$ ev, $\varkappa \approx 10^5$ cm^{-1}, and F ≈ 1 w/cm^2, we obtain $N \approx 10^{16}$ cm^{-3}. Thus, the discovery of paramagnetic resonance by means of modern techniques is quite practicable. In order to decrease the radiationless de-excitation of excitons it is desirable to choose impurity-free crystals and to use low temperatures. It should be kept in mind that just as in the case of polarons, no broadening of the paramagnetic absorption lines will exist because of the hyperfine interaction between an exciton and the spins of the surrounding nuclei.

Literature for Chapter VI

1. Griswold, T. W., A. F. Kip, C. Kittel. Phys. Rev. 88, 951, 1950.
2. Kip, A. F., T. W. Griswold, A. M. Portis. Phys. Rev. 92, 544, 1953.

3. Feher, G., T. W. Griswold. Phys. Rev. 93, 952, 1954.
4. Gutowsky, S., P. J. Frank. Phys. Rev. 94, 1067, 1954.
5. Schumacher, R. T., T. R. Carver, C. P. Slichter. Phys. Rev. 95, 1089, 1954.
6. Feher, G., A. F. Kip. Phys. Rev. 95, 1343, 1954.
7. Kip, A. F. Defects in Crystalline Solids, Bristol, 38, 1955.
8. Feher, G., A. F. Kip. Phys. Rev. 98, 337, 1955.
9. Levy, R. A. Phys. Rev. 102, 31, 1956.
10. Garif'yanov, N. S. Zh. Eksp. Teoret. Fiz. 32, 149, 1957.
11. Garif'yanov, N. S., M. A. Starikov. Zh Eksp. Teoret. Fiz. 35, 798, 1958.
12. Yafet, Y. Phys. Rev. 85, 478, 1952.
13. Bardeen, J. J. Chem. Phys. 6, 367, 1938.
14. Brooks, H. Phys. Rev. 94, 1411, 1954.
15. Argyres, P., A. Kahn. Phys. Rev. 98, 226, 1955.
16. Overhauser, A. W. Phys. Rev. 89, 689, 1953.
17. Korringa, J. Physica 16, 601, 1950.
18. Elliott, R. J. Phys. Rev. 96, 266, 1954.
19. Andreyev, V. V., V. I. Gerasimenko. Zh. Eksp. Teoret. Fiz. 35, 1209, 1958.
20. Al'tshuler, S. A. Zh. Eksp. Teoret. Fiz. 20, 1047, 1950.
21. Pines, D. Phys. Rev. 95, 1090, 1954.
22. Dyson, F. J. Phys. Rev. 98, 349, 1955.
23. Bloembergen, N. J. Appl. Phys. 23, 1379, 1952.
24. Silin, V. P. Zh. Eksp. Teoret. Fiz. 30, 421, 1956.
25. Azbel', M. Ya., V. I. Gerasimenko, I. M. Lifshits. Zh. Eksp. Teoret. Fiz. 31, 357, 1957; 32, 212, 1957; Azbel', M. Ya. Zh. Eksp. Teoret. Fiz. 32, 1259, 1957.
26. Azbel', M. Ya., I. M. Lifshits. Zh. Eksp. Teoret. Fiz. 33, 792, 1957.
27. Owen, J., M. Browne, W. D. Knight, C. Kittel. Phys. Rev. 102, 1501, 1956.
28. Owen, J., M. Browne, A. F. Kip. J. Phys. Chem. Solids 2, 85, 1957.
29. Knight, W. D. Phys. Rev. 76, 1259, 1949.
30. Kip, A. F. Rev. Mod. Phys. 25, 229, 1953; Kip, A. F., C. Kittel, A. M. Portis, R. Barton, F. H. Spedding. Phys. Rev. 89, 518, 1953.
31. Salikhov, S. G. Zh. Eksp. Teoret. Fiz. 26, 447, 1954.
32. Al'tshuler, S. A. Zh. Eksp. Teoret. Fiz. 26, 439, 1954.
33. Al'tshuler, S. A. Zh. Eksp. Teoret. Fiz. 28, 49, 1955.
34. Portis, A. M., A. F. Kip, C. Kittel, W. H. Brattain. Phys. Rev. 90, 988, 1953.
35. Willenbrock, F. K., N. Bloembergen. Phys. Rev. 91, 1281, 1953.
36. Fletcher, R. C., W. A. Yager, G. L. Pearson, A. N. Holden, W. T. Read, F. R. Merritt. Phys. Rev. 94, 1392, 1954.

37. Fletcher, R. C., W. A. Yager, G. L. Pearson, F. R. Merritt. Phys. Rev. 95, 844, 1954.
38. Pearson, G. L., J. Bardeen. Phys. Rev. 75, 865, 1949.
39. Honig, A., A. F. Kip. Phys. Rev. 95, 1686, 1954.
40. Lüttinger, J. M., W. Kohn. Phys. Rev. 96, 802, 1954; 97, 883, 1955.
41. Slichter, C. P. Phys. Rev. 99, 479, 1955.
42. Feher, G., R. C. Fletcher, E. A. Gere. Phys. Rev. 100, 1784, 1955.
43. Honig, A., J. Combrisson. Phys. Rev. 102, 917, 1956.
44. Abragam, A., J. Combrisson. Compt. Rend. 243, 576, 1956.
45. Feher, G., R. C. Fletcher. Bull. Am. Phys. Soc., ser. II, 1, 125, 1956.
46. Pines, D., J. Bardeen, C. P. Slichter. Phys. Rev. 106, 489, 1957.
47. Abrahams, E. Phys. Rev. 107, 491, 1957.
48. Seitz, F. Rev. Mod. Phys. 18, 284, 1946; 26, 7, 1954.
49. Hutchison, C. A. Jr. Phys. Rev. 75, 1769, 1949.
50. Tinkham, M., A. F. Kip. Phys. Rev. 83, 657, 1951.
51. Schneider, E. E., T. S. England. Physica 17, 221, 1951.
52. Hutchison, C. A. Jr., G. A. Noble. Phys. Rev. 87, 1125, 1952.
53. Kip, A. F., C. Kittel, R. A. Levy, A. M. Portis. Phys. Rev. 91, 1066, 1953.
54. Jen, C. K., N. W. Lord. Phys. Rev. 96, 1150, 1954.
55. Lord, N. W. Phys. Rev. 105, 756, 1957.
56. Wertz, J. E., R. A. Weeks, P. Auzins, R. H. Silber. Phys. Rev. 107, 1535, 1957.
57. Ard, W. B. Jr. J. Chem. Phys. 23, 1967, 1955.
58. Portis, A. M. Phys. Rev. 91, 1071, 1953; 100, 1219, 1955; Portis, A. M., D. Shaltiel. Phys. Rev. 98, 264, 1955.
59. Feher, G. Phys. Rev. 105, 1122, 1957.
60. Lord, N. W. Phys. Rev. Letters 1, 170, 1958.
61. Gordy, W., W. Smith, R. Trambarulo. Microwave Spectroscopy, Gostekhizdat, Moscow, p. 248, 1955.
62. Pekar, S. I. Studies of the Electronic Theory of Crystals, Gostekhizdat, Moscow-Leningrad, 1951.
63. Muto, T. Progr. Theor. Phys. 4, 243, 1949; Ynui, T., I. Uemura. Progr. Theor. Phys. 5, 252, 395, 1950.
64. Kahn, A. H., C. Kittel. Phys. Rev. 89, 315, 1953.
65. Dexter, D. L. Phys. Rev. 93, 244, 1954.
66. Krumhansl, J. A. Phys. Rev. 93, 245, 1954.
67. Deygen, M. F. Zh. Eksp. Teoret. Fiz. 33, 773, 1957.
68. Fermi, E. Z. Phys. 60, 320, 1930.
69. Pekar, S. I. Zh. Eksp. Teoret. Fiz. 17, 868, 1947; Pekar, S. I., M. F. Deygen. Zh. Eksp. Teoret. Fiz. 18, 48, 1948.
70. Deygen, M. F., L. A. Shul'man. Optika i Spektroskopiya 3, 21, 1957.
71. Zevin, V. Ya. Optika i Spektroskopiya 3, 660, 1957.

72. Shul'man, L. A. Optika i Spektroskopiya 3, 684, 1957.
73. Gourary, B. S., F. J. Adrian. Phys. Rev. 105, 1180, 1957.
74. Adrian, F. J. Phys. Rev. 106, 1356, 1957.
75. Adrian, F. J. Phys. Rev. 107, 488, 1957.
76. Blumberg, W. E., T. R. Das. Phys. Rev. 110, 647, 1958.
77. Glinchuk, M. D., M. F. Deygen. Zh. Tekh. Fiz. 28, 1981, 1958.
78. Lord, N. W. Phys. Rev. 106, 1100, 1957.
79. Schneider, E. E. Phys. Rev. 93, 919, 1954.
80. Känzig, W. Phys. Rev. 99, 1890, 1955.
81. Cohen, M. H. Phys. Rev. 101, 1432, 1956.
82. Castner, T. G., W. Känzig. J. Phys. Chem. Solids 3, 178, 1957.
83. Woodruff, T. O., W. Känzig. Rept. General Electr. Res. Lab. 39, No. 1827, 1957.
84. Suffczynski, M. Postepy fiz. 9, 27, 1958.
85. Inui, T., S. Harasawa, Y. Obata. J. Phys. Soc. Japan 11,612,1956.
86. Känzig, W., T. O. Woodruff. Phys. Rev. 109, 220, 1958.
87. Kawamura, H., O. Ishiwatari. J. Phys. Soc. Japan 13, 574, 1958.
88. Griffiths, J. H. E., J. Owen, I. M. Ward. Nature 173, 439, 1954; Defects in Crystalline Solids 9, Bristol, 81, 1954.
89. O'Brien, M. C. M., M. H. L. Pryce. Defects in Crystalline Solids, Bristol, 88, 1954.
90. O'Brien, M. C. M. Proc. Roy. Soc. A231, 404, 1955.
91. Weeks, R. A. J. Appl. Phys. 27, 1376, 1956.
92. Molin, Yu. N., V.V. Voyevodskiy. Zh. Tekh. Fiz. 28, 143, 1958.
93. Schulz-du Bois, E., M. Nisenoff, H. Y. Fan, K. Lark-Horowitz. Phys. Rev. 98, 1561, 1955.
94. Weeks, R. A. J. Appl. Phys. 27, 1376, 1956.
95. Smaller, B., M. S. Matheson, E. L. Yasaitis. Phys. Rev. 94, 202, 1954.
96. Matheson, M. S., B. Smaller. J. Chem. Phys. 23, 521, 1955.
97. Hutchison, C. A. Jr., R. C. Pastor. Phys. Rev. 81, 282, 1951.
98. Garstens, M. A., A. H. Ryan. Phys. Rev. 81, 888, 1951.
99. Levinthal, E. C., E. H. Rogers, R. A. Ogg, Jr. Phys. Rev. 83, 182, 1951.
100. Hutchison, C. A. Jr. J. Phys. Chem. 57, 546, 1953.
101. Hutchison, C. A. Jr., R. C. Pastor. Rev. Mod. Phys. 25, 285, 1953; J. Chem. Phys. 21, 1959, 1953.
102. Galkin, A. A., Ya. A. Shamfarov, A. V. Stefanishina. Zh. Eksp. Teoret. Fiz. 32, 1581, 1957.
103. Blume, R. J. Phys. Rev. 109, 1867, 1958.
104. Kaplan, J., C. Kittel. J. Chem. Phys. 21, 1429, 1953.
105. Ogg, R. A. J. Chem. Phys. 14, 114, 295, 1946; J. Am. Chem. Soc. 68, 155, 1946.
106. Deygen, M. F. Zh. Eksp. Teoret. Fiz. 26, 293, 300, 1954; Ukr. Fiz. Zhur. 1, 245, 1956.
107. Deygen, M. F., S. I. Pekar. Zh. Eksp. Teoret. Fiz. 34, 684, 1958.

108. Kim, Y. W., R. Kaplan, P. J. Bray. Bull. Am. Phys. Soc. 3, 178, 1958.
109. Noble, G. A. Bull. Am. Phys. Soc. 3, 178, 1958.
110. Watkins, G. D. Bull. Am. Phys. Soc., Ser. II, 2, 345, 1957; Zudwig, G. W., H. H. Woodbury. Bull. Am. Phys. Soc., Ser. II, 3, 135, 1958; Phys. Rev. Letters 1, 16, 1958; J. Phys. Chem. Solids 8, 490, 1959; Phys. Rev. 113, 1014, 1959; Feher, G., D. K. Wilson, E. A. Gere. Phys. Rev. Letters 3, 25, 1959; Koth, L. M., B. Lax. Phys. Rev. Letters 3, 217, 1959.

CHAPTER VII

Free Radicals

7.1. Introduction. Hyperfine Structure of a Paramagnetic Resonance Line in Solutions of Free Radicals

The study of free radicals, i.e., molecules in which at least one electron has an uncompensated spin, is one of the most important realms of application of paramagnetic resonance, and at the present time it attracts the attention of a very large number of investigators. It is estimated that more than a hundred papers are devoted to this subject. In this book, therefore, we shall not given an exhaustive statement of all the results obtained. For details we primarily refer the reader to Ingram's book [1], as well as the reviews by Wertz [2] and by Blyumenfel'd and Voyevodskiy [3].

The diversity of substances considered in this chapter is so great that it is exceedingly difficult to classify them rigorously.

Paramagnetic resonance was first observed in free radicals in 1947 by Kozyrev and Salikhov [4] in the case of pentaphenylcyclopentadienyl $C_{35}H_{25}$. In solid $C_{35}H_{25}$, they detected a single line having a g factor which differed little from 2 within the low limits of accuracy of the measurement. From this it was concluded that this free radical possesses mainly spin magnetism in accordance with measurements of its static magnetic susceptibility.

In 1949 a systematic study of paramagnetic resonance spectra in free radicals was initiated. Up to the present time many classes of these substances have been studied, for example, organic derivatives of divalent nitrogen, radical-ions of hydrocarbons, semiquinones, peroxide-type compounds, biradicals, etc.

The essential feature of paramagnetic resonance spectra in free radicals is that the g factor is very close to the value for a free electron $g_{spin} = 2.0023$; i.e., purely spin magnetism is present. Thus, for ordinary organic free radicals, containing only C, H, O, and N atoms, the difference $g - g_{spin} = \Delta g$ does not exceed 0.002-0.003. This almost complete absence of orbital magnetism is caused by the low symmetry of free-radical molecules, which effects the complete removal of the orbital degeneracy; in addition in many cases the symmetry reduction is undoubtedly caused by the Jahn-Teller effect. In accordance with such strong suppression of the orbital moment, the spin-orbit coupling in free radicals is small and the spin-lattice relaxation time is small (usually of the order 10^{-7} sec).

The second feature characteristic of almost all free radicals in the condensed phase in a pure undiluted state is the extreme narrowness of the paramagnetic resonance line: the line width as a rule is of the order of one (or a few) gauss. This magnitude is roughly 1/100 of the value calculated from the magnetic dipolar interactions and neglecting exchange. Thus, in free radicals we have an example of a system with large exchange forces. As a result their absorption line shape is almost Lorentzian, and the line width is determined by the spin-lattice interactions [5].

It must be mentioned that, apart from exchange in free radicals, there exists another important mechanism of narrowing of a paramagnetic resonance line, which was considered in [6]. It consists in a reduction of the effectiveness of the local magnetic field owing to the motion of a strongly delocalized unpaired electron inside a molecule of a free radical. Some experimental confirmation of the existence of this mechanism exists.

The narrowness of the lines makes the height of the resonance peaks in free radicals very large and facilitates their detection. Thus, α,α-diphenyl-β-picrylhydrazyl (DPPH) is widely used as a standard calibrated substance in paramagnetic resonance investigations. The characteristic line can be observed in modern instruments with the presence of only 10^{-13} mole of DPPH. Paramagnetic resonance is therefore the best of the existing methods for the detection of free radicals (at least in the condensed phases).

The value of paramagnetic resonance for chemistry is not limited to the detection of free radicals in the solid states. The investigation of paramagnetic resonance spectra in solutions containing free radicals gives very valuable information concerning their nature and properties. This information is obtained first by means of a study of the hyperfine structure of the paramagnetic resonance spectra. Well-resolved hyperfine structure is observed only at a sufficiently low free-radical concentration N in solution (usually for $N \leq 10^{-3}$ mole/liter), when the exchange interactions between the free radicals are almost completely eliminated. Thus, the number of hyperfine components of the line is often very large and their relative intensities are different. The emergence of such a structure is explained by the substantial delocalization of the unpaired electron, which interacts with the total spin I_{total} of several of the atomic nuclei occurring in the composition of the molecule. An analysis of the observed hyperfine structure therefore enables us to draw conclusions concerning both the nature of the radical and the character of the delocalization of the molecular orbital of the unpaired electron. This is illustrated most simply in the example of α,α-diphenyl-β-picrylhydrazyl, whose structure can be illustrated by formula A. Formula B represents p-benzosemiquinone.

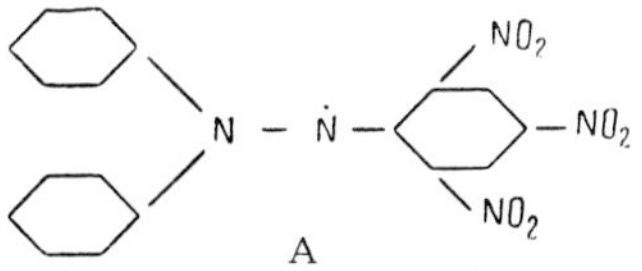

A

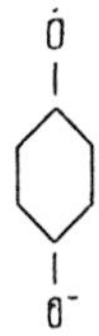

B

The spectrum observed in dilute solutions of radical A consists of five lines with the intensity ratios 1:2:3:2:1. It can be explained by assuming that the density of the unpaired electron cloud is distributed equally between the two central nitrogen atoms. Since the nuclear spin of N^{14} equals unity we must have $2\,I_{total} + 1 = 5$ hyperfine components. The ratio of the individual component intensities follows directly from consideration of Figure 7.1, which gives first the hyperfine splittings of the ground level due to the first N^{14} nucleus, and then the superimposed splittings of the same magnitude, due to the second N^{14} nucleus.

In a solution containing a negative ion of *p*-benzosemiquinone, five peaks are also observed, but with the intensity ratios 1:4:6:4:1. Simple considerations similar to the above show that in this case the interactions between the electron spin and each of the four protons of the molecule are identical; i.e., the density of the unpaired electron is distributed over the entire ring (we recall that the C^{12} and O^{16} nuclei have spins equal to zero, and therefore do not influence the hyperfine structure).

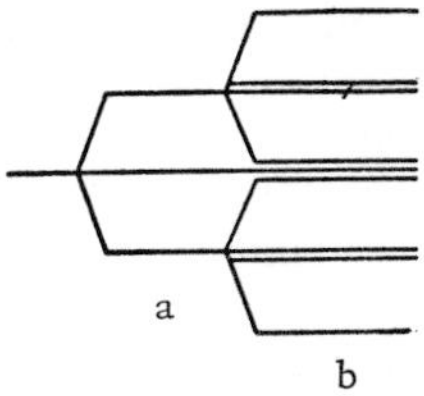

Fig. 7.1. Diagram of the hyperfine splittings produced by: a) the first N^{14} atom and b) the second N^{14} atom, with $A_1 \approx A_2$.

If the electron does not interact equally with all the nuclear spins, the spectral pattern is more complex. In particular, if the constant of the hyperfine interaction with one group of nuclei possessing the total spin I_1 turns out to be much greater than the constant of interaction with the other group, possessing a total spin I_2, then the hyperfine structure resulting from the stronger interaction consists of $2I_1 + 1$ components, and each of these breaks down into $2I_2 + 1$ closely situated peaks, due to the weaker interaction. Finally, if the constants of interaction between the electron spin and each of the atomic nuclei *a, b, c* . . . of the molecule, encompassed by the delocalized orbit, turn out to be different and have no integral relationship to one another, we should have a spectrum consisting of $(2I_a + 1)(2I_b + 1)(2I_c + 1)$ . . . components.

Strictly speaking, direct conclusions concerning the distribution of the electron density from paramagnetic resonance data can be drawn only when the delocalized orbital reacts with nuclei that are chemically completely equivalent (as, for instance, in the case of p-benzosemiquinone). For chemically nonequivalent atoms, however (such as the nitrogen atoms in DPPH), such a treatment is only very approximate [3].

We now proceed to the subject of the causes of the emergence of hyperfine structure in paramagnetic resonance spectra of aromatic free radicals, such as the aromatic hydrocarbon negative ions.

In order that nonzero hyperfine splittings might exist, the density of electrons at the positions of the nuclei must also be finite. Hence, a direct interaction between the unpaired π electron of the aromatic free radical and the ring of protons is impossible, as the latter are situated in the plane of the ring, where the density of the π electron cloud is equal to zero. Thus, at first glance, it appears that hyperfine structure in the paramagnetic resonance structure of aromatic free radicals in general should not occur. Nevertheless, experiment shows that it does.

The attempt to explain the observed effect by means of a consideration of the proton vibrations normal to the plane of the ring did not meet with success. It was assumed therefore (in analogy with the assumption of the theory of hyperfine structure in ionic crystals, considered in Chapter III) that in reality the unpaired electron of aromatic radicals has a small admixture of the excited σ state. A quantitative calculation of the configurational interaction for aromatic radicals was made by Weissman [7], McConnell [8] and others [9, 10].

According to [7], the ground-state configuration of a free aromatic radical may be designated: (filled orbitals) $\sigma_B{}^2\pi$, where σ_B is the bonding CH molecular orbital. A possible excited configuration which is mixed with the ground state is: (filled orbitals) $\sigma_B{}^1\pi(\sigma_A)^1$, where σ_A is the antibonding orbital, Since one of the conditions of configurational interaction is the requirement that both interacting states possess the same symmetry with respect to reflection in the plane of the ring, the admixture state: (filled orbitals) $\sigma_B{}^1\pi^2$ is impossible.

It follows from the theory that the hyperfine splitting A', expressed in gauss, produced by a proton belonging to a given carbon atom is directly proportional to the density ρ_i of the unpaired electron cloud at the position of the nucleus:

$$A' = Q\rho_i. \tag{7.1}$$

Here Q is a constant, identical for all aromatic free radicals, which according to a numerical calculation is approximately equal to 28 gauss. This value is the separation between the hyperfine structure peaks under the condition that $\rho_i = 1$; i.e., the density of the electron cloud as a whole is associated with one C atom; if, however, the density at one atom is less than unity, the constant A' should also be correspondingly smaller. Therefore, if the unpaired electron is delocalized over the entire ring, the separation between the outer peaks of the hyperfine structure again should be close to 28 gauss.

For most of the aromatic free radicals that were studied, experiment gave very good agreement with theory (see Table 7.3). In some cases, however, for example the peri-naphthene ion, the over-all hyperfine splitting turned out to be considerably greater than 28 gauss. This was explained by the possibility of a negative spin density on a carbon atom. Negative spin density arises from the perturbing action of an unpaired electron on the paired-electron orbitals. This perturbation leads to the partial unpairing of the initially paired spins, and thus there arises a new density of the unpaired electron with spin direction opposite to that which existed for the perturbed electron. The new density therefore has a negative sign. The initial positive density in turn increases, so that the algebraic sum of the densities at all the atoms of the ring remain as before equal to unity. But for hyperfine interactions the sign of the spin density is irrelevant so that the over-all hyperfine splitting is proportional to the sum of the absolute values of the spin densities, and as a result of this perturbation it becomes greater than 28 gauss [11].

The theory of configurational interaction does not explain, however, the hyperfine splittings arising from protons located in groups that have replaced cyclic hydrogen atoms, such as the CH_3 groups that replace the hydrogen atoms on the benzene ring in tetramethylbenzosemiquinone:

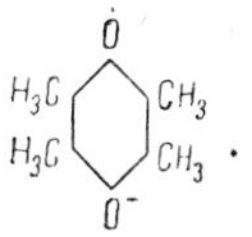

The mechanism that provides hyperfine interaction with the protons of the substituent results in a direct overlapping of the $2p_z$ orbital of the ring carbon atom with the linear combination of orbitals of three protons of the methyl group. Since the p_z orbital is part of a system containing an unpaired electron, the appearance of a spin density in the methyl group becomes possible. As a result of the rotation of the methyl group with respect to the ring, overlapping of electron clouds may occur for all three hydrogen atoms of CH_3. This mechanism caused by the hyperconjugation phenomena has been analyzed in greater detail in [48, 49].

The paramagnetic resonance spectra discussed up to this point were observed in liquid systems of low viscosity containing free radicals, where only the isotropic part of these hyperfine interactions plays a role since the anisotropic part is effectively averaged out by the Brownian motion. In [12], devoted to paramagnetic resonance in the inorganic free radical ClO_2 (chlorine dioxide), it is shown that in dilute liquid solutions of this radical four hyperfine structure peaks are observed (of $Cl^{35,37}$ with $I = 3/2$) with a separation between the peaks $A' = 17$ gauss and a width of each peak $\Delta H = 8$ gauss. After freezing the solutions, A' becomes equal to 52 gauss with a corresponding increase of ΔH. Both the increase of ΔH and of A' are explained by the removal of the averaging effect of Brownian motion by the freezing process.

A similar result was obtained by Berthet [13], who investigated the hyperfine structure of the free radical $(CH_3OC_6H_4)_2NO$ in solid and in liquid solutions. Whereas in a liquid solution the constant $A' = 11$ gauss and the intensities of all three peaks from the N^{14} nucleus are equal to one another, in a solid solution $A' = 18$ gauss with a different intensity of the components. It is also worthy of mention that the observed hyperfine structure appears in solid solutions for a 25% concentration of the free radical, whereas in liquid solutions it is detected only for the concentration 0.3%. This difference possibly is evidence of the fact that in liquid solutions the free radicals occur in the form of individual molecules only at appreciable dilutions.

7.2. Free Radicals in Pure Form

Before citing the results obtained for different classes of pure free radicals, it is advantageous to discuss the most extensively studied of these substances, α,α-diphenyl-β-picrylhydrazyl (DPPH), which is chemically one of the most stable free radicals and is widely used for an evaluation of the sensitivity of magnetic spectrometers, for an evaluation of the number of paramagnetic centers in samples under investigation, and finally in some cases for the determination of g factors.

Resonance in solid DPPH was first measured in 1950 [14] when the g factor in polycrystalline samples was found to equal 2.0036 ± 0.0003 and the line width was $\Delta H = 2.7$ gauss. Furthermore, in DPPH single crystals a small anisotropy was also found to exist both in the g value and in the values of ΔH [15, 77]. The longitudinal relaxation time T_1 was measured by the saturation method and it was found to equal $6.3 \cdot 10^{-8}$ sec, which is close to the value of T_2 as would be expected for a system with spin exchange [15] (see Sec. 5.3). The theory of the absorption line of DPPH in weak fields was developed in [16] and later confirmed experimentally [17].

A characteristic feature of paramagnetic resonance of solid DPPH which for a long time was unexplained was the dramatic difference in the ΔH values (from ~ 1 to ~ 7 gauss) obtained by various investigators. The principal reasons for these discrepancies was explained in the work of Arbuzov, Valitova, Garif'yanov and

Kozyrev [18], who studied the effect of the solvent[1] from which DPPH is crystallized on ΔH. The results of these measurements made on comminuted crystalline powders under vacuum are given in Table 7.1.

Table 7.1

Width of the Paramagnetic Resonance Line in DPPH Samples Obtained from Various Solvents

Solvent	ΔH, gauss		
	ν = 300 Mc		ν = 9400 Mc
	295° K	90° K	295° K
Benzene	6.8	4.6	4.7
Toluene	2.9	2.6	2.6
Xylene (mixture)	2.5	2.2	2.3
Pyridine	5.3	5.0	5.0
Bromoform	2.2	2.5	2.5
Carbon tetrachloride	1.9	2.7	2.3
Chloroform	1.7	2.1	2.0
Carbon disulfide	1.3	1.3	1.5

It is apparent from the table that the nature of this solvent strongly influences the line width; this should be expected, however, since it is well known that some solvents enter the DPPH crystalline lattice (thus, it is not without interest that in not a single case has chemical analysis given proof that the solvent appears in the lattice in stoichiometric proportions).

The DPPH samples under investigation are divided into two groups: in the first group (cyclic solvents) a narrowing of the lines occurs with cooling and with increase of frequency; in the second (noncyclic solvents) both relations are reversed. The small narrowing with increase of frequency which is observable in the first group qualitatively corresponds to the theory of Kube and Tomita for purely isotropic exchange (see Chapter V) and occurs probably as a consequence of the disappearance in strong fields H_0 of the nonsecular line broadening. The narrowing with cooling may be

[1] For two of the solvents—benzene and carbon disulfide—this effect had been detected previously in [19].

understood as a consequence of the dependence of the nonsecular broadening on the correlation time.

The frequency dependence of the DPPH line narrowing in the second group, however, cannot be so simply explained. It might be regarded as a consequence of the large anisotropy of the g factor in the second group, but measurements by Yablokov [20] in DPPH single crystals have shown that this anisotropy is roughly the same for the benzene sample ($g_{\parallel} = 2.0031 \pm 0.0003$; $g_{\perp} = 2.0039 \pm 0.0003$) and for the chloroform sample ($g_{\parallel} = 2.0030 \pm 0.0002$; $g_{\perp} = 2.0040 \pm 0.0002$). Thus, at present there is no complete explanation of the line width in the various forms of DPPH.

The nature of the solvent is not the only factor influencing ΔH in DPPH. As was established in [21, 18], in finely divided crystalline samples belonging to the second group, a reversible line broadening is observed, due to the adsorption of O_2 molecules from air. The evacuation of air narrows the line to a value of ΔH roughly corresponding to a coarse-grain crystalline sample. This effect is similar to that observed previously in coals [22] and explained by the shortening of the spin-lattice relaxation time in DPPH under the influence of the magnetic moments of O_2 molecules. In fact, the saturation method has shown that simultaneously with the broadening of the absorption lines of O_2, a shortening of T_1 also occurs. Oxygen causes an especially strong broadening of the narrowest line obtained in samples crystallized from carbon disulfide [18]. For a sample crystallized from chloroform over the temperature range 90 - 273° K, the effect of oxygen is enormously greater than at temperatures above 273° K [21].

It follows from the foregoing that use of DPPH as a standard requires an indication of its method of production, knowledge of the chemical composition of the sample, and the use of samples protected from contact with oxygen. The most suitable standard evidently is DPPH crystallized from benzene, in which the effect of oxygen adsorption is insignificant.

It is necessary to realize that the dependence of ΔH on the specific details of production and on the medium from which the sample is crystallized is not restricted to DPPH, but may occur also in other radicals. Thus, for pentaphenylcyclopentadienyl, values for ΔH were obtained of several tens of gauss in [4], 0.62 gauss in [23] and 5 gauss and above in [24] (depending on the solvent).

Unfortunately, in most of the work on DPPH and its derivatives no indication has been given of the solvent from which the radical was crystallized.

Besides DPPH a number of polycrystalline free radicals have been investigated [25], which have similar structures such as

Table 7.2

Radical	g	δH, gauss	Reference
Benzoquinhydrone, adsorbed on $Ba(OH)_2 \cdot 8H_2O$	2.003	several	[28]
Biphenylenetriphenylethyl	2.00	5	[30]
Wurster's blue (perchlorate)	2.003	2.7	[32]
Wurster's blue (picrate)[a]	2.0033	6	[33]
Wurster's blue (ferricyanide)[b]	2.0028	2.7	[33]
Di-p-anisyl nitrogen oxide (single crystal)	$g_{\parallel} = 2.0095$; $g_{\perp} = 2.0035$		[34]
Di-p-xenylphenylmethyl	2.00	several	[32]
Biphenylenetriphenylmethyl	—	5	[32]
Diphenylquionxalinium chlorostannite	2.0036		[33]
Banfield-Kenyon radical[c]	2.0057	8.9	[32, 33]
2-Nitrophenanthrophenazinium chlorostannite	2.0032		[33]
Pentaphenylcyclopentadienyl[d]	2.0025		[4, 23, 24]
Porphyrexide[a]	2.0065	17.0	[33, 35]
Porphyrindene[a, e]	2.0057	10.7	[32, 35]
Tetramethylbenzidine formate	2.00	3.4	[32]
Tetramethylbenzidine perchlorate[f]	2.00	—	[32]
Tetraphenylstilbonium peroxylamine disulfonate	2.00	100	[32]
Thymoquinhydrone, adsorbed on $Ba(OH)_2 \cdot 8H_2O$			[28]
Tri-*p*-xenylmethyl	2.0031	5.7	[32]
Tri-tert-butylphenoxyl[a]	2.0052	7.7	[23]
Triphenylamine perchlorate[g]	2.003	2	[32]
Tri-*p*-anisylaminium perchlorate[g]		0.68	[36]
Tri-*p*-aminophenylaminium perchlorate		0.33	[36]
Tris-*p*-nitrophenylmethyl	2.0037	0.7	[32]
Phenanthraquinhydrone, adsorbed on $Ba(OH)_2 \cdot 8H_2O$			[28]
N-Phenyl-*N*-9-decalyl-*N*-oxoaminyl	2.0036		[37]
2-(Phenyl nitrogen oxide)-2-methylpentan-4-one oxime *N*-phenyl ether (single crystal)	$g_x = 2.0042$; $g_y = 2.0064$; $g_z = 2.0083$		[34]
Chromocene $Cr(C_6H_6)_2I$	1.975	38	[58]
Chromocene $Cr(C_6H_5{-}C_6H_5)_2I$	1.987	28	[58]
Chromocene $Cr(C_6H_5{-}C_6H_5)_2OC_6H_5$	1.993	26	[58]

[a] The table lists the line width at half power.
[b] The original reference gives the line width at half power as 3.7 gauss.
[c] Reference [32] gives $g = 2.000$; [33] gives $g = 2.0057$.
[d] Reference [23] gives $\Delta H = 0.62$ gauss.
[e] Reference [32] gives $g = 2.001$.
[f] Reference [32] gives ΔH = several gauss.
[g] δH was measured at 15 Mc (it is larger at $9.4 \cdot 10^9$ Mc).

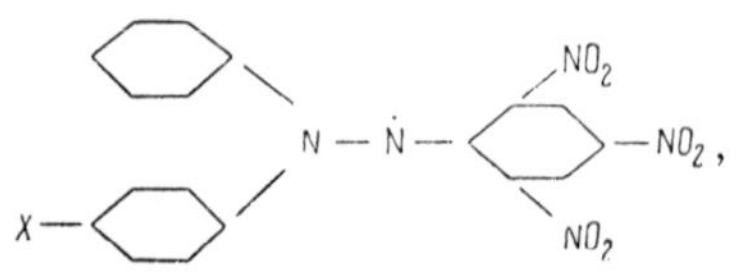

where X is Cl (g = 2.0042; δH= 1.2 gauss), Br (g = 2.002; δH= 2.2 gauss), OCH_3 (g = 2.000; δH = 2.6 gauss) or F (g = 2.000; δH = 4.1 gauss). Here δH is the line width between the inflection points. Investigations have also been made of diphenylhydroxypicrylhydrazyl powders: g is the same as in DPPH, δH = 3 gauss [26] and in a single crystal of N-picryl-9-aminocarbazyl, g ranges from 2.0041 to 2.0024, and δH= 0.5 gauss [27, 28]. The last substance differs from DPPH very little, having the following structural formula

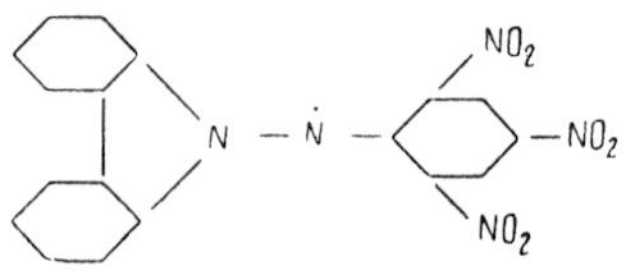

Nevertheless, its line width is considerably less than that in any variety of DPPH.

Some results of measurement of paramagnetic resonance in solid organic free radicals of other types are given in Table 7.2. This table does not claim exhaustive completeness.

7.3. Free Radicals in Solutions

In Sec. 7.1 we pointed out that from the chemical point of view the greatest interest lies in an investigation of the hyperfine structure of paramagnetic resonance lines that can be observed in solutions at sufficiently low concentration of the free radicals. Here we shall quote some results obtained in a study of solutions of such free radicals.

We have seen that DPPH in solution gives five lines. The closely related compound N-picryl-9-aminocarbazyl gives seven lines, which corresponds to a ratio of two for the interaction constants A_1' and A_2' with the nuclei of the first and second nitrogen atoms. The maximum possible number of lines, nine, was obtained in solutions of a diphenyldinitrosulfophenylhydrazyl salt

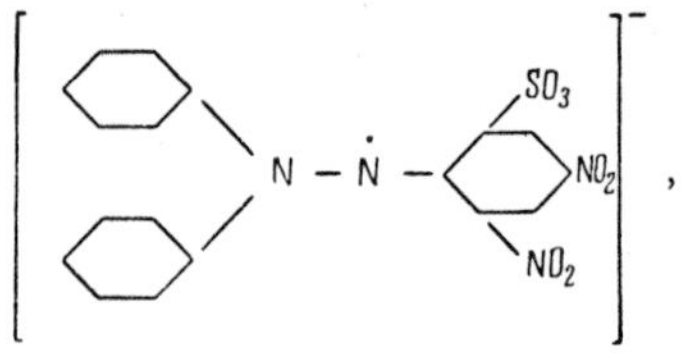

where the constants of interaction with the nitrogen atoms were A_1 = 12 gauss, and A_2 = 8 gauss [38, 39]. From this example it is apparent how sensitive the hyperfine structure is to the slightest change in the distribution of electron densities in the molecule.

Solutions containing ions of aromatic hydrocarbons are of great interest for verification of the theory of hyperfine structure. One of the first to be studied [40] was the negative naphthalene ion, which is obtained from the action of an alkali metal on a solution of naphthalene in tetrahydrofuran or dimethoxyethane

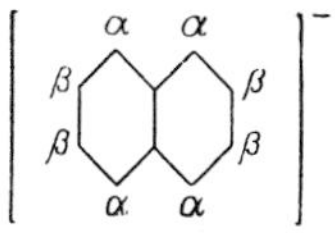

The nature of the metal and solvent do not alter the spectrum, which consists of 17 lines with the relative intensities

$$1:1:1:2:2:1:2:2:1:2:2:1:2:2:1:1:1$$

and with a separation between the outer peaks (over-all splitting) equal to 27.2 gauss. This magnitude is in good agreement with the theoretical value of the over-all splitting (28 gauss). The number and intensity of the lines were explained on the basis of an approximate molecular orbital calculation, performed long before in 1931 by Hückel [41]. In the case of equal hyperfine structure constants A_α and A_β stemming from the α and β protons of the naphthalene ion, nine lines should appear; when $A_\alpha \gg A_\beta$ one should obtain five groups of lines, each containing five closely spaced components. The number 17 corresponds to the ratio $A_\alpha/A_\beta = \rho i_\alpha/\rho i_\beta$ = 3:1, which agrees with the calculations of Hückel. A more accurate value of the ratio A_α: A_β, found from a detailed analysis of the paramagnetic resonance spectrum, is 5.01:1.79.

Partial replacement of C^{12} by C^{13} in the naphthalene ion permitted the hyperfine structure constant resulting from interaction between the electron spin and the spin of the C^{13} nucleus (I = 1/2) to be found. This value was 7.1 gauss, from which the density of the electron cloud at the C^{13} nucleus was calculated. Similar investigations have been made of a number of other negative aromatic ions (see Table 7.3), and determinations have been made of the electron densities at protons, which also turned out to be in good agreement with the calculations on the basis of [41]. Moreover, from paramagnetic resonance experiments it became possible to establish a scale of aromatic electronegativities, and if we assume that the lifetime of an electron in the ion determines the line width, then it also determines the rate of transition of the electron between the aromatic molecule and the ion [42].

Table 7.3
Stable Free Radicals in Solution [1][a]

Radical	ΔH or separation between outer HFS peaks, gauss	Number of HFS components	Reference
A) Aromatic ions			
Anthracene	26	21	[63]
Benzene	22.5	7	[64]
m-Dinitrobenzene	25	8	[65]
Diphenyl	21	9	[63]
Naphthalene	27	17	[66]
Naphthalene containing C^{13} [b]	34.3	34	[67]
Deuterated naphthalene	29	15—16	[66], [63]
Nitrobenzene	25	10	[66]
Perinaphthene	49	7×4	[68]
Perylene [c]	24	9	[44]
Tetracene [d]	25	31	[44]
Trinitrobenzene	25	8	[66]
B) Semiquinones			
1) *p*-Benzosemiquinone	9.48	5	[69]
Monomethyl-*p*-benzosemiquinone	14	many lines	[70]
Tetramethyl-*p*-benzosemiquinone	23	13	[70]
Monochloro-*p*-benzosemiquinone	6.0	4	[51]
Trichloro-*p*-benzosemiquinone	2.11	2	[71]
Tetrachloro-*p*-benzosemiquinone	0.4	1	[51]
2, 5-Di-tert-butyl-*p*-benzosemiquinone	4.3	3×19	[71]
2) 1, 4-Naphthosemiquinone	8	3×5	[72]
2, 3-dimethyl-1, 4-naphthosemiquinone	12	7×5	[72]
3) *o*-Benzosemiquinone	10	3×3	[73]
4-tert-Butylsemiquinone	6	2×11	[73]
3-Phenyl-p-benzosemiquinone	8	7	[73]
Oxidized 1, 2, 3, -benzenetriol	7	2×3	[62]
C) Triarylamine perchlorates			
Trianisyl	20	3	[74]
Tridiphenyl	20	3	[74]
D) Wurster's salts (pos. ions)			
Unsubstituted	28	15	[75]
N-Methyl substituted	46	24	[75]
N N-Dimethyl substituted	73	27	[75]
N, *N'*-Dimethyl substituted	76	9×3	[75]
N, *N*-Dimethyl-*NN'*-deutero	51	7×3	[75]
Tetramethyl substituted	88	13×3	[75]
E) Various other radicals			
Carbazyl	60	7	[38]
Difluorenyl nitrogen	9	10	[40]
Dimesitylmethyl	48	2×35	[76]
Di-*p*-anisyl nitric oxide	14	—	[65]
Diphenyldinitro-sulfonylhydrazyl	60	9	[38]
1, 1-Diphenyl-2-picryl hydrazyl	58	5	[77]
Peroxylamine disulfonate	26	3	[78]
Phenazine	60	5	[79]
Sodium trimesityl boron	42	4	[40]
Triphenylmethyl	25	21×4	[76]

[a] [More recent work, such as that reported by A. Carrington, F. Dravnieks and M. C. R. Symons in J. Chem. Soc. 947(1959), resolved some of the free radicals listed into many additional lines.]
[b] [21 lines actually observed in [6-7] — ed.]
[c] [ΔH=28.7 in H_2SO_4 and 2.6 for negative ion [44] — ed.]
[d] [ΔH=29.0 in H_2SO_4 and 24.7 for negative ion [44] — ed.]

By treating aromatic hydrocarbons with concentrated H_2SO_4, one may obtain the positive aromatic hydrocarbons ions, which also are, of course, free radicals. A number of such radicals have been investigated by the paramagnetic resonance method [43,44].

Some additional organic substances of other classes were treated with sulfuric acid (for instance, anthraquinone, thiophene and many others), and produced paramagnetic resonance spectra [45, 46]. In these cases, however, positive ions having the character of a radical are not obtained, but, instead, radical products of oxidation of the corresponding organic substances, as was convincingly shown in [47].

A large amount of work has been carried out on the resonance of solutions containing different semiquinones and their derivatives. The experimental values of the hyperfine structure constants have been compared with those calculated on the basis of the theory of hyperconjugation, developed in [48, 10], and they are in good agreement [49].

The spectral picture is often found to be very complex. Thus, for monomethyl-p-benzosemiquinone one must assume that the hyperfine structure constants for two of the ring protons are $A'_1 = A'_2 =$ 2.48 gauss, for the third ring $A'_3 = 1.73$ gauss; and for the methyl protons this structure constant is $B' = 2.02$ gauss [50]. The spectrum simplifies when the substituents are chlorine atoms, since the hyperfine splittings due to them are small and do not give resolved lines, but contribute only to the width of the component. Thus, in trichlorobenzosemiquinone only two components due to the single proton ring are observed [51]. On the other hand, fluorine-substituted semiquinones reveal hyperfine structure due to both the protons and the F^{19} nuclei, owing to the large magnetic moment and the small spin ($I = 1/2$) of the latter [1].

Of the numerous other classes of free radicals studied in solutions, we shall limit ourselves to only a few, referring the reader to Ingram's book [1] for more detailed discussion. Thus, we shall indicate that the spectrum in solutions of triphenylmethyl [52] and some other radicals reveals an anomalously large hyperfine splitting.

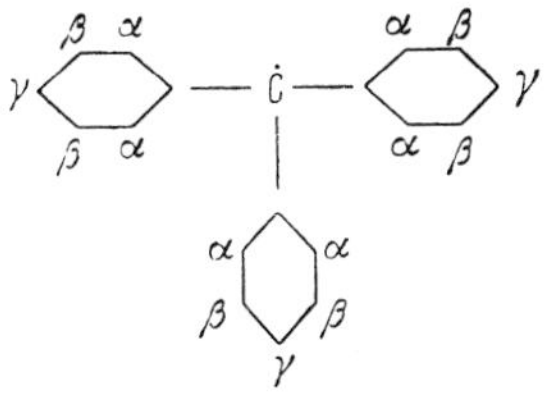

Under the assumption that the corresponding H atoms in all three rings are equivalent, triphenylmethyl must give $(2I_\alpha + 1)(2I_\beta + 1) \times (2I_\gamma + 1) = 196$ lines. They are not completely resolved, the over-all splitting being equal to 25 gauss. But an investigation of a sample containing C^{13} in the methyl position has shown the emergence of a doublet from the C^{13} nucleus with a splitting of 22 gauss, which indicates that an appreciable fraction of the unpaired electron density is indeed centered on the methyl carbon, and consequently $\sum \rho_i$ at the position of the remaining atoms must be substantially less than one. The explanation of the triphenylmethyl spectrum, which we shall not dwell on, has been given in [53, 54].

In radicals both in the solid form and in solutions which have been considered up to the present time, the g factor is very close to 2.0023. The greatest deviations from this value are observed in solutions of radicals containing sulfur and in peroxide type radicals [55]. This indicates considerably greater localization of the unpaired electrons in the latter cases. Radicals containing sulfur were obtained by dissolving thiophene, thiocresol, thionaphthol and diphenyl disulfide in concentrated sulfuric acid [45, 46]. They all give a paramagnetic resonance spectrum consisting of two groups of lines with $g_1 = 2.0151$ and $g_2 = 2.0081$ (g is determined from centers of the the groups). These groups appear to arise from two different radicals, since the second group was found to be more stable with time and persisted when the first had completely disappeared. The group of five lines with $g = 2.0081$ is created by a thianthrene ring with four protons. The group with $g = 2.0151$ evidently is due to the $(C_6H_5\dot{S})H^+$ radical with appreciable localization of the unpaired electron on the sulfur atom.

We note that in addition to the organic derivatives of sulfur having a radical character, paramagnetic resonance has been detected also in pure molten sulfur [56, 57], being observed at temperatures ranging from 189 to 414°C. One line was recorded (the spin of the S^{32} nucleus equals zero) with a shape close to Lorentzian and with $g = 2.024$. Both the line width and g factor are temperature independent. This resonance is due to the partial rupture of the bonds of the ring molecule S_8. A solution of sulfur in fuming sulfuric acid [1] also reveals two lines (for 20% SO_3) with g factors ranging from 2.003 to 2.018 for one line and from 2.025 to 2.032 for the other. The latter is apparently due to the rupture of the S_8 ring, and the former is due to some other radical containing sulfur.

There is great interest in the investigation carried out by Voyevodskiy and his collaborators [58, 59] in studies of solutions containing chromium aromatic compounds with a "sandwich" structure. Compounds of this type (metallocene) have the structure $(C_6H_6)_2M$ or $(C_5H_5)_2M$, etc., where the metallic ion M is situated between two parallel ring structures. The nature of the covalent bond between the metal with the addends in these compounds cannot be described in the framework in the theory of ordinary two-electron bonds. Quantum mechanical calculations relevant to this type of compound are presented in [60].

Investigation [58, 59] of paramagnetic resonance spectra in chromocene cations of the type

$$\begin{bmatrix} C_6H_5X \\ Cr \\ C_6H_5X \end{bmatrix}^+$$

where X = H, C_6H_6, cyclo-C_6H_{11}, COOH, and others, has shown the existence of hyperfine structure with the number of components corresponding to the number of protons in the two rings; the binomial distribution of the intensities of the components leads to the conclusion that all these protons are equivalent. The total spin density of the two rings is 1.92. From this it follows that on the Cr atom there is localized 0.92 of the density of an unpaired electron of opposite spin orientation.

In [61] it was shown that the width of the components of the paramagnetic resonance spectrum in chromocenes depends strongly not only on the substituent, but also on the nature of the solvent and on the temperature.

Besides the stable radicals in liquid solutions, we sometimes succeed in detecting radicals formed in the course of a reaction. Thus, for example, in [62] a study has been made of the paramagnetic resonance of pyrogallol, which oxidizes in air in aqueous and alcohol solutions. At room temperature the lifetime of the free radical turned out to be of the order of several minutes; $g = 2.005$; the spectrum consists of two triplets. In most cases, however, in solutions of low viscosity the unstable radicals have so short a lifetime that their nonequilibrium concentration lies at the limits of sensitivity of modern equipment. Moreover, the short lifetime causes a broadening of the absorption line, which even further hampers detection. The study of unstable radicals was therefore carried out by the usual method of rapid freezing of solutions.

To conclude this section we reproduce Table 7.3 (p. 304), taken from [1]. It illustrates the experimental results obtained in the study of several types of stable free radicals in solutions.

7.4. Irradiated Organic Substances. Radicals in Polymers and Carbons. Biradicals and Triplet States. Biological Materials

1. Irradiation of different organic substances by ultraviolet light, X rays and γ rays often causes a breakdown of their molecular structure, which leads to the formation of free radicals. The

study of such radicals by the paramagnetic resonance method is of great scientific and practical interest; at present there is a substantial literature devoted to this subject. The substances are usually studied either in the solid phase or in highly viscous liquids, since in these cases it is possible to produce a high concentration of radicals by irradiation.

Ultraviolet investigation of materials is preferred to work with X and γ rays, since in the first case, because of the small magnitude of the quantum, the disintegration of molecules and the formation of free radicals are much more selective in character and thus provide spectra that are simpler and easier to interpret. Indeed, in the case of X rays, and especially γ rays, a whole gamut of different free radicals is sometimes obtained, resulting in an extremely complex paramagnetic resonance pattern.

The first work on the study of free radicals in irradiated substances was conducted in 1951 by Schneider and his collaborators [80], who investigated paramagnetic resonance in polymethylmethacrylate polymer irradiated by X rays. The study of irradiated substances has been taken up on an extensive scale, however, only since 1955.

It has been found that a number of substances (ethyl iodide, benzylamine, benzyl chloride and others), dissolved in appropriate hydrocarbon mixtures (the most suitable was found to be a mixture of five parts ether, five parts isopentane and two parts ethanol)[1] and converted to the vitreous state by deep freezing give a paramagnetic resonance spectrum after irradiation with ultraviolet light [81]. A similar effect has been detected also in high-temperature organic gasses [82]. Further work has shown that in addition to the primary radicals formed by the direct action of ultraviolet quanta, secondary radicals emerge from the reaction of the primary radicals with the solvent [83]. Thus, it was found possible to obtain paramagnetic resonance spectra also from radicals of substances on which ultraviolet light had not directly acted. As a primary agent for the formation of radicals, hydrogen peroxide was found to be especially active, yielding the $\dot{O}H$ radical upon ultraviolet irradiation.

The nature of the secondary radicals may be determined from the hyperfine structure of the spectrum. Thus, in a vitreous solution of hydrogen peroxide in the alcohol $(CH_3)_2HCOH$ a spectrum of seven lines from six protons has been detected after irradiation; it obviously is attributed to the $(CH_3)_2COH$ radical.

The line width in solid and vitreous systems containing free radicals is greater than that in their liquid solutions, on account of the absence of narrowing due to Brownian motion. All the widths

[1] Special experiments have demonstrated that ultraviolet light does not affect the molecules of the solvent.

observed in glasses, however, are smaller than would be expected for a completely rigid arrangement of the atoms. This may be explained by an internal rotation of protons in the free radical molecules; this rotation is also preserved at low temperatures [84].

In this connection an investigation of the dependence of the secondary spectra on the temperature of the vitreous system is of interest. Such a study gives information concerning the internal motions in the glass, and sometimes makes it possible to separate the effects obtained from the separate components of the superposed spectrum, since the temperature dependence of the line width is different in different radicals. In particular, in [84] it was shown that the secondary radicals in a H_2O_2 solution in methanol are $\dot{C}H_2OH$ and the biradical $\dot{C}H_2 \ldots H\dot{C}$.

We shall proceed to results obtained in the case of irradiation by X and γ rays. The polymethylmethacrylate spectrum, obtained in 1951 [80], is so complex that its interpretation was not given until seven years later [85]. It turned out to be due to the $R \cdot CH_2 - \dot{C}(CH_3) - (COOCH_3)$ radical. It is easier to interpret the spectra of amino acids irradiated by X rays. Thus, in glycine a triplet due to the $\dot{C}H_2$ radical has been detected [86]. Anisotropy of the spectrum in an irradiated single crystal of glycine has been reported in [87].

An investigation of γ-irradiated frozen paraffin hydrocarbons [88, 89] has shown that when the hydrocarbon chain contains a not too large number of atoms, the spectrum has one central component of maximum intensity; in higher molecular radicals, however, there are two central components. This is evidence that in the first case the number of equivalent protons, which are close to the unpaired electron, is even, and in the second it is odd. From this it may be assumed that in hydrocarbons with a short chain, we chiefly obtain radicals of the type $\dot{C}H_2 - CH_2 - \ldots$, and in higher molecular weight compounds we obtain radicals of the type $\ldots - CH_2 - \dot{C}H - CH - \ldots$ The simplest of the hydrocarbons, methane, gives a paramagnetic resonance spectrum after γ irradiation at the temperature 20.4°K [90]; it consists of four components with the intensity ratio 1 : 3 : 3 : 1, which corresponds to the expected ratio for the radical $\dot{C}H_3$.

Thus, paramagnetic resonance enables one to establish the nature of radicals formed when solid organic substances are irradiated. We shall mention here still other papers on paramagnetic resonance in substances irradiated by x and γ rays. In [91] the following were studied: methyl alcohol, which gives three hyperfine components; ethyl alcohol (five components); acetamide (three components); propionamide (five components); acetanilide (three components; and sodium methoxide (three components). In [86] spectra were obtained of dimethyl-Hg (five components) and diethyl-Hg (three components). In [94] the following were investigated: glycine (three components); alanine (five components); valine (complex spectrum); leucine (two groups of five or more lines);

isoleucine (without a resolved structure); cystine (asymmetric structure with four components); glycolic acid (two components); and glycocyanine (two components). There is no doubt that the systematic study of the influence of irradiation will be extended further [93]. In particular, it is important for the investigation of polymers, which we shall now consider.

2. As is well known from chemical considerations, processes of polymerization of molecules often occur in free radicals. The paramagnetic resonance study of the kinetics of this process, however, is hampered by the low free-radical concentration. Therefore, we restrict ourselves to the determination of free radicals which are formed at the end of growing polymer chains and are fixed in the substances as a consequence of steric causes. This "freezing" takes place when the partially polymerized material forms a gel or when the polymer is insoluble in the monomer and precipitates around the growing chains.

The first investigation of this type refers to the gels of polyvinyl [94]. Glycol dimethacrylate gives a spectrum consisting of two partially overlapping groups, containing five or four lines; the spectrum was found to be independent of the initiator of the polymerization and is identical with the spectrum of irradiated polymethlmethacrylate. Both groups were recognized as belonging to one radical

$$
\begin{array}{c}
\text{COOR} \\
| \\
-\text{CH}_2-\overset{\cdot}{\text{C}} \\
| \\
\text{CH}_3
\end{array}
$$

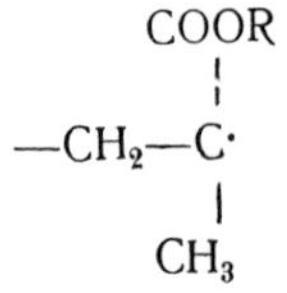

due to the hyperconjugation of the p_π orbital of the C atom with 5 nearby protons from the CH_2 and CH_3 groups [85].

Apart from investigation of free radicals frozen in gels or in the precipitates of polymers, one may identify the radicals arising in the final polymers during irradiation. An interesting example of such an investigation is the work on γ-irradiated frozen teflon ($77^\circ K$) [95]. After thawing with exclusion of air an eleven-line spectrum was obtained; ten of the lines formed two partially overlapping groups of five lines and arise from the radical. . . $- CF_2 - \overset{\cdot}{C}F - CF_2 -. . .$, in which the central F^{19} nucleus produces the main doublet splitting, and the four more remote fluorine nuclei split each doublet line into a quintuplet. Eleven lines are associated with the peroxide radical $- \overset{|}{\underset{|}{C}} - O\overset{\cdot}{O}$, since under the action of atmospheric oxygen the total spectrum of irradiated teflon is converted into a single asymmetric line that coincides in position with the eleventh line of the oxide-free spectrum [95, 96]. The asymmetry of the lines is related to the large localization of the unpaired electrons in the oxygen.

In addition to this case paramagnetic resonance spectra of the following polymers have been studied after irradiation: polymethacryclic acid, polyethylmethacrylate [97], polymethylchloroacrylate, polyacrylic acid, polyvinyl alcohol, hydrolyzed polyvinyl acetate, polystyrene, polythene, nylon, and polyacrylonitrile [98].

Free radicals obtained by polymerization of the following monomers have been studied by the method of freezing in gels or in precipitates: acrylonitrile, methacrylonitrile, vinyl bromide [85], acrylic acid [1], methyl methacrylate [94] and several other polymers.

The variation of concentration of free radicals during the course of polymerization has been studied in the case of copolymerization of methyl methacrylate and glycol dimethacrylate [99]. The action of inhibitors on the process of polymerization was investigated in [100].

3. The discovery of a large resonance effect in carbonized organic materials, made independently in [101-103], was rather unexpected.

In low-temperature pyrolysis products the g factor of a single observed line is very close to 2.0023, and the line width lies between 1 and 100 gauss. The intensity of the effect corresponds to the number of paramagnetic centers, which varies from 0 to 10^{20} per g of material and increases rapidly as the carbon concentration increases from 80 to 94% [104]. X-ray investigations show that in this region of concentration there is indeed initiated the formation of large groups of carbon rings (four or more rings). We note that the spin-lattice relaxation time must decrease with an increase of free carbon concentration [105]. The shortest times T_1 of the order of 10^{-7} sec, are found in anthracite-type coals [106, 107]. They give very narrow lines (δH from 0.7 to 0.3 gauss) with strong exchange interactions ($T_1 \approx T_2$).

It appears that the disorganized ring structure in the random arrangement of the carbon ring groups weakens the exchange and lengthens the spin-lattice relaxation time in carbonized substances containing a small concentration of free carbon. The properties of the paramagnetic resonance lines change as a function of the carbonization temperature and the intensity of the line increases as the temperature rises from about 350 to about 550°C [108]. This is just the temperature range in which the volatile product of pyrolysis are driven off and a carbon ring structure begins to form. Above about 600°C a sharp drop in the intensity of this effect is noted. This decrease is also observed if the concentration of free carbon in the sample exceeds 94%. The last two circumstances evidently are related to the formation of graphitic sheets containing multilayer three-dimensional ring structures. These structures can lead to the partial pairing of free electrons and, hence, to a weakening of paramagnetic resonance.

The intensity of the effect rises rapidly as the atmospheric oxygen is pumped out. The influence of the oxygen is reversible [109, 110, 106]. Two possible mechanisms can be postulated for the effect of O_2 or other paramagnetic gases (in particular, for example, NO_2 [106]) that have an effect entirely similar to oxygen.

The first type of mechanism is purely physical; it consists in the disturbance of the energy of an unpaired electron by the motion of a biradical molecule of adsorbed O_2 relative to the electron, or alternatively, the motion of an electron relative to an immobile fixed O_2 molecule. This disturbance will reduce the lifetime of the electron's excited state, i.e., shorten the spin-lattice relaxation time T_1. If this physical mechanism takes place, the number of unpaired spins in the irradiated substance and hence the area of the resonance absorption curve will remain the same when the line width δH broadens.

The other possible interaction mechanism is a chemical effect. Some very weak "quasi-chemical" bonds [1] are assumed to be formed between the oxygen and carbon (since they break down when the oxygen is pumped out). In these bonds the spin of the uncompensated electron of the free radical is no longer effective, since it pairs itself with one of the spins of the O_2 molecule. The remaining unpaired second electron of O_2 is strongly localized on the oxygen atom and therefore gives a strongly anisotropic and hence unobservable line. When such a mechanism takes place, the area of the resonance line should decrease. Austen and Ingram [111] were able to find carbon samples in which oxygen interacts with the free radicals both by the "physical" and by the "chemical" mechanism.

A number of investigations devoted to the effect of the chemical treatment of carbon have shown that, in general, paramagnetic resonance in them is not related to any individual chemical group, but is due to the existence of uncompensated and strongly delocalized electrons in condensed carbon rings as a whole [1]. Unpaired spins are formed by the breakage of bonds along the edge of the condensed rings, which to a large extent leads only to the growth of ring structure. But in individual cases it may also promote the emergence of uncompensated spins. Another possiblity is that unpaired electrons may originate from defects in the ring packing because the existence of separate five- or seven-membered rings in the ring structure should produce trivalent carbon atoms. A "broken bond" electron should have a π orbital (which entails very strong delocalization) plus the admixture of a σ state. The presence of a very strong exchange in most of the carbons that were studied [106] shows that the electron clouds of the intervening ring clusters overlap to an appreciable extent.

Paramagnetic resonance has also been observed in graphite and other high-temperature carbons made at $t > 1400°C$ [112]. It is not attributed to conduction electrons as was first assumed, but instead to defects of the graphite lattice [113]. Unpaired electrons in this case have much stronger localized σ orbitals. No resonance has been observed in carbons obtained in the temperature range 1000-1400°C.

In the future, investigations of paramagnetic resonance in different carbon blacks may play a very important role. Carbon blacks apparently are a mixture of high and low-temperature carbon, since they are prepared by a very rapid heating at 1000-1700°C. Their spectra, however, are very similar to those of low-temperature carbons; in particular, the spectrum is very sensitive to oxygen, whereas oxygen has no influence on the paramagnetic resonance in graphite. The existence in carbon blacks of unpaired electrons with delocalized π orbitals must undoubtedly play a role in the reinforcement action of carbon blacks when they are introduced into rubber as fillers [1].

We note that paramagnetic resonance has been detected in a number of tarry substances (petroleum asphalt, carbolite, etc.) and in petroleum [106] .

4. An unusual type of organic paramagnetic substance is the biradical—a molecule containing not one but two unpaired electrons. Among the biradicals, one may structurally distinguish a graduation of substances, beginning with those in which the spins of both pairs of electrons are very far apart and do not form a resultant molecular spin of unity and finally those in which the spins interact very strongly. The most reliable results on paramagnetic resonance have been obtained for biradicals with noninteracting spins. These include, for instance, 4,4′-polymethylene-bis-triphenylmethyl biradicals and p-substituted polyphenols, studied in [114]. All the g factors of these substances are very close to 2.0023, which indicates that virtually no coupling exists between the spins. The character of their structure is the same as in monoradicals, but, of course, with double the intensity calculated for one molecule.

Among the substances in which there is no basis for assuming that the coupling between the spins of the molecules is negligibly small, paramagnetic resonance has been detected in the so-called Chichibabin hydrocarbon [115]

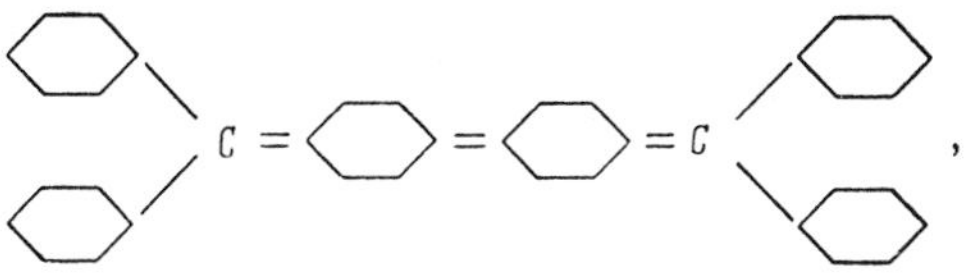

which in the excited triplet state must have the following structure:

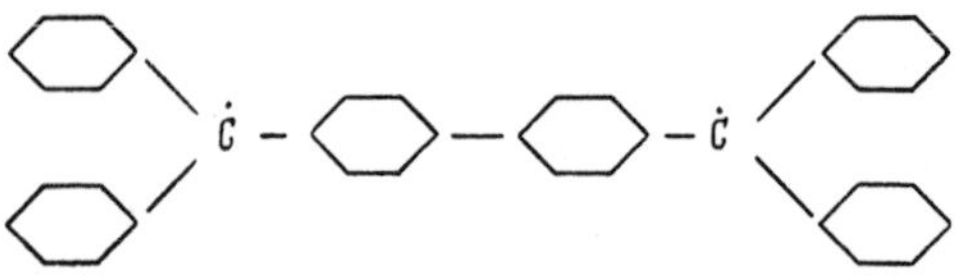

The observed resonance signal corresponds to 4% of the molecules in the triplet state. In the opinion of Ingram [1], there is a distinct possibility that this signal may have been due to some paramagnetic impurity. On the basis of a number of negative results on paramagnetic resonance which were obtained by optical excitation of the molecule to the triplet state, he assumed that in such molecules there occurs a very powerful relaxation mechanism which leads to so strong a line broadening that they become unobservable. In addition to Chichibabin's hydrocarbon, a number of other compounds exist in which the presence of excited triplet states may be postulated and which reveal paramagnetic resonance. These include, in particular, two highly conjugated systems: 1,9-bis(2-furyl)-5-oxo-1,3,6,8-nonatetraene and 1,9-diphenyl-5-oxo-1,3,6,8-nonatetraene, in which a weak resonance effect has been noted in [116].

Furthermore, a number of solid molecular compounds between various phenylenediamines and halide-substituted quinones, investigated by Bijl, Kainer and Rose-Innes [149], also revealed paramagnetic resonance. The spectrum has been interpreted as due to the formation of biradical ionic molecules as a result of the transfer of an electron by donors (phenylendiamines) to acceptors (quinones). Finally, paramagnetic resonance in such compounds as heated bianthrone ($g = 2.0036$; $\Delta H = 10$ gauss) [29], violanthrene ($g = 2.00$; $\Delta H = 26$ gauss) [31] and violanthrone ($g = 2.00$; $\Delta H = 30$ gauss) [31] can conclusively be attributed to no other cause than the existence in these compounds of a certain fraction of the molecules in the triplet state.

5. In concluding this section, we refer to the investigation of paramagnetic resonance in biological materials, which undoubtedly has a great future and has already given interesting results. Thus, in [117], investigations have been made of free radicals that are intermediate products in oxidation-reduction processes occurring in adrenalin, vitamin K and other biologically important materials. In [118] free radicals from albumin were observed in lyophilized tissues and fluids of animals and plants. In [119] studies were made of the time dependence of the concentrations of free radicals in the case of illumination of an aqueous suspension of chloroplasts and the decrease of this concentration after switching off the illumination. There is also great biological interest in investigations of iron in hemin, methemoglobin, and their derivatives, the results of which are given in the tables of Chapter IV of this book.

There is special interest in the works of Blyumenfel'd and his co-workers devoted to the subject of paramagnetic resonance in irradiated and nonirradiated albumins and also compounds of albumin with ribonucleic acids [120-123]. Since we cannot elaborate on the statements of this paper, we must mention that they reveal entirely new perspectives regarding a number of subjects of theoretical biology, in particular, heredity.

Finally we point out that an attempt has been made [1] to establish a correlation between the content of free radicals in tissues and the growth of cancerous cells. However this attempt did not meet with success.

7.5. Inorganic Free Radicals. Paramagnetic Gases

Up to the present time we have considered organic radicals. The class of inorganic radicals is substantially smaller, but in addition to a small number of stable radicals, it also includes a number of unstable radicals formed in a discharge, during irradiation, in the course of chemical reactions, etc. Among these radicals there are some that are very important chemically. In the class of free radicals one may conditionally include various atomic substances. Paramagnetic gases constitute a special class of free radicals as regards their spectra. In the present section, we shall briefly consider first free inorganic radicals in condensed phases, and then paramagnetic gases.

1. The spectrum of atomic hydrogen obtained during the γ irradiation of H_2SO_4, $HClO_4$ and H_3PO_4 acids frozen at 77°K turned out to be a doublet with splitting $A' = 500$ gauss and $g = 2.00$ [124, 125]. The maximum intensity of the effect in H_2SO_4 is observed for the ratio $H_2SO_4:H_2O = 1:5$; on further dilution the effect weakens, and in pure ice it vanishes. These measurements were made in the microwave region. At low frequencies (350 Mc) the effect due to atomic hydrogen in pure ice was detected with $A' = 30$ gauss [126]. The appearance of this resonance only at weak fields H can apparently be explained by the large anisotropy of the g factor for "atomic" hydrogen observed in pure ice. The effects of atomic hydrogen in deuterium in frozen systems have been observed in [127, 128].

The radical products that are formed in a discharge in water vapor condensed at 77°K were investigated in [129]. These authors discovered one line with $g = 2.0085$ and with a weak bend corresponding to $g = 2.027$. On heating up to 138°K the resonance disappeared. Both D_2O and H_2O_2 gave similar results. In [130] in an investigation of the products formed at low temperature from H_2O, H_2O_2 and D_2O vapors dissociated in a glow discharge, one line with a weak additional maximum on one of its wings was also obtained. This maximum has been explained by the authors of [130] as a consequence of the g-factor anisotropy and not as an indication of the presence of a second radical. The observed effect has been attributed on the basis of chemical considerations to the $H\dot{O}_2$ radical, and not to $\dot{O}H$.

Irradiated nitrates of some salts gave a spectrum, attributed to NO_2 and consisting of a triplet with $A' = 50$ gauss [131, 132].

Among the stable inorganic radicals, the superoxides and ozonates of alkali metals (types MO_2 and MO_3, respectively) must be mentioned. In the first case the spectrum is due to the $\dot{O}_2^-$ radical-ion, and consists of one asymmetrical line with $g_{\parallel} = 2.157$ and $g_{\perp} = 2.002$ [133]. In ozonates (NaO_3 and KO_3), the line was found to be somewhat more symmetric: $g_{\parallel} = 2.003$, $g_{\perp} = 2.015$ [134]. Sodium dithionite, in which the resonance is evidently due to the SO_2^- ion, gave a line with $g = 2.01$ and $\Delta H = 12$ gauss [135].

Investigations of chlorine dioxide (ClO_2) have been mentioned above (see page 297 [12]).

Finally, we shall mention the inorganic ion radical $[(SO_3)_2NO]^{2-}$ since several papers are devoted to investigating it in solution. It gives a triplet pattern resulting from the interaction between the unpaired electrons and the spin of the N^{14} nucleus. The energy levels of the system in the case of a weak field investigation accurately obey the Breit-Rabi formulas for the case $I = 1$, $S = 1/2$, as has been shown in [135]. Lloyd and Pake [136] have analyzed in detail the paramagnetic relaxation mechanisms in solutions containing the $[(SO_3)_2NO]^{2-}$ ion.

2. According to the definition given at the beginning of this chapter, the diatomic and polyatomic molecules of several gases are free radicals, inasmuch as they contain uncompensated electron spins. These gases include, in particular, O_2, NO, NO_2, ClO_2, and the vapors of several paramagnetic compounds. In addition to such stable gaseous free radicals, there also exist a large number of unstable radical materials that exist in gaseous media, such as, $\dot{C}H_3$, $\dot{O}H$, etc., some of which have been studied in the condensed phase, as was discussed above.

Paramagnetic gases differ from the paramagnetic substances discussed previously by the strong coupling between the magnetic moment of the unpaired electron and the angular momenta of the rotational motions of the molecule. As a result, the system of levels observed in an EPR investigation of a gas turns out to be very complex.

Resolved lines of the paramagnetic resonance spectra in gases are successfully observed only at reduced pressures p. At $p > 20$ mm Hg, no resolved line has ever been observed in even a single case; in practice, the pressures that are employed usually do not exceed 1 mm Hg. This is the source of the difficulty of experimental work with gases (if we allow for the large number of lines of the spectrum), in that it requires extremely sensitive equipment. A large part of the resonance work on gases has been carried out by Beringer and Castle.

Of all the gases studied, nitrogen peroxide NO_2 is characterized by the weakest coupling between the electron spin and the rotation of the molecule. At the pressure $p = 10$ mm Hg a triplet structure due to the nitrogen nucleus is observed; at $p = 1$ mm Hg it is partially resolved into a large number of lines; Beringer and Castle have interpreted this as a Paschen-Back effect on the three magnetic moments in the molecules: that of the electron spin, that of the nuclear spin and that due to the rotation of the molecule. The energy level system can be described by the equation

$$E_{M_S, M_I, M_J} = g\beta HM_S + AM_S M_I + BM_S M_J, \tag{7.2}$$

where M_J is the rotational quantum number of the molecule. A complete resolution of the separate lines was not successfully achieved [137, 138].

The NO molecule has one unpaired electron and its ground state is $^2\Pi$. It is split by spin-orbit coupling into two doublet levels with a separation of 120 cm^{-1}; the lower level $^2\Pi_{1/2}$ is diamagnetic, because the projections of the spin and orbital moments along the axis are equal and opposite; the upper level $^2\Pi_{3/2}$ is paramagnetic. The upper doublet is split further into a number of subcomponents by interaction with the rotational motion. Thus states are formed with the total angular momentum J. The $J = 3/2$ level has $g = 4/5$; this sublevel is split by the external magnetic field H into a triplet fine structure which was observed in [139]. Each of these triplet peaks in turn has a triplet hyperfine splitting due to the N^{14} nucleus. The theory of the Zeeman effect in NO has been given in [140].

The O_2 molecule is a biradical; it contains two unpaired electrons with parallel spins, and has zero angular momentum along the axis. Its ground state is therefore $^3\Sigma$. Its orbital moment combines with the spin moment to give levels corresponding to $J = K$, $K \pm 1$, where K is the total orbital angular momentum quantum number (molecular + electron). The $K \pm 1$ levels are nearly degenerate and are separated by 2 cm^{-1} from the $J = K$ level. It is therefore possible to observe absorption in zero external magnetic field H at a wavelength of about 5 mm. Application of the field H splits the J level and induces magnetic dipole transitions between the sublevels. In the field region $H \approx 3000$ gauss the spin and orbital motions are decoupled, which gives rise to a large number of resonance lines (about 40), due to the rotational levels. These lines have been described in [141], and the theory of the spectrum is given in [141-143].

In addition to stable paramagnetic gases, Beringer and his co-workers also investigated atomic hydrogen [144], oxygen [145], and nitrogen [146] in the gaseous phase. The free atoms were produced in a U-shaped high-voltage gas discharge tube in which the corresponding molecular gases were located. This tube was connected directly to a vertical tube passing along the axis of a TE_{011} cylindrical resonator. Recombination on the glass walls was prevented as far as possible by the use of suitable anticatalysts.

Dehmelt [147] proposed the addition of inert gases at pressures of 10-100 mm Hg to the gas being studied (at a partial pressure of about 0.01-0.1 mm Hg). At these pressures it is possible to maintain a high-temperature arc. It is therefore possible to dissociate any type of molecule by purely thermal means. At the same time, the inert gas reduces the possibility of recombination, by retarding diffusion to the walls. He employed this method to study atomic phosphorus ($^4S_{3/2}$). The line was found to be a hyperfine doublet with $A' = 20$ gauss. Another method was used in [148] for the study of atomic iodine; the method employs photodissociation with the aid of ultraviolet irradiation of the J_2 vapors directly in a cavity resonator.

Literature for Chapter VII

1. Ingram, D. J. E. Free Radicals as Studied by Electron Spin Resonance, London, 1958.
2. Wertz, J. E. Chem. Rev. 55, 829, 1955.
3. Blyumenfel'd, L. A.,V. V. Voyevodskiy. Uspekhi Fiz. Nauk 68, 31, 1959.
4. Kozyrev, B. M., S. G. Salikhov. Doklady Akad. Nauk SSSR 68, 1023, 1947.
5. Bloembergen, N., S. Wang. Phys. Rev. 93, 72, 1954.
6. Walter, R. I., R. S. Codrington, A. F. D'Adamo, H. C. Torrey. J. Chem. Phys. 25, 319, 1956.
7. Weissman, S. I. J. Chem. Phys. 25, 890, 1956.
8. McConnell, H. M. J. Chem. Phys. 24, 764, 1956.
9. Jarrett, H. S. J. Chem. Phys. 25, 1289, 1956.
10. Bersohn, R. J. Chem. Phys. 24, 1066, 1956.
11. McConnell, H. M., D. B. Chestnut. J. Chem. Phys. 27, 384, 1957; 28, 107, 1958.
12. Bennett, J. E., D. J. E. Ingram, D. Schonland. Proc. Phys. Soc. A69, 556, 1958.
13. Berthet, G. Arch. Sci. 10, 98, 1957.
14. Holden, A. N., C. Kittel, F. R. Merritt, W. A. Yager. Phys. Rev. 77, 147, 1950.
15. Livingston, R., H. Zeldes. J. Chem. Phys. 24, 170, 1956.
16. Garstens, M. A., L. S. Singer, A. H. Ryan. Phys. Rev. 96, 53, 1954.

17. Becker, S. Phys. Rev. 99, 1928, 1955.
18. Arbuzov, A. Ye., F. G. Valitova, N. S. Garif'yanov, B. M. Kozyrev. Doklady Adad. Nauk, SSSR 126, 774, 1959.
19. Lothe, J. J., G. Eia. Acta Chem. Scand. 12, 1535, 1958.
20. Yablokov, Yu. V. Conference on Paramagnetic Resonance, Kazan, 1959.
21. Garif'yanov, N. S., B. M. Kozyrev, Doklady Akad. Nauk SSSR 118, 738, 1958.
22. Uebersfeld, J. Compt. Rend. 241, 371, 1955.
23. Wertz, J. E., C. F. Kolsch, J. L. Vivo. J. Chem. Phys. 23, 2194, 1955.
24. Arbuzov, A. Ye., F. G. Valitova, N. S. Garif'yanov, B. M. Kozyrev. Conference on Paramagnetic Resonance, Kazan, 1959.
25. Chirkov, A. K., R. O. Matevosyan. Zh. Eksp. Teoret. Fiz. 33, 1053, 1957.
26. Berthe, G. Arch. Sci. 9, 92, 1956.
27. Cohen, V. W., C. Kikuchi, J. Turkevich. Phys. Rev. 85, 379, 1952.
28. Bijl, D., H. Kainer, A. C. Rose-Innes. Nature, London, 174, 830, 1954.
29. Nielsen, W. G., G. K. Fraenkel. J. Chem. Phys. 21, 1619, 1953.
30. Meyer, L. H., A. Saika, H. S. Gutowsky. J. Phys. Chem. 57, 481, 1953.
31. Yokozawa, Y., L. Tatsuzaki. J. Chem. Phys. 22, 2087, 1954.
32. Chu, T. L., G. E. Pake, D. E. Paul, J. Townsend, S. I. Weissman. J. Phys. Chem. 57, 504, 1953.
33. Holden, A. N., W. A. Yager, F. R. Merritt. J. Chem. Phys. 19, 1319, 1951.
34. Van Roggen, A., L. van Roggen, W. Gordy. Phys. Rev. 105, 50, 1957.
35. McLean, C., T. Rotgieser, G. Y. W. Kor. Appl. Sci. Res. 5, 469, 1956.
36. Codrington, R. S., J. D. Olds, H. C. Torrey. Phys. Rev. 95, 607, 1954.
37. Trkal, V. Cesksl. rasop. Fys. 7, 748, 1957.
38. Jarrett, H. S. J. Chem. Phys. 21, 761, 1953.
39. Kicuchi, C., V. W. Cohen. Phys. Rev. 93, 394, 1954.
40. Weissman, S. I., J. Townsend, D. E. Paul, G. E. Pake. J. Chem. Phys. 21, 2227, 1953.
41. Hückel, E. Z. Phys. 70, 204, 1931.
42. Ward, R. L., S. I. Weissman. J. Am. Chem. Soc. 76, 3612, 1954.
43. Yokozawa, Y., I. Miyashita. J. Chem. Phys. 25, 796, 1956.
44. Weissman, S. I., E. de Boer, J. J. Conradi. J. Chem. Phys. 26, 963, 1957.
45. Hirshon, J. M., D. M. Gardner, G. K. Fraenkel. J. Am. Chem. Soc. 75, 4115, 1953.

46. Wertz, J. E., J. L. Vivo. J. Chem. Phys. 23, 2193, 1955.
47. McLean, C., J. U. van der Waals. J. Chem. Phys. 27, 827, 1957.
48. McConnell, H. M. J. Chem. Phys. 24, 632, 1956.
49. Tuttle, T. R., S. I. Weissman. J. Chem. Phys. 25, 189, 1956.
50. Venkataraman, B., G. K. Fraenkel. J. Chem. Phys. 24, 737, 1956.
51. Wertz, J. E., J. L. Vivo. J. Chem. Phys. 23, 2441, 1955.
52. Jarrett, H. S., G. J. Sloan. J. Chem. Phys. 22, 1783, 1954.
53. Brovetto, P., S. Ferroni. Nuovo Cimento 5, 142, 1957.
54. McConnell, H. M., D. B. Chestnut. J. Chem. Phys. 27, 984, 1957.
55. Bamford, C. H., A. D. Jenkins, D. J. E. Ingram, M. C. R. Symons. Nature, London, 175, 894, 1955.
56. Ingram, D. J. E., M. C. R. Symons. J. Chem. Soc. 2437, 1957.
57. Gardner, D. M., G. K. Fraenkel. J. Am. Chem. Soc. 78, 3279, 1956.
58. Tsvetkov, Yu. D., V. V. Voyevodskiy, G. A. Razuvayev, Yu. V. Sorokin, G. A. Domrachev. Doklady Akad. Nauk SSSR 115, 118, 1957.
59. Voyevodskiy, V. V., Yu. N. Molin, V. M. Chibrikin. Optika i Spektroskopiya 5, 90, 1958.
60. Dyatkina, M. Ye. Uspekhi Khim. 27, 57, 1958.
61. Chibrikin, V. M., A. I. Burshteyn, S. P. Solodovnikov. Cited in [3].
62. Hoskins, R. H., B. R. Loy. J. Chem. Phys. 23, 2461, 1955.
63. De Boer, E. J. Chem. Phys. 25, 190, 1955.
64. Weissman, S. I., T. R. Tuttle, E. de Boer. J. Phys. Chem. 61, 28, 1957.
65. Pake, G. E., S. I. Weissman, J. Townsend. Disc. Faraday Soc. 19, 147, 1955.
66. Tuttle, T. R., R. L. Ward, S. I. Weissman. J. Chem. Phys. 25, 189, 1956.
67. Tuttle, T. R., S. I. Weissman. J. Chem. Phys. 25, 190, 1957.
68. Sogo, P. B., M. Nakazaki, M. Calvin. J. Chem. Phys. 26, 1943, 1957.
69. Venkataraman, B., G. K. Fraenkel. J. Am. Chem. Soc. 77, 2707, 1955.
70. Venkataraman, B., G. K. Fraenkel. J. Chem. Phys. 23, 588, 1955.
71. Fraenkel, G. K. Ann. N. Y. Acad. Sci. 67, 553, 1957.
72. Wertz, J. E., J. L. Vivo. J. Chem. Phys. 24, 479, 1956.
73. Hoskins, R. H. J. Chem. Phys. 23, 1975, 1955.
74. Gilliam, O. R., R. I. Walter, V. W. Cohen. J. Chem. Phys. 23, 1540, 1955.
75. Weissman, S. I. J. Chem. Phys. 22, 1135, 1954.
76. Jarrett, H. S., G. J. Sloan. J. Chem. Phys. 22, 1783, 1954.
77. Hutchison, C. A., R. C. Pastor, A. E. Kowalsky. J. Chem. Phys. 20, 534, 1952.

78. Pake, G. E., J. Townsend, E. I. Weissman. Phys. Rev. 85, 682, 1952.
79. Fellion, Y., J. Uebersfeld. Arch. Sci. 10, 95, 1957.
80. Shneider, E. E., M. J. Day, G. Stein. Nature, London, 168, 645, 1951.
81. Ingram, D. J. E., W. S. Hodgson, C. A. Parker, W. T. Rees. Nature, London, 176, 1227, 1955.
82. Bijl, D., A. C. Rose-Innes. Nature, London, 175, 82, 1955.
83. Gibson, J. F., D. J. E. Ingram, M. C. R. Symons, M. G. Townsend. Trans. Faraday Soc. 53, 914, 1957.
84. Fujimoto, M., D. J. E. Ingram. Trans. Faraday Soc. 54, 1304, 1958.
85. Ingram, D. J. E., M. C. R. Symons, M. G. Townsend. Trans. Faraday Soc. 54, 409, 1958.
86. Gordy, W., W. B. Ard, H. Shields. Proc. Nat. Acad. Sci. 41, 983, 1955.
87. Uebersfeld, J., E. Erb. Compt. Rend. 242, 478, 1956.
88. Chernyak, N. Ya., N. N. Bubnov, L. S. Polak, Yu. D. Tsvetkov. Optika i Spektroskopiya 6, 564, 1959.
89. Chernyak, N. Ya., N. N. Bubnov, L. S. Polak, N. D. Tsvetkov. Doklady Akad. Nauk SSSR 120, 346, 1958.
90. Smaller, B., M. S. Matheson. J. Chem. Phys. 28, 1169, 1958.
91. Luck, C. F., W. Gordy. J. Am. Chem. Soc. 78, 3240, 1956.
92. Gordy, W., C. G. McCormik. J. Am. Chem. Soc. 78, 3243, 1956.
93. Rexroad, H.N., W. Gordy. Proc. Nat. Acad. Sci. 45, 256, 1959.
94. Fraenkel, G. K., J. M. Hirshon, C. Walling. J. Am. Chem. Soc. 76, 3603, 1954.
95. Bubnov, N. N., Yu. D. Tsvetkov, Yu. S. Lazurkin, M. I. Mokul'skiy, V. V. Voyevodskiy. Doklady Akad. Nauk SSSR 122, 1053, 1958.
96. Ard, W. B., H. Shields, W. Gordy. J. Chem. Phys. 23, 1727, 1955.
97. Abraham, R. J., H. W. Melville, D. M. Ovenall, D. H. Whiffen. Trans. Faraday Soc. 54, 409, 1958.
98. Abraham, R. J., D. H. Whiffen. Cited in [1].
99. Atherton, N. M., H. W. Melville, D. H. Whiffen. Trans. Faraday Soc. Cited in [1].
100. Harle, O. L., J. R. Thomas. J. Am. Chem. Soc. 79, 2973, 1957.
101. Ingram, D. J. E., J. E. Bennett. Phil. Mag. 45, 545, 1954.
102. Uebersfeld, J., A. Etienne, J. Combrisson. Nature, London, 174, 614, 1954.
103. Winslow, F. H., W. O. Baker, W. A. Yager. J. Am. Chem. Soc. 77, 4751, 1955.
104. Austen, D. E. G., D. J. E. Ingram, J. G. Tapley. Trans. Faraday Soc. 54, 400, 1958.
105. Uebersfeld, J., E. Erb. Compt. Rend. 243, 2043, 1956.

106. Garif'yanov, N. S., B. M. Kozyrev. Zh. Eksp. Teoret. Fiz. 30, 272, 1956.
107. Garif'yanov, N. S., B. M. Kozyrev. Zh. Eksp. Teoret. Fiz. 30, No. 6, 1956.
108. Ingram, D. J. E., J. G. Tapley, R. Jackson, R. L. Bond, A. R. Murnaghan. Nature, London, 174, 797, 1954.
109. Singer, L. S., W. T. Spry. Bull. Am. Phys. Soc. 214, 1956.
110. Uebersfeld, F., E. Erb. J. Phys. Rad. 16, 340, 1955.
111. Austen, D. E. G., D. J. E. Ingram. Chem. and Ind. 981, 1956.
112. Castle, J. G. Phys. Rev. 92, 1063, 1953; 94, 1410, 1954.
113. Ubbelohde, A. R. Nature, London, 180, 380, 1957.
114. Jarrett, H. S., G. F. Sloan, W. R. Vanghan. J. Chem. Phys. 25, 695, 1956.
115. Hutchison, C. A., A. Kowalsky, R. C. Pastor, G. W. Wheland. J. Chem. Phys. 20, 1485, 1952.
116. Kozyrev, B. M. Doklady Akad. Nauk SSSR 81, 427, 1955.
117. Blois, S. Bioch. and Biophys. Acta 18, 165, 1955.
118. Commoner, B., J. Townsend, G. Pake. Nature, London, 174, 4432, 1954.
119. Commoner, B., J. J. Heise, J. Townsend. Proc. Nat. Acad. Sci. 41, 983, 1955.
120. Blyumenfel'd, L. A., A. Ye. Kalmanson. Doklady Akad. Nauk SSSR 117, 72, 1957.
121. Blyumenfel'd, L. A., A. Ye. Kalmanson. Biofizika 2, 552, 1957.
122. Blyumenfel'd, L. A., A. Ye. Kalmanson. Biofizika 3, 87, 1958.
123. Blyumenfel'd, L. A., A. Ye. Kalmanson, Sheng Pei-chen. Doklady Akad. Nauk SSSR 129, 1144, 1959.
124. Livingston, R., H. Zeldes, E. H. Taylor. Phys. Rev. 94, 725, 1954.
125. Livingston, R., H. Zeldes, E. H. Taylor, Disc. Faraday Soc. 19, 166, 1955.
126. Smaller, B., M. S. Matheson, E. U. Yasaitis. Phys. Rev. 94, 202, 1954.
127. Jen, C. K., S. N. Foner, E. L. Cochran, V. A. Bowers. Phys. Rev. 104, 846, 1954.
128. Matheson, M. S., B. Smaller. J. Chem. Phys. 23, 521, 1955.
129. Livingston, R., Y. Ghormeley, H. Zeldes. J. Chem. Phys. 24, 483, 1956.
130. Gorbanev, A. I., S. D. Kaytmazov, A. M. Prokhorov, A. B. Tsentsiper. Zh. Fiz. Khim. 31, No. 2, 1957.
131. Ard, W. B. J. Chem. Phys. 23, 1967, 1955.
132. Bleaney, B., W. Hayes, P. M. Llewellyn. Nature, London, 179, 140, 1957.
133. Bennett, J. E., D. J. E. Ingram, M. C. R. Symons, P. George, J. S. Griffith. Phil. Mag. 46, 443, 1956.
134. Hodgson, W. G., A. Neaves, C. A. Parker. Nature, London, 178, 489, 1956.

135. Townsend, J., S. I. Weissman, G. E. Pake. Phys. Rev. 89, 609, 1953.
136. Lloyd, J. P., G. E. Pake. Phys. Rev. 94, 579, 1954.
137. Beringer, R., J. G. Castle. Phys. Rev. 78, 581, 1950.
138. Beringer, R., J. G. Castle. Phys. Rev. 80, 114, 1950.
139. Beringer, R., E. B. Rawson, A. F. Henry. Phys. Rev. 94, 34, 1954.
140. Margenau, H., A. Henry. Phys. Rev. 78, 587, 1950.
141. Beringer, R., J. S. Castle. Phys. Rev. 81, 82, 1951.
142. Henry, A. F. Phys. Rev. 80, 396, 1950.
143. Tinkham, M., M. W. P. Strandberg. Phys. Rev. 97, 937, 1955; 97, 951, 1955; 99, 537, 1955.
144. Beringer, R., H. A. Heald. Phys. Rev. 95, 1474, 1954.
145. Rawson, E. B., R. Beringer. Phys. Rev. 88, 677, 1952.
146. Heald, M. A., R. Beringer. Phys. Rev. 96, 645, 1954.
147. Dehmelt, H. G. Phys. Rev. 99, 527, 1955.
148. Bowers, K. D., R. A. Kamper, C. D. Lustig. Proc. Phys. Soc. B70, 1177, 1957.
149. Bijl, D., H. Kainer, A. C. Rose-Innes. J. Chem. Phys. 30, 765, 1959.

CHAPTER VIII

Double Resonance. Some Applications of Paramagnetic Resonance

8.1. Introduction

Up to this point we have considered resonance absorption of a periodic electromagnetic field at one specific frequency. In addition, various applications have been found for double resonance, which consists of the simultaneous resonance absorption of electromagnetic radiation at two different frequencies. The most important examples of double resonance will be considered: 1) the Overhauser effect and other dynamic methods of polarizing nuclei; 2) paramagnetic amplifiers (masers); and 3) optical studies of paramagnetic resonance.

In the Overhauser effect, electron and nuclear paramagnetic resonance are examined simultaneously. Consequently, one of the frequencies used lies in the microwave region and the other lies in the high radio-frequency region. The polarization of atomic nuclei is an interesting application of this effect.

Paramagnetic resonance is used in engineering for the construction of amplifiers with exceptionally low noise levels. In these amplifiers one usually utilizes variable fields at two different frequencies lying in the microwave region. Radiation at one frequency is used to supply energy to the paramagnetic substance, and the other frequency is used for amplification.

In many experiments the substance under investigation was subjected to the simultaneous resonance action of optical and microwave radiation. The union of optical and microwave methods of investigation was very fruitful and in a short time made it possible to obtain some interesting data both in the realms of atomic spectroscopy and the theory of atomic collisions.

8.2. Dynamic Methods of Polarization of Nuclei

1. Overhauser effect in metals and semiconductors

We assume that the substance contains both particles having an electronic magnetic moment and also particles possessing a nonzero nuclear moment. In a particular case the electronic and nuclear moments may belong to the same atom. In many instances the mechanisms of electron and nuclear spin-lattice relaxation are such that saturation of the electron paramagnetic resonance leads to appreciable polarization of the nuclei. This effect was first theoretically treated for metals by Overhauser [1].

At first glance the enhancement of the nuclear polarization when the electron resonance is saturated may seem paradoxical, since equalization of the populations of different energy sublevels of the spin system signifies an increase of its temperature. As the temperature increases, the population difference of the different nuclear Zeeman sublevels should diminish. Van Vleck [2] resolved this paradox by pointing out that in this case a single electron-nuclear spin system does not exist. Three weakly interacting systems particpate in the processes of interest to us, namely, the K system, associated with the kinetic energy of the conduction electrons of the metals; the Z system, whose energy is due to the interaction between the electrons and the external static magnetic field (Zeeman energy of the electrons); and finally the N system, to which the Zeeman energy of the nuclei belongs. The different temperatures T_K, T_Z and T_N may be inherent to these systems.

Overhauser [3] showed that nuclear spin-lattice relaxation in metals is mainly due to the interaction between the nuclear moments and the conduction electrons:

$$\mathscr{H}_{eN} = a\hat{\boldsymbol{I}}\hat{\boldsymbol{S}} = a(\hat{I}_Z\hat{S}_Z + \hat{I}_+\hat{S}_- + \hat{I}_-\hat{S}_+), \tag{8.1}$$

where

$$a = \frac{8\pi}{3}\beta\beta_N g g_N \delta(r). \tag{8.2}$$

Here r is the distance from the conduction electron to the nucleus and $\delta(r)$ is the delta function. Interaction (8.1) is a contact interaction and is isotropic, which makes it apparent that the sum $S_Z + I_Z$ is a constant of motion. Thus, from the law of the conservation of angular momentum it follows that under the influence of interaction (8.1) only the following transitions are possible:

$$M, m \longleftrightarrow M - 1, m + 1. \tag{8.3}$$

The reorientation of the electron spin is accompanied by a reversal in the nuclear spin direction.

It must be kept in mind that the electron Zeeman energy $E_Z = g\beta H_0 M$ is approximately 10^3 times greater in absolute value than the nuclear Zeeman energy $E_N = -g_N\beta_N H_0 m$.[1] A simultaneous reorientation of the electron and nuclear spins is therefore possible

---

[1]It should be remembered that g_N may be either positive or negative.

if the K system, which acquires the excess liberated energy, also takes part in this process. Suppose process (8.3) is accompanied by a change of the kinetic energy of the conduction electrons $E_K \longleftrightarrow E_{K'}$. Then from the law of conservation of energy we obtain

$$E_{K'} - E_K - g\beta H_0 - g_N \beta_N H_0 = 0. \tag{8.4}$$

Let N_K, N_M and N_m be the number of particles per unit volume in the K, M and m states, respectively. For each pair of interacting particles the probabilities of forward and reverse processes (8.3) are identical. The number of forward transitions will therefore be proportional to $N_K N_M N_m$ and the number of reverse processes proportional to $N_{K'} N_{M-1} N_{m+1}$. Under steady-state conditions,

$$N_K N_M N_m = N_{K'} N_{M-1} N_{m+1}. \tag{8.5}$$

Since

$$\left.\begin{aligned} \frac{N_K}{N_{K'}} &= \exp\left(\frac{E_{K'} - E_K}{kT_K}\right) = \exp\left[\frac{(g\beta + g_N\beta_N) H_0}{kT_K}\right], \\ \frac{N_M}{N_{M-1}} &= \exp\left(-\frac{g\beta H_0}{kT_Z}\right), \ \frac{N_m}{N_{m+1}} = \exp\left(-\frac{g_N \beta_N H_0}{kT_N}\right), \end{aligned}\right\} \tag{8.6}$$

it follows from (8.5) that

$$\frac{1}{T_N} = \frac{g\beta + g_N \beta_N}{g_N \beta_N T_K} - \frac{g\beta}{g_N \beta_N T_Z}. \tag{8.7}$$

Under the conditions of saturation of the electron resonance $T_Z \rightarrow \infty$. If we take into account the fact that $g_N \beta_N \ll g\beta$, we obtain

$$T_N = T_K \frac{g_N \beta_N}{g\beta}. \tag{8.8}$$

Thus, saturation of the electron resonance causes a reduction of the temperature of the nuclear Zeeman system by a factor of $g\beta / g_N \beta_N$. Hence, if we assume that $g\beta H_0 \ll kT_K$, we obtain

$$\frac{N_m}{N_{m+1}} = 1 - \frac{g\beta H_0}{kT_K}. \tag{8.9}$$

Polarization of the nuclei occurs as if their magnetic moments were increased by a factor of $g\beta / g_N \beta_N$. We note that the nuclear g factor may be either positive or negative. Consequently the temperature of the nuclear Zeeman system may take both positive and negative values. For simplicity the Boltzmann distribution was used in the derivation of (8.9). It is easy to verify that the Fermi distribution leads to the same result.

Under the influence of the RF field, which saturates the electron resonance, for the most part, transitions occur from the lower electron Zeeman level to the upper one. Relaxation transitions of the electron occur in the reverse direction with great probability, resulting in the establishment of a stationary state. Among the various relaxation mechanisms the one based on the electron-nuclear interaction (8.1) is essential for the Overhauser effect. Electrons jump from the upper Zeeman level to the lower and thereby continuously turn the nuclear spins toward one direction. The nuclear polarization will grow until the number of transitions $M, m \rightarrow M-1, m+1$ which occur under the influence of this relaxation mechanism becomes equal to the number of inverse transitions. In fact, it is clear that as the difference between T_N and T_K grows, the number of transitions contributing to the equalization of these temperatures will also increase. The Overhauser affect is an irreversible process of continuous transfer of electron Zeeman energy to lattice vibrations. This effect therefore may be easily interpreted by the methods of thermodynamics and statistical physics [4-9]; it may serve as a good illustration of the principal tenets of these theories. For a general theory of the Overhauser effect, it is essential to consider relaxation processes in two spin systems [10, 11], i.e., in systems containing two species of particles possessing different magnetic moments.

In the derivation of (8.9) we have assumed that for nuclei the relaxation mechanism based on interaction (8.1) is unique. The relaxation time due to this mechanism will be denoted by T'_1. Actually there exist other mechanisms of spin-lattice coupling. If we denote the over-all spin-lattice relaxation time by T_1, and in addition take into account the fact that the saturation parameter q_{12} of electron resonance may differ from zero, instead of (8.9) we obtain

$$\frac{N_m}{N_{m+1}} = 1 - \frac{g\beta H_0}{kT_K}(1-q)\frac{T'_1}{T_1} - \frac{g_N \beta_N H_0}{kT_K}. \tag{8.10}$$

This formula is applicable only to samples whose linear dimensions d are small compared with the skin depth δ. Azbel', Gerasimenko and Lifshits [12] showed that the Overhauser method permitted polarization of a nucleus in samples for which $d \gg \delta$. The electron mean free path in a metal is indeed much shorter than the distance traversed by the electron between two collisions which alter the orientation of the electron spin. Thus, the magnetic moments give a peculiar, anomalous skin effect. The nuclear polarization in samples of arbitrary thickness is calculated in [12].

The increase of nuclear polarization as a result of saturation of the electron Zeeman energy levels should change the shape of the electron paramagnetic resonance line [13], since the field produced by the polarized nuclei will be superimposed on the external magnetic field.

The Overhauser effect was first studied experimentally in lithium [14]. To avoid the difficulties associated with the simultaneous use of a resonant cavity and a coil, the experiments were conducted at relatively low frequencies, namely 13.4 Mc and 7.96 kc. Figure 8.1 gives a photograph illustrating how strongly the nuclear resonance signal is enhanced as a result of the saturation of the electron resonance. Later the Overhauser effect was studied in detail in Na and Li [15].

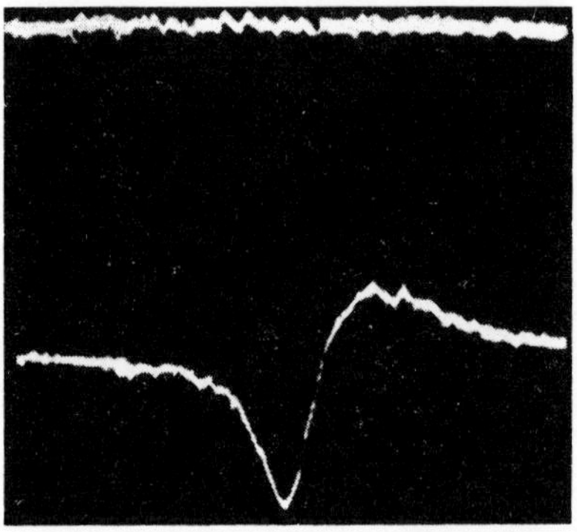

Fig. 8.1. Overhauser effect in lithium [14]. The upper trace shows the nuclear resonance signal hidden in the noise. In the lower one this signal is enhanced by electron resonance saturation.

Use of the Overhauser effect to increase nuclear polarization was extended to semiconductors, which affords the following advantages: 1) the poor conductivity removes difficulties associated with the skin effect at ultrahigh frequencies; 2) the small number of conduction electrons leads to very large nuclear relaxation times, which permits a separation both in amplitude and in time of the nuclear polarization induced by the high-frequency field from that appearing in subsequent observational experiments on this polarization employing a relatively low-frequency field.

Experiments have been performed in silicon crystals with phosphorus impurity [16]. The polarization of the Si^{29} nuclei was preserved for several minutes.

We should note the erroneous conclusions of Honig [17] from electron resonance experiments on arsenic-doped silicon. The measurements showed that the resonance absorption line has four hyperfine components in conformity with the magnitude of the nuclear spin of As^{75}, equal to 3/2. With repeated passage through the same lines, the absorption diminishes according to the exponential law $1 - e^{-t/\tau}$, where $\tau = 16$ sec. If during a time interval much less than 16 sec we vary the field H_0 in order to pass successively through two neighboring hyperfine components, the intensity of the second peak increases strongly. Honig initially supposed that he had found a method of 100% polarization of nuclei at moderately low temperatures. He assumed that transitions between the electron Zeeman sublevels, excited by the RF resonance field, cause the nuclear spins to rapidly build up as a result of the IS hyperfine interaction. The appropriate calculations have been performed by Kaplan [18]. However, subsequent experiments by Honig and Combrisson [19] have shown that we are dealing exclusively with a long electron relaxation time.

2. Overhauser effect in nonmetals

The Overhauser effect may occur in substances which are neither metals nor semiconductors [20-22]. In fact the following circumstances are essential in the Overhauser effect in metals: 1) one of the electron-spin relaxation mechanisms must depend on electron spin coupling with the nuclear moments, which requires conservation of the total angular momentum; 2) this latter interaction must play a decisive role in nuclear spin relaxation processes; 3) the possibility of conserving energy during these relaxation transitions must be ensured by the continuity of the conduction electron kinetic energy spectrum; 4) under saturation conditions, the relaxation transitions from the upper Zeeman level to the lower must occur at a greater rate than those in the reverse direction.

Completely analogous conditions exist in many nonmetals: 1) the conservation of the sum of the electron and nuclear spins is not necessary for an enhancement of nuclear polarization; it is only important that the probabilities of transfer of the nuclear spin $m \to m'$ and $m \to -m'$ be nonidentical; 2) the hyperfine interactions determine the nuclear relaxation not only in metals, but also in many other substances; 3) conservation of energy during the simultaneous flip of electron and nuclear spins may be guaranteed by the transfer of excess energy to the lattice vibrations in solids or to the Brownian motion in liquids and gases; 4) if the lattice is in a state of thermodynamic equilibrium then the a priori probabilities of relaxation transitions from the upper Zeeman levels to the lower ones is always greater than the probability of the reverse transitions.

Abragam [23] has treated in detail several important cases of the Overhauser effect in nonmetals. The following assumptions were made: a) the nuclear spin $I = 1/2$; b) the external magnetic field is strong so that to a good approximation the projections of the electronic and the nuclear spins along the H_0 direction are good quantum numbers; c) the nuclear moments have no direct coupling to the lattice vibrations so the nuclear relaxation occurs via the magnetic interaction of the nuclear and electronic spins, which is written generally as

$$\hat{\mathscr{H}}_1 = \hat{\boldsymbol{I}} a \hat{\boldsymbol{S}}, \tag{8.11}$$

where a is a symmetric tensor. The operator $\hat{\mathscr{H}}_1$ can be written as

$$\hat{\mathscr{H}}_1 = -g_N \beta_N \hat{\boldsymbol{I}} \hat{\boldsymbol{H}}_e, \tag{8.12}$$

where $\hat{\boldsymbol{H}}_e = -(a/g_N\beta_N)\,\hat{\boldsymbol{S}}$ may be called the magnetic field produced by the electron at the nucleus. The field H_e is a random function of time, and as a result random variations of both the tensor a and the direction of the spin S are possible. We shall speak of a relaxation of the first type if it is due to variations of the tensor a caused by the lattice vibrations in solids or by Brownian motion in liquids. Relaxation of the second type corresponds to flips of the electron spin occurring as a result of the ordinary mechanism of electron spin-lattice interaction which is independent of coupling with the nuclear moments.

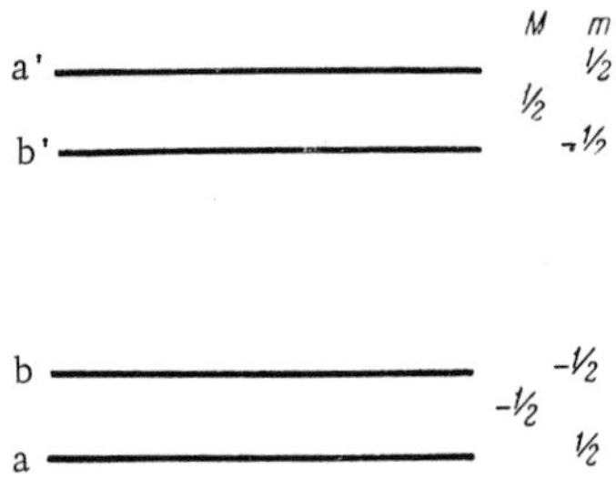

Fig. 8.2. Energy level diagram for the case S = 1/2, I = 1/2.

We shall denote the states (M = 1/2, m = 1/2), (- 1/2, 1/2), (1/2, - 1/2), (- 1/2, - 1/2), by a', a, b', b (Figure 8.2), the total population of levels a and a' by N_+, and that of levels b and b' by N_-. In addition we shall introduce the probabilities of relaxation transitions between different electronic sublevels by

$$\left.\begin{aligned} A_{aa'} &\approx A_{bb'} = Ae^{-\varepsilon} \approx A(1-\varepsilon), \\ A_{a'a} &\approx A_{b'b} = A(1+\varepsilon), \quad \varepsilon = \frac{g\beta H}{2kT}. \end{aligned}\right\} \tag{8.13}$$

For the probabilities of other relaxation transitions we take

$$\left.\begin{aligned} &A_{a'b'} \approx A_{b'a'} \approx A_{ab} \approx A_{ba} = \lambda_1 A, \\ &A_{b'a} \approx \lambda_2 A(1+\varepsilon), \quad A_{ab'} \approx \lambda_2 A(1-\varepsilon), \\ &A_{a'b} \approx \lambda_3 A(1+\varepsilon), \quad A_{ba'} \approx \lambda_3 A(1-\varepsilon). \end{aligned}\right\} \tag{8.14}$$

If the electron transitions $a \to a'$ and $b \to b'$ are saturated by the RF field, as Abragam has shown, the nuclear polarization is determined by the following expression:

$$\frac{N_+}{N_-} = 1 - \frac{2\varepsilon(\lambda_3 - \lambda_2)}{2\lambda_1 + \lambda_2 + \lambda_3}. \tag{8.15}$$

We shall consider the following special cases.

1. In metals, which we have treated earlier, there occurs a relaxation of the first type determined by the interaction (8.11) so that $\lambda_1 = \lambda_3 = 0$ and hence

$$\frac{N_+}{N_-} = 1 + 2\varepsilon, \tag{8.16}$$

which agrees with Eq. (8.9).

2. In liquids, if we assume that the nuclear relaxation is of the first type and is determined by the magnetic dipole interactions between the nuclei and the paramagnetic impurities, the ratios of the quantities λ_1, λ_2 and λ_3 are 3 : 2 : 12, i.e., as the mean values of the square of the matrix elements of operators $\hat{c}_{jk}$, $\hat{b}_{jk}$, and $\hat{e}_{jk}$ (5.9). For the nuclear polarization we obtain

$$\frac{N_+}{N_-} = 1 - \varepsilon. \tag{8.17}$$

3. In diamagnetic crystals containing paramagnetic impurities, the relaxation is of the second type. In this case $\lambda_3 = \lambda_2$ and no Overhauser effect exists. This result may be explained in the following manner. We shall consider transitions which lead to a flip of the nuclear spin $1/2 \to -1/2$:

$a' \to b \to b'$ and $a \to b' \to b$. The transitions $b \to b'$ and $b' \to b$ occur under the action of the saturating RF field and are not accompanied by a change in orientation of the nuclear spin. The transitions $a' \to b$ and $a \to b'$ occur as a result of coupling with the lattice vibrations. Since the relaxation is of the second type and is due to magnetic interactions between the electronic and nuclear spins, the probabilities of both these processes turn out to be identical ($\lambda_2 = \lambda_3$); as a result, the lattice acquires no energy, which means that additional polarization of the nuclei due to saturation of the electronic resonance is impossible.

4. For substances containing paramagnetic atoms with nonzero nuclear spins, the calculations were performed under the assumption that the hyperfine structure of the resonance line is resolved and has an isotropic character. In this case $\lambda_3 = 0$ and the polarization equals

$$\frac{N_+}{N_-} = 1 + \frac{2\varepsilon\xi}{2+\xi}, \tag{8.18}$$

where $\xi = \lambda_2/\lambda_1$. If one of the electron transitions, but not both, is saturated,

$$\frac{N_+}{N_-} = \frac{1+\varepsilon\xi}{2+\xi}. \tag{8.19}$$

The theory of relaxation transitions between the hyperfine energy sublevels has been given by Valiyev [24], who calculated the value of $\lambda_1 A$ for typical ions of the iron group and rare earth group. Corresponding calculations for ions in S states were made by Bashkirov [25]. The Overhauser effect has also been treated theoretically for the case $S = 1/2$, $I = 1$ with the Cu^{64} ion as the example. Thus, it is shown that simultaneous saturation of one electron and one nuclear resonance yields nuclear polarization of the same magnitude as in the case of saturation of all the electronic transitions [26].

Khutsishvili [27] considered the subject of polarization of nuclei belonging to paramagnetic atoms in nonmetals by means of saturation of only one of the hyperfine structure lines. He found that it is most convenient to saturate the line $m = 0$ if the nuclear spin I is even, and the line $m = \pm 1/2$ if I is odd.

The Overhauser effect in nonmetals has been studied experimentally in a number of cases: in protons of the free radical of α,α-diphenyl-β-picrylhydrazyl [28], in protons [29], in Li^7 and F^{19} nuclei [30][a] in solutions containing the free radical $K_2(SO_3)_2NO$, and in protons of benzene absorbed on charcoal [31].

3. Method of adiabatic (fast) passage (Endor)

The Overhauser method of nuclear polarization is applicable if the mechanism of nuclear spin-lattice relaxation obeys certain conditions. The (Endor) method proposed by Feher [32], based on the adiabatic fast passage of the paramagnetic resonance line (see Sec. 8.4), is applicable to substances which exhibit resolved hyperfine lines regardless of the mechanisms of nuclear and electronic spin-lattice relaxation. The method is illustrated in Figure 8.3, which shows the Zeeman energy levels vs. applied magnetic field H_0 in the case $S = 1/2$, $I = 1/2$. We denote by ν_e and ν_N the frequencies of the microwave and radiofrequency fields, both of which are perpendicular to H_0. If we sweep the field H_0 through the value H_1, we will induce the electronic transitions $M = -1/2$, $m = 1/2 \leftrightarrow M = 1/2$, $m = 1/2$. If we do this under adiabatic fast-passage conditions, the electronic magnetization vector will be turned through 180°, which causes a reversal of the populations of the corresponding sublevels. Now the population difference of each pair of nuclear sublevels belonging to the same electronic state will be determined by the electronic rather than the nuclear Boltzmann factor, which may be easily detected by the nuclear resonance method. However, the populations of both $m = +1/2$ sublevels equals that of the $m = -1/2$ sublevels, so that the sample as a whole does not exhibit nuclear polarization. In order to obtain a net polarization, we must sweep the magnetic field through the nuclear resonance corresponding to the field H_2, in an adiabatic fast passage. Since the energy spacing

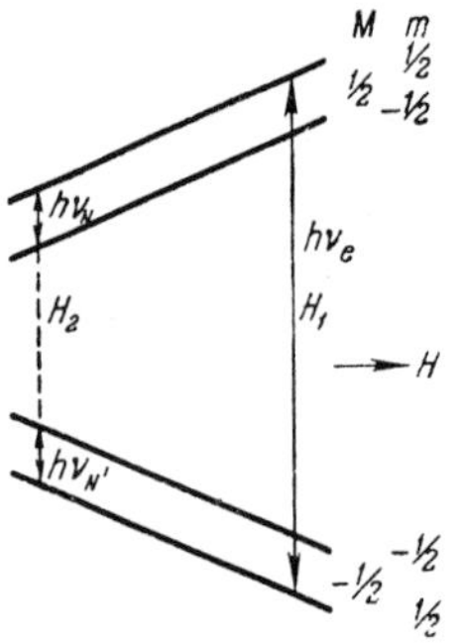

Fig. 8.3. Diagram of polarization of nuclei by the method of adiabatic passage.

---

[a] [In [30] NMR (at 72 gauss) of protons in $K_2(SO_3)_2NO$ solutions, of F^{19} in organic substances such as $C_6H_4(CF_3)_2$, and of Li^7 in solutions of LiOH was observed.]

$h\nu_N$ between one pair of nuclear sublevels does not equal the spacing between the other pair, there arises a nuclear polarization equal to[a]

$$\frac{N_+}{N_-} = 1 - 2\varepsilon. \tag{8.20}$$

This polarization decays during a time interval approximately equal to the nuclear relaxation time, and it may be reestablished by repeated sweeps of the field H_0.

If an adiabatically fast transition $\Delta m = 1, \Delta M = 0$ is realized, the electron resonance lines changes greatly. This provides us with a sensitive method of studying nuclear resonance by observing electron paramagnetic resonance absorption.

An experimental verification of the method of adiabatic passage was accomplished by Feher and Gere [33]. The experiments were performed on a phosphorus-doped silicon crystal containing about $3 \cdot 10^{16}$ atoms of P^{31} per cm^3. Previous papers (Sec. 6.3) showed the possibility of observing hyperfine structure of the paramagnetic resonance line in this substance arising from the interaction of the donor electron with the magnetic moment of the P^{31} nucleus, and in addition the electron spin relaxation time was found to be very long.

In the experiments of Feher and Gere the external field at which the transitions were observed was about 3130 gauss, and the temperature of the sample was 1.25°K. The electron resonance line was observed by the superheterodyne method without the use of magnetic field modulation. The microwave cavity was made of pyrex with a thin silver layer coated on the inner surface. A slit permitted the penetration inside the cavity of the RF field necessary for the stimulation of transitions between the nuclear sublevels. The amplitudes of the microwave and radio-frequency fields in the sample were of the order 0.001 gauss. The steady field H_0 was swept in the course of about 4 sec from the initial value 3150 gauss to 3110 gauss, and then returned again to 3150 gauss.

The results of the experiments verified the calculations of Feher. When no RF field existed the amplitude of the electron spin resonance line during the second passage through the resonance changed slightly. If the RF field acted in the interval between the first and second passage and induced the transition $h\nu_N$ (see Figure 8.3), then during the second passage the intensity of the electron spin resonance line dropped sharply, which indicates the existence of nuclear polarization. A similar method was applied in [34].

4. Method of parallel fields (dynamic polarization of forbidden transitions)

Jeffries [35] proposed for nuclear polarization the use of forbidden transitions which occur with a parallel arrangement of the periodic and static magnetic fields, since then the hyperfine

[a][More precisely, $N_+/N_- = (1 - \epsilon)/(1 + \epsilon)$.]

interactions slightly mix states with different values of M and m. If the hyperfine interaction operator is $A\hat{I}_z\hat{S}_z + B(\hat{I}_x\hat{S}_x + \hat{I}_y\hat{S}_y)$, then the wave functions which equal $\psi(M, m)$ in the zeroth approximation become in the first-order approximation $\psi(M, m) + \alpha(B/H)\ \psi(M \pm 1, m \mp 1)$.

As an illustration we shall consider the case $S = 1/2$, $I = 1/2$ (Figure 8.4). The solid arrows depict transitions which are possible with the usual mutually perpendicular arrangement of the periodic and static magnetic fields ($\Delta M = 1$, $\Delta m = 0$). The dashed arrows illustrate forbidden transitions which arise for the parallel arrangement of the field. From the form of the perturbed wave functions we obtain $\Delta(M + m) = 0$. If the RF field saturates the transition $M = -1/2, m = +1/2 \rightarrow M = 1/2, m = -1/2$, there immediately arises a polarization[a]

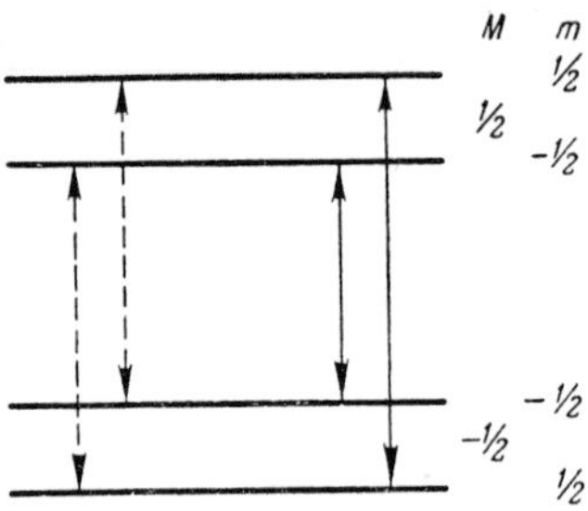

Fig. 8.4. Nuclear polarization scheme for the method of parallel fields (dynamic polarization of forbidden transitions).

$$\frac{N_+}{N_-} = 1 - \varepsilon.$$

If the polarized nuclei are radioactive, the polarization may be detected by observing the γ-ray anisotropy. The effect will be proportional to the number of radioactive decays instead of the number of atoms participating in the paramagnetic resonance absorption. Thus, the polarization method is particularly appropriate for the study of short-lived nuclei.

The method of Jeffries has been employed for the polarization of radioactive Co^{60} nuclei contained in a single crystal of $La_2Mg_3(NO_3)_{12} \cdot 24D_2O$ [36]. The abundance ratio for magnesium to isomorphically substituted cobalt isotopes was the following: $Mg : Co^{59} : Co^{60} = 10^4 : 50 : 1$. The measurements were conducted at the frequency $9.3 \cdot 10^9$ cps at the temperature 1.6°K. The Z axis of the crystal was oriented perpendicular to the static and oscillatory magnetic fields. The paramagnetic absorption in Co^{60} is very weak and could not be measured directly. The paramagnetic resonance was determined from the γ-ray anisotropy. The spectrum contained $2I = 10$ lines as expected from the known value of the Co^{60} nuclear spin. The following ratios were obtained for the relative intensities of the lines: 83 : 100 : 83 : 52 : 18, which is in good agreement with those predicted by theory [37].

5. Abragam and Proctor method [38]

We shall assume that the substance contains electronic and nuclear unpaired spins. For simplicity we take these spins to be $S = 1/2$ and $I = 1/2$. Suppose some interaction such as magnetic

[a][More precisely, $N_+/N_- = (2 - \epsilon)/(2 + \epsilon)$.]

dipole-dipole coupling exists between the electronic and nuclear spins. This coupling mixes the electronic and nuclear states, so that the wave functions take the form $\psi(M, m) + \alpha\psi(M', m')$, where $\alpha \ll 1$.

We assume that a periodic field of frequency $\nu = \nu_e + \nu_N$ is imposed perpendicular to the static field H_0. There is then a certain probability P, proportional to α^2, that a simultaneous reorientation of the electron and nuclear spins will begin. We shall denote the electron spin-lattice relaxation time by T_{1e}, and the corresponding time for the nucleus by T_{1N}. Suppose $1/T_{1N} < P < 1/T_{1e}$. Then, obviously, after dynamic equilibrium has set in, the ratio of populations of the Zeeman levels of the nuclei will be the same as in the electronic levels.

This type of effect may be achieved if we supply an energy with the frequency difference $\nu_e - \nu_N$. Thus, obviously, a reflipping of the electron spin will be accompanied by a reorientation of the nuclear spin in the opposite direction.

Abragam and Proctor [38] experimentally checked their method in a LiF single crystal. The experiments were conducted at the frequency $\nu = \nu_e \pm \nu_N = 9.4$ Mc. The nuclear polarization of Li^6 was enhanced by approximately $\gamma(F^{19}) : \gamma(Li^6) = 6.5$-fold.

Further development of this method is described in papers [120]. In particular, the aluminum nucleus was polarized in chromium-doped corundum [121].

8.3. Maser Amplifiers and Oscillators

Conventional radio-engineering devices which contain electronic tubes, klystrons, magnetrons, etc., transform the kinetic energy of charged particles into RF electromagnetic energy. For many reasons the possiblity of obtaining RF electromagnetic energy from the internal energy of atoms and molecules in excited states is very attractive. This idea was first realized by means of molecular beams[1] [39-41]. Masers have found a number of important applications because of their unusually high frequency stability, but they cannot be widely used in technology because of the extremely low power and the limitation of possible operating frequencies. Such a device may in principle be used as an exceptionally low-noise amplifier. Practical applications of this amplifier do not exist, however, because of the extremely narrow frequency bands amplified by it and the impossibility of tuning it.

In recent years it has become possible to use paramagnetic resonance in solids to produce very low-noise amplifiers, which are

---

[1]Such a device is outside the definition of what is customarily called a "maser," which means microwave amplification by stimulated emission of radiation.

distinguished by much greater bandwidths and the possibility of easily tuning the operating frequency over wide limits. Together with maser amplifiers, maser oscillators also may find technical application, in particular, in the millimeter and submillimeter wavelength regions.

The principle of operation of maser amplifiers and oscillators consists in the following. In Sec. 1.5 we saw that in contrast to the optical region, the probabilities of spontaneous transitions in the RF region are neglibibly small. Therefore, here we may discuss the use of induced radiation. Moreover, since each atom radiates independently of the others in optical light sources the radiation is incoherent, while in the RF region the radiation is coherent and definite phase relations exist between the induced radiation and the resulting RF electromagnetic field.

We shall now consider a substance containing a large number of unpaired spins, each of which possesses a definite system of energy levels. Suppose E_m and $E_n\,(E_m > E_n)$ are a pair of levels whose spacing lies in the RF region.[1] N_m and N_n are the numbers of unpaired electrons, per unit volume, located on the levels E_m and E_n. We suppose that the substance was brought by some means to a nonequilibrium state, in which the number of unpaired spins in the upper level is greater than those in the lower level. A discussion of the various methods of so exciting the substance will be given in the following sections. We also assume that relaxation mechanisms are not very effective and that consequently the transition of a paramagnetic substance into the equilibrium state is brought about by internal interactions which occur relatively slowly. Suppose now that a weak RF signal of frequency $\nu_{mn} = (E_m - E_n)/h$ is incident on the substance. This signal gives rise to transitions $E_m \longleftrightarrow E_n$, whose probabilities are the same for both possible directions, but inasmuch as $N_m > N_n$, the paramagnetic resonance absorption will be negative. In other words, radiation will occur, whose power may be evaluated in accordance with (1.6), (1.7) and (1.11) from the formula

$$P_{\mathrm{rad}} = \frac{\pi^2 (N_m - N_n) |< m \,|\, \mu_x \,|\, n >|^2 \, \nu_{mn} q H_r^2}{h \Delta\nu}. \tag{8.21}$$

We note that, strictly speaking, the quantities $(N_m - N_n)$, $< m\,|\mu_x|\,n >$ and $\Delta\nu$ cannot be regarded as independent of one another. In fact, the larger the spin S of the paramagnetic species, the greater the matrix elements of the magnetic moment. But the increase in S, i.e., the increase in the number of spin levels, brings about a decrease of N_n and N_m. At the same time the enhancement

[1]We know that such splittings are achieved in readily attainable magnetic field strengths.

of S may cause an increase of the resonance line width $\Delta\nu$. When speaking of the width of the resonance line, as we already know (see Sec. 5.8), we should differentiate between "inhomogeneous broadening," due to the inhomogeneity of the field acting on the various unpaired spins, and "homogeneous broadening," which arises from dipole-dipole and exchange interactions between identical particles and from other causes. The sources of the inhomogeneous broadening—spins of nuclei belonging to diamagnetic atoms, inhomogeneity of the applied magnetic field, inhomogeneity of the crystalline field, etc.—begin to play a lesser role as the concentration of the unpaired spins increases. An increase of concentration and consequently also ($N_m - N_n$), starting at a certain minimum value, is accompanied by an increase of line width $\Delta\nu$.

The amplifier which is simplest and at the same time possesses many advantages may be visualized as a waveguide filled with an appropriate paramagnetic substance. A traveling wave as it moves forward will exponentially accumulate power so that, neglecting waveguide losses, the power gain is equal to

$$g_a^2 = \exp(\alpha, l), \tag{8.22}$$

where l is the waveguide length, $\alpha = AP_{\text{rad}}/P_{\text{inc}}$, and A is the transverse cross section of the waveguide. The power of the incident wave equals

$$P_{\text{inc}} = \frac{1}{8\pi} AcH_r^2. \tag{8.23}$$

It follows from (8.21) and (8.23) that

$$\alpha = \frac{8\pi^3 (N_m - N_n) |< m | \mu_x | n >|^2 \nu_{mn} q}{ch\,\Delta\nu}. \tag{8.24}$$

Calculations show that for substantial values of ($N_m - N_n$)/$\Delta\nu$ to obtain appreciable amplification, the length of the waveguide must be very large, on the order of several meters.

To decrease the dimensions of the amplifier, cavity resonators are used in place of waveguides. If the nonmagnetic losses in the substance and losses in the walls of the resonator are smaller than the power radiated by the paramagnetic substance, the energy stored in the resonator will increase, and in such a case induced radiation of the unpaired spins is caused not only by a weak RF signal, but also by the action of radiation previously emitted by the paramagnetic substance. Thus, a resonator filled with an active paramagnetic substance may be regarded as an oscillatory system with positive feedback coupling.

This system may be characterized by a negative quality factor Q_m, connected with the magnetic losses through the quality factor Q_0 resulting from the nonmagnetic losses inside the resonator, and the quality factor Q_e due to external losses arising from coupling to the waveguide or to the coaxial line. According to (1.10) we have

$$-\frac{1}{Q_m}=\frac{4P_{\text{rad}}}{\nu(\overline{H_r^2})_V}, \tag{8.25}$$

where $(\overline{H_r^2})_V$ is the value of H_r^2 averaged over the volume of the cavity resonator. Our system will operate as an oscillator if the self-excitation condition is fulfilled:

$$-\frac{1}{Q_m}>\frac{1}{Q_0}+\frac{1}{Q_e}. \tag{8.26}$$

The power of the generated oscillations will be limited by the saturation effect, since when the populations of levels E_m and E_n begin to equalize, the induced emission power ceases to increase. Saturation is caused by the nonlinearity of the self-oscillatory system under consideration and in this way determines the amplitude of the steady-state oscillations in the resonator. The system will operate as an amplifier if

$$\frac{1}{Q_0}+\frac{1}{Q_e}>-\frac{1}{Q_m}>\frac{1}{Q_0}. \tag{8.27}$$

If we denote the power gain as before by g_a^2, it is easy to deduce the following formula for the resonator amplifier[1]

$$g_a=\frac{Q_e^{-1}-Q_0^{-1}-Q_m^{-1}}{Q_e^{-1}+Q_0^{-1}+Q_m^{-1}}. \tag{8.28}$$

The bandwidth of amplifier B may be defined as the ratio of frequency ν to the over-all Q factor of the device:

$$B=\nu\left(\frac{1}{Q_e}+\frac{1}{Q_m}+\frac{1}{Q_0}\right). \tag{8.29}$$

Usually Q_0 is rather large, so that the last two formulas take the following simple form:

$$g_a=\frac{Q_m-Q_e}{Q_m+Q_e}, \tag{8.28a}$$

$$B=\nu\left(\frac{1}{Q_e}+\frac{1}{Q_m}\right). \tag{8.29a}$$

---

[1] This formula refers to an amplifier which is switched on with the help of a ferrite circulator (isolator).

Multiplying these expressions we obtain

$$g_a B = \nu \left(\frac{1}{Q_e} - \frac{1}{Q_m} \right). \tag{8.30}$$

If the amplification is large, Q_e and $|Q_m|$ should be almost identical, so that we have

$$g_a B = \frac{2\nu}{Q_e} = \frac{2\nu}{|Q_m|}. \tag{8.31}$$

We see that the product of the square root of the amplification factor and the bandwidth is a quantity which is approximately constant for an amplifier, when the configuration of the cavity resonator and the volume of the paramagnetic substance are fixed. It is apparent from (8.28) and (8.29a) that if the amplification is large, the amplification factor g^2_a and the bandwidth B are very sensitive to relatively small variations of Q_e and Q_m. No matter how large the variations of g_a and B become, however, their product remains almost constant.

Maser amplifiers and oscillators have important advantages. First, the amplifiers are free of many noise sources which are inherent to electronic devices, and their noise temperature is several degrees Kelvin. Second, maser oscillators and amplifiers have no restrictions regarding high frequencies, because the frequencies of the generated and amplified oscillations are determined by the spacings between the spin energy levels. These spacings may be made rather large by the selection of the material and the increase of the static magnetic field within available limits.

Up to the present time no maser oscillators of practical significance have been realized. Consequently, in the following we shall discuss only amplifiers, and specifically we shall discuss those of the resonator type.

The main advantage of maser amplifiers is their high sensitivity, which is related to a low inherent noise level. A number of investigations [43–45] have been especially devoted to this subject. The low noise level in these devices is ensured first of all by the fact that in contrast to electronic tube and semiconductor devices, there exist no free charges and therefore no shot effect, no flicker noise, no excess noise, etc. The lower limits of paramagnetic maser amplifier noise levels are determined by spontaneous emission. The noise in paramagnetic maser amplifiers may be characterized by an effective noise temperature T_n, whose magnitude equals approximately the absolute value of the effective spin temperature T_s. Moreover, application of the low (helium) temperatures necessary for effective operation of the amplifier (increase of the population difference of the levels, lengthening of the relaxation time T_1) promotes a reduction of the noise level.

Strandberg [45] calculated the noise figure F of a paramagnetic maser amplifer.[1] He obtained the following formula for a resonant amplifier:

$$\mathrm{F} = \left(\frac{g_a+1}{g_a}\right)^2 \frac{1}{tp_\nu(T_a)} \Big\{(1-t)p_\nu(T_t)+tp_\nu(T_a)+ + \frac{Q_e}{Q_0}\left[p_\nu(T_c)-p_\nu(T_m)\right]-\left(\frac{g_a-1}{g_a+1}\right)p_\nu(T_m)+ +(g_a+1)^{-2}p_\nu(T_0)\Big\}. \tag{8.32}$$

The values of many of the quantities occurring in this formula may be understood from a schematic illustration of the amplifier (Figure 8.5), where T_a, T_t, T_c are the temperatures of the antenna (source of the signal), of the transmission line and of the paramagnetic substance, respectively; T_0 is the temperature at the resonator output (load temperature); t is the power loss factor in the transmission line, i.e., the ratio of the output power to the input power of the transmission line. The parameter T_m has the dimensionality of temperature and may be determined from the following formula

$$\frac{N_m-N_n}{N_m+N_n} = \tan\mathrm{h}\left(\frac{h\nu_{mn}}{2kT_m}\right). \tag{8.33}$$

If η is the number of spin levels of one frequency,

$$N_m+N_n \approx \frac{2N_0}{\eta}. \tag{8.34}$$

From formulas (8.33), (8.34), (8.21), (8.25) we obtain

$$T_m = -\frac{h\nu_{mn}}{2k}\left[\tan\mathrm{h}^{-1}\frac{\eta h\Delta\nu}{8\pi^2 qN_0Q_m\,|\,(m\,|\,\mu_x\,|\,n)\,|^2}\right]^{-1}. \tag{8.35}$$

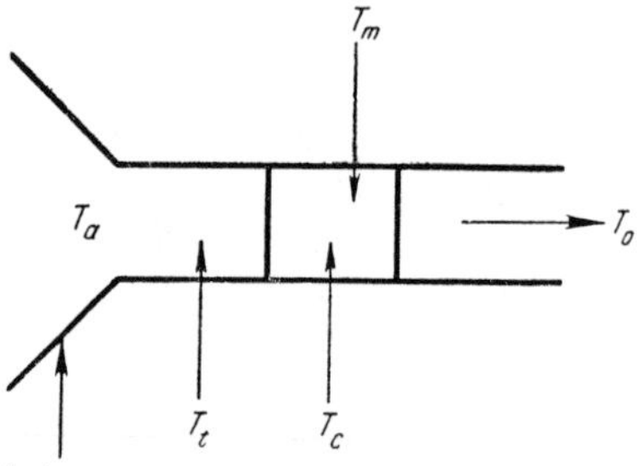

Fig. 8.5. Temperature parameters which determine the noise figure of a paramagnetic maser amplifier.

[1] Errors in the formulas of [45] are corrected in [46].

In conformity with Planck's formula, the mean energy of the oscillator at the temperature T is

$$p_\nu(T)=\frac{h\nu}{\exp(h\nu/kT)-1}. \tag{8.36}$$

Usually $h\nu \ll kT$, so that $p_\nu(T)=kT$. Moreover, if we assume first that the transmission line losses are small and $t\approx 1$, and second that the amplification is substantial and $g_a \gg 1$, then (8.32) takes a simpler form:

$$\mathrm{F}=1-\frac{T_m}{T_a}\left(1+\frac{Q_e}{Q_0}\right)+\frac{T_c}{T_a}\frac{Q_e}{Q_0}, \tag{8.37}$$

and consequently the noise temperature becomes

$$T_n=(\mathrm{F}-1)T_a=-T_m\left(1+\frac{Q_e}{Q_0}\right)+T_c\frac{Q_e}{Q_0}\ldots \tag{8.37a}$$

It is easy to see that by a proper selection of the amplifier parameters, the noise figure F can be made almost unity and $T_n \approx T_m$. An additional source of noise arises if excitation of the working substance is effected by the saturation method (see Sec. 8.5). Weber [46] has shown that the corrections to formula (8.32) resulting from this have no practical significance.

The most important problems arising in the construction of a paramagnetic maser amplifier are the choice of the working substance and the selection of a means of exciting it. It is obvious that a great diversity of methods of exciting unpaired spins occurs in the case of particles with effective spin $S' > 1/2$, i.e., when the number of spin levels is greater than 2. In the following sections, therefore, we shall consider separately two- and three-level maser amplifiers.

8.4. Two-Level Maser Amplifiers

All the proposed methods of exciting paramagnetic species with the effective spin $S' = 1/2$ consist in a population inversion of the Zeeman energy sublevels. In the equilibrium state the ratio of the populations of the lower (1) and upper (2) spin levels equals

$$\frac{N_1}{N_2}=\exp\left(\frac{g'\beta H_0}{kT}\right)=\exp\left(\frac{h\nu_0}{kT}\right). \tag{8.38}$$

The problem is to invert this ratio for a more or less long time interval. We shall discuss three possible methods of inversion of the spin level population.

a) Nonadiabatic change in direction of the static magnetic field

The simplest method of achieving this goal is a rapid (non-adiabatic) reversal of the applied static magnetic field H_0. The ratio N_1/N_2 thus becomes reversed, the more populated lower level becomes the upper, and vice versa. The change in field H_0 must occur so quickly that the condition of nonadiabaticity is fulfilled [47]. In our case this is

$$\frac{1}{H_0}\frac{dH_0}{dt} \gg 2\pi \cdot \nu_0 . \tag{8.39}$$

This condition is more easily fulfilled, the smaller the precession frequency ν_0, i.e., the smaller the field H_0. But the field H_0 cannot be as small as one wishes since it must substantially exceed the width of the resonance line: $H_{min} \gg \Delta H$.

It is most expedient, therefore, to proceed in the following manner: slowly decrease the field H_0 adiabatically to the magnitude H_{min}; then nonadiabatically quickly change $H_{min} \rightarrow -H_{min}$; after that slowly reduce the field adiabatically to $-H_0$. Obviously, this entire procedure must take place during a time which is much shorter than T_1. As an example, we take $\Delta H \approx 0.1$ gauss, $H_{min} \approx 0.5$ gauss. Then in order to change the field H_0 by 1 gauss, according to (8.39) a time interval of approximately $5 \cdot 10^{-8}$ sec is required. Such a type of field change may be produced by modern pulse techniques.

The method described by us has until now found application only in the realm of nuclear paramagnetism. This method has a great advantage, however, over other methods of excitation of unpaired spins since it does not require the use of an auxiliary RF field. It may be expected that the nonadiabatic change in direction of the magnetic field will be used for the construction of ultrahigh-frequency microwave oscillators.

b) Adiabatic fast passage

Bloch [49] has shown that an inversion of the spin level populations may be achieved through a rapid but adiabatic passage through the resonance produced by a variation in frequency of the microwave field or the intensity of the static field. Without deliberating on the calculations which lead to this result via a solution of Eq. (5.1) (see for example [50, 51]), we shall illustrate this method by a classical model.

The behavior of a dipole in the magnetic field H is conveniently studied by changing to a coordinate system rotating with a certain angular velocity ω. In the rotating coordinate system the motion of the dipole will be determined by the same equations of motion as in the inertial coordinate system, if we assume that an effective field instead of the field H acts upon the dipole [52]

$$\boldsymbol{H}_{\text{eff}} = \boldsymbol{H} - \frac{\omega}{\gamma}, \quad \gamma = \frac{g'\beta}{\hbar}. \tag{8.40}$$

The magnetic moment of the dipole will precess with an angular velocity $\omega_{\text{eff}} = \gamma H_{\text{eff}}$. Suppose now, as usual, $\boldsymbol{H} = \boldsymbol{H}_0 + \boldsymbol{H}_1$, where $\boldsymbol{H}_0$ is the static field, and field $\boldsymbol{H}_1$ is small and rotates uniformly with the velocity ω in a plane perpendicular to $\boldsymbol{H}_0$. Figure 8.6 illustrates three possible cases:

$$\gamma H_0 > \omega, \quad \gamma H_0 = \omega, \qquad \gamma H_0 < \omega.$$

We see that if H_{eff} undergoes a slow adiabatic change, the sign of the magnetization vector changes after passage through the resonance, and consequently the distribution of particles over the spin levels becomes inverted: $N_2 > N_1$. The adiabatic variation of H_{eff} means that the relative decrease of H_{eff} during the time $1/\omega_{\text{eff}}$ must be small. The smallest value of H_{eff} is H_1. The adiabatic condition in our case, therefore, is

$$(\gamma H_1)^{-1} \ll \Delta t \tag{8.41}$$

if Δt denotes the time necessary for a change of the field H_0 by a magnitude equal to the half-width ΔH of the resonance line. Moreover,

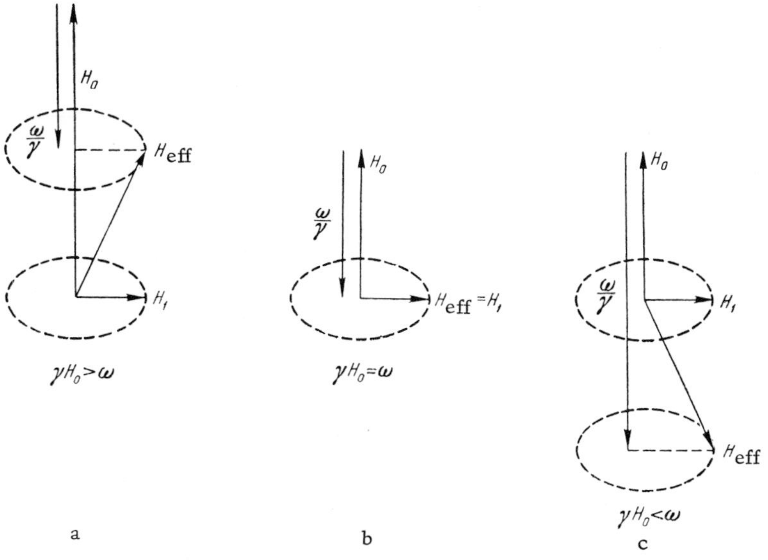

Fig. 8.6. Effective magnetic field in a coordinate system rotating with angular velocity ω around the field H_0.

passage through the resonance must be fast, inasmuch as the following condition must be fulfilled:

$$\Delta t \ll T_1. \tag{8.42}$$

The method of adiabatic fast passage has the following advantages: 1) it is not necessary to obtain good stabilization of the frequency ν of field H_1; 2) the time of passage Δt may be varied over a wide range.

c) 180° pulse

The paramagnetic substance is assumed to be at resonance. If we transform to a coordinate system rotating with the resonance frequency, then $H_{\text{eff}} = H_1$. Hence, only the steady magnetic field H_1 will act on the magnetic dipole (Figure 8.6b). The magnetization vector will precess around H_1 with angular frequency $\omega_1 = \gamma H_1$. If in place of the continuously acting periodic magnetic field we use a pulse of length

$$t_\pi = \frac{\pi}{\gamma H_1}, \tag{8.43}$$

the direction of the magnetization vector is changed by 180°, and an inversion of the spin levels occurs. The inversion is not complete, however, if 1) H_1 is not appreciably greater than the width of the resonance ΔH, and if 2) condition (8.43) is not fulfilled to a high degree of accuracy. It goes without saying that the pulse length t_π must be much less than the relaxation time T_1. The 180° pulse method is more suitable than the adiabatic fast passage method in that it requires a smaller periodic magnetic field power and a smaller time interval for inversion of the spin levels [50].

Operation of the two-level maser amplifier may be visualized in the following manner. Initially the working substance is found in a state of equilibrim. Then during the time t_1 one of the methods considered by us inverts the spin levels. After this, during the time $t_2 \ll T_1$ the process of amplification occurs. Then during the time t_3 thermal equilibrium is reestablished. We shall see that the two-level maser amplifier is operated on an intermittent basis. The time intervals t_2 of active operation are separated by "dead" intervals $t_3 + t_1$. If the restoration of thermal equilibrium occurs in an undisturbed substance, the time t_3 will be very large, on the order of T_1. Two methods of accelerating the restoration of equilibrium have been proposed.

The first method consists in optical illumination of the paramagnetic substance. This method is suitable when the working substance is an impurity semiconductor, for instance silicon doped with elements of group V (P, As, Sb) or with lithium. These semiconductors have a thermal relaxation time T_1 of several seconds at liquid helium temperature and at concentrations $N_0 \approx 10^{17} - 10^{18}$ cm^{-3} (see Sec. 6.2). By optically irradiating the crystal, the thermal relaxation time T_1 is shortened to several microseconds. If we allow for the fact that the time t_1 is in the worst case of the order of milliseconds, we see that the dead time may be made negligibly small, and the maser amplifier will operate almost continuously.

The second method of shortening t_3 consists in the following. Crystals containing two types of paramagnetic particles are used as the working substance. Let the relaxation time T_1 of one type of particle (A) be several orders of magnitude greater than that of particles of the other type (B). These two types of particles clearly will have different spin level systems. Particles of type A are used as the active paramagnetic centers of the maser amplifier. At the end of the period t_2 the static field H_0 is changed so that the spacing between the spin levels of particles A becomes equal to the spacing between any pair of spin levels of particles B. Then as a result of the spin-spin interaction the energy from particles of type A is transferred to particles of type B, and hence transferred very rapidly to the lattice. This kind of shortening of the relaxation time has been studied experimentally in a number of cases [53].

We shall obtain a condition for the existence of amplification, by assuming that the relaxation losses can be neglected. $(\overline{H_1^2})_S$ is the square of the periodic magnetic field strength, averaged over the volume of the paramagnetic sample. Let us assume that $|\langle m|\mu_x|n\rangle| = \beta$, $N_m - N_n = 1N_0 h\nu/2kT$. It then follows from (8.27), (8.25) and (8.21) that amplification will occur if

$$N_0 > \frac{kT\Delta\nu}{2\pi^2 q\beta^2\nu Q_0} \frac{(\overline{H_1^2})_V}{(\overline{H_1^2})_S}. \tag{8.44}$$

The first attempt to construct a maser was made using phosphorus-doped silicon under the following experimental conditions [54]: $\nu = 9000$ Mc, $Q_0 = 10{,}000$, $T = 2°$K, $\Delta\nu \approx 4 \cdot 10^6$, $(\overline{H_1^2})_S \approx (\overline{H_1^2})_V$. After substitution of these data, condition (8.44) becomes: $N_0 > 10^{17}$ cm^{-3}. In these experiments this condition was not fulfilled, and hence the desired amplification not detected. A positive result was obtained by Feher et al. [55], who replaced natural silicon by isotopically pure (99.88 ± 0.08%) Si^{28}, resulting in the narrowing of the paramagnetic resonance line from 2.7 to 0.22 gauss, since the inhomogeneous broadening due to the hyperfine interaction between the electronic shell of phosphorus and the Si^{29} nuclei disappeared. The experiments were conducted under the following conditions: $N_0 = 4 \cdot 10^{16}$ cm^{-3}, $T_1 \approx 1$ min at the temperature 1.2°K, $\nu = 9000$ Mc, and $Q_0 \approx 20{,}000$. The unpaired spins were excited by the adiabatic fast passage method.

Quartz and magnesium oxide, whose paramagnetic centers were created by strong neutron irradiation, were successfully used as the working substance for a two-level maser [56]. Inversion of the levels was accomplished by the adiabatic passage method. The frequency of the amplified signal was $\nu = 9000$ Mc, the loaded Q of the resonant cavity was ≈ 6000, and the temperature was 4.2°K. In the experiments with quartz the number of unpaired electrons $N_0 \approx 10^{18}$. The inverted state was maintained for about 2 milliseconds. If the signal was amplified 1.2 milliseconds after inversion of the levels, $g_a B \approx 5 \cdot 10^6$ sec^{-1} with an amplification which varied from 8 to 21 db. In experiments with MgO, $N_0 \approx 10^{17}$. The inverted state was maintained for about 2.5 milliseconds. An amplification of 20 db was observed within 125 microseconds after inversion of the levels.

In conclusion we note that the construction of a continuously operating two-level maser [57], based on the use of mechanically rotating equipment, has been proposed.

8.5. Three-Level Maser Amplifiers

1. Principle of operation

If the number of paramagnetic spin levels is greater than two, the method of saturating electron resonance may be used for excitation of the working substance. We assume that the particles have three spin levels (Figure 8.7). We assume also that with the aid of a sufficiently strong oscillatory field of frequency ν_{31}, saturation is obtainable, resulting in equalization of the populations of levels E_1 and E_3: $N_1 \approx N_3$. Then obviously, either $N_2 < N_3$ and it is possible to produce an amplifier of signals of frequency ν_{32}, or $N_2 > N_1$ and the amplification of signals of frequency ν_{21} is possible. The idea of producing a molecular oscillator with this method of excitation was first suggested by Basov and Prokhorov [58]. The possibilities of constructing a three-level maser, excited by the saturation method, were considered by Bloembergen [59]. The advantages of such a type of maser amplifier are continuity of operation and the possibility of using substances with relatively short relaxation times. These relaxation times must be long enough so that there is a practical possibility of saturating the paramagnetic resonance.

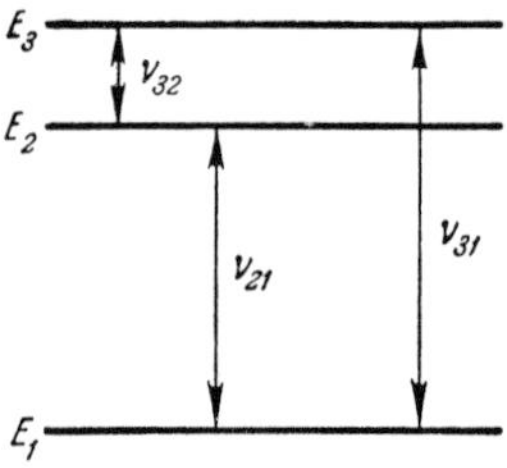

Fig. 8.7. Spin levels of unpaired electrons which constitute the operating substance of a three-level maser.

We shall find the condition of excitation of a three-level maser amplifier. Let A_{ik} be the probability of a particle undergoing a transition during 1 sec from level E_i to level E_k under the influence of lattice vibrations (see Sec. 5.3), and let p_{ik} be the probability of a transition between the same levels under the influence of the RF fields, calculated using (1.3). If $h\nu_{ik} \ll kT_c$, then the populations of the individual levels will obey the equations

$$\left.\begin{aligned}
&N_1 + N_2 + N_3 = N_0,\\
&\frac{dN_3}{dt} = A_{13}\left(N_1 - N_3 - \frac{N_3}{3}\frac{h\nu_{31}}{kT_c}\right) + \\
&\quad + A_{23}\left(N_2 - N_3 + \frac{N}{3}\frac{h\nu_{32}}{kT_c}\right) + p_{31}(N_1 - N_3) + p_{32}(N_2 - N_3),\\
&\frac{dN_2}{dt} = A_{23}\left(N_3 - N_2 + \frac{N}{3}\frac{h\nu_{32}}{kT_c}\right) + \\
&\qquad + A_{21}\left(N_1 - N_2 - \frac{N}{3}\frac{h\nu_{21}}{kT_c}\right) + p_{32}(N_3 - N_2),\\
&\frac{dN_1}{dt} = A_{13}\left(N_3 - N_1 + \frac{N}{3}\frac{h\nu_{31}}{kT_c}\right) + \\
&\qquad + A_{21}\left(N_2 - N_1 + \frac{N}{3}\frac{h\nu_{21}}{kT_c}\right) - p_{31}(N_1 - N_3).
\end{aligned}\right\} \tag{8.45}$$

If we assume that $p_{31} \gg p_{32}$ и $p_{31} \gg A_{ik}$, we obtain

$$N_1 - N_2 = N_3 - N_2 = \frac{hN_0}{3kT_c}\,\frac{A_{21}\nu_{21} - A_{23}\nu_{32}}{A_{12} + A_{23}}. \tag{8.46}$$

This magnitude will be positive and consequently negative absorption will occur at the frequency ν_{32} if

$$A_{21}\nu_{21} > A_{32}\nu_{32}. \tag{8.47}$$

If the reverse inequality is valid, negative absorption will occur at the frequency ν_{21}. Substituting (8.46) into (8.21) and using (8.25) and (8.27), we obtain the following conditions for the existence of amplification:

$$\frac{4\pi^2 qN_0 \,|\langle 2 | \mu_x | 3\rangle|^2}{3kT\,\Delta\nu}\,\frac{(\overline{H_1^2})_S}{(\overline{H_1^2})_V}\,\frac{A_{21}\nu_{21} - A_{23}\nu_{32}}{A_{12} + A_{23}} \gg \frac{1}{Q_0}. \tag{8.48}$$

If the number of spin levels is greater than three, completely analogous calculations may be conducted, which, however, become very cumbersome.

In the derivation of Eq. (8.47) we have neglected cross relaxation. Eq. (8.45) should be replaced by Eqs. (5.119); then in place of (8.47), we obtain

$$A_{21}\nu_{21} > \left(A_{32} + w + \frac{1}{3}\sum_{l} w_{ij}\right)\nu_{32}. \tag{8.47a}$$

Since the probabilities of cross relaxation transitions increase rapidly with an increase in unpaired spin concentration, from this it becomes clear why an appreciable increase in concentration of the spins leads to a cessation of the amplifier operation.

The linear amplifier theory presented by us may be regarded as correct if the pumping power of frequency ν_{31} is sufficient to overwhelm the spin-lattice relaxation and produce saturation, but still is not so large that it exceeds the spin-spin interaction and causes coherent ordering of the spin system. In other words, the mean time interval necessary for the reorientation of the spin under the influence of the saturating RF field must be greater than the spin-spin relaxation time. If this condition is not fulfilled, non-linear effects arise [60], which cause the paramagnetic maser to be of the parametric type. The linearity may be easily maintained if the spin-lattice interactions are far weaker than the spin-spin interactions. The latter conditions is usually fulfilled in many substances at low temperatures and for intermediate concentrations of unpaired spins.

It is noteworthy that the temperature T_m, which determines the minimum value of the noise figure, in the case of excitation of the amplifier by the saturation method may turn out to be much lower that the temperature T_c of the operating substance. In fact, if we assume $kT_m \gg h\nu_{32}$, then from (8.33), (8.34) and (8.46) we obtain (if $\eta = 3$)

$$T_m = T_c \frac{A_{12} + A_{23}}{\frac{\nu_{21}}{\nu_{32}} A_{21} - A_{23}}. \tag{8.49}$$

If we can neglect the quantity A_{23} in this expression, with an appropriate selection of the energy spacing, we obtain $T_m \ll T_c$.

2. Choice of substances

The foremost problem which must be solved in the design of a maser is the selection of a substance possessing suitable properties. The working substance of a three-level maser must satisfy the following basic requirements: a) the number of spin levels of the paramagnetic particle must be greater than two, and consequently particles with an effective spin $S' = 1/2$ are excluded; b) the splittings of the spin levels in the crystalline field in the absence of an external magnetic field (initial splittings) must be of the order $h\nu_{31}$, in order to easily achieve saturation of the paramagnetic resonance at the frequency of the pumping radiation; if the initial splittings are small, the magnetic dipolar transitions differ appreciably from zero only between neighboring spin levels; c) the probabilities of the spin-lattice relaxation transitions must be sufficiently small in order for saturation to set in at the available pumping powers; d) the relationship between the probabilities of relaxation transitions for different pairs of spin levels must satisfy condition (8.47); e) the number of magnetically nonequivalent ions in a unit cell must be as small as possible; f) the absence of hyperfine structure of the energy levels is very beneficial; g) the width of the individual spin levels, due to spin-spin interactions, must be sufficiently small so that 1) the spin levels do not overlap; and 2) saturation is rather easily attainable; it is necessary, therefore, that the substance selected be magnetically diluted with an isomorphic diamagnetic material; h) finally, there are certain requirements that are unrelated to the magnetic properties of the substance such as chemical stability, low dielectric loss and sufficient mechanical strength.

It should be noted that the longitudinal relaxation mechanism is of great value for maser operation. If this mechanism is determined by the rate of transfer of energy from the system of equivalent lattice oscillators to the liquid helium bath, saturation of the resonance, due to transitions between the levels E_1 and E_3, may influence the populations of the other levels (see Sec. 5.4). Unfortunately, the existing experimental data are incomplete and meager so the nature of paramagnetic relaxation in different substances still remains debatable. Bloembergen [61] asserts that the very fact that three-level masers exist at temperatures below 4.2°K indicates that longitudinal relaxation in paramagnetic crystals is not determined by coupling between the effective lattice oscillators and the helium bath. It is possible that the bottleneck in the process of energy transfer from the spin system to the lattice is the phonon-phonon interaction. Strandberg et al. [62, 63], while analyzing the results of experiments involving three-level masers, reached the conclusion that phonon-phonon processes play an essential role. On the basis of the latter investigation, Bloembergen [122] concluded that all the effects discovered by Strandberg et al. can be explained by cross relaxation.

Among the various paramagnetic substances it appears that only crystals containing ions of intermediate groups may satisfy the state requirements. The most intensively studied have been compounds of the iron group elements. As we know, in most crystals iron group ions have an environment of octahedral symmetry so these compounds will be discussed first.

In this case ions with the electron configuration d^1, d^2, d^6, d^7 possess extremely short spin-lattice relaxation times (see Sec. 5.3). It is therefore natural to exclude from consideration compounds of Ti^{3+}, V^{4+}, V^{3+}, Fe^{2+} and Co^{2+}. The suitable compounds that remain are those of the ions V^{2+}, Cr^{3+}, Cr^{2+}, Mn^{3+}, Mn^{2+}, Fe^{3+}, Ni^{2+} and Cu^{2+}. Of these ions, copper has spin $S = 1/2$, and its compounds are therefore not suitable for a three-level maser; however, the existence of hyperfine structure of the paramagnetic resonance line in copper apparently may enable one to use its salts for the creation of a maser at the frequencies from 10^8 - 10^9 cps [64]. Furthermore, vanadium and manganese ions are not very suitable because they have a large nuclear spin (V^{51}: $I = 7/2$, Mn^{55}: $I = 5/2$). Thus, the best choice of the compounds that remain consists of divalent and trivalent chromium, trivalent iron and divalent nickel ions.

In Sec. 3.9 we noted the necessity of distinguishing between paramagnetic complexes with a small fraction of covalency and those with strong covalent bonds. Of the compounds with strong covalent bonds, only those containing Cr^{3+} are suitable for our purposes since atoms with the configurations $d\epsilon^1$ and $d\epsilon^5$ will have an effective spin $S = 1/2$. Atoms with the configurations $d\epsilon^2$ and $d\epsilon^4$ have $S = 1$, but the initial splittings of the spin levels are apparently too large. The atom Cr^{3+} has the configuration $d\epsilon^3$, and is in the effective S state with spin $S = 3/2$. It is analogous to Fe^{3+} and Mn^{2+} ions in compounds with weak bonding.

We shall discuss in somewhat greater detail the different compounds of the selected iron groups ions.

Cr^{2+}. S = 2. Salts of divalent chromium are chemically less stable than the others. Moreover, in this ion the lower orbital level in a cubic field is a doublet and the orbital degeneracy is removed by a weak field of lower symmetry, with the result that one may expect the initial splittings of the spin levels in the crystalline field to be too large. Up to the present time the verification of this lies in a single investigation of the substance $CrSO_4 \cdot 5H_2O$, which possesses the spin Hamiltonian constant $D = 2.24\ \mathrm{cm}^{-1}$ and requires the use of a 4-mm pumping wavelength.

Cr^{3+}. S = 3/2. Compounds of this ion have been thoroughly studied; they possess relatively long spin-lattice relaxation times and the initial splittings of many of them lie in the convenient range of standard microwave frequencies. Of the compounds of this ion, chromium hexacyanide and corundum with the impurity Cr^{3+} have already been used as maser working substances.

Fe^{3+}. S = 5/2. The free ion is in the S state. The relaxation times are of the same order as in Cr^{3+}. The initial splittings of the spin levels are large in some cases. The Fe^{3+} compounds may be of interest for construction of a maser without the use of a steady magnetic field [65, 42] or with the use of weak magnetic field, because even in the absence of a magnetic field the Fe^{3+} ion has three spin levels.

Ni^{2+}. S = 1. At first glance compounds of Ni^{2+} are most suitable for use as working substances, in view of the fact that this ion has only three spin levels. An attempt to produce a maser with nickel fluosilicate [68], however, did not meet with success because the spin-lattice relaxation time T_1 is too short and because of the internal stresses in the crystal, which lead to excessive broadening of the paramagnetic resonance line. It is well known that there are a large number of paramagnetic salts of divalent nickel, in which the only magnetic property that has been studied until now is the static susceptibility. It is possible that in contrast to nickel fluosilicate some of these salts may turn out to be suitable. We note that if the symmetry of the crystalline field surrounding the Ni^{2+} ion is so low that the spin Hamiltonian contains type $E(S_x^2 - S_y^2)$ terms, the spin degeneracy will be removed even in the absence of an external magnetic field. Such compounds of Ni^{2+} appear well suited for maser use without a steady magnetic field [65].

Until now we have considered octahedral paramagnetic complexes. Analysis of the energy level structure of iron group ions in a tetrahedral environment shows that for various reasons (short spin-lattice relaxation time, large hyperfine structure, etc.), the only types of compounds of this group found to be suitable are those of divalent iron salts, diluted, of course, in the appropriate diamagnetic lattice.

Of the group of rare earth elements only compounds of the Gd^{3+} and Eu^{2+} ions occurring in the S state may be used since in the remaining ions of this group the spin-lattice relaxation time is excessively short. Eu^{2+} is less suitable because of appreciable hyperfine structure. The spin of Gd^{3+} is $S = 7/2$ and in the absence of an external magnetic field there are four spin levels, which makes Gd^{3+} compounds suitable for construction of a maser without a magnetic field.

Strong covalent bonding is characteristic of magnetic complexes of the palladium and platinum group compounds. Consequently, in conformity with the considerations with respect to iron group compounds, only complexes with the electronic configuration $d\epsilon^3$ are suitable for our purposes, i.e., complexes containing trivalent molybdenum, trivalent tungsten and pentavalent ruthenium. Complexes containing Re^{4+} are not suitable because the nuclear spin of Re^{185} and Re^{187} equals 5/2.

The majority of the actinide group elements are radioactive. Uranium compounds have been studied very little. It is possible that some of the compounds of trivalent and tetravalent uranium may turn out to be suitable.

Concluding the summary of substances having prospective use for three-level masers, we might also mention crystals with a cubic type lattice, MgO, CaO, CaF_2, to which the ions Cr^{3+}, Fe^{3+}, Gd^{3+}, Mn^{2+}, etc., have been added. The paramagnetic resonance absorption lines observable in these cases are very narrow (Cr^{3+}, for example, has a line width of 3 gauss). It is possible that these substances may find application in masers at relatively low frequencies.

3. Selection of the steady magnetic field orientation

The following important characteristics depend on the orientation of the steady magnetic field with respect to the crystal axes:

position of the spin energy levels, the probabilities of transitions between the levels under the action of the periodic magnetic field and the probabilities of transitions due to lattice vibrations. Almost no study has been made of the probabilities of relaxation transitions between different spin levels as a function of the steady magnetic field. The position of the spin levels and the probabilities of magnetic dipole transitions between these levels may be calculated if the spin Hamiltonian parameters are known (see Chapter III).

When choosing the magnetic field direction it is not only essential that there exist suitable energy level spacings giving the required values of the frequencies ν_{32} (or ν_{21}) and ν_{31}, but it is also important that the magnetic dipole transition probabilities p_{32} (or p_{21}) and p_{31} (1.3) be large. If p_{32} (or p_{21}) is small, the gain will be small, and if p_{31} is small, a large pumping power is required in order to obtain the saturation effect. Therefore, as mentioned above, the splittings of the energy levels caused by the application of an external static magnetic field should not greatly exceed the initial crystalline field splittings. If the external magnetic field is very large, the spin levels will be almost equally spaced, and in practice, transitions due to the RF field will be possible only between neighboring levels, so that pumping will not be realizable.

In the case $S \leq 3/2$ the spin Hamiltonian has the simplest form since the part of it $\hat{\mathscr{H}}_{\mathrm{cr}}$ corresponding to the crystalline field interaction energy contains only quadratic terms in the component of the spin vector $\hat{\mathbf{S}}$. If the field has trigonal or tetragonal symmetry, $\mathscr{H}_{\mathrm{cr}} = D\,[\hat{\mathbf{S}}_z^2 - \frac{1}{3}S(S+1)]$, where the symmetry axis coincides with the Z direction. If the static magnetic field $\mathbf{H}_0 \parallel Z$, the spin Hamiltonian is represented by a diagonal matrix, and consequently, the simple selection rule $\Delta M = \pm 1$ is valid for the magnetic dipole transitions. The possibilities of selecting suitable transitions to obtain the required values of ν_{32} (or ν_{21}) and ν_{31} are clear from Fig. 1.3. If the spin Hamiltonian also contains a rhombic term $E\left(\hat{S}_x^2 - \hat{S}_y^2\right) \equiv 1/2\,E\left(\hat{S}_+^2 + \hat{S}_-^2\right)$, the latter obviously mixes the states in which the quantum numbers of the projection of the spin on the Z axis differ by $\pm$ 2, i.e., states with ($M = -1$, $M = +1$) in the case of $S = 1$ and states with ($M = -3/2$, $M = 1/2$, $M = -1/2$, $M = 3/2$) in the case of $S = 3/2$. The number of pairs of levels between which transitions are allowed now increases.

We note that in the case of an even number of electrons the rhombic field completely removes the spin degeneracy, so that for ions with $S = 1$ in the absence of a magnetic field we have already three separate spin levels. As we have pointed out, this opens up the possibility of using compounds of these ions as the working substance of a maser which does not use a magnetic field.

Suppose now that the field H_0 is perpendicular to the trigonal or tetragonal axis of the crystal. If as before we take $H_0 \parallel Z$, the term $[\hat{S}_z^2 - 1/3\, S\,(S+1)]$ changes into $1/2\, [\hat{S}_+^2 + \hat{S}_-^2]$ and mixes states with $\Delta M = \pm 2$ even in the absence of the rhombic field.

In the case $S = 5/2$ (and $S = 7/2$) the form of the spin Hamiltonian is considerably more complicated, since it will be represented by a polynomial of the fourth (sixth) power with respect to the component of the spin vector $\boldsymbol{S}$. The position of the spin levels and the selection rules will depend substantially on the relation between the magnitudes of the various parameters of the spin Hamiltonian.

For certain orientations of the steady magnetic field a symmetrical energy splitting is possible, enabling the pumping of one frequency to simultaneously cause transitions between the two pairs of spin levels. Use of such a symmetrical version enhances the gain by several factors.

As we shall see, when initial crystalline splittings of the spin levels exist, resonance absorption is possible not only for mutually perpendicular static and periodic magnetic fields. To find the optimum conditions of operation of a maser, it is also important to

Table 8.1

Initial Splittings of the Spin Levels in Substances Containing Fe^{3+}, Ni^{2+}, Gd^{3+}

Ion	Substance	Initial splittings, cm^{-1}		
		Δ_1	Δ_2	Δ_3
Fe^{3+}	$RbFe(SO_4)_2 \cdot 12H_2O$	0.043	0.002	
	$NH_4Fe(SO_4)_2 \cdot 12H_2O$	0.085	0.014	
	$KFe(SO_4)_2 \cdot 12H_2O$	0.043	0.025	
	$Fe[(CH_3CO)_2CH]_3$	0.28	0.14	
	$BaTiO_3$	0.332	0.166	
	$SrTiO_3$	0.023	0.044	
	$(NH_3CH_3)Fe(SO_4)_2 \cdot 12H_2O$	0.134	0.48	
	Al_2O_3	0.38	0.63	
	$Al_2Be_3(SiO_3)_6$	0.05	0.06	
	$MgWO_4$	2.05	2.52	
Ni^{2+}	$(NH_4)_2Ni(SO_4)_2 \cdot 6H_2O$	1.5	0.97	
	$(NH_4)_2Ni(SeO_4)_2 \cdot 6H_2O$	0.91	1.64	
	$Tl_2Ni(SeO_4)_2 \cdot 6H_2O$	2.5	0.2	
	$K_2Ni(SO_4)_2 \cdot 6H_2O$	2.95	1.1	
	$NiSO_4 \cdot 7H_2O$	2.0	3.0	
Gd^{3+}	$Mg_3Gd_2(NO_3)_{12} \cdot 24H_2O$	0.0766	0.0479	0.0246
	$GdCl_3 \cdot 7H_2O$	0.0827	0.0504	0.0243
	$GdCl_3$	0.0087	0.00077	0.00065
	$Gd(C_2H_5SO_4)_3 \cdot 9H_2O$	0.131	0.085	0.0466
	$Gd_2(SO_4)_3 \cdot 8H_2O$	0.291	0.055	0.908

take into account the absorbed power of the RF field as a function of its orientation with respect to the steady magnetic field and the crystalline axes.

In conclusion we note that apparently there is great practical value in masers which operate without an externally applied static magnetic field [42]. Such masers possess a number of advantages: 1) no electromagnet is necessary, so they avoid the difficulties associated with the attainment of great magnetic field homogeneity and current stabilization in conjunction with a large working space; 2) single crystals are unnecessary; 3) all ions of the unit cell are used; 4) superconductors may be used for construction of microwave circuits; 5) the dimensions of the Dewar are not restricted by the pole gap; 6) there is no broadening caused by a discrepancy of the angles between the crystalline axes and the magnetic field.

Table 8.1 gives the initial splittings of unpaired spin levels for substances used up to the present time which are capable of finding application in masers without field.

4. Gadolinium ethylsulfate maser

The first three-level maser [66, 67] was constructed of diamagnetic lanthanum ethylsulfate containing 0.5% gadolinium and 0.2% cerium. The Gd^{3+} ions play the role of active unpaired spins. A static magnetic field of intensity 1800 gauss is positioned perpendicular to the symmetry axis of the crystal. Of the eight spin levels of Gd^{3+}, which we shall designate according to the value of the magnetic quantum number in a strong magnetic field, three neighboring ones were used: $M = -5/2$, $-3/2$ and $-1/2$. The pumping frequency $\nu(-1/2, -5/2) = 11{,}500$ Mc, the signal frequency $\nu(-3/2, -5/2) = 6000$ Mc; the magnetic field of the signal is positioned perpendicular, and the pumping magnetic field is parallel, to the static field H_0. The frequencies $\nu(-1/2, -3/2)$ and $\nu(-3/2, -5/2)$ are so close to one another that a prerequisite for population inversion of the levels $M = -5/2$ and $M = -3/2$, according to (8.43), is $A(-1/2, -3/2) \gg A(-3/2, -5/2)$. This requirement can be easily fulfilled with the aid of a small amount of Ce^{3+} impurity. These experimental conditions are such that the spacing between the spin levels of Ce^{3+} are indeed equal to the spacing $(-1/2, -3/2)$ of the Gd^{3+} ion. The spin-lattice relaxation time of Gd^{3+} at liquid helium temperatures is approximately 10^{-4} sec; the relaxation time of Ce^{3+} is several orders of magnitude shorter. According to the resonance spin-spin interaction of gadolinium and cerium there occurs a rapid excitation of the spin levels of Ce^{3+} due to the transitions $M = -1/2 \rightarrow M = -3/2$ of the Gd^{3+} ion. In turn, the excited Ce^{3+} ions very quickly transfer energy to the lattice vibrations.

An RF field of 88-mw power was used for the pumping. The Q of the resonant cavity was $Q_0 \approx 6000$. The gain was approximately

20 db with a bandwidth of about 10^5 cps. The effective noise temperature of the entire equipment, including the circulator and the controlling equipment, was equal to about 150°K, but it could be reduced appreciably by many means.

Because of its chemical instability, gadolinium ethylsulfate has hardly any practical value as the working substance of a maser.

5. Chromium hexacyanide maser

The exceptionally long longitudinal (spin-lattice) relaxation time, of about 0.2 sec at 1.25°K, attracts attention to chromium hexacyanide as a maser working substance [68]. In practice the diamagnetic salt $K_3Co(CN)_6$ containing 0.5% Cr was used. The $Cr(CN)_6$ complex has a strong covalent bond (see Sec. 3.9), and consequently the electron configuration $d\epsilon^3$ gives a vanishing resultant orbital moment and a resultant spin $S = 3/2$. Of the four spin levels the upper three $M = 3/2$, $1/2$, and $-1/2$ were used. The signal frequency was $\nu(3/2, 1/2) = 2800$ Mc, the pumping frequency $\nu(3/2, -1/2) = 9400$ Mc. In this case no special devices were needed to fulfill condition (8.47), because $\nu(1.2, -1/2) \gg \nu(3/2, 1/2)$. The central part of the maser—the resonant cavity—requires special

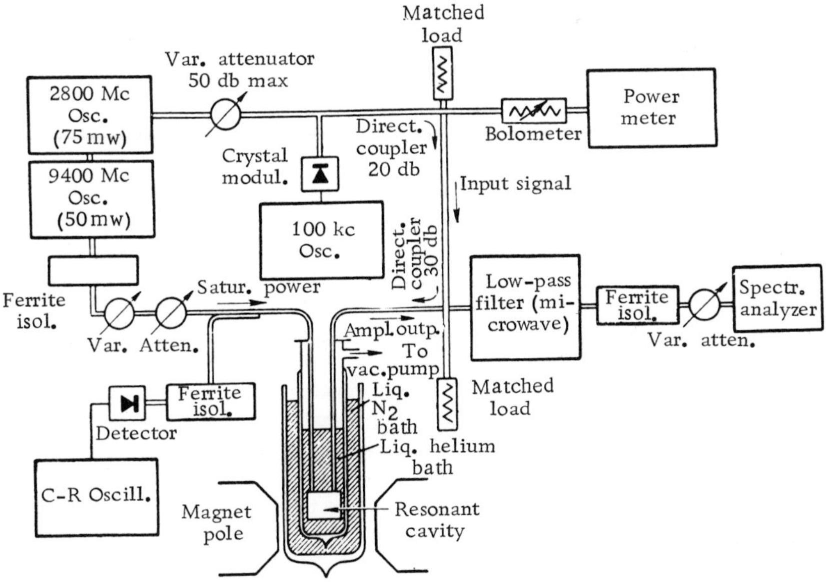

Fig. 8.8. Block diagram of the microwave amplification apparatus [68].

construction to make possible the simultaneous excitation of vibrations at both the signal frequency and the pumping frequency.

Figure 8.8 gives a block diagram of the equipment used to obtain a gain of 37 db with a bandwidth of $2.5 \cdot 10^4$ cps. The saturating power was 1 mw. There was no noticeable change in the gain when the signal power was raised from 10^{-11} to 10^{-10} w; with a further increase of power the gain diminished and the bandwidth broadened.

It has been shown experimentally that the relation $g_a B$ = const (8.31) is correct to a high degree of accuracy if the volume of the paramagnetic substance and the configuration of the resonant cavity remain unchanged. Thus, it was found that $g_a B = 1.8$ Mc. The theoretical calculation gives a value close to this: ~ 2.6 Mc.

Chromium hexacyanide has been used [69] also to construct a maser operating at the frequency 1373 Mc (close to the frequency of the interstellar hydrogen line). The pumping was performed at 8000 Mc. At a pumping power of 9 mw the equipment was converted into an oscillator. Chromium hexacyanide has also been used by other authors to build masers [62, 70].

6. Ruby maser

Corundum doped with chromium (ruby) was used to construct a maser for various frequencies [71, 72]. Ruby is distinguished by the following positive qualities: 1) an initial crystalline splitting of the order of the frequencies most used in practice; b) a relatively long longitudinal relaxation time, 0.1 sec at 4.2°K; c) the unit cell contains only one ion of Cr^{3+} or Al^{3+}, which is isomorphic with it; d) low dielectric losses; e) high mechanical strength and chemical stability; f) good thermal conductivity.

Makhov et al. [71] have constructed a maser with the signal frequency $\nu(-1/2, 1/2) = 9300$ Mc, and the pumping was effected at the frequency $\nu(-3/2, 1/2) = 24{,}000$ Mc. A static magnetic field of intensity 4200 gauss was directed at an angle of 54°44′ relative to the trigonal axis of the crystal. The chromium concentration in the sample was 0.1%. A klystron supplied the pumping power of 120 mw and the gain reached 20 db.

Prokhorov et al. [72] operated a maser at the frequency $\nu(-1/2, 1/2) \approx 3000$ Mc and the pumping frequency $\nu(3/2, -1/2) = 15{,}000$ Mc. When the temperature was reduced to 2°K the system was self-excited and operated as an oscillator.

Recently a report was made [117] of a traveling-wave ruby maser (i.e., waveguide type waveform), having the following parameters: ~25-db gain, bandwidth approximately 23 Mc, noise temperature ~10°K, retunability of the operating frequency within limits of several percent near the operating frequency ~ 6000 Mc. Practical realization of such a maser became possible by use of delay systems.

Graphs have been plotted of the dependence of the splitting of the spin levels on the field H_0 and its inclination to the optic axis of the ruby crystal [118], and investigations have also been made of the effect of Co^{2+} and other impurity ions on the probability of a relaxation transition [119].

7. Maser using corundum doped with Fe^{3+}

Korniyenko and Prokhorov [34] have constructed a maser at the signal frequency $\sim$10,000 Mc and the pumping frequency $\sim$25,000 Mc using corundum doped with iron ions as the working substance. The optic axis of the crystal made a small angle with the direction of the steady magnetic field. Let us denote the spin levels by the magnetic quantum numbers attributable to them in a strong field H_0. For amplification the levels with $M = -3/2, -1/2$ were used; for pumping: $M = -5/2, -1/2$. We note that because Fe^{3+} ions have a spin Hamiltonian containing terms which are not only of axial but also of cubic symmetry, the transitions between any pairs of chosen levels will be resolved.

8.6. Optical Methods of Studying Paramagnetic Resonance

A number of interesting results have been obtained in recent years from experiments involving gases simultaneously acted upon by electromagnetic radiation of two different frequencies, one lying in the optical and the other in the radio-frequency region. Such a type of investigation was conducted both with atoms (or molecules) with nonmagnetic ground-state singlets and those with paramagnetic ground states. In the first case the RF resonance occurs in optically excited atoms, and in the second case in atoms in the ground state.

1. Resonance in optically excited atoms

Paramagnetic resonance experiments in optically excited atoms were proposed in 1949 [73, 74]. They can be described as follows. Let us consider an ensemble of diamagnetic atoms placed in a static magnetic field H_0 and subjected to the action of polarized light at the resonance transition frequency. The excitation of the atoms will obviously be selective. If the atoms are paramagnetic in the excited state, only some of the Zeeman sublevels will be occupied. Consequently, the radiation arising during fluorescence of the atoms will be polarized. The RF field inducing the transitions between the Zeeman sublevels changes the nature of the polarization of the emitted light. Thus, measurement of the emitted light polarization enables one to establish the onset of magnetic resonance.

The method of investigation described by us was first realized experimentally by Brossel and Bitter [75], who applied it to the even isotope of mercury. By means of linearly polarized light they excited the ultraviolet resonance line of 2537 Å ($6^1S_0 \rightarrow 6^3P_1$). The field H_0 is positioned parallel to the electric vector of the light wave. Thus, as is well known [76], only the Zeeman sublevel $M = 0$ is excited. The radiation thus contains only the π component. Then an oscillatory magnetic field of frequency $\nu = 2.9625 \cdot 10^{10}$ cps was applied perpendicular to the field H_0. With a change in the intensity of H_0 the resonance condition $h\nu = g\beta_0 H_0^*$, was fulfilled, where $g = 1.5$ is the Landé factor for the $^3P_1$ state. Owing to the $\Delta M = \pm 1$ transitions induced by the RF field, circularly polarized components appear in the optical radiation. Figure 8.9 gives the energy level scheme, where the dashed lines depict transitions induced by the RF field. In Figure 8.10, Curve *I* gives the intensity of the σ component as a function of field H_0. The maximum intensity corresponds to the field strength H_0^* which satisfies the resonance condition.

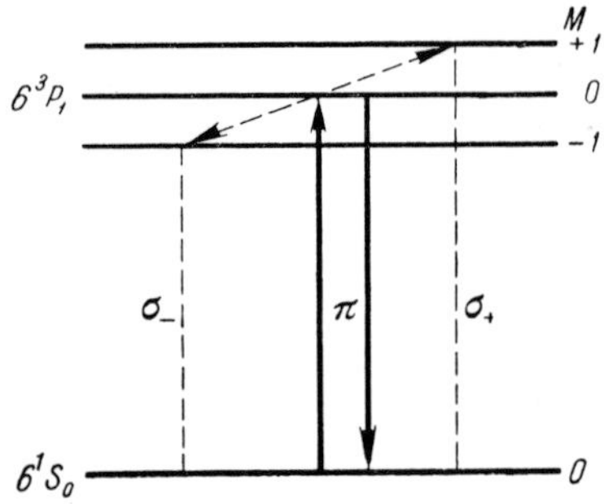

Fig. 8.9. Diagram of magnetic resonance in optically excited mercury atoms.

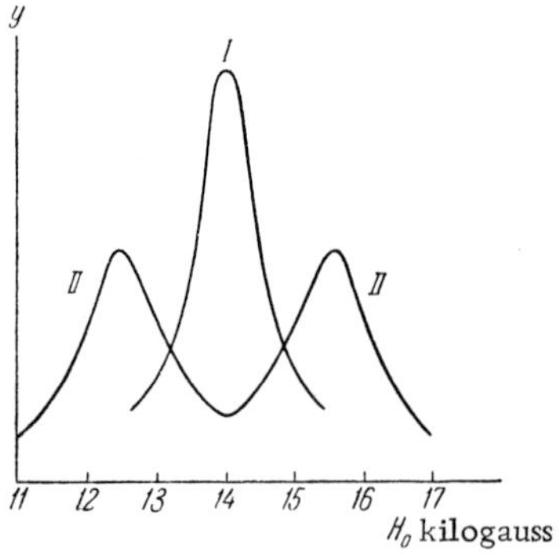

Fig. 8.10. Stark effect on the mercury resonance line at 2537 A. I—Curve of dependence on the field H_0 of σ component of emission, arising under magnetic resonance conditions; II—Curve of the same relation when an electric field E = 40 kv/cm is imposed.

This method also makes possible a precise study of the Stark effect. Blamont [77] produced an electric field $E = 40$ kv/cm parallel to H_0. When the field E does not exist, the energy spacings $0 \rightarrow 1$ and $-1 \rightarrow 0$ are identical, so that one resonance line I is observed (Figure 8.10). The shift of levels $M = 0$ and $M = \pm 1$ caused by the electric field E is different; therefore, two resonance lines appear (Curve II in Figure 8.10). The Stark effect was shown to be quadratic within the limits of experimental error. The interval between the resonance peaks equals

$$\nu_2 - \nu_1 = 2KE^2, \tag{8.50}$$

where the Stark constant $K = (2.13 \pm 0.05) \cdot 10^5$ cps/kv $\cdot$ cm^{-1}.

2. Shape of the magnetic resonance line

If the gas is highly rarefied, so that $N_0 < 10^{12}$, the width of the optical resonance line $h\Delta\nu = g\beta\Delta H$ is determined by the lifetime of the excited state t_0. According to the uncertainty principle

$$t_0 \approx \frac{1}{\pi\Delta\nu} = \frac{h}{\pi g\beta\Delta H}. \tag{8.51}$$

If the width ΔH is evaluated from curve I of Figure 8.10, the lifetime of level 6^3P_1 is found to be $t_0 = 1.19 \cdot 10^{-7}$ sec, which is in good agreement with purely optical data. The double resonance method was also employed [78] for a determination of the much shorter lifetime in the excited level 7^3S_1.

It is easy to show [75] that the shape of the resonance line is given by the following expression:

$$y = \frac{1}{t_0}\int_0^\infty P(M, M', t)\, e^{-\frac{t}{t_0}}\, dt, \tag{8.52}$$

where y is the relative intensity of the line, and $P(M, M', t)$ is the probability that the transition $M \rightarrow M'$ occurs during the time t. This probability is calculated from the well-known Majorana formula [79]. In this way, for the $6^3P_1 \rightarrow 6^1S_0$ line we obtain

$$y = \frac{\gamma^2 H_r^2\left(\gamma^2 H_r^2 + \frac{4}{t_0^2} + 4\omega^2\right)}{\left(\gamma^2 H_r^2 + \frac{1}{t_0^2} + \omega^2\right)\left(\gamma^2 H_r^2 + \omega^2 + \frac{4}{t_0^2}\right)}. \tag{8.53}$$

Here $\omega = 4\pi(\nu - \nu_0)$. Under resonance conditions $\omega = 0$, and consequently,

$$y_{\text{res}} = \frac{\gamma^2 H_r^2}{\frac{1}{t_0^2} + \gamma^2 H_r^2}. \tag{8.54}$$

If the amplitude of the periodic field is small, the width of the resonance curve can be determined from the following approximate formula:

$$(\Delta\nu)^2 = \frac{4}{t_0^2}\left[1 + 1.45\,(\gamma H_r t_0)^2\right]. \tag{8.55}$$

If the Zeeman levels are displaced due to the Stark effect, formulas (8.53) to (8.55) must of course be altered [80].

3. Multiple coherent photon scattering

Blamont [77] by studying the dependence of the line width $y_0(H)$ on the vapor density in the even isotopes of mercury obtained an unexpected result: as the density increases, the resonance line becomes markedly narrower. Thus, for instance, when the number of atoms per cm^3 is increased from 10^{11} to 10^{13}, the line width decreases by a factor of three. As the vapor density rises, the number of atomic collisions increases. Under described experimental conditions this source of line broadening evidently is insignificant. Detailed investigations undertaken by Brossel et al. [81] have shown that the line narrowing depends on the dimensions of the resonant cavity; it is determined by the concentration of only the isotope under investigation and is entirely unrelated to the quantity of other isotopes. All these facts have been explained by the prominent role played by multiple coherent photon scattering in these experimental conditions [82].

The process of multiple photon scattering may be visualized in the following manner: a photon is absorbed by atom A, which fluoresces during the time interval t_0; after this, the photon is absorbed by another atom B, etc. It is essential that the scattering be coherent; then the width of the resonance line will be determined not by the lifetime t_0, but rather by the "duration of coherence" $t_k > t_0$. A theoretical analysis of multiple coherent scattering was performed long ago by Weisskopf [83].

It is noteworthy that for $N_0 > 10^{14}$, atomic collision processes begin to markedly influence the line width.

4. Study of hyperfine splittings

Until now we have assumed that the energy levels under investigation do not have hyperfine structure. If, however, the nuclear spin is not equal to zero, hyperfine splittings can be measured with great accuracy by the double resonance method. These measurements are of particular value when in the ground state $J = 0$ or $1/2$, and consequently, only the study of excited states makes possible a determination of the quadrupole moments of nuclei. This method was employed for the analysis of the hyperfine structure of the $^3P_1$ level of the zinc atom [84] and the $^2P_{3/2}$ level of alkali metal atoms, namely: sodium [85], potassium [86], rubidium [87], and cesium [88]. In this manner the nuclear quadrupole moments were determined; the following values were obtained: Na^{23}, $Q = (0.11 \pm 0.01) \cdot 10^{-24}$ cm^2; K^{39}, $Q = (0.11 \pm 0.035) \cdot 10^{-24}$ cm^2; Rb^{85}, $Q = (0.29 \pm 0.02) \cdot 10^{-24}$ cm^2; Rb^{87}, $Q = (0.14 \pm 0.01) \cdot 10^{-24}$ cm^2; Cs^{133}, $Q = (-0.003 \pm 0.002) \cdot 10^{-24}$ cm^2. This series of papers includes the investigation of the Stark effect for levels of odd isotopes of mercury, which as we know, possess hyperfine structure [89].

Rabi [90] supplemented his original beam method by the optical excitation of atoms. Measurements conducted in this manner give values for the quadrupole moments of alkali nuclei which are in agreement with those cited above.

5. Orientation of atoms in the ground state

The treatment of magnetic resonance in optically excited atoms will now be extended to ground atomic levels. First of all, we shall discuss the method of optical pumping, which makes possible the orientation of atoms in the ground state. This method is illustrated with the $D_2(^2P_{3/2} \leftrightarrow {}^2S_{1/2})$ line of sodium. For simplicity at first we shall neglect the hyperfine structure of the level. Suppose the sodium atoms are situated in a static field H_0. A diagram of the Zeeman splittings and of the possible electron dipole transitions that arise in this case is given in Figure 8.11. We assume that there is propagated along the field H_0 a circularly polarized beam of light, which causes the σ^+ transitions, indicated in Figure 8.11 by solid arrows. In the case of fluorescence of the atoms that have been excited in this manner a large portion of them goes over to the state $M = +1/2$. After a multiple repetition of this process the level $M = -1/2$ becomes empty and all the atoms collect on the level $M = +1/2$. Thus, as a result of the optical pumping, all the atoms will be oriented opposite to the field, and saturation magnetization will occur. In actuality, this orientation of the atoms is never complete, mainly because of collisions with the walls of the vessel. Nevertheless, experiments show that the orientation will be appreciable. The extent of the orientation of the atoms can be judged from the character of the polarization of radiation emitted by the optically excited atom. In our example of the sodium D_2 line, if the orientation of the atoms is 100%, the radiation will contain only the σ component.

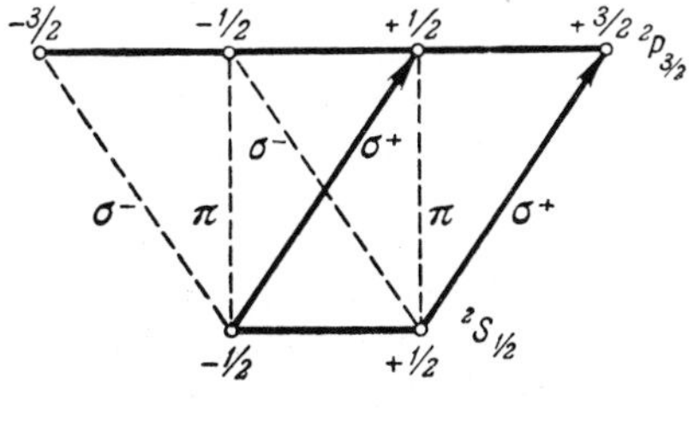

Fig. 8.11. Diagram of the optical pumping in sodium atoms via excitation of the σ^+ transition $^2P_{3/2} \leftrightarrow {}^2S_{1/2}$ by polarized light.

The idea of orienting atoms by means of optical pumping was put forward by Kastler [91]. The first experiments were conducted with atomic beams of sodium [92, 93]. They were successfully repeated with sodium vapor, which appreciably simplified the experimental technique [94]. Subsequently, besides Na atoms [95], other alkali metals were studied: K [96], Rb [97], and Cs [98]. Thus, various versions of the optical pumping method have been proposed and realized [99, 100]. In particular, it was shown that under the action of natural light which is propagated along the magnetic field, a "build-up" of the atoms occurs.[1]

6. Orientation of nuclei

If the nuclei have nonzero spin, then as a result of the interaction between the electron and nuclear moments, the orientation of the atoms will be accompanied by an orientation of the nuclei. Attempts have been made to determine this orientation from the γ-ray anisotropy in nuclei of alkali metal atoms [102]. The result was negative, apparently because of the adsorption of atoms on the walls of the vessel.

If the ground state is diamagnetic, the method of optical pumping enables us to obtain a purely nuclear orientation. The first experiments with odd isotopes of mercury did not meet with success because of insufficient light intensity [103]. A positive result was obtained [104] for mercury enriched with the Hg^{201} isotope to 90%. The optical excitation was produced by natural light propagating along the direction of the magnetic field. In this manner a build-up of the nuclei was achieved in these experiments.

7. Magnetic resonance in atomic ground states

Paramagnetic resonance absorption increases appreciably because of optical pumping. Usually, however, the detection of magnetic resonance is accomplished by optical methods based on the depolarization of resonance (optical) radiation as a consequence of transitions between the Zeeman levels under the influence of RF fields. The first experiments, performed on Na atoms [105], revealed that in addition to the resonance peaks corresponding to $\Delta M = \pm 1$ transitions, for sufficient RF field intensity, there appear peaks associated with the transitions $\Delta M = \pm 2, 3, \ldots$ The additional peaks appear as the result of the absorption of 2, 3, . . . RF quanta. A theoretical analysis has shown [106] that the intensity of the n-th order resonance is proportional to $(H_1/H_0)^{2^n}$.

Winter [107] has predicted the possibility of resonance at multiple frequencies even when each atom contains only two

---

[1] The build-up of atoms, as distinct from their polarization, means that levels with magnetic quantum numbers M and $-M$ have the same population; levels with different $|M|$ are unequally occupied.

magnetic sublevels. If this effect is to appear the RF field should not be circularly polarized, but should contain photons of different polarizations. The effect has been experimentally observed in Na atoms [108].

8. Influence of foreign gases

The double resonance method which we have described is very suitable for studying the influence of foreign gases on the orientation of atoms under investigation. If the atoms are oriented and exist in an excited state, it is well known that a depolarization of the resonance radiation occurs as a result of collisions with the molecules of the foreign gas [76], since these collisions mix states with different M values.

Foreign gases have a double influence on the oriented atoms that exist in the ground state:

a) first, they exert a deorienting action, as they also do in the case of excited atoms;

b) second, they play the role of a buffer by inhibiting collisions of the atoms with the walls of the vessel.

For a relatively low density of foreign gases, the buffer action plays a prominent role and leads to an increase of the resonance radiation intensity by factors of 10-15 [99, 109]. If in the absence of impurities the rectilinear motion of the atoms is interrupted primarily by collisions with the walls of the vessel in the presence of foreign gases, the trajectory of the atoms takes on a zig-zag form and the orienting action of the incident light is therefore extended. This effect is greater the larger the mass of the foreign gas molecules. Atoms in the $^2S_{1/2}$ state are less sensitive to collisions. Dicke [110] predicted that the collisions should cause not only a rise in intensity, but also a narrowing of the resonance line. Before long this effect was detected experimentally [111].

In conclusion we shall discuss some prospects for the development of the double-optical RF resonance method.

a) The measurement accuracy of ordinary optical spectroscopy is limited by Doppler line broadening. This drawback is absent in the double resonance method, which makes it valuable for metrology.

b) Investigations on vapors in the presence of foreign gases give valuable experimental material for the theory of collisions of oriented atoms. The weak influence of collisions on the orientation of atoms may be used for the orientation of radioactive nuclei and for the production of polarized electrons [112].

c) In the experiments described above, the optical methods play a double role: 1) they are used for selective excitation of atoms;

2) they serve to detect an RF resonance. Interesting results can be obtained by a combination of optical methods with other methods of both selective excitation of atoms and detection of magnetic resonance.

We shall indicate some of the possible combinations that have yielded positive results:

1) Selective excitation of atoms may be carried out by the Frank and Hertz method of inelastic electron collisions; the detection of a magnetic resonance, by the optical method. Dehmelt [113] used this method to investigate magnetic resonance in the 6^3P_2, metastable states of mercury, and Pebay-Peyroula [114] made measurements for the 6^3P_1 level.

2) We have already mentioned the combination of optical excitation and the detection of resonance by the Stern-Gerlach beam method, which was realized by Rabi [90].

3) Selective excitation may be accomplished by the optical method, and the detection of paramagnetic resonance by the usual method [115].

d) There is great interest in the application of optical pumping to solids. The suitability of a substance for this purpose is determined by two conditions: 1) the spin-lattice relaxation time must be longer than the duration of one cycle of optical pumping; 2) there must exist in practice optical transitions in an appropriate frequency range. A preliminary discussion [116] has shown that these conditions first of all may be satisfied by ions of salts in the S state. Apparently the most suitable are salts of divalent europium.

We note that the passage to solids is particularly important for experiments with oriented nuclei, since the use of gases is not convenient because of the deorienting effect of adsorption on the walls of the vessel.

e) With the optical pumping method it is easy to obtain a large population of the upper Zeeman levels relative to the lower levels. This affords the possibility of using this effect to construct a low-noise maser amplifier or oscillator [112]. The necessity of using rarefied gases to avoid multiple incoherent scattering of photons greatly limits the practical applicability of such devices. They, however, may turn out to be most valuable as frequency standards.

Literature for Chapter VIII

1. Overhauser, A. W. Phys. Rev. 92, 411, 1953.
2. Van Vleck, J. H. Nuovo cimento 6, suppl., 1081, 1957.
3. Overhauser, A. W. Phys. Rev. 89, 689, 1953.
4. Brovetto, P., G. Cini. Nuovo cimento 11, 618, 1954.
5. Brovetto, P., S. Ferroni. Nuovo cimento 12, 90, 1954.
6. Kittel, C. Phys. Rev. 95, 589, 1954.
7. Klein, M. J. Phys. Rev. 98, 1736, 1955.

8. Slichter, C. P. Phys. Rev. 99, 1822, 1955.
9. Barker, W. A., A. Mencher. Phys. Rev. 102, 1023, 1956.
10. Solomon, I. Phys. Rev. 99, 559, 1955.
11. Little, W. A. Proc. Phys. Soc. B70, 785, 1957.
12. Azbel', M. Ya., V. I. Gerasimenko, I. M. Lifshits, Zh. Eksp. Teoret. Fiz. 31, 357, 1956; 32, 1212, 1957.
13. Kaplan, J. I. Phys. Rev. 99, 1322, 1955.
14. Carver, T. R., C. P. Slichter. Phys. Rev. 92, 212, 1953.
15. Carver, T. R., C. P. Slichter. Phys. Rev. 102, 975, 1956; N. A. Bekeshko, Ye. I. Kondorskiy. Zh. Eksp. Teoret. Fiz. 32, 611, 1957.
16. Abragam, A., J. Combrisson, I. Solomon. Compt. Rend. 245, 157, 1957; 246, 1035, 1958.
17. Honig, A. Phys. Rev. 96, 234, 1954.
18. Kaplan, J. I. Phys. Rev. 96, 238, 1954.
19. Honig, A., J. Combrisson. Phys. Rev. 102, 917, 1956.
20. Bloch, F. Phys. Rev. 93, 944, 1954.
21. Overhauser, A. Phys. Rev. 94, 1388, 1954.
22. Korringa, J. Phys. Rev. 94, 768, 1954.
23. Abragam, A. Phys. Rev. 98, 1729, 1955.
24. Valiyev, K. A. Uch. Zap. Kharkov State Univ. 117, 145, 1957; Fiz. Metall. Metalloved. 6, 193, 1958.
25. Bashkirov, Sh. Sh. Uch. Zap. Kharkov State Univ. 117, 154, 1957.
26. Bashkirov, Sh. Sh., K. A. Valiyev. Zh. Eksp. Teoret. Fiz. 35, 678, 1958.
27. Khutsishvili, G. R. Zh. Eksp. Teoret. Fiz. 34, 1653, 1958.
28. Beljers, H. G., I. vander Kint, J. S. van Wieringen. Phys. Rev. 95, 1683, 1954.
29. Allais, E. Compt. Rend. 246, 2123, 1958.
30. Landesman, A. Compt. Rend. 246, 1538, 1958.
31. Motchane, J. L., E. Erb., J. Uebersfeld. Compt. Rend. 246, 1833, 2121, 1958.
32. Feher, G. Phys. Rev. 103, 500, 1956.
33. Feher, G., E. A. Gere. Phys. Rev. 103, 501, 1956.
34. Korniyenko, L. S., A. M. Prokhorov. Zh. Eksp. Teoret Fiz. 36, 919, 1959.
35. Jeffries, C. D. Phys. Rev. 106, 164, 1957.
36. Abraham, M., R. W. Kedzie, C. D. Jeffries. Phys. Rev. 106, 165, 1957.
37. Steenberg, N. R. Proc. Phys. Soc. A65, 791, 1952.
38. Abragam, A., W. G. Proctor. Compt. Rend. 246, 2253, 1958.
39. Weber, J. Trans. Inst. Radio Engin. Prof. Group on Electron Devices, PGED-3, June, 1953.
40. Basov, N. G., A. M. Prokhorov. Zh. Eksp. Teoret. Fiz. 27, 431, 1954; Doklady Akad. Nauk SSSR 101, 47, 1954; Disc. Faraday Soc. 19, 99, 1955; Uspekhi Fiz. Nauk 57, 485, 1955; Zh. Eksp. Teoret. Fiz. 30, 560, 1956.

41. Gordon, J. P., H. J. Zeiger, C. H. Townes. Phys. Rev. 95, 282, 1954; 99, 1253, 1955.
42. Bogle, S. S., H. F. Symmons. Proc. Phys. Soc. 73, 531, 1959; Austr. J. Phys. 12, 1, 1959.
43. Shimoda, K., H. Takahasi, C. H. Townes. J. Phys. Soc. Japan 12, 686, 1957.
44. Pound, R. V. Ann. Phys. 1, 24, 1957.
45. Strandberg, M. W. P. Phys. Rev. 106, 617, 1957; 107, 1483, 1957.
46. Weber, J. Phys. Rev. 108, 537, 1957.
47. Landau, L., Ye. Lifshits. Quantum Mechanics, Moscow, Gostekhizdat, 1948.
48. Purchell, E. M., R. V. Pound. Phys. Rev. 81, 279, 1951.
49. Bloch, F. Phys. Rev. 70, 460, 1946.
50. Andres, E. Nuclear Magnetic Resonance, IL, Moscow, 1957, 150.
51. Lösche, A. Kerninduktion, VEB, Berlin, 1957, 62.
52. Rabi, I., N. F. Ramsey, J. Schwinger. Rev. Mod. Phys. 26, 167, 1954.
53. Feher, G., H. E. D. Scovil. Phys. Rev. 105, 760, 1957.
54. Combrisson, J., A. Honig, C. H. Townes. Compt. Rend. 242, 2451, 1956.
55. Feher, G., J. P. Gordon, E. Buehler, A. Gere, C. D. Thurnmond. Phys. Rev. 109, 221, 1958.
56. Chester, P. F., P. E. Wagner, J. G. Castle Jr. Phys. Rev. 110, 281, 1958.
57. Bolef, D. I., P. F. Chester. IRE Trans. Microw. Theory and Techn. 47, 1958.
58. Basov, N. G., A. M. Prokhorov, Zh. Eksp. Teoret. Fiz. 28, 249, 1955.
59. Bloembergen, N. Phys. Rev. 104, 324, 1956.
60. Javan, A. Phys. Rev. 107, 1579, 1957; Clogston, A. M. J. Phys. Chem. Solids 4, 271, 1958; A. M. Prokhorov. URSI Meeting, Boulder, Colo., IX, 1957.
61. Bloembergen, N. Phys. Rev. 109, 2209, 1958.
62. Strandberg, M. W. P., C. F. Davis, B. W. Faughman, R. L. Kyhl, G. J. Wolga. Phys. Rev. 109, 1988, 1958.
63. Strandberg, M. W. P. Phys. Rev. 110, 65, 1958.
64. Bashkirov, Sh. Sh., K. A. Valiyev. Zh. Eksp. Teoret. Fiz. 35, 302, 1958.
65. Bowers, K. D., W. B. Mims. Conference Electronic Tube Research, Berkeley, Calif., VI, 1957.
66. Scovil, H. E. D., G. Feher, H. Seidel. Phys. Rev. 105, 762, 1957.
67. Scovil, H. E. D. Trans. Inst. Radio Eng. Prof. Group on Microwave Theory and Techniques 6, 29, 1958.
68. McWhorter, A. L., J. M. Meyer. Phys. Rev. 109, 312, 1958.
69. Artman, J. O., N. Bloembergen, S. Shapiro. Phys. Rev. 109, 1392, 1958.
70. Autler, S. H., N. McAvoy. Phys. Rev. 110, 280, 1958.

71. Makhov, G., C. Kikuchi, J. Lambe, R. W. Terhune. Phys. Rev. 109, 1399, 1958.
72. Zverev, G. M., L. S. Korniyenko, A. A. Manenkov, A. M. Prokhorov. Zh. Eksp. Teoret. Fiz. 34, 1660, 1958.
73. Brossel, J., A. Kasler. Compt. Rend. 229, 1213, 1949.
74. Pryce, F. Phys. Rev. 77, 136, 1950.
75. Brossel, J., F. Bitter. Phys. Rev. 86, 308, 1952; Brossel J. Ann. Phys. 7, 622, 1952.
76. Mitchell, A., M. Zemansky. Resonance Radiation and Excited Atoms, Chap. 5, 1937.
77. Blamont, J. E. These (Paris, 1956); Blamont, J., J. Brossel. Compt. Rend. 238, 1487, 1954; Arch des. Sci. Geneve 9, fasc. special, 152, 1956; 243, 2038, 1956.
78. Brossel, J., C. Julienne. Compt. Rend. 242, 2127, 1956.
79. Majorana, J. E. Nuovo cimento 9, 43, 1932.
80. Blamont, J., J. Winter. Compt. Rend. 244, 332, 1957.
81. Guichon, M., J. E. Blamont, J. Brossel. J. Phys. Rad. 18, 99, 1957; Boutron, F., J. Brossel. Compt. Rend. 245, 2250, 1957; Barrat, J., J. Brossel. Compt. Rend. 246, 2744, 1958.
82. Rollet, N., J. Brossel, A. Kastler. Compt. Rend. 242, 240, 1956.
83. Weisskopf, V. Ann. Phys. 9, 23, 1931.
84. Bockmann, K., H. Kruger, E. Recknagel. Nuovo cimento 6, suppl. ser. X, 1155, 1957.
85. Sagalyn, P. L. Phys. Rev. 94, 885, 1954.
86. Ritter, G. J., G. W. Series. Proc. Phys. Soc. A68, 450, 1955; Proc. Roy. Soc. A238, 473, 1957; Series, G. W. Phys. Rev. 105, 1128, 1957.
87. Meyer-Berkhout, U. Z. Phys. 141, 185, 1955.
88. Althoff, K. H. Z. Phys. 141, 33, 1955.
89. Blamont, J. E., J. Brossel. Compt. Rend. 243, 2038, 1956.
90. Perl, M. L., I. I. Rabi, B. Senitzky. Phys. Rev. 98, 611, 1955; 103, 315, 1956; 104, 553, 1956.
91. Kastler, A. J. Phys. Rad. 11, 225, 1950; Physica 17, 191, 1951.
92. Brossel, J. A., A. Kastler, J. Winter. J. Phys. Rad. 13, 668, 1952.
93. Hawkins, W. B., R. H. Dicke. Phys. Rev. 91, 1008, 1953; 98, 478, 1956.
94. Barrat, J., J. Brossel, A. Kastler. Compt. Rend. 239, 1196, 1954.
95. Kastler, A. J. Opt. Soc. Amer. 47, 460, 1957.
96. Arditi, M., T. R. Carver. Phys. Rev. 109, 1012, 1958.
97. Skalinski, T. Compt. Rend. 245, 1908, 1957.
98. Diamand, F., J. M. Legendre, T. Skalinski. Compt. Rend. 246, 90, 1958.
99. Brossel, J., J. Margerie, A. J. Kastler. Compt. Rend. 241, 865, 1955.

100. Dehmelt, H. G. Phys. Rev. 105, 1487, 1957; Bell, W. E., A. L. Bloom. Phys. Rev. 107, 1559, 1957; 109, 219, 1958; Franzen, W., A. G. Emslie. Phys. Rev. 108, 1453, 1957.
101. Margerie, J., J. Brossel, A. Kastler. Compt. Rend. 241, 474, 1955; Hawkins, W. B., R. H. Dicke. Phys. Rev. 91, 1008, 1953; Hawkins, W. B. Phys. Rev. 98, 478, 1955.
102. Brossel, J., J. L. Mosser, J. Winter. J. Phys. Rad. 16, 814, 1955.
103. Bitter, F., J. Brossel. Phys. Rev. 85, 1051, 1952; Bitter, F., R. F. Lacey, B. Richter. Rev. Mod. Phys. 25, 174, 1953.
104. Cagnac, B., J. Brossel, A. Kastler. Compt. Rend. 246, 1827, 1958.
105. Brossel, J., B. Cagnac, A. Kastler. Compt. Rend. 237, 984, 1953; J. Phys. Rad. 15, 6, 1954.
106. Besset, C., J. Horowitz, A. Messiah, J. Winter. J. Phys. Rad. 15, 251, 1954; Salwen, H. Phys. Rev. 99, 1274, 1955; Hack, M. N. Phys. Rev. 104, 84, 1956.
107. Winter, J. Compt. Rend. 241, 375, 600, 1955.
108. Margerie, J., J. Brossel. Compt. Rend. 241, 373, 566, 1955; Winter, J., J. Brossel. Arch. Sci. Geneve 9, fasc. spec., 148, 1956.
109. Bender, P. L. Thesis, Princeton University, 1956; Cohen-Tannoudji, C., J. Brossel, A. Kastler. Compt. Rend. 244, 1027, 1957; Hartman, F., M. Rambosson, J. Brossel, A. Kastler. Compt. Rend. 246, 1522, 1958.
110. Dicke, R. H. Phys. Rev. 89, 472, 1953.
111. Wittke, J. P., R. H. Dicke. Phys. Rev. 96, 530, 1954; Wittke, J. P. Thesis, Princeton University, 1954.
112. Kastler, A. Holweck Lecture, Proc. Phys. Soc. A67, 853, 1954.
113. Dehmelt, H. G. Phys. Rev. 103, 1125, 1956.
114. Pebay-Peyroula, J. C., J. Brossel, A. Kastler. Compt. Rend. 244, 57, 1957.
115. Shimoda, K., T. Nishikawa. J. Phys. Soc. Japan 6, 512, 1951.
116. Series, G. W., M. J. Taylor. Colloque CNRS, No. 86, Paris, 1958.
117. De Grasse, R. W., E. O. Schulz-du Bois, H. E. D. Scovil. Bell. Syst. Technic. Journ. 38, 305, 1959.
118. Schulz-du Bois, E. O. Bell. Syst. Technic. Journ. 38, 271, 1959.
119. Schulz-Du Bois, E. O., H. E. D. Scovil, R. W. DeGrasse. Bell. Syst. Technic. Journ. 38, 335, 1959.
120. Erb, E., J. L. Motchane, J. Uebersfeld. Compt. Rend. 246, 3050, 1958; Uebersfeld, J. Rev. Univers. Mines. 15, 594, 1959; Abraham, M., M. A. H. McCausland, F. N. H. Robinson. Phys. Rev. Letters 2, 449, 1959.
121. Cowen, J. A., W. R. Schafer, R. D. Spence. Phys. Rev. Letters 3, 13, 1959.

122. Bloembergen, N., S. Shapiro, P. S. Pershan, J. O. Artman. Phys. Rev. 114, 445, 1959.

Books and Review Articles on Paramagnetic Resonance

1. Gordy, W., W. V. Smith, R. F. Trambarulo. Microwave Spectroscopy, John Wiley & Sons, New York, 1953.
2. Bleaney, B., K. W. H. Stevens. Paramagnetic resonance, Rep. Progr. Phys. 16, 108, 1953.
3. Bowers, K. D., J. Owen. Paramagnetic resonance II, Rep. Progr. Phys. 18, 304, 1955.
4. Ingram, D. Spectroscopy at Radio and Microwave Frequencies, Butterworths Scientific Publications, London, 1955.
5. Ingram, D. J. E. Free Radicals as Studied by Electron Spin Resonance, London, 1958.
6. Wertz, J. E. Nuclear and electronic paramagnetic resonance, Chem. Rev. 55, 829, 1955.
7. Pryce, M. H. L. Paramagnetism in crystals, Nuovo cimento 6, suppl. No. 3, 817, 1957.
8. Gorter, C. J. Paramagnetic relaxation, Nuovo cimento 6, suppl. No. 3, 887, 1957.
9. Van Vleck, J. H. Line-breadths and the theory of magnetism, Nuovo cimento 6, suppl. No. 3, 993, 1957.
10. Van Vleck, J. H. The concept of temperature in magnetism, Nuovo cimento 6, suppl. No. 3, 1081, 1957.
11. Low, W. Paramagnetic Resonance. Academic Press, New York-London, 1960.
12. Khutsishvili, G. R. Overhauser effect and related phenomena, Uspekhi Fiz. Nauk, 61, 9, 1960.

Subject Index